The Chemical Senses and Nutrition

The Chemical Senses and Nutrition

Edited by Morley R. Kare and Owen Maller

> Dr. Kare is professor of physiology at North Carolina State University. Dr. Maller is a research associate in psychology at Duke University.

with a Bibliography on the Sense of Taste prepared by Rose Marie Pangborn and Ida M. Trabue

The Johns Hopkins Press, Baltimore

This book has been brought to publication with the generous
assistance of a grant from The Nutrition Foundation, Inc.

Foreword

The growth of modern human populations, if not severely curbed, will soon require the exploitation of many novel foods, perhaps more nutritious than those of our present diets but strange to many tastes. Palatability thus becomes of prime importance, and scientific research into the bases of the act of eating more and more necessary.

The present symposium reflects a broad interdisciplinary attack on many aspects of the chemical senses, taste and color. It explores the nature of the stimuli that provoke such motivations as hunger and satiety. It examines the interrelationships between sensory receptors, the hypothalamus, and other and higher brain centers, and the neuromuscular and glandular effectors involved in eating. Psychological aspects are obviously involved, for who is not aware of the importance of habit and conditioning in matters of food preferences; and cultural, ethnological factors loom large. Genetics too must enter in; not only are there clearly wide interspecific differences in capacities to sense and discriminate various chemical compounds, but there are also great differences between individuals of the same species in respect to the thresholds at which particular substances are detected or at which attraction gives rise to avoidance. These differences, though in general modifiable by experience and learning, are also frequently constitutional and innate, as some of the present contributors have shown. Moreover, just as there are forms of color blindness, the investigation of which has revealed much about vision, so there are forms of taste blindness that are beginning to reveal much about our chemical senses. Surgical devices, which can entirely eliminate taste without impairing hunger, or which interfere with satiety or bypass completely the oral and pharyngeal steps in eating by putting food directly through a fistula into the stomach, greatly extend our knowledge. Delicate electrical leads from single nerve fibers reveal that of the three sensory cells attached to a single hair in an insect's chemoreceptor, one cell detects sugars and cations, another responds to water, and the third detects anions. The refinement and application of such methods to vertebrate chemoreception may be possible in time.

The chemical senses must be as ancient as animal life itself, long antedating vision and hearing or even the sense of equilibrium. They must be as ancient as the internal proprioceptors themselves, for animals depend upon eating their way through life, and chemical senses turned toward the outer world are as necessary as chemical senses informing the animal of its inner well-being or discomfort. A crawling worm, a sessile hydroid—the simplest imaginable multicellular animal, in fact—needs only tactile and chemical senses directed outward toward its environment. All other more complex senses are derivative. A simple, free nerve ending suffices for touch and taste, and some of the recent researches reported here show that in the absence of the more complex taste buds chemoreception still persists, apparently on the basis of the free nerve endings of the oral mucosa. Though the tongue is well known to be the chief organ of taste, with four distinct modalities, the term "palatability" is not a complete misnomer since the palate's free nerve endings can in fact function as simple chemoreceptors.

It is remarkable that in a symposium devoted to "The Chemical Senses and Nutrition" so comparatively little has been said about olfaction. True, it is a far more complex sensory system than that of taste, and its modalities are almost innumerable and unclassifiable. Recent researches on the olfactory mechanisms by Adrian and others have nevertheless shed much light on these complex problems. It is very interesting that the discrimination of even non-volatile solutions, such as that of sodium chloride, is shown to depend more on odor than on taste when the concentrations are very low. The olfactory organs of the lower vertebrates, the agnatha and the cartilaginous and bony fishes, are chemoreceptors that respond to substances in solution and differ from taste receptors more in location than in any intrinsic way. The evolutionary advent of amphibians and air-breathing reptiles accelerated the evolution of special sensory receptors adapted to detection of odors, often of infinitesimal strength, wafted on the breezes. The strength of natural selection in this direction is evident from the dependence of so many species of land animals upon odors attracting them to mates, and especially of carnivorous and scavenging mammals in seeking their prey. Still, first things first: simple chemoreception, as exemplified by taste, was the primary evolutionary step, and a satisfactory analysis of taste will clarify the nature of olfactory reception and its role in the regulation of food intake.

Man himself, the most domesticated of mammals, seems to stand at a fresh crossroad in the evolution of the regulation of eating. Satiety is no longer a sufficient guard against overeating, and hunger is no longer a sufficient bulwark against dietary insufficiencies. Man has provided himself with too many foods unknown in the natural environment, too many natural goods appealing to his appetite but unbalanced or deleterious when consumed in great quantity. Even milk and milk products, as adult foods, come under grave suspicion. Man is too adaptable in diet, in spite of his cultural conservatism in matters of food and appetite, to pick and choose safely on the basis of flavor and appetite as guides to nutrition. His very readiness to learn and to become conditioned is a trap. Especially because he lives to a greater average age of eighty, ninety, or even one hundred years, and seeks to maintain mental and physical vigor to the end of his days, only a most thorough scientific analysis of the components and proportions of an optimum diet will suffice. The optimum will differ for particular conditions and particular genotypes. Science must therefore become, in respect to nutrition, an adjunct to chemoreception and the regulatory feedbacks. For that end our knowledge is far from adequate, but to it the contributors to this symposium have added a great deal.

Bentley Glass

State University of New York at Stony Brook
February, 1967

Preface

Many of us carry out informal experimentation with taste and smell; however, systematic research on the function of these senses in the intact animal has received limited consideration. One obvious direction for such work is the interaction between the chemical senses and the nutritive processes. Much of the scientific investigation in these two areas has developed independently. Research on the chemical senses is strongly oriented toward either behavioral or electrophysiological elucidation on the nature of taste and smell sensations. Investigations of the nutritive processes have been largely biochemical and generally divorced from consideration of the chemical senses.

Research workers from zoology, psychology, physiology, nutrition, entomology, medicine, genetics, and food science are investigating similar sensory phenomena from their particular perspectives. Normally their publications are widely scattered in diverse journals; no single source presenting the interdisciplinary range of this subject is currently available for either the student or the scientist.

While many symposia are, by design, gatherings of scientists in a common area of research, the meeting upon which this book was based attempted to bring together workers who normally have limited scientific contact. Specialists in areas related to the subject of the chemical senses or the nutritive processes were invited. Attendance was limited in the hope that a spontaneous exchange of ideas might take place. The difference in levels of training and interest of the participants required that the speakers avoid jargon and that they emphasize concepts rather than detailed research data.

The symposium was structured, in the sense that each paper was to be directed to one of four questions:

1. What phylogenetic and evolutionary changes have the chemical senses undergone? Is taste a necessary function?

2. How do the chemical senses interact with the metabolism, nutrition, and physiology of the organism?

3. What limitations do experiential factors of the organism impose upon the information obtained from the chemical senses?

4. How do the chemical senses or receptors in the nervous system interact with one another in the control of food and water intake?

As was expected, the scientists did not remain within this narrow framework; however, reasonable continuity and substantial cohesion was maintained.

This book is based on the proceedings of the meeting held at Cornell University in June, 1966. The discussions have been condensed, largely by eliminating perfunctory remarks and inquiries about minor details. However, the participants were invited to supplement their discussions with citations from pertinent literature. Some of the individual authors expanded their papers for publication.

In the desire for rapid publication, we probably have added to the pitfalls encountered in publishing a symposium. For example, the participants have seen the discussion only once since the meeting, and we are certain that in blending the corrections of several dozen participants, full justice to every intent of meaning was not met. The authors have had an opportunity to review their own papers. The editors assume responsibility for any misinterpretations in the discussion sections. We hope that the book has faithfully captured the tempo of the meeting and that it manages to make available to a larger audience a comprehensive as well as current presentation of the diverse areas of research on the chemical senses. The material presented does provide insight into the complex interrelationship of the senses and nutrition. We feel that the usefulness of the book, particularly to students, has been enhanced by the comprehensive bibliography on taste compiled by R. M. Pangborn and I. M. Trabue.

The contribution of all the participants to both the symposium and the subsequent publication is acknowledged. We are especially grateful for the cooperation of Drs. S. Lepkovsky, R. B. MacLeod, R. H. Barnes, J. Brobeck, and R. M. Pangborn in organizing the meeting. Also, assistance in editing by Drs. L. de Ruiter and H. R. Behrman is acknowledged. We would be remiss not to comment on the academic hospitality of the School of Nutrition at Cornell University. For help in so many ways, we would also thank Mrs. J. Perry.

The conference and the preparation of the manuscript for publication were supported financially by the Nutrition Foundation. (Created and supported by the food and allied industries, it is dedicated to advancing the science of nutrition and to furthering its use in preserving the health and welfare of mankind. It does this primarily through grants to scientists in colleges and universities.) The assistance of Drs. P. B. Pearson and H. L. Sipple of the Foundation was offered from the beginning and throughout the undertaking. Assistance was also received from the National Institutes of Health (Neurological Disease and Blindness NB 03896).

Morley R. Kare

Raleigh, North Carolina
February, 1967

Participants

E. F. Adolph
Department of Physiology
The University of Rochester
Rochester, New York

John E. Bardach
School of Natural Resources
    and Department of Zoology
The University of Michigan
Ann Arbor, Michigan

Richard H. Barnes
Graduate School of Nutrition
Cornell University
Ithaca, New York

H. R. Behrman
Sensory Physiology Laboratory
North Carolina State University
    at Raleigh
Raleigh, North Carolina

L. M. Beidler
Department of Biological Sciences
Florida State University
Tallahassee, Florida

John R. Brobeck
Department of Physiology
University of Pennsylvania
Philadelphia, Pennsylvania

H. H. Chauncey
Veterans Administration
Central Office
Washington, D.C.

Alan N. Epstein
Department of Biology
University of Pennsylvania
Philadelphia, Pennsylvania

Robert P. Erickson
Department of Psychology
Duke University
Durham, North Carolina

Roland Fischer
Department of Psychiatry
Division of Behavioral Sciences
The College of Medicine
The Ohio State University
Columbus, Ohio

Melvin J. Fregly
Department of Physiology
University of Florida,
    College of Medicine
Gainesville, Florida

Sebastian P. Grossman
Department of Psychology
The University of Chicago
Chicago, Illinois

Bruce P. Halpern
Department of Psychology
    and Division of Biology
Cornell University
Ithaca, New York

Charles Hamilton
Veterans Administration Hospital
Coatesville, Pennsylvania

Alfred E. Harper
Department of Biochemistry
University of Wisconsin
Madison, Wisconsin

Robert I. Henkin
Clinical Endocrinology Branch
National Heart Institute
Bethesda, Maryland

Edward S. Hodgson
Department of Biological Sciences
Columbia University
New York, New York

Keiichiro Hoshishima
Department of Hygiene
Fukushima Medical College
Fukushima City, Japan

Harry L. Jacobs
Department of Psychology
The University of Illinois
Urbana, Illinois

Morley R. Kare
Sensory Physiology Laboratory
North Carolina State University
  at Raleigh
Raleigh, North Carolina

J. Lát
Institute of Physiology,
Czechoslovak Academy of Sciences
Prague
Czechoslovakia

Samuel Lepkovsky
Department of Poultry Husbandry
University of California
Berkeley, California

Robert B. MacLeod
Department of Psychology
Cornell University
Ithaca, New York

Owen Maller
Department of Psychology
Duke University
Durham, North Carolina

N. B. McCutcheon
Rockefeller University
New York, New York

Robert S. Morison
Division of Biological Sciences
Cornell University
Ithaca, New York

David G. Moulton
Department of Biology
Clark University
Worcester, Massachusetts

Rose Marie Pangborn
Food Science and Technology
University of California
Davis, California

Paul B. Pearson
The Nutrition Foundation, Inc.
New York, New York

Carl Pfaffmann
Rockefeller University
New York, New York

Leendert de Ruiter
Department of Zoology
State University of Groningen
Groningen, The Netherlands

Kamal N. Sharma
Department of Physiology
St. John's Medical College
Bangalore, India

Horace L. Sipple
The Nutrition Foundation, Inc.
New York, New York

I. Snapper
Consultant in Residence
Fort Hamilton Veterans
  Administration Hospital
Brooklyn, New York

James A. F. Stevenson
Department of Physiology
The University of Western Ontario
London, Canada

Contents

Part One

1: Introductory Remarks

by John R. Brobeck

IN THESE first few minutes I wish to try to bring our interests into common focus on the topics and problems with which we are concerned. I have chosen to do this by using a diagram that I put together some years ago. This is a picture of a baby (Fig. 1–1), or at least of the feeding performance of a baby. It begins on the left side with taste and touch. The large square is intended to represent the central nervous system; the arrows simply mean "leads to."

Taste and touch lead to grasping and sucking, and sucking leads to filling, secretion, digestion, absorption, metabolism—and eventually to increase in body size. This list could be extended almost indefinitely because one can amplify each of the components that I have placed in the diagram. For our discus-sion today, the important point is that there are interrelations between what is taking place in the digestive tract and the sensory input here at the left side of the diagram. If you touch a baby's cheek, the baby will respond to this touch and turn its head toward the source. Or, if something is placed between the baby's lips, the lips and jaw will grasp it and sucking will begin. The grasping and sucking both bring about positive reinforcement, or a positive feedback, that increases the grasping and sucking. This is partly mechanical in origin and partly due to taste; no doubt it is also due to olfaction.

On the other hand, all of these responses, feeding back in a negative way, eventually limit the processes that were going forward. The diagram is incom-

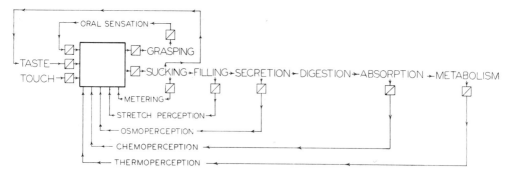

Fig. 1–1. Diagram illustrating mechanisms controlling food intake. Each arrow signifies "leads to." Feeding is initiated by touch, taste, or other oral sensation (or olfaction) at left of diagram [1].

3

plete because it does not show, for example, that the stomach has some preferred degree of filling; there is a positive feedback to get it up to that size and a negative feedback to keep it from being stretched. This may also be true of all the other kinds of reactions.

In this conference we are focusing our attention especially on the initial sensory input, its influence upon the central nervous system, and the positive and negative feedbacks upon mechanisms of food intake. We are not especially concerned with secretion, digestion, and absorption, except as they may affect what happens initially. There is a fair possibility, I believe, that what goes on in the distal end of this sequence does affect the sensitivity of the nervous system to what is being put in at the proximal end.

I wish to discuss even more briefly what seem to me to be the three most important problems in the control of food intake that are related to olfaction and taste. In the past twenty-five to thirty years we have learned much about food intake. Yet I still feel that I don't know very much about what is going on in the animal. We have learned how to study food intake, what factors must be controlled in order to get consistent results, what we can expect from an animal under a variety of environmental, dietary, and metabolic conditions. But as to the nature of the physiological mechanisms, we are almost completely ignorant.

Sometimes I have the feeling that I am planning ingenious experiments rather than informative ones. Some time ago, incidentally, Adolph told me that he supposed no one would ever reproduce our experiments, because of their highly individualistic character. You know that this is not true of his own experiments because parts of them have been reproduced in all of our laboratories. The study of feeding has developed and spread to a point where experiments are being repeated and where we have even created a field of study. Nevertheless, we need to direct our attention to fundamental questions.

Of the three problems I wish to discuss, the first is illustrated by the feeding cycle of an animal that lives always in the presence of food or by the behavior of a breast-fed infant on an ad libitum schedule. Some time ago when I was a medical student, I had occasion to examine a baby that had fallen onto a cement sidewalk. The baby appeared to be unconscious; there was what seemed to be a hypotonia of all muscles; and as I watched the baby I saw what I took to be periodic respiration of the Cheyne-Stokes type. I decided that the baby had a serious head injury. But in a few minutes I learned that the baby had merely been asleep during my examination. It awakened and was perfectly normal. This brought to my attention the fact that from a neurological point of view the sleeping state is one of profound disturbance! The same point is true of the feeding behavior of a satiated animal. The animal appears to be blind, anosmic, without taste, and incapable of perceiving the presence of food. Yet, in a few minutes or an hour or so, the animal's condition is completely changed, and an active search for food begins. This is sometimes called the off-on phenomenon or the short-term control of feeding. It seems to me that we should have as one of our objectives the characterization of these two states, so that we can say, "this is a description of the animal that will eat, this is a description of the animal that won't eat, and this is how these two states differ." At the moment such a distinction is impossible.

The second question is illustrated in Fig. 1–2. This is the food intake of a normal animal shifted from a low density to a high density diet. The animal

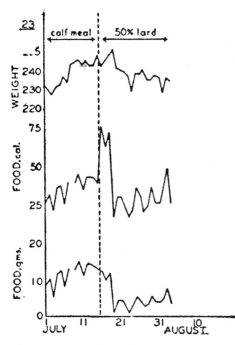

Fig. 1–2. "Caloric adjustment" occurred after a 3-day lag when 50 per cent lard was added to diet of female rat [3].

was on calf meal and was then shifted to a diet containing 50 per cent lard; this is one of Strominger's experiments. When the diet was changed, the caloric intake went way up; then it dropped after three days. In many animals it comes to the previous level, sometimes a bit above the control. But the food intake in grams always falls off dramatically, just as it did here. What happens to an animal in the course of three days of feeding on a high fat diet? How does he know that he must adjust his intake to a lower level in grams? I would like to know the answer to this because, insofar as I can tell, the animals with ventromedial lesions do not show this correction. Data from several different laboratories suggest that once the change to high fat is made the food intake of the ventromedial animals simply goes up and remains high. To my mind this is perhaps the only really good clue we have as to the nature of the deficit in an

animal with these hypothalamic lesions. Also we have a number of animals in which the intake, whether in grams or in volume, continues apparently without change as one alters the fat content of the diet.

BODY WEIGHTS, FOOD INTAKES AND FINAL BODY FAT CONTENTS OF PREVIOUSLY FORCE FED RATS ALLOWED ACCESS TO FOOD.

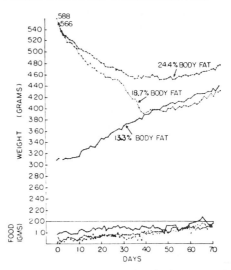

Fig 1–3. Reduced food intake in rats made obese by tube feeding. Food intake recovered when body weight returned to normal level [2].

In Fig. 1–3 an experiment that seems to me to be even more profound in its implications is described. This is an experiment of Cohn and Joseph in which they fed animals by gastric intubation, made them fat, and then gave them free access to food. The graph shows that the animals did not eat a normal amount of food until their body weight returned to normal. Teitelbaum and Hoebel achieved the same results by giving insulin [4]. You may not agree with me about this, but I believe that these are the only good data that show that there is a regulation of body weight or fat content. Other data are often mentioned in this regard, but they all have other possible interpretations. I have not been able to discover an alternate interpretation for this phenomenon, other than that the animal is sensitive to some derivative of the amount of fat or of energy stored in the body; this is, of course, long-term regulation.

What I am asking for and seeking is an explanation of the short-term and the long-term components of the regulation, of the off and on processes that determine feeding behavior, and of adjustment of intake to the composition of the diet. With this we must discover what the relations are between the feeding systems within the brain as many of us have studied them, the digestive system where food is processed, and the specialized sensations from the oral and nasopharyngeal regions of the body. If these sensations involved in the control of

food intake have not yet received the attention they deserve, it can be the function of this conference to begin to correct the oversight.

REFERENCES

1. Brobeck, J. R. Review and synthesis, in *Brain and Behavior*, Brazier, M. A. B. (ed.). American Institute of Biological Sciences, Washing, D.C., pp. 389–409, 1962.
2. Cohn, C., and Joseph, D. Influence of body weight and body fat on appetite of "normal" lean and obese rats. *Yale J. Biol. Med.*, **34:** 598–607, 1962.
3. Strominger, J. L., Brobeck, J. R., and Cort, R. L. Regulation of food intake in normal rats and in rats with hypothalamic hyperphagia. *Yale J. Biol. Med.*, **26:** 55–74, 1953.
4. Teitelbaum, P. Disturbances in feeding and drinking behavior after hypothalamic lesions, in *Nebraska Symposium on Motivation*. University of Nebraska Press, Lincoln, pp. 39–65, 1961.

2: *Chemical Senses in the Invertebrates* by *Edward S. Hodgson*

IT SEEMS appropriate to begin a discussion of the chemical senses by asking a very simple question: What were the *first* chemoreceptors to appear in evolution? A comparison of their microanatomy and functions with the similar features of mammalian taste or smell receptors might yield clues as to what mechanisms are *essential* for the functions of the chemical senses. Such a comparison should also show from what roots our own capacities for perceiving chemicals have developed.

COELENTERATES

The first chemical senses must have evolved in coelenterate animals, or their close relatives, during pre-Cambrian or early Cambrian times, no less than 500 million years ago. Our best source of information concerning those early chemoreceptors consists, therefore, of present-day coelenterates. The sensory cells (sometimes called *palpocils*) of coelenterates are all modified neurons. They are characteristically small, elongated, and have elaborate specializations at their tips. Their small size has prevented analysis with modern electrophysiological methods. Consequently, it is impossible to know exactly to which modalities of stimuli a single cell responds. Hyman [14] assumes that palpocils de-

tect mechanical, chemical, and temperature changes and notes that they do not seem to be morphologically differentiated among themselves for these various functions.

In the fresh-water coelenterate *Hydra*, Lentz and Barrnett [17] found only one cell type at the inner or outer surface of the animal that in any way conforms in structure to a receptor, even when the cells were studied by means of electron microscopy. Each of the receptor cells has a specialized apex with a modified cilium containing nine peripheral fibers and at least four central fibers. The apical region also contains many microtubules parallel to the long axis of the cell. Mitachondria, ribosomes, and vesicles are abundant in the cytoplasm. With minor variations, such as the number of central fibers in distal cilia, this description could fit the basic ultrastructure of many mammalian chemoreceptors [3]. If, indeed, the coelenterate receptors, which have been best studied under electron microscopy, function as chemoreceptors, one possible generalization emerges—the basic cell specializations that account for sensitivity to chemicals were present in the earliest evolved chemoreceptor cells.

To what chemical stimuli were these early chemoreceptors sensitive? The most primitive coelenterates, like most of their present-day descendents, were marine animals. Therefore, normal stimuli for their chemoreceptors must have been compounds that were moderately stable in sea water. The compounds must also have been widespread in small invertebrate organisms, eggs, fish, and bits of animal flesh, such as constitute the prey of modern jellyfishes and hydroids. According to existing data, proteins or protein breakdown products appear to be the most likely candidates for the sensory cues.

Loomis [19] and Lenhoff [16] reported that under certain conditions, which must be carefully controlled, the feeding reflex of *Hydra* is activated by the tripeptide reduced glutathione. They conclude that a chemoreceptor with a high order of specificity for the λ-glutamyl moiety, or "backbone," of the glutathione must exist. The observation that glutamic acid and glutamine function as competitive inhibitors of the glutathione response, while neither cysteine nor glycine have this effect, supports such an interpretation.

Although attempts have been made to relate data on the distribution of the glutathione-activated response to the sequence in which feeding mechanisms evolved in coelenterates, there appears to be no over-all significance of glutathione alone. Pantin and Pantin [21] found that a number of amino acids, notably tyrosine, elicited feeding responses in the sea anemone *Anemonia*. Inorganic compounds and carbohydrates are relatively ineffective in that regard. Some observations (discussed in reference [16]) suggest that feeding responses by the colonial hydroid *Cordylophora* are activated by the amino acid proline; methionine may play a similar role for corals.

Several compounds may be effective stimulants for a limited surface area of a single coelenterate. Isolated tentacle preparations from the large tropical sea anemone *Condylactis* exhibit bending responses (as during feeding of the intact animals) when exposed to glycine, sulfhydryl-containing amino acids, and certain short-chain tertiary amines, such as trimethyl amine oxide [11]. It seems unlikely that the full spectrum of effective chemical stimuli for the earliest chemoreceptors has, even yet, been discovered. Accumulating evidence, however, remains consistent with the idea that widely distributed components of proteins were prominent among the sensory cues for these early carnivorous animals.

Even though we remain ignorant of the exact functional significance of ultrastructural components of the coelenterate receptor cells, the same might be said of many receptors in mammals. If, for example, the accumulation of mitochondria in the receptor cells suggests very active metabolic processes, and the microtubules suggest the presence of transport systems within the receptors, such observations at the present time are really outlines of basic problems, worthwhile in terms of the future investigation of many experimental preparations.

ARTHROPODS

Progressing some distance along one of the main pathways of evolution to the arthropods, a rather similar pattern is found. The exact receptors in crustacea have to be inferred from ablation, histological, and behavioral data. Again, protein breakdown products or components are the effective stimuli. Chemoreceptors on the antennules and legs of crayfish are responsive to glycine and glutamic acid, as tested by behavioral and electrophysiological methods [9]. Case [2] made similar observations on crabs; Laverack [15] concluded that trimethyl amine and the closely related betaine are stimulatory in some crabs also. Levandowsky and Hodgson [18] found that glutamic acid and/or short-chain tertiary amines elicited discharges in chemoreceptors of the spiny lobster *Panulirus*. The neural responses shown in Fig. 2–1 are typical of the information

a synapse. The receptor organ would, according to this view, resemble an "open-ended" neural junction.

The similarity between stimulating amines and ACh is not the only resemblance between excitants for neurons

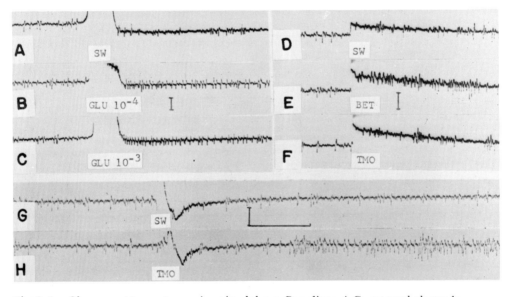

Fig. 2–1. Chemoreceptor responses in spiny lobster, Panulirus. *A-C, external electrode on an antennule; D-F, the same, from a different animal; G-H, records from dactyl (leg). Chemical stimuli, 10^{-3} M, except as otherwise noted. Vertical calibrations $= 50\mu$ V; horizontal calibrations, 25 msec; GLU = gluatamic acid; BET = betaine; TMO = trimethylamine oxide. Deflections of traces over stimulus labels mark stimulus artifacts.*

that can be obtained from crustacean preparations, even without precise localization of individual receptor cells. As with the coelenterates, these particular sensitivities "make sense" from an ecological standpoint because of the wide distribution of the effective amino acids and amines—the latter compounds, in fact, account for much of the characteristic odor of decaying fish!

Laverack [15] has also drawn attention to the fact that some of the stimulating amines resemble acetylcholine in their molecular architecture. Since ACh is well known as a synaptic transmitter substance, the suggestion has been made that the chemoreceptor membrane functions like the postsynaptic membrane of

and chemoreceptors. Microelectrophoretic injection of acidic amino acids, such as glutamic, cysteic, and aspartic, close to neurons in the mammalian central nervous system, will cause the neurons to discharge repetitively [5]. The action of the amino acids in these cases appears to occur on specific receptor sites on the external surfaces of the neurons. Clearly, the gap between "ordinary" neurons and the chemoreceptor cells discussed thus far no longer appears as great as it once did.

With the evolution of the terrestrial arthropods, on the other hand, the chemical senses attained what is perhaps their highest and most elaborate degree of specialization among the invertebrates.

In one experimental preparation, that of taste or "contact" chemoreceptors on mouth parts of flies, it became possible for the first time to carry out precise electrophysiological studies on anatomically defined single chemoreceptor cells. Dethier and co-workers have provided the most detailed information on the anatomy and the uses of these chemoreceptors in feeding, with the blowfly *Phormia* being the principal experimental animal [4]. In brief, the longer sensory hairs on the labellum of the blowfly contain three to five receptor cells. One of these was found to be a mechanoreceptor located near the base of the hair [23], while the others are chemoreceptors having dendrites extending to the tip of the sensory hair.

By a combination of electrophysiological recording methods and behavioral observations, the functions of the two to four chemoreceptor cells in a single hair have been worked out. Earlier details have been reviewed by Dethier [4] and by Hodgson [10]. Combined with more recent data, the observations lead to the following conclusions: The two receptors most generally connected to the tips of the sensory hairs are sensitive to sugars and cations [7,13]; another chemoreceptor cell is sensitive to water [20]; the remaining chemoreceptor, when present, is sensitive to anions [22].

Typical impulses from these chemoreceptors are shown in Figs. 2–2 and 2–3. Sugar and water receptor impulses appear in Fig. 2–2. The cation and anion receptor impulses are seen in Fig. 2–3. Note that the impulses from different receptor cells can be differentiated on the basis of amplitude and shape. For example, spike potentials from the anion receptor (Fig. 2–3) have a slightly longer

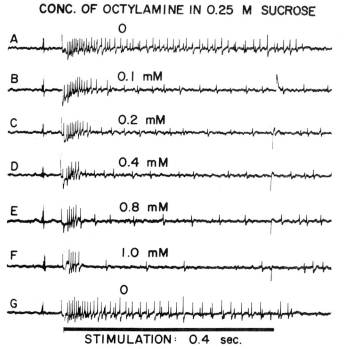

CONC. OF OCTYLAMINE IN 0.25 M SUCROSE

A   0

B   0.1 mM

C   0.2 mM

D   0.4 mM

E   0.8 mM

F   1.0 mM

G   0

STIMULATION: 0.4 sec.

Fig. 2–2. Sugar and water receptor responses from the blowfly labellum, showing inhibition by octylamine. The small spikes are from the water receptor and large spikes from the sugar receptor. Note the higher concentrations of hydrocarbon necessary to inhibit the water response. (Courtesy of Dr. R. Steinhardt.)

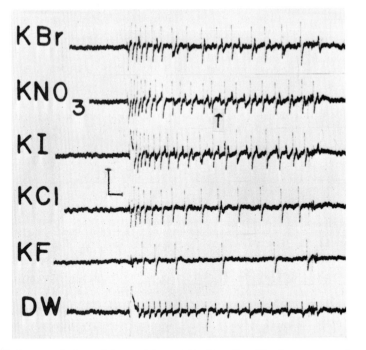

Fig. 2–3. *Responses of electrolyte receptors of the blowfly. All salt concentrations are 0.3 molal and appear in the order of application of stimulation. The arrow points to a typical anion receptor impulse recorded from KNO₃ stimulation. (Courtesy of Dr. R. Steinhardt.)*

duration, as well as a much lower amplitude, compared to impulses from the cation receptor.

MECHANISMS OF EXCITATION

The significance of these four chemosensory cells is not simply that they characterize the few channels through which a fly tastes food. Of more general importance is the availability of a conveniently accessible experimental preparation for studying the molecular mechanisms of excitation in chemoreceptors. Some of the ideas about these mechanisms have been undergoing substantial revisions within the past few years [10]. Because they appear to shed some light on the initial, and most basic, stages of food detection, it is worthwhile to note the *trends* of the current interpretations, if not their details.

The sugar receptor is not equally sensitive to all sugars. Molecules possessing an α-D-glucopyranoside linkage are most stimulating. Since structural configuration of sugar molecules is most important, and there are several instances of competitive inhibition by closely related sugars, enzymatic reactions were initially thought to be involved in the linking of carbohydrates to specific receptor sites. Lack of inhibition by metabolic inhibitors of the glycolytic cycle, and additional evidence, suggest otherwise. Dethier [4] has proposed that the sugar molecules are linked to receptor sites by weak forces, such as Van der Waal forces, to form complexes that depolarize the membrane. However, this is still an active area of investigation and no conclusion is more than tentative.

Effects of electrolytes were once related predominantly to mobilities of cations. Gillary [8] found that, in addition to cations, the anions are very important stimulants. Steinhardt [22] found that anions stimulated the "fourth" chemoreceptor cell in some hairs—the one receptor that had not been characterized previously. Steinhardt also noted that complete sequences of stimulating efficiencies of different ions could not be explained by ionic mobilities. For example, Cs^+ would be a very effective cation stimulus if stimulation depended upon ionic mobility or penetration of lipid material, since Cs^+ has a small shell of hydration. However, Cs^+ is the least stimulating of a large series of cations tested!

A more adequate explanation of ionic effectiveness is derived from Eisenman's theory of ionic selectivity based on studies with glass electrodes [6]. According to this theory, the sequences of ionic penetration would depend primarily upon the effective electrostatic field strength (anionic radius) of fixed negative charges in the glass electrodes, or, in the case of the receptor, in the receptor membrane. Deductions from this theory have been used to accurately predict the stimulating effectiveness of some cations [22]. The sequence of anion effectiveness also matches a "fixed charge" theory.

In the water receptor, the receptor sites could be responding to water as a chemical or to the osmotic pressure of the stimulating solution. A completely satisfactory choice between these alternatives has yet to be established. However, it does seem noteworthy that under some conditions the activity of the water receptor is inhibited by solutes, particularly electrolytes, as would be consistent with the second alternative.

A general problem with all receptor types is the fate of the stimulating ion or molecule. How strong and how permanent is its union with the receptor membrane? Is it metabolized by the receptor cell or sloughed off and disposed of by some mechanism external to the receptor? The speed of "recovery" of electrical phenomena after withdrawal of a stimulus from the receptor—within a few milliseconds—argues for the latter type of mechanism, although some active "pump" to clear the receptor membrane is not ruled out.

Critical data on this problem might be expected from following the movement, in or around the receptors, of compounds labeled with radioactive tracers. Because of the likelihood of some sort of flow system for removing stimuli from the chemoreceptor membranes in the labellar receptors, we have recently been using tritiated water in our experiments. When tritiated water is applied to the tips of the hairs, we can find no evidence of accumulation during stimulation of the water receptors within normal physiological limits. When $H_2{}^3O$ (1 curie/ml) is injected into the proboscis, behind the labellum, it gradually moves out into the sensory hairs. Both within the hairs and when collected from the hair tips, tritium can be readily differentiated from background radioactivity by a scintillation counter (see Fig. 2–4). The rate of movement of the fluid into the sensory hair can be speeded up by clipping the tip of the sensillum. From these experiments, it seems clear that the actual chemoreceptor membrane of the receptor cell must be bathed in a slowly flowing liquid. This liquid would be expected to influence access to the sensitive sites of the membrane, and to remove some of the chemicals from the receptor area.

ELECTRICAL ACTIVITIES

The labellar receptors also provide a convenient introduction to the electrical activities of chemoreceptors. Ingenious

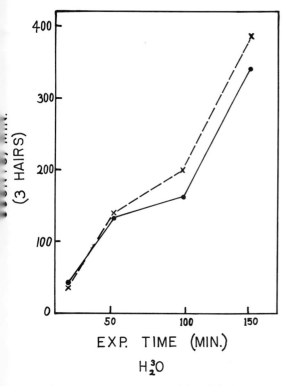

(3 HAIRS)

EXP. TIME (MIN.)

H₂O

Fig. 2–4. Movement of tritium-labeled water from the proboscis of a blowfly into the sensory hairs of the labellum. Data from two counting runs on three sensory hairs were recorded when tritium was injected at 0 minutes.

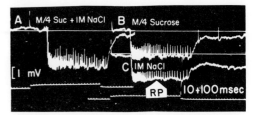

Fig. 2–5. Receptor potentials and spike potentials from labellar hair of Lucilia *(blowfly), recorded by Dr. H. Morita. A single stimulus has been used to obtain records on the right. The left record was obtained by applying a mixture of salt and sugar to show partial summation of receptor potentials. (Courtesy of Dr. H. Morita.)*

techniques of recording, most recently employed in studies by Morita and his collaborators [10], have been particularly helpful in this connection. These workers showed that the initial electrical symptoms of receptor excitation are sustained potentials that can be recorded along the sides of the sensory hairs. These initiate the spike potentials, or impulses, near the receptor cell body. Both the slow, sustained potentials and the faster, action potentials are shown in Fig. 2–5.

Under some conditions the slow potentials are analogous to the "generator potentials" of other primary receptor cells. When more than one receptor cell contributes to the over-all sustained potential, or when inhibition is associated

with the slow potential, it is more accurate to designate the initial electrical effect of stimulus application as merely a "receptor" potential.

The relationship between the receptor potential in a dendrite and the spike potential that it evokes near the cell body is shown on the right side of the diagram in Fig. 2–6. Excitatory stimuli (*ES*) or inhibitory stimuli (*IS*) reach specific receptor sites (*RS*). The receptor potential (*RP*) in the dendrite (*D*) may be either a depolarizing generator potential (*GP*), leading to stimulation (*ST*), or a hyperpolarizing inhibitory potential (*IP*). Stimulation produces action potentials, or spike potentials (*AP*) in or near the cell body (*CB*). In most cases stimulation causes *increased* frequencies of action potentials, as compared to any spontaneous frequency (*SF*) of receptor firing. However, there may actually be *decreased* frequencies of firing as a result of receptor exposure to certain compounds such as long-chain hydrocarbons.

INTEGRATION AND MODULATION OF AFFERENT IMPULSES

Comparison of the fly's labellar chemoreceptors with mammalian taste receptors is made in the lower section of the

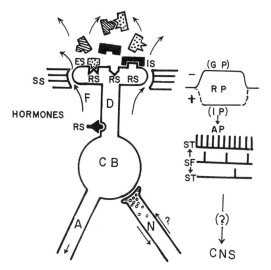

Fig. 2–6. Diagram of some basic properties of chemoreceptor cells. A receptor cell is indicated in the center, and electrical events in various parts of the cell are shown on the right. Explanation of symbols and further details are found in the text. (Redrawn from Hodgson [10].)

diagram (Fig. 2–6). In the fly the afferent axon (A) proceeds without known synapses to the brain. In mammalian taste receptors there is a junction between the actual receptor and an afferent neuron (N), with the latter carrying the pattern of impulses to the brain. The absence of such junctions in the insect preparation rules out one source of a complicating integration of nerve impulses between the receptor and the electrical recording point. Nonetheless, the actual coding of the afferent impulses, which leads to food ingestion or food avoidance, is far more complex than might be expected from the small number of cells involved.

As was shown quite early, stimulating sugars elicit normal feeding responses in food-deprived animals. The same result follows stimulation of the water receptor. With the discovery of the two types of electrolyte receptors, however, the behavioral role of each kind was called into question. The receptor firing to cations does evoke avoidance behavior in many cases, but not in all cases. The

amount of food depletion, the stimulus concentration, and other factors are all important in this case. However, anion stimulation always indicates unacceptable solutions. The anion receptor, then, is the only labellar chemoreceptor that evokes rejection behavior under all the circumstances tested thus far [22].

To these complexities we must add the fact that one molecular species in a stimulating solution may block access of ions or other molecules to the receptor membrane, thereby making it difficult to predict the results—even at the receptor level—of stimulation by normally occurring mixtures of chemicals. Inhibiting compounds may have differential effects upon one type of receptor, as when long-chain hydrocarbons inhibit the responses of sugar receptors, but they leave the water receptors relatively unaffected. Such a case is illustrated by the effects of octylamine, shown in Fig. 2–2. Assuming that the ultimate behavioral reactions to chemical stimuli depend upon the balance and pattern of afferent impulses from all four receptor types, the subtleties of even such a simple sensory system are obvious.

A quite different type of modulation of receptor activity has been observed recently in the insect experimental preparations. The effective agent is a hormone. Of course, enhancement of afferent olfactory activity during stimulation of the sympathetic fibers of the ethmoid nerve in mammals has been known for some time [1]. Hormones from the sympathetic nerve endings might have only an indirect effect upon the chemoreceptors in mammals, acting through effects on blood circulation in the area or some other mechanism.

With the labellar chemoreceptors, the effect must be directly on the receptor cells. Perfusion of the labellum with epinephrine and closely related sympathomimetic compounds may double the frequency of impulses from receptors responding to a standard electrolyte solution [12]. It should be noted that epinephrine and related catechol amines are found in neurosecretory organs of insects, and presumably they would be distributed widely through the open hemolymph system. The flow of materials through receptor organs, such as that illustrated by the data in Fig. 2–4, would be supporting evidence for such an assumption.

In the diagram of chemoreceptor mechanisms (Fig. 2–6) it has been necessary to add some important factors to the area surrounding the receptor cell rather than to the interior of the receptor. The fluid (F) passing the receptor distally is indicated by curved arrows. Supporting structures (SS) and hormones are also included. Exploration of the normal roles of these components is only beginning.

In summary, it is needlessly simplistic to study a single chemoreceptor cell without referring to others in the receptor organ or to such other factors as feedings, hormone level, etc., in the experimental animals. The behavioral studies still are most important in giving direction to electrophysiology. It may appear that these considerations defeat the purpose by making the seemingly simple invertebrate chemoreceptors almost as complicated as mammalian taste buds. Yet there is still a *relative* simplicity associated with the small number of cells in some invertebrate preparations. There is also considerable convenience in using the invertebrate preparations to study the many basic mechanisms that occur in the operation of the chemical senses throughout the animal kingdom.

Discussion

Jacobs: Do you feel that the function of the flushing mechanism is limited to washing away the stimulating solution, or might it change extracellular ionic concentration and perhaps shift adaptation level, thus determining the responsiveness of the receptor to the subsequent stimulus? Have you measured the liquid in terms of the ionic concentrations?

Hodgson: No, we have not. We simply have not been able to collect enough of the liquid yet. It is possible that the composition of the fluid over the receptors might influence the adaptation levels or other aspects of receptor function. The long-range implication seems to be that, no matter how much we might like to confine studies only to the receptor level, we are actually forced to think about the whole sensory system and also the accessory systems, which influence input so profoundly.

Beidler: It is interesting that in the olfactory system of many animals, particularly birds, the sustentacular cell that surrounds the receptor cell also secretes. In the taste cell of mammals there is some indication that this may also be the case. I was interested in this secretion because it raises the question of what is the normal environment of your receptors. Also, you refer to receptors going positive and negative, but you don't really know where zero is? So these are just terms.

Hodgson: Zero is simply the potential recorded in the absence of any external stimulation. The zero level is reasonably constant, even though this is not an intracellular recording. The fluctuations, either positive or negative, are quite reproducible for a given chemical stimulus. Hence, they provide the closest electrical indications of initial receptor mechanisms that anyone has yet obtained with an invertebrate preparation.

Beidler: G. Eisenman's approach *(Symposium on Membrane Transport and Metabolism,* S. Kleinzeller and A. Kotyk [eds.], Academic Press, New York, 1962) is identical to that which we used in our taste receptor experiments and is also identical to the approach of Gilbert Ling (*A Physical Theory of the Living State*, Random, 1962, p. 383).

Hodgson: It is encouraging that, quite independently, we may be achieving some concepts of general validity regarding the mechanisms by which ions stimulate.

Beidler: What did you mean by open-end synapse?

Hodgson: Nothing more than that the receptor membrane functions like the postsynaptic membrane in a neuron-to-neuron junction. Instead of being excited by a chemical transmitter substance from another neuron, as is the postsynaptic membrane, the chemoreceptor is excited by chemicals moving freely in the environment. When we know more about transmitter substances, as well as about the sensitivities of chemoreceptors in "lower" invertebrates, we may better be able to judge whether the analogy can tell us anything about the early evolution of chemoreceptors.

Pfaffman: Do you have any evidence or suspicion as to whether the flushing action is an intracellular or extracellular process? In our studies of the effect of saliva on reactivity of taste cells, we have evidence of a possible extracellular electrolyte influence. Have you any evidence in your preparations as to whether the hemal elements continuously produce and extrude cytoplasmic material in a manner analogous to that found in nerve fibers (PTO) reported by Paul Weiss?

Hodgson: We have no evidence concerning the origin of the fluid. Each sensory hair has another cavity in it, beside the one occupied by the dendrites. It has been suggested that this could serve for fluid transport to the tip, but the fluid could also come from the actual receptor cells.

Halpern: I think the amino acids do have a capacity to penetrate the mammalian taste receptor cells. If ^{14}C-glycine is placed on the rat tongue for a few minutes, we find activity inside the cell after about three minutes. This is about the time that glycine reaches maximum response magnitude (Halpern *et al., J. Gen. Physiol.,* 45:681, 1962), and it may be that getting it in requires about this much time in the mammal. At the Olfaction and Taste Meeting in Japan, a flushing mechanism was described for insect olfactory chemoreceptors. Is it necessarily a simple electrolyte? It may have considerable characteristics of its own in terms of absorbing various substances and changing the time in which different substances will affect the receptor surface.

Hodgson: We have looked for tritium uptake from labeled stimuli but thus far have no convincing evidence of it. This may mean only that the amounts taken up are too small to differentiate from background activity, but we are continuing this approach.

The observation of oozing from the sensory hairs was made by Brunhild Stuerckow (in *Olfaction and Taste, II,* T. Hayashi [ed.], Pergamon Press, 1967 [in press]), and I am glad to acknowledge that her findings gave us hope that we could use tracers to follow movement of chemicals in these taste organs.

Epstein: I have a carrot and a stick for Hodgson. First, the carrot: It is good news that the fourth cell has been identified and I would like to know more about it. The stick is a word of caution about accepting the Loomis-Lenhoff glutathione story of feeding in hydra. There was a time when we thought we finally had an animal in which feeding could be understood as an elegant and very simple chemical reflex. Forrest *(Biol. Bull.,* **122:** 343, 1962) has shown and recalled evidence a hundred years old showing that glutathione is neither necessary nor specific for feeding in this animal. That is, the feeding movements can be elicited by pieces of chemically pure filter paper, by bits of boiled egg white, or by chemicals unrelated to glutathione, such as nicotinic acid, riboflavin, and just plain sodium chloride. It seems that the glutathione produces what is best described as a paralysis of mouth opening and not really the full feeding reflex.

Hodgson: To take the carrot first, the fourth receptor cell studies have a history of only a few months. The function of this receptor was recognized by Steinhardt (unpublished Ph.D. thesis, Columbia University, 1966). Evidence that anions, as well as cations, are effective stimuli had been obtained by Gillary (unpublished Ph.D. thesis, The Johns Hopkins University, 1966) —contrary to several earlier reports on insect and mammalian salt receptors. Impulses from the "anion receptor" had not been clearly recognized, however, because of their small amplitude and easy confusion with the water receptor impulses. Steinhardt found that the NH_4^+ ion does not inhibit the water receptor, and by using NH_4NO_3 he could get many impulses from both receptor types, with the expected occasional summations of anion and water spikes. By varying the anion components of salts, while holding the cations constant, he found that the frequency of discharges of the "new" receptor varied according to the anion present $(I^- \geqq NO_3^- > Br^- > CI^- > F^-)$. One word of caution: While the fourth cell does respond to anions, this may not be its complete repertoire, even though it appears so now.

Regarding the stick part of the question, I think that suspended judgment is in order. Clearly, Forrest has shown that reduced glutathione is not so uniquely specific a normal feeding stimulant as was once thought. On the other hand, Lenhoff has shown that the glutathione response is very dependent upon the microenvironment of the animal, and comparisons are difficult unless this is rigorously controlled. Within those controlled limits, the glutathione response seems a useful one for analyzing feeding responses in what amounts to physical chemical terms.

Epstein: Have you been able to see that anion cell discharging in your old records? Do you see it, looking retrospectively at your work with chloride salts?

Hodgson: Yes.

REFERENCES

1. Beidler, L. M. Physiology of olfaction and gustation. *Ann. Otol. Rhinol. Laryngol.,* **69:** 1–12, 1960.
2. Case, J. F. Properties of the dactyl chemoreceptors of *Cancer antennarius* Stimpson and *C. productus* Randall. *Biol. Bull.* (Woods Hole, Mass.), **127:** 428–46, 1964.
3. DeLorenzo, A. J. D. Studies on the ultrastructure and histophysiology of cell membranes, nerve fibers, and synaptic junctions in chemoreceptors, in *Olfaction and Taste,* Zotterman, Y. (ed.). Macmillan, New York, pp. 5–18, 1963.
4. Dethier, V. G. *The Physiology of Insect Senses.* John Wiley & Sons, New York, 266 pp., 1963.
5. Eccles, J. C. *The Physiology of Synapses.* Academic Press, New York, 316 pp., 1964.
6. Eisenman, G. Cation selective glass electrodes and their mode of operation. *J. Biophys.,* **2** (2): 259–332, 1962.
7. Evans, D. R., and Mellon, D., Stimulation of a primary taste receptor by salts. *J. Gen. Physiol.,* **45:** 487–500, 1962.
8. Gillary, H. L. "Quantitative electrophysiological studies on the mechanism of stimulation of the salt receptor of the blowfly."

Unpublished thesis, The Johns Hopkins University, 94 pp., 1966.

9. Hodgson, E. S. Electrophysiological studies of arthropod chemoreception. III: Chemoreception of terrestrial and fresh-water arthropods. *Biol. Bull.* (Woods Hole, Mass.), **115**: 114–25, 1958.

10. Hodgson, E. S. The chemical senses and changing viewpoints in sensory physiology. *Viewpoints in Biology*, **4**: 83–124, 1965.

11. Hodgson, E. S., and Hodgson, V. S. Unpublished data, 1966.

12. Hodgson, E. S., Ishibashi, T., and Wright, A. Unpublished data, 1966.

13. Hodgson, E. S., Lettvin, J. Y., and Roeder, K. D. The physiology of a primary chemoreceptor unit. *Science*, **122**: 417–18, 1955.

14. Hyman, L. H. *The Invertebrates. I: Protozoa Through Ctenophora*. McGraw-Hill, New York, 726 pp., 1940.

15. Laverack, M. S. Aspects of chemoreception in crustacea. *Comp. Biochem. Physiol.*, **8**: 141–51, 1963.

16. Lenhoff, H. M. Activation of the feeding reflex in *Hydra littoralis*, in *The Biology of Hydra*. University of Miami Press, Miami, pp. 203–32, 1961.

17. Lentz, T. L., and Barrnett, R. J. Fine structure of the nervous system of *Hydra*. *Amer. Zoologist*, **5**: 341–56, 1965.

18. Levandowsky, M., and Hodgson, E. S. Amino acid and amine receptors of lobsters. *Comp. Biochem. Physiol.*, **16**: 159–61, 1965.

19. Loomis, W. F. Glutathione control of the specific feeding reactions of hydra. *Ann. N.Y. Acad. Sci.*, **62**: 209–28, 1955.

20. Mellon, D., and Evans, D. R. Electrophysiological evidence that water stimulates a fourth sensory cell in the blowfly taste receptor. *Amer. Zoologist*, **1**: 372, 1961.

21. Pantin, C. F. A., and Pantin, A. M. P. The stimulus to feeding in *Anemonia sulcata*. *J. Exp. Biol.*, **20**: 6–13, 1943.

22. Steinhardt, R. A. Physiology of labellar electrolyte receptors of the blowfly, *Phormia regina*. Unpublished thesis, Columbia University, 85 pp., 1966.

23. Wolbarsht, M. L., and Dethier, V. G. Electrical activity in the chemoreceptors of the blowfly. I: Responses to chemical and mechanical stimulation. *J. Gen. Physiol.*, **42**: 393–412, 1958.

Research in the author's laboratory, some of which is reported here for the first time, was supported by Grant E–2271 from the National Institutes of Health, U.S. Public Health Service. Drs. H. Morita and R. Steinhardt kindly provided figures to illustrate their own work.

3: The Chemical Senses and Food Intake in the Lower Vertebrates by John E. Bardach

THE TERM "lower vertebrates" will be taken here to comprise the poikilothermous classes of the subphylum Vertebrata, namely lampreys and hagfishes (Agnatha); the sharks, rays, skates, and chimaeras (Chondrichthyes); the lungfishes, lobefins, and higher bony fishes (Osteichthyes); the frogs, toads, and salamanders (Amphibia); and the snakes, lizards, turtles, and crocodiles (Reptilia). The first three classes are entirely aquatic but still, generally, lay their eggs and spend their early lives in the water. Only two genera of salamanders and one of toads are ovoviviparous; and even those amphibians that live on land do so in moisture-laden niches. The reptiles are either ovoviviparous or land breeders, though some, like the sea turtles, seek the water soon after they hatch.

The lower vertebrates not only comprise the great majority of present-day and fossil backboned animals, they also fill the widest possible variety of habitats, from the depths of the oceans to high mountaintops and from tropical rain forests to deserts. Consequently, their feeding adaptations are legion and their foods range from detritus (e.g., lamprey larvae) to blood and tissue fluids (adult lampreys), from algae (certain bony fishes) to leaves (certain lizards), and from carrion (hagfishes) to large living prey (sharks and snakes).

On the grounds of variety alone, one may well suspect that no generalizations that relate the chemical senses of these animals to their food intake are possible, except, perhaps, on the cellular, biophysical level [21], at least not any that would apply to the subphylum as a whole and be narrow enough to be meaningful. Moreover, there are variations in the spectra of taste sensitivity even within one species, such as those noted by Konishi and Zotterman [28] between Swedish and Japanese strains of carp.

An equally serious obstacle to an attempt at generalization is the lack of pertinent information, even about entire subclasses. For instance, the Elasmobranchii, which include the sharks, are often large predators, dangerous to man, and known to be attracted under certain conditions to blood and tissue fluids in the water. One would think that this attribute alone would have led to thorough studies of their feeding behavior and physiology. Yet a recent reviewer of their olfactory, gustatory, and chemical senses [44] stresses that current physiological knowledge about shark chemoreception and feeding is sparse indeed. If this pertains to a group as important to man as the sharks, one may imagine the gaps in such information concerning the remainder of the lower vertebrates.

Nevertheless, an attempt will be made here to put some order into the miscellany. The chemical senses of lower vertebrates as they are related to feeding will be discussed, with emphasis on the relative roles of smell and taste in locating food and on the final acceptance or rejection of food in some aquatic, semiaquatic, and terrestrial members of the group. A phylogenetically arranged *anatomical* overview of potential assistance to human-or-mammal-oriented readers will precede the main discussion of *behavior* and *physiology*. The attention given to the different groups reflects both the interests of the reviewer and the degree to which the groups have been studied.

CHEMOSENSORY ANATOMY OF THE LOWER VERTEBRATES

Agnatha The lampreys are often bloodsuckers as adults but have detritus-feeding larvae that spend several years buried in the bottom of streams (e.g., *Petromyzon marinus),* while the hagfishes are predators or carrion eaters. Their single, medially situated olfactory organ still bears marks of bilateral symmetry [25]. It ends either in a blind sac (lampreys) or connects with the pharynx (hagfishes). Lampreys develop their nasal apparatus only when they are transformed into adults, at which time they acquire the species-specific range of nasal folds, which are lined with ciliary supporting cells and typical vertebrate olfactory sense cells, except at the fold's periphery. A blind nasal sac, extending caudally beneath the brain and bearing dorsally a cartilaginous capsule with the olfactory folds, is emptied and filled by the alternating contraction and relaxation of the branchial basket. The olfactory cells in the black-pigmented epithelium give rise to two short, many-bundled olfactory nerves leading to the olfactory bulb. The single nasal organ of the hagfishes shows more bilateral symmetry in its folding pattern than does that of lampreys; the olfactory nerve enters the bulbus in several separate roots, each of which is connected to its own set of glomeruli [37].

No references to electromicroscope studies of lamprey or hagfish olfactory cells were located.

Among non-olfactory, presumably chemosensory, structures of the Agnatha there are: in larval lamprey, taste buds in the pharynx and gill cavities that spread also to the outer skin in the adult [2] and a profusion of free nerve endings especially concentrated in the oral tentacles [37]; on the tentacles of hagfishes, some cells that grossly resemble olfactory cells and others that appear like the gustatory cells of more advanced groups, some occurring singly and some in buds in the epithelium. They are mostly, though not all, innervated by cranial nerves.

Chondrichthyes Most sharks and rays have ventral mouths, and their narial pits lie at varying distances from the oral opening [38,44] (Fig. 3–1). A first group has them far anteriorly, on the snout, as in the tiger shark (*Galeocerdo cuvieri*) or the hammerheads (*Sphyrna*), the latter to be discussed in more detail below. The nares of the second group, to which the smooth dogfish (*Mustelus canis*) belongs, lie close to but not directly at the mouth, while in the third group, the one that includes many rays, the pit so closely adjoins the mouth that water from it drains into the latter.

The nasal pits are oval, sometimes lozenge-shaped, and lie across the snout or point obliquely toward the mouth; in the last group they lie almost at right angles to the mouth. Folds in the nasal pits lie predominantly at right angles to

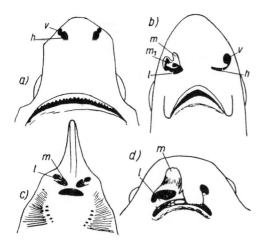

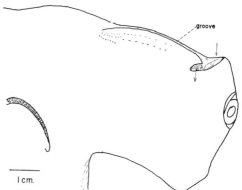

Fig. 3–2.   Ventral view of the head of a
hammerhead shark (Sphyrna lewini) showing
groove leading to nostril. (From Sharks and
Survival, P. W. Gilbert [ed.] [44].)

Fig. 3–1.   Position of nares in various
elasmobranchs: (a) Spinax niger,
(b) Mustelus, (c) Rhinobatus, and
(d) Myliobatis; h = posterior nasal opening,
l = lateral fold, m, m_1 = median fold, and
r, r_1 = anterior nasal opening. (From
Schnakenbeck, after Plate [38].)

the longitudinal axis of the pit; these
folds in turn are thrown into secondary
folds which carry the olfactory epithelium. The narial pits are covered by
variously folded and molded skin flaps
so that water courses through them from
a lateral entrance to a medial exit; some
pits may be almost divided into two
chambers by these skin flaps. Skin
grooves leading to the pits help to channel the flow of water, which in turn is
drawn in, to a greater or lesser extent
depending on the position of the nares,
by the stream of water inspired through
the mouth. Ciliary movements within
the pits also serve to channel the water.

The hammerhead may be singled out
because of its peculiar head shape. The
entrances to the nose lie laterally at the
head's leading edge where a pronounced
groove deflects water outwardly, directly
into the large nasal pits; the water then
leaves the nose medially (Fig. 3–2). If
any fish is anatomically endowed to detect differences in scent concentration on
both its right and left sides, it is this
genus of predatory sharks, some species

of which are reported to have reached
twenty feet in length; the water inlet
into the right nose would thus be separated from that of the left nose by a
distance of several feet.

The chemical senses are important in
the lives of most sharks and rays. Their
olfactory sacs are large, and from them
short nerves lead to correspondingly sizable bulbs that are clearly bilobed in
some species and somewhat bilobed in
others; the olfactory tracts are relatively
long. In some sharks, e.g., the blacktip
(Caracharinus melanopterus), of rare but
authenticated man-eating fame, the olfactory lobes are clearly the largest portion of the brain.

Taste buds of the Chondrichthyes are
found in the folded epithelial lining of
the mouth and pharynx, especially associated with papillae that occur on the
roof and, more numerously, on the floor
of the mouth. They are innervated by
cranial nerves VII, IX, and X. On the
outer body surface of sharks are found
the so-called pit organs [14]. They are
arranged in various species-specific patterns, more regularly rowlike in some
sharks than in others. They were originally reported to be taste organs, but recent neuroanatomical and histological

investigations [45] see them rather as mechanoreceptors of close relation to those of the lateral line.

Osteichthyes Of all the classes of vertebrates, the bony fishes have the greatest number of species; the anatomical differences in their chemical sense organs are accordingly varied. The review or summary descriptions of Hasler [15], Teichmann [42], and Holl [22] (the latter for the olfactory organ only) should be consulted for further detail.

The primary plan of the fish nose is still that of a covered pit, not connected with the mouth. The olfactory sac, or pit, is large and elongate, extending from the tip of the snout to the orbit of the eye in the eels and morays (Anguilliformes), the fishes with the most acute sense of smell. In contrast, certain puff-ers (Tetraodontidae), highly visually oriented reef fishes, have lost the nasal sac completely; there remains only a minute epidermal patch from which the nearly invisible olfactory nerve originates. These puffers also have no olfactory bulb. Many patterns of intermediate anatomical development reflect the relative role of olfaction in the lives of fishes (Fig. 3–3).

The olfactory folds vary greatly in direction and number, with macro-osmatic species such as the eels having the most numerous lamellae (140 of them in *Conger*), predominantly set at right angles to the long axis of the nasal chamber. The presumably anosmic stickleback normally has two folds (Fig. 3–4). The number of folds and receptor cells varies also with age.

There are three types of arrangement

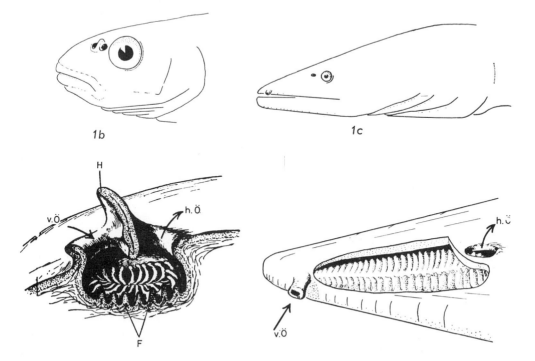

Fig. 3–3. Nasal anatomy of bony fishes. Left. Position and internal structure of the nose in the minnow (Phoxinus phoxinus). Right. The same for the eel (Anguilla anguilla). F = folds of olfactory rosette; H = skin-fold which deflects water into nose; h.ö = posterior opening; v.ö = anterior opening. (From H. Teichmann, "Die Umschau," in Wissenschaft in Technik, Frankfurt ams Main, 62: 568, 1962.)

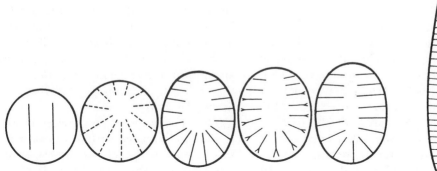

Fig. 3–4. Number and arrangement of folds in the noses of various fishes.
From left to right: *Stickleback* (Gasterosteus aculeatus), *Pike* (Esox lucious), *Rainbow trout* (Salmo gairdneri), *Perch* (Perca fluviatilis), *the minnow Elritze* (Phoxinus phoxinus), *Eel* (Anguilla anguilla). *(From H. Teichmann [40].)*

of the olfactory epithelium: (1) continuous except for the folds' distal and lateral parts (e.g., the perch, *Perca*); (2) in large fields between the folds (pike, *Esox*); and (3) in small fields on the folds and in the valleys, with the sense cells arranged somewhat like taste buds (carp, *Cyprinus*). The epithelium is made up of basal, supporting, and sensory cells; the supporting cells may or may not be ciliated and may have mucus cells interspersed among them [22] (Fig. 3–5). For the organization of the fish forebrain and the smell-related nerve paths in the brain, see Ariens-Kappers, Huber, and Crosby [2] and Aronson [3].

Water may pass through the nasal chambers (1) by deflection from a skin fold that bridges the chamber (goldfish, *Carassius*); (2) by suction, with the help of accessory, fluid-filled sacs that work like a hydraulic system (flounder, *Pleuronectes*); and (3) by channelings assisted by ciliary motion (eel, *Anguilla*). Combinations of these methods also occur [29].

The early development of the lungfish (*Protopterus*) nose resembles that of teleosts, but later the anterior nares come to lie on the upper lip, almost at the entrance of the mouth, while the posterior ones have migrated into the oral cavity and lie lateral to the vomerine teeth. Numerous well-developed lamellae in the olfactory rosette bear sense cells that extend only over the dorsal and lateral inner faces of the lamellae [12].

Taste buds of fishes lie in the mouth, the pharynx, the gill cavity, on the gill arches, on appendages such as barbels and/or fins, and also, in some fishes, on the body, being distributed down to the very tail [16,42]. They may be arranged singly or in groups, and their apexes may bulge out slightly or lie in a more or less pronounced pit (Fig. 3–6). The taste buds are innervated by cranial nerves VII, IX, and X; the recurrent *facialis* branch, or *ramus lateralis accessorius,* especially, innervates the buds on the trunk (100,000 or more in catfishes) or on the fins; these appendages, often modified into feelers (hake, *Urophycis*), also receive spinal nerves.

Fish can also taste without taste buds.

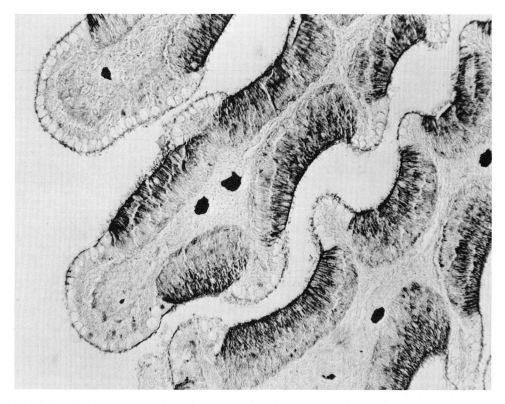

Fig. 3–5a.   Sagittal section through olfactory lamellae of the Coho salmon (Oncorhynchus kisutch) showing fields of olfactory cells; Bodian silver stain.

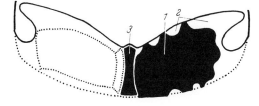

Fig. 3–5b.   Distribution of cell types on an olfactory lamella of the eel; 1 = olfactory epithelium, 2 = indifferent epithelium, and 3 = median raphe.

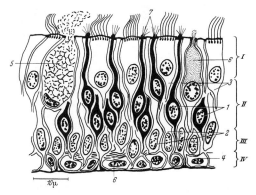

The spinal nerves innervate special epidermal "spindle" cells (Fig. 3–7) [49] on the head and body, and, in some cases (searobins, Triglidae), on the tentacular fin rays, where chemical sensitivity is reasonably high. The assumption that these cells are probably chemosensory is, so far, based on their structure, which has some similarities to that of the sensory cells in the taste buds. The latter

Fig. 3–5c.   Detail of area 1 in Fig. 3–5b; 1 = receptors, 2 = supporting cells, 3 = ciliated cells, 4 = basal cells, 5 = goblet cell, 6 = clubshaped secretory cells, and 7 = olfactory vesicle or cell with sensory hairs; I = zone of ciliated cell nuclei, II = zone of receptor cell nuclei, III = zone of nuclei of supporting cells, and IV = zone of basal cells. (Figs. 3–5b and 3–5c after Holl [22].)

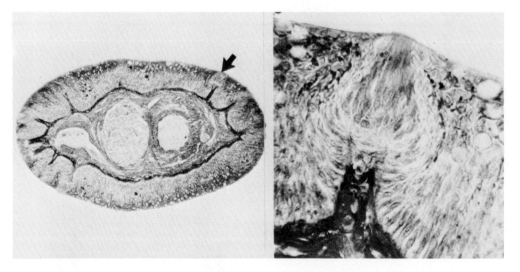

Fig. 3–6a.   Cross section through the barbel of a yellow bullhead (Ictalurus natalis); *the arrow points to a taste bud, note the large nerve trunk in the center. Eosin hematoxyline stain.*

Fig. 3–6b.   Detail of taste bud of the same animal, note the bulge at the apex of the bud.

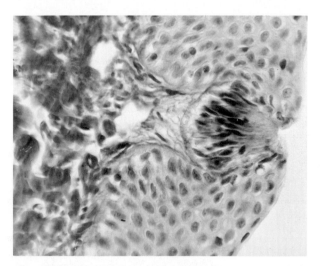

Fig. 3–6c.   Taste bud from the barbel of a sturgeon (Acipenser fulvescens), *note the apical depression, in contrast to b.*

have been the object of some electron microscope studies (Fig. 3–8). Desgranges [9] described variously shaped microvilli at the apexes of taste cells in the bullhead *(Ictalurus)*; Hirata [18] deals with innervation of the sense cells and with other aspects of the ultrastructure of sensory, supporting, and basal cells in fish taste buds. Two things should be mentioned: First, there are transitional cells at the border of the bud which may become either supporting or sensory cells; and second, the few species so far studied have fewer microvilli-like extensions per sensory cell than do mammals. The supporting cells have more but

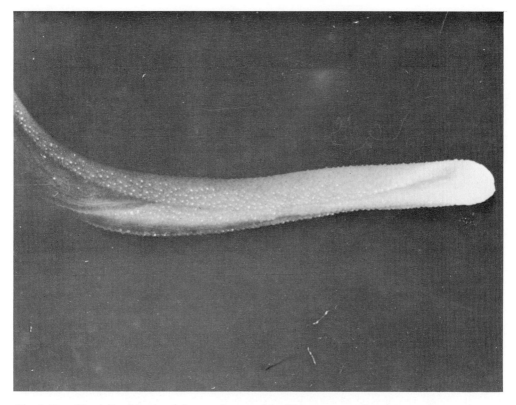

Fig. 3–7a. *Specialized pectoral finray of a searobin* (Prionotus carolinus); *note the small skin bulges on the fin which, as shown here, is ca. 3 cm long.*

smaller extensions than do the sensory cells.

Aside from small nerves that proliferate around taste buds [10], probably subserving touch, there are numerous free nerve endings in the skin of fishes [49], some of which have at times been implicated to subserve the so-called common chemical sense. Buddenbrock [8] denies, with good argument, that such a sense exists; but even if it did, it would not have much to do with food intake.

Amphibia The nares connect with the mouth cavity in all amphibians. The simplest condition is that of the gillbearing salamander (*Necturus*), which has an elongated nasal chamber with epithelial folds that bear budlike islands of olfactory cells among the supporting cells, an arrangement which closely resembles that of certain fishes. Macroosmatic urodeles such as the newt (*Triturus*) have a main nasal cavity with a respiratory passageway ventrolateral to it. In the land urodeles, especially, there occurs in this passage, separated from the main cavity by a fold, an area of olfactory and supporting cells that differs from that of the main cavity. This is the beginning of the organ of Jacobson, which here appears with a narrowed lumen, secretory and ciliary supporting cells, and densely packed olfactory cells (Fig. 3–9). The lacrymal duct opens into the nasal passage, somewhat anterior to Jacobson's organ [17].

The gross anatomy of the nasal organ of tailless amphibians is more complicated than that of their tailed cousins. Jacobson's organ extends medially and ventrally to the main nasal cavity and

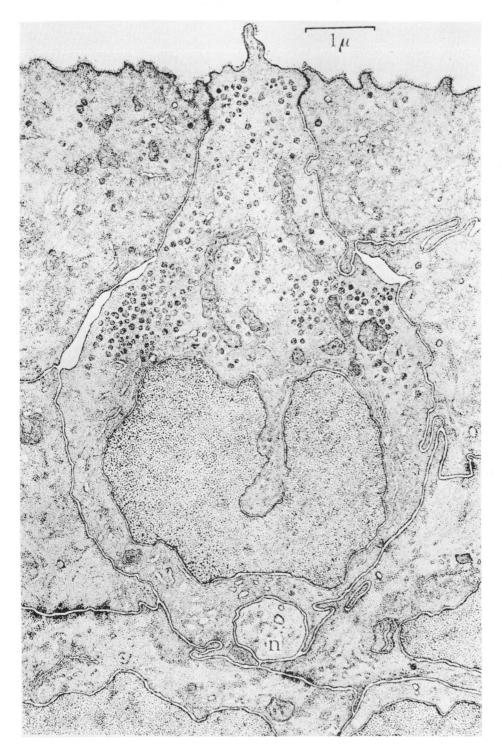

Fig. 3–7b.   *Presumed chemosensory cell in fish epidermis, also found on searobin fins;*
n = *nerve. (From Whitear [49] and personal communication.)*

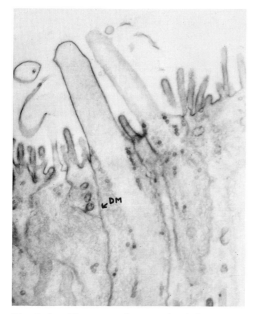

Fig. 3–8. Electron micrograph of the apex of a bullhead taste bud; note the sense cells with their large extensions and the cylinder of granules around a hyaline core and also the supporting cells with many smaller microvilli; DM = double membrane. (Courtesy of D. Webb, University of Michigan.)

the respiratory passage; it is well separated from the latter also. Several types of glands pour their secretions into the main and accessory nasal cavities; apparently Jacobson's organ especially needs copious lubrication (see below).

In the small group of legless caecilians, Jacobson's organ is connected to

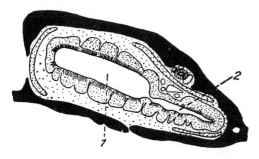

Fig. 3–9. Cross section through the central portion of the nasal cavity of the newt (Triturus alpestris): 1 = main cavity; 2 = Jacobson's organ; the black, outer region is bone. (From Herter, after Schuch [17].)

the so-called tentacle, a structure situated anterolaterally on the head. It is capable of rapid projection and retraction for several millimeters and is mainly used when the animal creeps forward. One should note that its poorly developed, skin-covered eyes are capable at best of conveying only general information about light intensities. Internally, the tentacular apparatus extends posteriorly, beneath the eye, and receives lubricating secretions from the orbital gland. One finds the speculation that the tentacle, as it is retracted, somehow transfers mucus saturated with odoriferous substances to the Jacobson's organ; a possible accessory olfactory function has been ascribed to the tentacle, aside from its very clearly tactile one [12].

Taste organs are restricted to the mouth cavities of amphibians; they are typically bud-shaped in urodeles, while they have been called taste discs on the tongue of frogs and toads because their cells are spread out rather than gathered together. In the discs, free nerve endings reach the periphery between supporting cells [7]. Herter [17], however, expresses doubts about the discs' gustatory function. Physiological details about amphibian taste and the role it may play in the acceptance or rejection of food will be treated in the next major division of this review.

Reptilia The nasal apparatus of reptiles, like that of the preceding classes, reaches various degrees of complexity [7]. Snakes and lizards, with the exception of chameleons, have a well-developed organ of Jacobson. In many snakes it lies fairly well forward, in the roof of the mouth, and has a narrow duct leading into a hollow globe that is lined with columns of olfactory epithelium and partly filled with a mushroom-shaped tissue plug or pad; various glands are associated with it.

Adult crocodiles have lost the vomeronasal, or Jacobson's organ, but they have pronounced conchae, well-separated respiratory and olfactory nasal ducts, and generally presage the condition of the mammalian nose with its turbinate bones. Turtles range from the desert to the sea and consequently have varied life histories and show varied development of the vomeronasal organ. Generally its form is that of a duct rather than a hollow sphere, as in snakes, and it is accessible from the main portion of the nose.

While under water, aquatic reptiles close their nostrils. Water snakes, for instance, have muscles as well as vascular pads that shut their nares. Correlations have been suggested, at least for turtles and snakes, between the degree of water life, which places less reliance on the sense of sight, and the development of Jacobson's organ, although the best-developed such structure occurs in the nearly blind, burrowing, snake-like lizard (Typhlops). It seems that the important influence here is not that of the terrestrial or aquatic environment, but the degree to which other senses, such as sight, will guide the animal.

A functional relationship between the tongue and the vomeronasal organ of reptiles is described by Kahmann [30] (see also the next section). The tips of many snakes' tongues lie on small pads near the median mandible and fit into corresponding depressions in the roof of the mouth. When the tongue is everted, reaches for a trace of scent, and then is retracted, the chemical is passed into the organ of Jacobson by other pads in the mouth.

Taste structures occur in the mouths of all reptiles, though in widely differing numbers. Venomous snakes have taste buds all over their mouths and even on the sheaths of their poison fangs while crocodiles, surely gulpers of prey par excellence, have them only in two small patches on the pterygoid bone, on the level at which the teeth of the upper jaw end.

The occurrence and variable development of the vomeronasal organ in reptiles and amphibians still require mention of a division in the innervations and central connections of smell. The vomeronasal, though part of cranial nerve I, is well separated from it and eventually leads to different nuclei. In addition the trigeminal nerve plays a role in olfaction and probably also in taste [2]. The only attempt, in the lower vertebrates, at a physiological approach to this complex system was made by Tucker [46], who admits that his experiments were but exploratory.

FOOD INTAKE AND THE CHEMOSENSORY BEHAVIOR AND PHYSIOLOGY OF THE LOWER VERTEBRATES

General Remarks In the feeding behavior of animals, as in human affairs, possesion is nine points of the law; but to possess food one must first find it. All senses are involved in that quest to some extent, but some animals rely more on chemical senses than others. Since water is not as good an optical medium as is air, one may expect nocturnal or deep-water aquatic predators, or animals with a special diet, to use chemical senses in food hunting more than do herbivores with catholic tastes, or filter feeders and plankton eaters.

It is noteworthy here that some fishes defy the general distinction between smell as a distance sense and taste as a close-range sense, for they can navigate by taste over distances reliably observed to be at least fifty times their own body length, and they can follow a chemical gradient, without a current to orient them, by taste alone.

Once the animal has found food, by visual, mechanical, or, as in some fishes, even electrical clues, it may still have to test its find just before or after taking it into the mouth. The decision as to palatability is based, at least in part, on taste. The "feel" of the food, that is, its impression on the mechanical senses in and around the mouth, is often as important to an animal as taste—or more so—and is very closely associated with it. Other animals, however, such as some sharks, fishes, amphibians, and reptiles, are indiscriminate gulpers.

Following Food-Scent Trails Controlled observations of the mode of search among the lower vertebrates were made with snakes, by dragging a dead mouse [30]; with newts, by dragging juicy pieces of earthworm over a bending path [17]; and with sharks, by releasing the scent of food into a current [21].

Food-scent trails in water or air can rarely be as clearly delimited or as narrow as they are on the ground, and animals searching for a chemical in these fluids need to spread their sensors as widely as possible. Antennae, barbels, threadlike fins are all gross anatomical adaptations to this exigency. In addition, the receptors themselves need to be acute, and the peripheral and central apparatus need to be geared for sensing frequent and rapid changes. Fishes (and flying insects), furthermore, detect these changes in scent concentration in three dimensions whereas a newt, a snake, or a dog searching along a narrow scent trail on the ground stays more confined to one plane and has fewer eddies to contend with. When the animal loses a trail on the ground, he changes direction and usually finds the narrow scent spoor again. Among vertebrates, the ability to assay for changes in "chemical space" seems to have evolved to the highest degree in certain fishes. Fig. 3–10 illustrates a behavior common to the above-mentioned animals, and others,

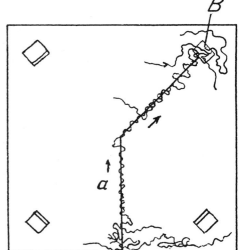

Fig. 3–10a. *A European common viper* (Vipera aspis) *tracking the spoor of a mouse killed by it, which had been dragged to the box* (B). *(From Buddenbrock, after Baumann [8].)*

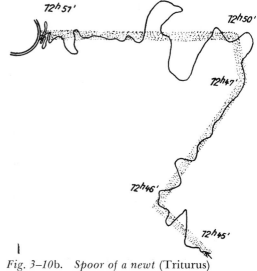

Fig. 3–10b. *Spoor of a newt* (Triturus) *following an experimentally produced earthworm scent trail. (From Herter [17].)*

when they follow a scent. It seems to result generally from the comparison of successive sensory inputs, not from simultaneous comparison between right and left as in binaural hearing. The relative closeness of the nares of most vertebrates makes it difficult for them to have one nostril inside a smell corridor and the other one outside. Beneath a certain level of evolution, e.g., reptiles, the vertebrates cannot move their heads very well; rather, if they lose a scent as they crawl, slide, or swim, they turn, and depending on their size with relation to the trail, they manage either a U-turn, several S's, or one or more figure eights; insects behave similarly.

The path swum by a bullhead in search of food scent released upstream illustrates both the overshooting and the resulting figure-eight pattern (Fig. 3–11).[1]

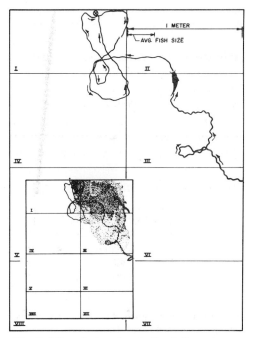

Fig. 3–11b. *Swimming path of the same animal after 0.1 M cysteine (50 ml delivered over 10 min) in a dye was released into the tank where a current flowed from top to bottom.*

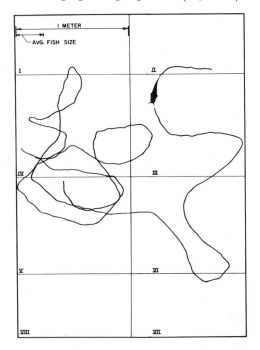

Fig. 3–11a. *Swimming path of a blind bullhead* (Ictalurus nebulosus) *in a tank without a chemical stimulus.*

According to observations in our laboratory, the first evidence of scent detection is a speeding up of the water drawn through the nasal cavity (Chen, Master's thesis [in preparation]). Then the animal starts swimming slowly in and out

of a tongue of scent, with accentuated to-and-fro movements—for the fluorescent trace is thick; then, as the trace becomes thinner, it speeds up and hence leaves the scent area; it returns, overshoots, and repeats these movements, narrowing the path as it nears the point from which the chemical is being released.

When a catfish spreads its lateral barbels in its food search, they reach the greatest anterolateral extension when the animal makes contact with the surface film, as it does frequently (Fig. 3–13); they give the animal an isosceles "detection triangle," at whose corners the tips of the lateral barbels and the tail are assemblages of taste buds. The barbel tips form the corners of the triangle on the short side and are about twelve times as far apart as the nares, whereas the distance from each barbel tip to the

[1] The track is a photographic trace made by sewing a fluorescent tag onto the head of a blinded fish and exposing the film in ultraviolet light for several minutes as the fish swam in a shallow tank (Fig. 3–12).

Fig. 3–12. Photograph to explain genesis of swimming paths traced in Figs. 3–13, 3–16, and 3–17. In this exposure, fluorescent food-scented dye was released into a slowly flowing current; the bullhead with its fluorescent head tag finds the source of the scent. The camera shutter was left open in ultraviolet light, and the exposure was terminated with a flash. (Photo, P. C. Davis, University of Michigan.)

tail, one of the triangle's long sides, is at least thirty times the internarial distance.

Such anatomical attributes enable the bullhead, after all, to detect chemical differences to either side of it by means of taste at least as well as might the hammerhead shark, mentioned above, by means of smell. Bullheads seem, indeed, to make simultaneous comparisons of a chemical's concentration to the right and left of them by taste alone (we used liver extract or cysteine—see below about the sensitivity to the amino acid); photographic tracks of blinded, anosmic bullheads show them to continue along the edges of fluorescent, dye-marked scent fields with one lateral barbel in and one out; they quickly find the scent source, often without deviation during the approach (Fig. 3–14).

One-sided deprivation of chemosensory input, as in the classical experiment in which Parker [36] plugged one naris of a shark and elicited frequent turnings to the intact side, is mentioned in support of a theory that some central neural mechanism enables the animal to average right and left inputs. In bullheads, however, such a unilateral deprivation must involve most of the taste sensors of one side before a lopsided search results (Fig. 3–15), though Teichmann and Teichmann [43] found no effect on the search pattern after one-sided smell elimination in the shark (*Scilliorhinus canicula*). Moreover, in bullheads unilateral deprivation of smell and/or taste sensors tends to change the slow initial to-and-fro search to one with more overshooting.

The usually turbid flow at the edges of currents, and the size of most fishes, speak against their simultaneously comparing what they detect with their right and left olfactory rosettes. Yet, it might be of considerable advantage to the animal to be able to do so, or at least to compare right and left sides in quick succession. The simplest method of comparing would be to close one or the other naris temporarily; however, this has not been observed. Another possibility would be to suppress impulses from each bulb alternately. Such efferent one-sided control apparently exists in mammals [31]; the slow to-and-fro initial search methods of bullheads suggest that lower vertebrates may do likewise.

Food-finding by olfaction alone has been demonstrated for salamander species with truly amphibious habits (*Triturus*). Animals with severed olfactory tracts had to be stimulated visually to snap up food morsels when on land; in the water they could be induced to feed only by water movements near them. Taste played no role in the food search, and the elimination of Jacobson's organ did not impair their ability to find food by smell [17] (see below for a comparison with snakes). The tracks of the animals following a scent show some S-like movements after overshooting the confines of the scent trail (Fig. 3–10). It is

Fig. 3–13. Brown bullhead with extended barbels searching for a food scent released on the surface. While the fish is on the surface, the nasal barbels remain in contact with the surface film while the laterals move up and down. (Photo, P. C. Davis, University of Michigan.)

difficult to judge whether simultaneous comparison between the stimulation of right and left olfactory epithelia took place; the salamander crawled along the edge of the track far enough to suggest that it did.

Generalizations about whether or not the feeding of *Anurans* is predominantly vision-based may be premature; the comparative anatomy of the noses and eyes and their associated nerves, in frogs and toads, suggests that some are smell feeders but others are sight feeders [17]. Furthermore, certain toads, such as the natterjack (*Bufo calamita*) searched for well-scented but invisible food.

Among reptiles, snakes certainly rely on a comparison of successive chemical stimuli; take the search of *Natrix natrix*, a land-dwelling relative of the American water snake, for a mouse that it had been allowed to hold briefly in its mouth. The snake followed the trail by frequently touching the ground with its tongue and retracting it. Removal of Jacobson's organ or the tongue, or both, eliminated its tracking ability (Fig. 3–16) [30].

It is difficult to determine whether an animal follows a gradient by means of Jacobson's organ and the tongue, since successive comparisons of the scent on

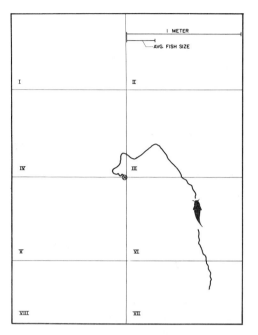

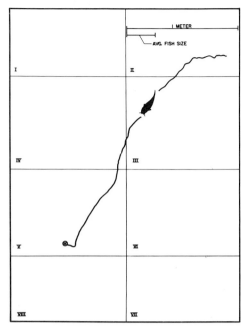

Fig. 3–14. Search pattern for liver extract by a blind brown bullhead without a current in the tank. The animal started searching for the scent 17 min 24 sec after the latter was released and found it within 9 sec.

Fig. 3–15a. Searching patterns for food extract of blind, anosmic brown bullheads (nares cauterized) with various barbels removed; no current is present in the tank. All barbels are amputated but taste buds on the body are intact and functional. Fish began search 4 min 34 sec after scent release and located scent source in 34 sec.

the track with its absence next to it could also lead to the prey without being a gradient toward the prey.

Visual, tactile, chemical, or other releasers, such as the emptying of poison glands by snakes that have them, may have to precede the search; the necessity for chemical releasers would indicate that the snake is sensitive to a particular compound. A viper (*Vipera aspis*) will follow very closely the track of a mouse it has just bitten but will almost disregard the trail of an unbitten mouse [30]. The behavior obviates further oral testing since Jacobson's organ and the tongue (which has no taste buds) combine in a joint olfactory-gustatory function.

Testing the Food Less is known about the "gating" function of taste in lower vertebrates, that is, about the acceptance or rejection of food items taken

into the mouth, than is known about the role of their chemical senses in the search for food. Predators of large prey, such as pike, bass, deepwater gulpers, sharks, certain lizards, snakes, and crocodiles, are likely to swallow their food very quickly without retaining it in the mouth; the finding of tennis balls, tin cans, and similar objects in the stomachs of sharks certainly speaks against their ability to discriminate by taste. Yet Tester [44] cites several experiments suggesting that taste, not smell, mediates food preferences; more precise and better-planned experiments are needed.

In tests of bony fishes, moray eels often spat out anchovies coated with plastic or paraffin [6], and sharks rejected alcohol-deodorized squid that they had already ingested [44]. Again it is difficult

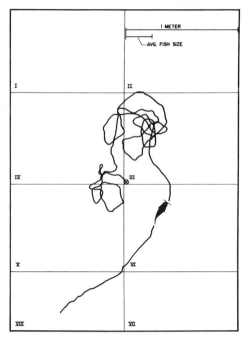

Fig. 3–15b. Searching patterns for food extract of blind, anosmic brown bullheads (nares cauterized) with only right-hand barbels removed. Note greater incidence of circling to the left. Fish began searching 4 min and 4 sec after the scent was released and found it within 1 min 29 sec.

to decide whether food morsels treated to be tasteless are rejected because of their tastelessness or because of tactile properties they have acquired in the treatment. Appetite must greatly influ-

ence the rate of ingestion and with it the opportunity of testing food by taste.

Amphibians are predators that generally gulp their prey. They have swallowed quinine-soaked food, though some salamanders have been shown to discriminate among the four basic taste substances [17]. Taste probably plays a minor role in many reptiles' choice of food. The few reptiles examined have relatively sparsely distributed taste buds; and vision, olfaction, often Jacobson's organ, and the pit organs of rattlesnakes all seem to be important in relation to taste. No pertinent critical experiments on reptilian taste were reported in the literature available to me.

CHEMOSENSORY PHYSIOLOGY RELATED TO FOOD INTAKE

The first part of this symposium, and the one in which this paper is placed, is concerned with evolution. This part also bears in its title the question "Is taste necessary?" A biologist would probably answer, "Yes, like sex, it is." He might elaborate as follows: In some lower vertebrates, as have already been discussed, taste has evolved as the dominant sense; in others, taste perception is only one of many equally important senses. Certain

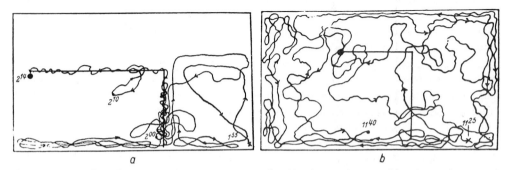

Fig. 3–16. Trail on land of a European water snake (Natrix natrix) searching for prey: (a) after being permitted to "mouth" a live mouse that was subsequently killed and dragged over the rectangular path to the black dot in the left of the picture where it was left to be found by the snake; (b) the same animal, but with Jacobson's organ cauterized, then put through the experimental paces described above. (From Lüdicke, after Kahmann [30].)

substances, such as cysteine, indole, and others, are perceived in low concentrations by both smell and taste, and salt acts on the noses of fresh-water fishes as well as on their taste buds. Sugars and bitter substances act only on taste receptors, but not on all kinds of them (see below).

Macro-osmatic fishes have remarkable olfactory acuity. Teichmann [42] trained immature eels to detect beta phenylethyl alcohol in a solution of 1.77×10^3 molecules per cubic centimeter of water. The narial lumen of the fish employed was such that the scent must have been detected from the presence of perhaps two or three molecules in the nasal chamber. Glaser [13] determined that the minnow *Phoxinus,* which has external taste buds but is not as "taste-oriented" as the bullhead, is from two dozen to well over two thousand times as sensitive to the taste of diverse substances as is man. It can detect quinine hydrochloride in a solution 24 times as dilute as that in which man can detect it; salt in a solution 205 times as dilute; glucose, 1,575 times; and fructose, 2,560 times.

Cysteine, ascertained by paper chromatography to occur in flesh extracts of various animals, elicits clear responses from the barbel taste nerves of the bullhead at a 5×10^{-5} M concentration (Fig. 3–17) [5]. Since bullheads have many thousand tastebuds from which responses are summated, their gustatory acuities probably surpass those of the minnow. Most likely their taste thresholds approach or equal those of blind cave fishes, which are considerably lower than those of Glaser's *Phoxinus* [23], and

thus, for some compounds, are perhaps a million-fold lower than those of man. Navigation in chemical gradients by taste alone, as described above, and the thresholds cited here, suggest that in some lower vertebrates, taste rivals smell in acuity.

But what about the gamut of taste sensations? Less versatile than smell, taste is nevertheless capable of conveying a considerable variety of chemical information. The four basic modalities may still be useful, conceptually, in dealing with the biophysics of taste, but the concept would need to be amplified considerably before one could hope to speculate profitably about how the animal might interpret taste sensations. Konishi and Zotterman [28] took recordings from the glossopharyngeal nerve of the carp and proposed seven different fiber types. There certainly appear to be more than four in fishes, including one that is highly sensitive to cysteine (see above). Certain virtually insoluble compounds, such as cholesterol (Fig. 3–18) and lipid-like substances, also excite fishes' taste sensors [5,28]; in this laboratory, recent investigations of bullheads' sensitivity to carbohydrates showed that their external taste nerves responded remarkably well to stimulation by glucosamine.

The integrated records of responses to different substances are characteristic enough of each in duration, rise in time to peak discharge frequence, etc. (Fig. 3–4) [5], so that these properties, evoked by stimulation with one pure or mixed substance, could be imparting to the animal at least some specific information about a substance. Other possibilities of

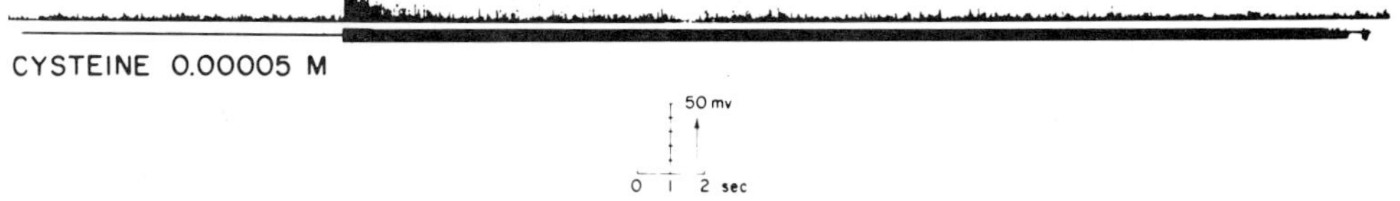

CYSTEINE 0.00005 M

50 mv

0   I   2 sec

Fig. 3–17. *Response of a few-fiber preparation from a brown bullhead barbel to 0.00005 M 1 cysteine. (From Bardach, Fujiya, and Holl [5].)*

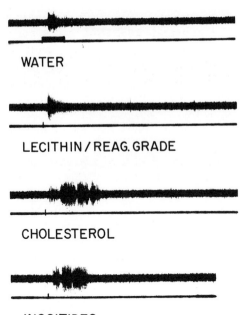

WATER

LECITHIN / REAG. GRADE

CHOLESTEROL

INOSITIDES

Fig. 3–18. Responses from a several-fiber preparation of a brown bullhead barbel to charged lipid compounds; camera speed 1 cm/sec; bar under water trace. (From Bardach, Fujiya, and Holl [5].)

information-processing in taste nerves that cannot be analyzed from integrated records, such as compound-specific discharge sequences and the interplay between inhibitory and excitatory fibers in a nerve bundle from a specific region, have not been investigated, though inhibitory effects on the continuous discharge patterns of fishes' taste nerves have been reported [27,28].

Carnivores are excited and attracted when they smell—or, as in some fishes, taste—flesh or other tissue extracts, which surely contain a welter of chemicals. Chemical fractionation of the extracts and testing of the constituents for their power of spontaneous attraction seem called for but have seldom been done. Kleerekoper and Mogensen [26] isolated some amino acids and amines (notably their amine F) that attract adult sea lampreys to their prey. The amine also influences the searching be-

havior of other fishes (Kleerekoper, personal communication). Certain amino acids elicit responses through smell or taste; serine is avoided by sharks [44] and salmon [24]. In our laboratory we have ascertained that bullheads can smell but not taste serine; the response then must be an olfactory one. Naïve bullheads approach a nozzle that releases cysteine into a current; probably they both smell and taste this potential attractant.

Along with taste buds, fishes also have spinally innervated taste structures without buds; the range of such structures is more restricted than that of cranially innervated taste buds [5]. These cells, presumably those described by Whitear [49], react to quinine but not to sugar. Glaser [13] described violent aversion reactions of fish to quinine. The fishes best known to have spinal taste nerves are the searobins. Past experiments on how they employ those nerves in searching for food are summarized in Bardach and Case [4].

The spontaneous discharge rates of fibers in the olfactory tracts of carp, goldfish, eel, and other fishes change when the nose is perfused with food extracts, and each of various fiber types reacts in its own specific manner [32]. Recordings of impulses from the olfactory tract of carp, though not in response to food scents, revealed both temporal and spatial coding in single nerves [34]. Stimulation with a scent causes slow potential changes in the olfactory epithelium of fishes [39] as it does in amphibians [35]; the relations of these changes to feeding are unknown.

Though frogs are well suited for electrophysiological experiments, and though vast numbers of them have been used in attempts to elucidate the biophysics of smell, we still know little or nothing about what chemicals attract or repel Amphibia. Frogs have taste fibers by which they can sense water [1]; it is not known whether these function in food intake or in the search for a preferred habitat. Brackish-water catfish have somewhat comparable fibers, which react to highly dilute salt solutions (Konishi, personal communication). Salamanders (*Triturus*) were taste tested for the four human taste qualities [17]; they could distinguish among them, though their thresholds were relatively high.

The only reptiles that have been subjected to electrophysiological tests of their taste or smell senses are land turtles, as already mentioned [46]; the olfactory and gustatory physiology of most reptiles remains to be explored. Perhaps the reason for the dearth of knowledge is much the same as for sharks—both kinds of animals are difficult to keep in capitivity, and their size and shape, as well as their more detailed anatomy, complicate neurophysiological studies.

Even though taste has become, in some fishes, a directional, distance sense, it retains its role in the close-range testing of food. In this role it is closely associated with the mechanical senses; in the hake, for example, proprioceptive or position-indicating fibers issue from taste bud-bearing pelvic fins (Fig. 3–19), and taste buds in the mouth, on the lips, and on the body have tactile fibers in or near them [5,19]. Not only are the fibers associated with taste buds peripherally, but their central connections with taste nuclei in the brain further underscore the close functional connection of chemical and tactile senses [2].

Discussion

Beidler: We know that animals, particularly man, have large numbers of so-called free nerve endings. The relation between these nerve endings and the epithelial cells is almost identical to that

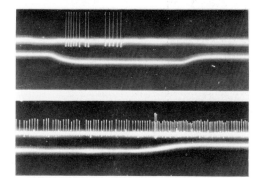

Fig. 3–19.   *Oscilloscope recordings from the nerves of the pelvic fin of a hake* (Urophycis chuss). Top. *Phasic mechanoreceptor response to 2 mm deflection of fin, as indicated in the lower trace.* Bottom. *Tonic and phasic units responding to 2 mm deflection of fin.* Horizontal bar = 250 msec; vertical bar = 0.5 mV. *(From Bardach and Case [4].)*

between the gustatory cell and the taste nerves in the taste buds. Maybe we should also consider free nerve endings as chemical receptors. Certainly this is true in the nose, because the nerve ending is sensitive to many more substances than the olfactory cell. This is also true for the eye and probably for any other area where the free nerve ending comes close to the surface. Therefore, it may be dangerous to relate only special receptors to fine sensitivities and not to worry about all the information that might come to the animal when we use chemical stimuli.

Bardach: It may be dangerous to relate only special receptors to the four taste modalities because, when staining a fish taste bud with Bodian silver stain or equivalent techniques, one finds many ramifying fibers around the taste bud. They nearly extend to the outer cells of the epidermis. We never know, when we pick up a fiber, whether it is tactile or chemical, and one suspects much information, even chemosensory in nature, may come to the animal from the free nerve endings. Some fish, such as the searobin, have taste structures on their extremities that are definitely not taste buds.

Henkin: The distribution of taste buds in the fungiform and circumvallate papillae suggests that there are significantly more taste buds in circumvallate than in fungiform papillae. There is a dense distribution of free nerve fibers in circumvallate papillae, a less dense distribution of free nerve fibers in fungiform papillae. Thus, there is a close similarity between quantitative distribution of taste buds and that of free nerve fibers in circumvallate and fungiform papillae. In tongue biopsies taken from the patients with familial dysautonomia, we have found only free nerve fibers. These patients are similar to the searobin you have described, for they do not possess taste buds. Whatever information these patients obtain about taste is through the utilization of these free nerve fibers. There is growing evidence to support the idea that sensory information in man can be acquired through the utilization of free nerve fibers. Weddell demonstrated that touch and temperature, as well as pain, could be perceived in the cornea, although only free nerve fibers have been demonstrated. (Weddell, *Ann. Rev. Psychol.,* 6: 119, 1955.) Thus, there is some precedent in man that taste sensation may in some cases be mediated over free nerve fibers where papillae and taste buds are absent.

Moulton: We seem to be concentrating on the nature and properties of the peripheral receptors, but if we are interested in the function of a chemosensory system in controlling food intake, perhaps we should also keep in mind the central mechanisms for processing the receptor input. As Bardach indicated, there are dramatic examples in the experiments of Kahmann (*Zool. Jahrb.,* 51: 173, 1932),

Bogert (*Ann. N.Y. Acad. Sci.,* 41: 329, 1941), and others of the elimination of feeding, trailing, and other behavior in snakes, following sectioning of the vomeronasal nerve or removal of the tips of the tongue. Apparently these patterns are normally triggered by odorants stimulating the vomeronasal organ. This does not necessarily imply that the animal lacks the peripheral equipment to detect the relevant cues: the olfactory organ is well developed. What the animal may lack are the central mechanisms for exploiting alternative inputs.

In contrast, ablation of the olfactory bulb in dogs (Kalina, *Zh. Vyssh. hervn. deyatel,* 11: 318, 1961), cauterization of the vomeronasal organ in the cat (Mihalkovics, *Anat. Hefte,* 11: 1, 1898), etc., are procedures which appear to have little or no detectable effect on behavior. This is not to say that the operations are without influence; but it does seem that we are dealing with a further example of the greater ability of mammals to exploit all available cues. It is possible for one sensory input to be substituted for another. Whether we wish to interpret this in terms of "innate" as against "learned" behavior is another matter. But if we ask, does a particular chemosensory system serve a necessary function, the answer will obviously depend (in part) on who is using the system.

Halpern: The containing cells which surround the spinally innervated contact chemoreceptors remind me of a structure Iggo has described (Brown and Iggo, *J. Physiol.,* 105: 228, 1963). There was a differentiated cutaneous receptor apparatus, which would degenerate when the innervating nerve was cut and then regenerate.

Harper: Do you find evidence of specificity in regard to the sensitivity of receptor cells to different amino acids?

This comes to mind because of the work that has been done with serine in spawning salmon.

Bardach: We have tried to see whether or not the olfactory organ of fishes responds to serine; so far we have used trout and bullheads. The olfactory tracts increase their spontaneous discharge rates when serine is applied to the olfactory folds. Serine is reported to repel salmon and sharks. Perhaps we have here a simple substance that is avoided by all fishes, but one should remember that not only the salmon might be prone to predation by mammals which have this substance in their skin rinse. Incidentally, serine has not given us responses from taste fibers. The best example of a taste specificity is the different sensitivity of the Swedish and Japanese carp to silkworm pupae extract, reported by Konishi and Zotterman (*Olfaction and Taste,* Macmillan, New York, 1963).

Harper: I was thinking more specifically of the sensitivity of a single species to a variety of individual amino acids.

Hodgson: Gilbert, Mathewson, and I have been studying electrical activity in olfactory bulbs and forebrains of sharks. We find that almost any single chemical stimulus in the nasal sacs will elicit recognizable changes in the neural activities of those areas. Yet the feeding response, which is quite dramatic, is given more selectively, especially to certain amino acids and amines. In other words, it looks as though the receptors were capable of detecting a wide variety of stimuli by the time the Elasmobranchs evolved, as though the specificity of behavioral responses depends primarily on central nervous mechanisms.

Sharma: I want to comment on specificity of the amino acids. When you are recording from the gut afferents, there do not seem to be specificities for the various amino acids. (Sharma and Nasset, *Amer. J. Physiol.,* **202**: 725, 1962.) We have tried single amino acid perfusions, for instance, glycine, histidine, and glutamic acids. One does find that the fiber spectra invariably are the same, though particular responses may differ quantitatively. How far this may be reflected in terms of sensitivity is a different question.

Bardach: We have observed some of the cranially innervated taste fibers of hake fins, which have taste buds, to give responses of varying degrees to a number of amino acids, such as aspartic acid, alanine, tryptophane, phenylalanine, and glycine, as well as to glutathione.

Jacobs: When you defined a chemoreceptor, you gave an example of inhibition. When you get inhibition from a chemical in solution put on a single fiber, is it as reasonable to call that a chemoreceptor when you get excitation? Recently it was shown in single-fiber analysis that with excised liver of guinea pigs in Ringer solution you get high activity in a fiber. With mannose you still get high activity in the fiber, but when you apply glucose the activity stops. You put Ringer back on, and the activity goes back up: definition, glucoreceptor. What about the logic in this system?

Halpern: In general, decreased firing rate of spontaneously active units is scarcely restricted to chemoreceptors. It is found in most afferent systems that one can transmit information as well by a decrease in activity as by an increase in activity. One cannot say that a decrease in activity is bad or that an increase is good. One cannot draw any motivational interpretations from the way in which the response goes. It is not unusual that the decrease in firing rate to some stimuli is contrasted to an increase in firing rate. If a system is spontaneously active, i.e., with some jitter in it, a small amount of energy change can cause it to go down or go up a little bit. This might be a more efficient system than one which has to start producing a change in the capacitance of the membrane and then start an active process going. This is probably just a matter of biological efficiency.

De Ruiter: Hodgson, would you comment on this point, as you have told us that decreased firing of a sugar receptor contains information to the fly?

Hodgson: This would certainly be a concrete illustration of the general principle that Halpern was discussing. Tranmission of information through *decreased* receptor firing can occur in two ways: in mixtures of chemical stimuli, when one component depresses the response to another component, as in the case of the fly, or, if spontaneous activity is present, there may be a decrease in the rate of firing, as in the case of the glucoreceptor Jacobs discussed.

Pfaffmann: I would make the admonition that your criteria probably have to be more specific as to the locus of the operation and the time course. You certainly change the firing rate of neurons by a lot of things that would not necessarily be considered a part of a normal receptor system.

Bardach: Yes, but so far we have talked about application of a compound and changes in firing rate, either positive or negative, and that seems to carry informational content.

Pfaffmann: Yes, but there is the question of change brought on by a changing chemical character somewhere in the system, not at the point of application.

De Ruiter: Let us consider in a comparative perspective one of the questions raised by Brobeck: How does the individual adapt to a change in diet? Either taste, or nutrient content, or both may be changed. Let us restrict ourselves to taste. Bardach has stated that the final decision, whether or not a food object will be swallowed, depends on its taste. Does this imply that lower vertebrates, kept indefinitely on a diet of poor palatability will actually eat less than individuals kept on more tasty, but nutritionally equivalent food, in contrast to mammals whose intake appears to be fairly independent of palatability?

Bardach: I have no such information, though some fish accept or reject certain food items, apparently by taste. Some fishes, such as the deep sea gulpers, or even our northern pike eat tremendous amounts at a time. They try to swallow prey their size or bigger. Obviously they hoard food for lean times and ingest it on the basis of sight or lateral line clues rather than those of smell or taste. I think, though, that those experiments that Brobeck mentioned, of regulation of caloric intake, should be done with lower vertebrates, perhaps even with these fishes that have chemical sensitivity outside their mouths.

De Ruiter: If food is swallowed beyond need or digestive capacity, it seems to me that this must be because its attractive taste or smell has an overriding influence on ingestion. Conversely, there are one or two cases in the literature on fish which suggest that there may be a lasting reduction of intake on low palatability diets (W. E. Ricker, *J. Fish., Res. Board Canada,* 5: 293–313, 1941; W. W. MacDonald, *J. Anim. Ecol.,* 25: 36–53,

1956; B. Holling, *Memoirs Entomol. Soc. Canada*, **45**: 3–60, 1965).

REFERENCES

1. Andersson, B., and Zotterman, Y. The water taste in the frog. *Acta Physiol. Scand.*, **20**: 95–100, 1950.
2. Ariens-Kappers, C. U., Huber, C., and Crosby, E. *The Comparative Anatomy of the Nervous System of Vertebrates, Including Man*. Macmillan, New York, 1936.
3. Aronson, L. R. The central nervous system of sharks and bony fishes with special reference to sensory and integrative mechanisms, in *Sharks and Survival*, P. W. Gilbert (ed.). Heath, Boston, pp. 165–241, 1963.
4. Bardach, J. E., and Case, J. Sensory capabilities of the modified fins of squirrel hake (*Urophycis chuss*) and searobins (*Prionotus carolinus* and *P. evolans*). *Copeia* 2: 194–206, 1965.
5. Bardach, J. E., Fujiya, M., and Holl, A. Investigations of external chemoreceptors of fishes. Proceedings of the Second International Symposium on Olfaction and Taste, Tokyo, pp. 647–65, 1966 (in press).
6. Bardach, J. E., Winn, H. E., and Menzel, D. W. The role of the senses in the feeding of the nocturnal reef predators *Gymnothorax moringa* and *G. vicinus*. *Copeia* 2: 133–39, 1959.
7. Boeke, J., Niedere Sinnesorgane, in *Handb. d. Vergl. Anat. d. Wirbeltiere*, L. Bolk, E. Göppert, E. Kallius, and W. Lubosch (eds.). Urban and Schwarzenberg, Berlin and Vienna, pp. 855–78, 949–88, 1934.
8. Buddenbrock, W. von. *Vergleichende Physiologie Bd. 1 Sinnesphysiologie*. Verl. Birkhäuser, Basel, pp. 465–66, 1952.
9. Desgranges, J. C. Sur l'existence de plusiers cellules sensorielles dans les bourgeons du gout des barbillons du poisson-chat. *C.R. Acad. Sc. Paris*, **261**: 1095–98, 1965.
10. Dogiel, A. S. Über die Nervenendigungen in den Geschmacks—Endknospen der Ganoiden. *Arch. Mikrosk. Anat.*, **49**: 769–90, 1897.
11. Fujiya, M., and Bardach, J. E. A comparison between the external taste sense of marine and freshwater fishes. *Bull. Jap. Soc. Sci. Fish.*, **32**(1): 45–56, 1966.
12. Gerard, P. Organe olfactif, in *Traite de zoologie*. XII: *Vertebres*. Masson, Paris, pp. 522–52, 1954.
13. Glaser, D. Untersuchungen ueber die absoluten Geschmacksschwellen von Fischen. *Z. vergl. Physiol.*, **52**: 1–25, 1966.
14. Grassé, P. P. Anatomie, ethologie, systematique, in *Traite de zoologie. XIII: Agnathes et poissons*. Masson, Paris, Part 2, pp. 1034–62, 1958.
15. Hasler, A. D. The sense organs: Olfactory and gustatory senses of fishes, in *The Physiology of Fishes*, II, M. E. Brown (ed.). Academic Press, New York, 1957.
16. Herrick, C. J. The organ and senses of taste in fishes. *Bull. U.S. Fish. Comm.*, **22**: 239–72, 1904.
17. Herter, K. Amphibia, in *Handb. d. Zool.*, VI. Walter de Gruyter, Berlin, pp. 200–12, 1941.
18. Hirata, Y. *Archivum Histologicum japonicum*, 1966 (in press).
19. Hoagland, H. Specific nerve impulses from gustatory and tactile receptors in catfish. *J. Gen. Physiol.*, **16**: 685–93, 1933.
20. Hobson, E. S. Feeding behavior in three species of sharks. *Pacific Science*, **17**(2): 171–94, 1963.
21. Hodgson, E. S. The chemical senses and changing viewpoints in sensory physiology, in *Viewpoints in Biology*, O. D. Carthy and C. L. Luddington (eds.). Butterworths, London, pp. 83–123, 1965.
22. Holl, A. Vergleichende morphologische und histologische Untersuchungen am Geruchsorgan der Knochenfische. *Z. Morph. Ökol. Tiere*, **54**: 707–82, 1965.
23. Humbach, I. Geruch und Geschmack bei augenlosen Höhlenfischen *Anoptichthys jordani* and *A. hubbsi*. *Naturwiss.*, **47**: 551, 1960.
24. Idler, D. R., Fagerlund, U. H., and Mayoh, H. Olfactory perception in migrating salmon. I: 1. Serine, a salmon repellent in mammalian skin. *J. Gen. Physiol.*, **39**: 889–92, 1956.
25. Kleerekoper, H., and Erkel, G. A. van. The olfactory apparatus of *Petromyzon marinus*. *Can. J. Zool.*, **38**: 209–23, 1960.
26. Kleerekoper, H., and Mogensen, I. A. The chemical composition of scent of freshwater fish with special reference to amines and amino acids. *Z. vergl. Physiol.*, **49**: 492–500, 1959.
27. Konishi, J., Uchida, M., and Mori, Y. Gustatory fibers in the sea catfish. *Jap. J. Physiol.*, **16**(2): 194–204, 1966.
28. Konishi, J., and Zotterman, Y. Taste functions in fish, in *Olfaction and Taste. I: Proceedings of the First International Symposium, Wenner Gren Center, Stockholm, 1962*, Y. Zotterman (ed.). Macmillan, New York, pp. 215–33, 1963.
29. Liermann, K. Über den Bau des Geruchsorganes der Teleostier. *Z. Anat.*, **100**: 1–39, 1933.
30. Ludicke, M. Serpentes (5), Ordnung der Klasse Reptilia, in *Handb. d. Zool.*, VII. Walter de Gruyter & Co., Berlin, pp. 116–123, 1962.
31. Mancia, M., Green, I. D., and Baumgarten, R. von. Reticular control of single neurons in the olfactory bulb. *Arch. Ital. Biol.*, **100**: 463–75, 1962.
32. Maljukina, G. A., and Solomatin, S. S. Toward a physiology of the olfactory analyzer

of fish. *Akademija Nauk S.S.S.R. Voprostji Ichtiologii, Odeljnji Ottisk, Moskva,* 4(3): 570–78, 1964.

33. Matthes, E. Geruchsorgan, in *Handb. d. Vergl. Anat. d. Wirbeltiere,* L. Bolk, E. Göppert, E. Kallius, and W. Lubosch (eds.). Urban und Schwarzenberg, Berlin and Vienna, pp. 879–948, 1934.

34. Nanba, R., Djahanparwar, B., and Baumgarten, R. von. Erregungsmuster einzelner Pasern des Tractus olfactorius lateralis des Fisches bei Reizung mit verschiedenen Geruchsstoffen. *Pfzüger's Archiv,* 288: 134–50, 1966.

35. Ottoson, D. Generation and transmission of signals in the olfactory system, in *Olfaction and Taste. I: Proceedings of the First International Symposium, Wenner Gren Center, Stockholm, 1962,* Y. Zotterman (ed.). Macmillan, New York, pp. 35–44, 1963.

36. Parker, G. H. The directive influence of the sense of smell in the dogfish. *Bull. U.S. Bur. Fish.,* 33: 61–68, 1914.

37. Pietschmann, V. Cyclostoma, in *Handb. d. Zool., VI.* Walter de Gruyter, Berlin, pp. 256–355, 1933.

38. Schnakenbeck, W. Pisces, in *Handb. d. Zool., VI.* Walter de Gruyter, Berlin, pp. 905–38, 1960.

39. Shibuya, T. The electrical responses of the olfactory epithelium of some fishes. *Jap. J. Physiol.,* 10: 317–26, 1960.

40. Teichmann, H. Vergleichende Untersuchungen an der Nase der Fische. *J. Morph. Ökol. Tiere,* 43: 171–212, 1954.

41. Teichmann, H. Ueber die Leistung des Geruchssinnes beim Aal (*Anguilla anguilla* L.). *Z. vergl. Physiol.,* 42: 206–54, 1959.

42. Teichmann. H. Die Chemorezeption der Fische. *Erg. d. Biol.,* 25: 177–205, 1962.

43. Teichmann, H., and Teichmann, R. Untersuchungen über den Geruchssinn der Haifische. *Pubbl. Staz. Zool. Napoli,* 31(1): 76–81, 1959.

44. Tester, A. L. Olfaction, gustation, and the common chemical sense in sharks, in *Sharks and Survival,* P. W. Gilbert (ed.). D. C. Heath & Co., Boston, pp. 255–82, 1963.

45. Tester, A. L., and Nelson, G. I. Free neuromasts (pit organs) in sharks. Paper presented at symposium: Current investigations dealing with Elasmobranch Biology. Sponsored by Office of Naval Research, AIBS and *Lerner* Marine Laboratory, Bimini, Bahamas, January 30–February 4, 1966.

46. Tucker, D. Olfactory, vomeronasal and trigeminal receptor responses to odorants, in *Olfaction and Taste. I: Proceedings of the First International Symposium, Wenner Gren Center, Stockholm, 1962,* Y. Zotterman (ed.). Macmillan, New York, pp. 45–69, 1963.

47. Von Baumgarten, R., Green, I. D., and Mancia, M. Recurrent inhibition in the olfactory bulb: II. The effects of antidromic stimulation of commissural fibers. *J. Neurophysiol.,* 25: 485–500, 1962.

48. Whitear, M. The innervation of the skin of teleost fishes. *Quart. J. Microsc. Sci.,* 93: 289–305, 1952.

49. Whitear, M. Presumed sensory cells in fish epidermis. *Nature,* 208(5011): 763–64, 1965.

I am grateful to the following: M. Fujiya, J. Case, A. Holl, R. Crickmer, A. Brown, J. Todd, G. Johnson, C. C. Chen.

4: Some Aspects of Chemoreception in Human Nutrition by Rose Marie Pangborn

GUSTATION AND olfaction have been designated as "lower senses," because they appear to influence human behavior to a minor degree as compared to visual, auditory, and other sensory stimuli. Primitive man may have been highly dependent on the chemical senses in hunting, selecting nutrients, detecting weather changes, avoiding enemies, and, perhaps, in his mating behavior. As the species evolved, however, chemoreception declined in importance for human survival, concomitant with the rise in visual ability.

VISION AND CHEMORECEPTION

To a large extent man recognizes, discriminates, and selects nutrients with the eye. Through conditioning and association, he expects an item of a certain shape and color to have a specific odor, taste, and texture. In foods, colors are identified with previously experienced quality and serve as instant indicators of good or bad, according to the product and its intended use. Through familiarity, the palate can convert the eye, particularly with regard to rare or exotic foods. For instance, there is little to commend the color of such foods as caviar, black olives, figs, or truffles, yet these items are accepted as delicacies by many consumers.

The psychological aspects of food colors have received little systematic attention in the laboratory. As might be expected, experimental subjects identified fruit flavors incorrectly when jellies were atypically colored [36]. Few of 200 pharmacy students could identify flavorings presented in colorless syrups, and even fewer responded correctly when solutions were presented in unusual colors [27]. Sherbets were prepared in six flavors, adding either no coloring, the appropriate color, or an inappropriate color [18]. As anticipated, miscoloring greatly interfered with correct flavor identification. Furthermore, properly colored sherbets rated highest in flavor acceptability whereas deceptively colored samples rated lowest. Work in our laboratory showed no color-sweetness associations in unflavored aqueous solutions [43].

In pear nectar, however, there was a pronounced tendency to designate the green-colored samples as the least sweet. In a second experiment, food colorings were added to a dry white table wine to simulate the appearance of reisling, sautern, sherry, rosé, claret, and burgundy wine types [44]. Subjects who seldom or never used wine demonstrated no color-sweetness relationships, but experienced wine judges, despite their greater sensory ability, attributed significantly greater sweetness to the rosé-colored wine and the least amount to the claret-colored wine.

Studies of a more basic nature [5] reported that an increase in ambient illumination was accompanied by an improvement in gustatory sensitivity. In a detailed study on the influence of ambient lighting on perceived intensity of the acid taste, Gregson [15] had twenty-four subjects evaluate three concentrations of citric acid under four levels of illumination. There was a small intersensory effect of light on relative intensity of taste that was facilitatory for most subjects but negative for others, and these intersensory effects were multiplicative, i.e., not readily explained as simple threshold-shift effects. Gregson raises a valid criticism of previous work in which mean responses rather than individual subject responses were used in data analyses, thereby causing a loss of information on individual differences in intersensory facilitation or inhibition. In a more recent experiment [16], inconclusive results were obtained on the effect of changes in white light intensity on acid taste detection. Under colored illumination, however, subjects used heteromodal cues as an alternative response basis when the primary discrimination task was relatively difficult.

If modern man is so visually oriented, of what value are the chemical senses? It is generally agreed that the senses of taste and smell function in the recognition, selection, and rejection of nutrients. Even in the absence of visual and auditory cues, animals distinguish food from non-food items. In dogs that had been "killed," then resuscitated, Murskii [40] reported that early recovery of the gustatory function was always associated with successful resuscitation. In cases where recovery was difficult and cortical cells did not regain full function, the ability to distinguish food from non-foods was sometimes disturbed. Apparently, corn is a non-food item for carnivores, while meat is a non-food item for ruminants. The question arises as to whether differences in the gustatory receptors exist among carnivores, herbivores, and omnivores.

PALATABILITY AND APPETITE

The word "palatability" originated from the mistaken notion that the palate was the organ of taste. In common usage palatability refers to over-all acceptance or degree of liking and depends upon the appearance, odor, taste, texture, temperature, and in selected cases, even the auditory properties of a food (e.g., "noisiest potato chips in the world," and "snap, crackle, and pop" of a dry cereal). Furthermore, the environmental setting and emotional state of the animal influence palatability. Appetite, on the other hand, generally refers to internal determinants of food acceptance and preference [59]. It is appropriate to speak of appetite when a preference is determined by deprivation or satiation, by surgical operation, or by special organic conditions such as pregnancy and lactation, disease, etc. The distinction between palatability and appetite does not imply that there are two kinds of affective processes; rather, there is one, with positive and negative signs but with a variety of conditions that influence affectively [59]. A number of workers [34] have demonstrated that both chemoreceptive and postingestional factors serve to check ingestion in rats. Mook [37] distinguishes between positive and negative oral factors as motivating food intake and adds postingestional osmotic effects and "dilute water" mechanisms as influencing factors.

To what extent does an animal utilize gustation and olfaction to meter food intake to meet his metabolic needs? Can man depend upon "palatability" to assure adequate nutrition? In 1897 Roberts [49] minimized palatability and ascribed inborn control when he wrote, "The generalized food customs of mankind are not to be viewed as random practices, adopted to please the palate or idle or vicious appetite. These customs must be regarded as the outcome of profound instincts which correspond to certain wants of the human economy. They are the fruit of a colossal experience accumulated by countless millions of men through successive generations." If we define instinct as innate, spontaneous behavior independent of the cultural environment, Roberts' two final statements would appear contradictory. Lepkovsky [29] stated, "Human populations have shown an amazing ability to choose foods in accordance with their physiological needs, providing their choice was not unduly influenced by education, imitation, social, religious, or other considerations." In our present society, the latter factors play a large, although poorly defined, role in both the qualitative and quantitative ingestion of food.

The environmental conditions of modern man, associated with automation, affluence, and increased leisure, have bred one of the most formidable nutritional problems of the Western world—excessive food intake and subsequent obesity. Twenty to twenty-five per cent of American adults over thirty years of age are sufficiently overweight as to affect their health [21]. Most Americans are exposed to an overabundance of high density food, and the majority lead sedentary lives, yet all are not obese. The role that the chemoreceptors play in regulation of quantitative food intake and subsequent weight control is not known.

The large number of publications between 1930 and 1940 on appetite and food intake prompted the editors of *Nutrition Reviews* [41] to advance six generalizations. I would like to paraphrase these statements and pose the question as to whether today, twenty-two years later, the same rules are applicable, and/or whether the list should be amplified.

1. Nutrition based upon appetites is not universally successful.
2. Appetites are often fickle and unpredictable.
3. Appetites may be trivial in origin.
4. Individual animals vary in their ability to make choices that will improve their nutritional status.
5. Factors affecting human appetites may be expected to be more numerous and more complex than those affecting the appetites of animals.
6. From the evidence, self-selection of diets appears to be inferior to scientific evaluation of diets for the maintenance of good nutrition.

Today no one would have the temerity to claim that the food choices of man are an infallible guide to correct nutrition. However, this does not imply that there is no relationship whatsoever between food selection and nutritional need.

The following factors have been outlined by Young [58] as regulators of food intake (1) affective arousals determined by excitation of the head receptors and by postingestion conditions; (2) neural organizations that facilitate or inhibit ingestion of foods; (3) chemical constitution of the organism as determined by genetic and dietary history; and (4) feeding habits and attitudes based upon dietary experience. With regard to the last factor, the emotionality of food consumption among human subjects should not be underestimated. The emotional aspects of the eating process are related to two basic facts: (1) the universal fear of starvation, and (2) the universal experience in each individual's early life that food intake requires the cooperation of another person [3]. In our own culture, most, if not all, social functions involve the intake of food—and frequently these are foods of high caloric density such as alcohol, sweets, and fats. To humans the symbolic aspects of food are often of such importance that a given food will be refused, regurgitated, or traumatic if its symbolic significance makes it unacceptable to the eater [38]. Gandhi was reported to eat beef on the basis of a rational, intellectual conviction that its nutritional excellence was a factor in the physical and energetic superiority of the Western cultures; his efforts were futile, however, as he became very ill from eating beef [30].

Although man cannot depend upon the wisdom of the body and must call upon the nutritionist to establish adequate dietaries, the nutritionist should be aware of the psychological factors that influence the feeding process. Traditionally, the nutritionist has been concerned with estimation of the organism's need for carbohydrates, proteins, lipids, minerals, and vitamins, while the subjective feelings of the patient have been not only neglected but specifically excluded. Since people eat food, not nutrients, it should not be surprising that pepper, garlic, onions, horse-radish, chili and pickles, all of insignificant nutritive value, have a greater influence on food acceptance than does a knowledge of protein, fatty acid, and vitamin requirements. During World War II, much to the dismay of the U.S. Army Quartermaster Corps, the best-fed soldiers in the world would not eat their nutritionally adequate rations. The nutritionists and dieticians often forget that under conditions of stress and physiological and social deprivations, such as exist in hospitals, mess halls, dormitories, etc., subjects place undue importance on the sensory attributes of their meals. Unfortunately, nutritionists trained in one country with a specific cultural and dietary pattern tend to impose this regimen on other cultures.

HUNGER, SATIETY, AND CHEMORECEPTION

The historical development of theories on hunger and appetite are covered by Carlson [4], who also presented detailed descriptions of the influence of sensory stimulation on the stomach activity of a patient with an obstructed esophagus who was fed by gastric fistula. Whenever pleasant-tasting food was placed in the patient's mouth, gastric contractions ceased. Marked inhibition was also shown when the patient chewed paraffin vigorously. An eighteen-year-old boy, who was fed through the jejunum because of a completely obstructed esophagus, weighed 70 lb at the onset of the experiment and reached 114 lb after six months [20]. He had a voracious appetite, eating constantly and consuming up to 24,300 calories in one day, despite the fact that all food ingested orally was regurgitated. Up to 3,000 calories were administered directly into the fistula. After consenting to an operation to correct his condition, his insatiable hunger disappeared and his weight rose to 120 lb on approximately 3,000 calories per day. The intragastric feeding of 33 per cent of the caloric requirement was found to have no appreciable effect on the oral food intake of dogs with gastric fistulas [52]. Larger percentages, 50 or 66 per cent of the caloric requirement, reduced the amount of food the dogs ingested orally, but these were not fully compensatory; even intragastric feeding of 133 per cent of the caloric requirement for one week did not abolish oral intake completely. The effect of intragastric administration of food on the oral intake of fistula dogs was studied over a three-month period. It was found that 175 per cent of the daily caloric requirement was needed to completely suppress oral intake [25]. Only a very slight rise in body weight was observed, a finding that has not been explained.

A hungry animal is considered to be in a state of high nervous irritability that leads to a heightened level of sensory and motor excitation. As glycogen stores are depleted, blood glucose levels decrease, circulating epinephrine rises and stimulates the reticular formation of the brain, which in turn produces cortical arousal and facilitates motor and sensory activity, thereby lowering the threshold for all external sensory stimuli. A satiated animal, by contrast, is relaxed, disinterested in the outside world, sleepy, and consequently should have a high sensory threshold. There are conflicting opinions on whether olfactory and gustatory acuity are reliable, reproducible indexes of metabolic needs or of hunger and satiety. An extensive review of the literature up to 1955 has been published [28].

It has been reported that salt deficiency does not alter the sensitivity of the taste receptors [46]. Furthermore, enhanced sugar preference following the ingestion of insulin was not associated with a change in taste sensitivity [47]. Mayer-Gross and Walker [33] made 202 observations in 100 patients in various stages of hypoglycaemia, covering all glucose levels from fasting to incipient hypoglycaemie coma. There was a preference for 30 per cent sucrose below a blood glucose level of 50 mg/100 ml, and a rejection of it above this critical level. The judgment of sweetness for 5 per cent sucrose and saccharine was also related to the blood glucose level but saccharine was rejected below the critical level. Yensen [54,56] placed two human subjects on a low-salt diet and observed that, during the period of salt deficiency, taste sensitivity for sodium chloride definitely increased, while sensitivity to sucrose, sulfuric acid, and quinine sulfate showed no change. Loss of body water was also accompanied by a decrease in sensitivity to salt, whereas sensitivity to sourness remained unchanged [55,57].

The work of Goetzl and colleagues is frequently cited because it revealed that both olfactory and gustatory thresholds of human subjects show diurnal variations that are closely dependent on food intake [10–14]. Freely selected meals, as well as the administration of sucrose solutions, were preceded by increased acuity and followed by decreased acuity. Further studies [22,31,32] showed that when 75 cc of 12 per cent ethyl alcohol was ingested in lieu of lunch, the decrease in olfactory acuity and in sweetness perception was of greater magnitude and of longer duration than that produced by freely selected noon meals. Conversely, ingestion of 150 cc of 0.3 per cent tannic acid in water prevented the decrease in olfactory acuity and interfered with satiety [23]. Goetzl's work is subject to criticism because of the use of the Elsberg [7] blast-injection technique for measuring olfactory acuity, wherein the subject responds to both olfactory stimulation and variations in air pressure. The measurements were made in an odor-contaminated environment, environmental temperature and humidity were not controlled, and the delivery of compounds to the nose under pressure was atypical of normal conditions of sniffing [26]. Goetzl's conclusions were based on only one threshold determination per subject per session, the subjects had no practice or training, and the overall dietary intake and general routine of the subjects were not controlled. Minor variations in acuity of the sense of taste for sucrose and sodium chloride, as well as in the threshold for the odor of coffee, were found to show no consistent relationship to the presence or absence of hunger sensations and appetite [24]. Once again, there was only one test day for each subject. Using hydrochloric acid as the taste substance and ground coffee as the odorous material, Hammer [19] also tested human subjects for critical flicker frequency, a visual test mediated by sensory receptors not on the food pathway. Hammer showed that the additive effects of food intake and fatigue caused odor, taste, and flicker-fusion thresholds to be higher before, and lower after, lunch was eaten. It has been observed that olfactory acuity to the odor of citral increased during periods of relative hunger compared to periods of satiation [50]. Using rather unsystematic procedures, Zilstorff-Pedersen [60] reported no changes in the odor thresholds of five subjects as a function of ingestion of lunch.

In successive determinations of sweet, salt, and bitter thresholds, at three-hour intervals during a 34-hour fast by nine subjects [35], no systematic changes for any of the tastes were found. Working with the odors of n-butonal, iso-amyl acetate, and oil of cloves, and with the tastes of sucrose, hydrochloric acid, and sodium chloride, Furchtgott and Friedman [9] found some tendency for thresholds to be lower before than after lunch. They did remark, however, that the effect was very small and is readily masked by other undefined factors.

In studies conducted in our laboratory, only one out of twelve subjects had a greater sensitivity to the odor of 2-heptanone before than after lunch [2]. Two subjects showed no difference whereas the remaining nine demonstrated acute sensitivity after rather than before lunch. The mean percentage of correct responses before and after lunch, 68.1 and 73.7, respectively, for an average N of 369 and 407, was significantly different at ($p < 0.001$). This is in agreement with Moore et al. [39], who tested the sensitivity of seven subjects to sucrose solutions before and after a lunch and a no-lunch condition. Sensitivity was higher in the afternoon than in the morning and was independent of whether or not lunch was consumed; these data indicated that diurnal effects, rather than eating per se, influenced sensitivity to sucrose. Pangborn [42] reported that thresholds for sucrose, sodium chloride, citric acid, and caffeine were reduced significantly with training. Fasting versus non-fasting conditions had no significant effect on difference thresholds or on identification thresholds in seven out of eight subjects.

OBESITY AND FOOD PREFERENCES

It has been speculated that overweight individuals not only like foods of high caloric density better than do people of normal weight, but also would be more likely to prefer high- to low-calorie foods when given a choice. The latter hypothesis has been difficult to test because accurate information is lacking on the dietary intake of heavy persons over prolonged periods. Guilt feelings associated with their overweight condition often cause these people to report less than the total quantity of food ingested and to withhold disclosure of consumption of food items high in fat or carbohydrates. For example, it was observed that the more time and detailed attention a skilled interviewer gave to obese women, the greater these women's caloric intake appeared to be [1]. The obese women who were interviewed had a caloric intake derived from fat, carbohydrates, and proteins in the same proportion as that of normal women. In other words, the difference between the intake of the two groups was quantitative rather than qualitative.

In a five-week field study of food monotony, eighty-six military personnel were limited to four daily menus, including only 41 foods (the normal Army ration contains 150 food items) [51]. Individual records were kept of the amount of each food consumed at each meal, and the acceptance of each item was measured on a nine-point scale of likes and dislikes. As might be anticipated, the correlation coefficients between acceptance ratings and consumption were highly significant $(r = + 0.69 - + 0.81)$. Dividing the men into two groups, those whose ratings declined most during the test period, and those whose ratings increased most, resulted in no significant differences in age, height, intelligence (AGCT scores), national background, or personality (MMPI scores). However, the group more subject to monotony was significantly heavier than the other group, suggesting that the heavier subjects had a greater interest in, and concern for, food.

To determine whether overweight people have a "sweet tooth," the degree of liking for four desserts varying in sweetness and the preference for sweeter samples expressed by 12,505 consumers were studied [45]. There was a tendency for the sweetest samples to be scored highest by overweight and lowest by underweight consumers; however, preference between two samples differing in sweetness was not influenced by body size. The tendency for the obese individuals to indicate a high acceptance for all samples suggested that overeating and subsequent obesity result from a greater liking for food in general rather than a particular preference for sweeter foods.

HEDONISM AND CHEMORECEPTION

Food can be used very effectively as a reward because of the strong affective or hedonic tone which is a basic property of taste and odor stimuli. Hunger is an unpleasant state and food ingestion supplies relief and comfort. Thus, there are hedonic changes associated with physiological and psychological states of depletion and satiation. However, there is no perfect correlation between the affective processes and the peripheral changes in the organism, possibly because, as has been suggested, the ultimate correlates of *felt* pleasantness are neural processes hidden deep within the subcortical brain centers [59].

Since hedonic tone can greatly influence consummatory response and, subsequently, nutrient intake, several investigators have studied this aspect of the reaction to chemical stimuli. We have often wondered whether a relationship existed among threshold responses, magnitude estimations of suprathreshold concentrations, and affective value of the same stimuli. During the past year we have had occasion to test this idea using a group of nine highly trained subjects, as part of a study of the influence of solution temperature on the taste of drinking water.[1] The consumer of drinking water of a high-mineral content is frequently heard to remark that chilling tap water greatly improves its palatability. It was of interest to us, therefore, to determine whether alteration in the temperature of solutions of sodium chloride would be reflected in threshold responses, subjective intensity, or hedonic value. The three psychophysical methods were presented in a randomized pattern over a six-month period. All test conditions were standardized, e.g., exactly 10 ml of solution was taken into the mouth and held for 5 sec, with 30-sec intervals between subsequent samples. Distilled water at the temperature of the test solutions was used for oral rinsing between samples, and swallowing was not per-

[1] This study was financed by U.S. Public Health Service grant EF 00802. Appreciation is extended to Mrs. Rosalind B. Chrisp for technical assistance.

mitted. We are currently in the process of applying statistical analyses to these data, but the main results are shown in Fig. 4–1, 4–2, and 4–3. Threshold deter-

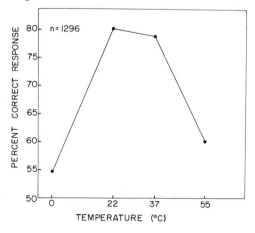

Fig. 4–1. *Effect of solution temperature on difference thresholds for sodium chloride. Each point represents an average of 1,296 individual judgments obtained by paired comparison techniques.*

minations were established by comparing solutions of sodium chloride with distilled water, at each of four temperatures—ice water, room temperature, body temperature, and as hot as could be tolerated in the mouth (0, 22, 37, and 55° C, respectively). The results in Fig. 4–1 show that the highest percentage of correct responses was obtained at the

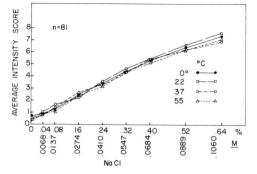

Fig. 4–2. *Subjective intensity of saltiness of suprathreshold concentrations of sodium chloride at four temperatures. Each point represents an average of eighty-one individual judgments.*

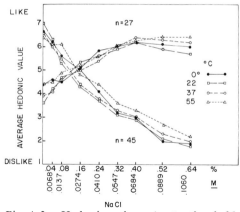

Fig. 4–3. *Hedonic ratings of suprathreshold concentrations of sodium chloride at four temperatures on a nine-point hedonic scale. Three Ss demonstrated increased liking and five Ss indicated decreased liking with concentration.*

two intermediate temperatures, consistent with reported psychophysical data [17] and neural responses [53]. With intensity judgments of solutions ranging from 0.0068 to 0.1060 M, however, temperature did not seem to influence the response (Fig. 4–2). Relative to hedonic responses (Fig. 4–3), a distinct biphasic distribution was obtained, with three subjects indicating an increased degree of liking with increasing sodium chloride content and five indicating the reverse. (The ninth subject, whose results are not included in Fig. 4–3, gave erratic responses.) The effect of temperature needs to be established mathematically; visually, it appears that the solutions at 55° C were disliked the least. This bimodal distribution of hedonic ratings of salt solutions is not unprecedented [8], as evidenced by Fig. 4–4. Opposing distributions were obtained for both sodium chloride and sucrose, with most subjects disliking the saline and liking the sugar solutions. In a recent study [6] eight subjects expressed preferences among seven concentrations of sodium chloride to give patterns of response depicted in Fig. 4–5. Note the

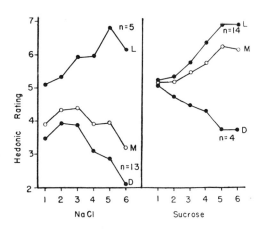

temperature results obtained from our laboratory, we can conclude that taste responses to stimulus concentration are not only dependent upon the psychophysical method employed (threshold, intensity, hedonic tone) but may vary significantly among individual subjects.

SUMMARY

I would like to call attention to some areas of chemoreception that are much in need of research, that would be of direct or indirect importance to human nutrition. A close scrutiny of the literature indicates a dearth of information on the interactive effects of gustation and olfaction, despite the fact that the two systems are so closely interrelated along the food pathways in so many species. The extent to which visual, auditory, tactile, and thermal factors impinge upon chemoreception is largely uninvestigated.

Fig. 4–4. Average hedonic ratings of increasing concentrations of sodium chloride and sucrose on a nine-point hedonic scale. M = mean rating for all eighteen Ss; L = mean rating for Ss liking solution; D = mean rating for Ss disliking solutions. (Source: Engen et al., in Pfaffmann, 1961.)

distinct lack of uniformity among individual subjects. It is clearly evident that stimulus concentration, as well as quality, is an important determinant of hedonic rating. On the basis of the

Although it would be expected that sensitivity to odor and taste stimuli would increase during hunger and/or deprivation and would decrease with satiation,

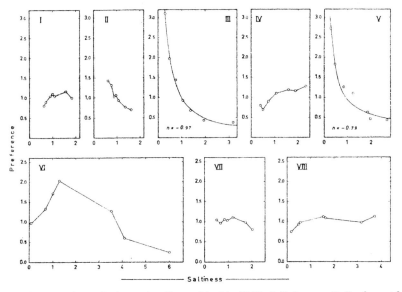

Fig. 4–5. Preferences for solutions of sodium chloride (0.05–0.65 per cent). Each graph represents the response of an individual S. (Source: Ekman and Akesson, 1964.)

conflicting evidence precludes any generalization. The extent to which the palatability of food or the pleasure derived from the eating process per se influences the excessive ingestion of calories is a subject of much speculation but of little unifying experimental evidence. No data appear to be available on the gustatory and olfactory sensitivity and discriminability of obese versus non-obese human subjects, or of fed versus fasting obese subjects as compared to normals. Much evidence suggests that the composition of the saliva bathing the taste receptors influences gustatory responses, raising the question as to whether quantitative and/or qualitative changes in the saliva and/or the blood alter taste and olfactory perception sufficiently to be reflected in food selection and intake. Are sensitivities to taste and olfactory stimuli, and perhaps in other sensory modalities, transmitted genetically, as conclusively demonstrated for the bitter taste of thiourea compounds? Are taste and olfactory sensitivities so subjugated by the eating patterns of the cultural environment to render them invalid as influencing factors in the regulation of food intake?

It is hoped that the foregoing discussion will stimulate further thought and research in this area. In 1944, Pyke [48] summarized a meeting of a nutrition panel of the British Society of Chemical Industries, with a statement that is quite appropriate for the present conference, "The science of nutrition has progressed a long way. It certainly has still a long way to go. Perhaps this meeting of the Nutrition Panel, where nutritionists, chemists, physiologists, psychologists and those forgotten folk who taste and choose and cannot explain, all met to talk together and partially to comprehend each other, may have served in some small way to send it off on a new, fruitful journey."

Discussion

Snapper: I don't want to discuss the excellent experiments you have made but I want to say a few words about two statements in your introduction. First, that "many Americans over thirty years of age are obese." The damage is already done before they are twenty years old. Of the soldiers who were killed in Korea, average age twenty-two years, 50 per cent had advanced arteriosclerosis. And I think the second statement that you made is a very dangerous one; that is, that we should listen to the nutritionists as far as our food is concerned. I will try to explain later that the poor condition of our health in this country is the fault of the nutritionists. If you will recall, in the colonized oriental countries the public health service and nutritionists gave the population advice to eat butter, and this was followed by a tremendous increase of fatalities. Nutritionists are very valuable people who try their best, but they make human errors. Therefore, one should not listen too attentively to the nutrionists but more to the instincts that are disappearing in our degenerating race.

Pfaffmann: In your data, the effect of temperature on the threshold for the NaCl solutions seems almost exactly like the electrophysiological recordings obtained by Abbott (unpublished Ph.D. thesis, Brown University, 1953), and Sato (*Olfaction and Taste,* Macmillan, New York, 1963). They got essentially that same function, i.e., very low sensitivity at either end of the curve, with an optimum at about the ranges you have demonstrated. The other point is the observation of the similarity of hedonic ratings. Do you have any indications why those subjects were so clearly different? When I did the hedonic rating, I made this kind of *post hoc* analysis but didn't have any subjects come back for re-examination. Do you have anything to say about what differentiates these subjects perhaps in other ways?

Pangborn: Not at present.

Halpern: Was the change of temperature in recognition threshold rather than in judged intensity? In the electrophysiological data (Abbott, *op. cit.;* Sato, *op. cit.;* Nejad, unpublished Ph.D. thesis, Florida State University, 1961), response magnitude was measured, not the quality of intensity or the ability to differentiate. I was surprised that, in terms of judged intensity, no difference was noted in your data. Might this be just at the low concentrations and at the very low temperatures? Was there any subjective report of taste given? Did the subjects report a loss in taste responses when it was very cold?

Pangborn: They did not comment about a taste loss. Indications of a loss do not show up in the responses on the numerical scale. They objected to the temperature of the 0° C solution per se, but this did not seem to be reflected in their intensity scoring or hedonic responses.

Chauncey: In some of our studies using rate of parotid gland secretion to evaluate stimulus intensity we observed a peculiar phenomenon. Sodium citrate solutions (5, 10, 15, and 20 per cent), citric acid solution (0.5, 1.0, 1.5, and 2.0 per cent), and sucrose solutions (5, 10, 15, and 20 per cent) were tested. We noted that all individuals tested were able to discern intensity changes, and there was no aversion to the taste when the pure solutions were employed. In contrast, when we mixed the sodium citrate and citric acid solutions and requested that the participants discriminate relative to the "sourness" and "saltiness" of the mixed solutions, many were unable to

do this. A frequent complaint was registered, stating that the taste was objectionable. I then decided to test myself and found that though I could easily distinguish the pure solutions, in all the mixture concentrations of sodium citrate and citric acid I was only able to perceive a bitter sensation and was unable to note any saltiness or sourness. This, apparently, was also happening to some of the participants. This data is suggestive that certain persons have a peculiar type of acid-salt taste-blindness which is manifest as a bitter sensation. It would be interesting to determine if this is a genetic factor such as the response to PROP. With citric acid–sucrose mixtures, all the individuals were able to discern sourness and sweetness. We found that the effect here was quite additive, with the exception, as Pangborn mentioned, that certain concentrations of these mixtures were highly unpalatable and were not liked by the subjects.

Henkin: We observed thresholds for salty, sweet, bitter, and sour in patients with and without dentures, and there is no question that the thresholds for sour and bitter are more significantly enhanced when a denture patient has his upper dentures out than when he has them in. The role that the palate plays in sour and bitter sensations is quite significant, and if you ask different patients about the taste, particularly sour and bitter, they will report that when their dentures are in they note a great decrease in their ability to taste.

Hamilton: Pangborn has demonstrated factors other than chemicals that are involved in taste. I should like to expand this with a few notes I've made on variables other than taste that are related to food acceptance and rejection.

Bates has stated that "Food and sex are different—almost any adult can tell them apart" (*Amer. Scholar*, **22**: 449, 1958). He then proceeds to describe the ways in which they are similar. Even the vocabularies are interchangeable, for example, the words "appetite," "hungry," "satiated," and "starved." One might observe that the female spider has taken the essay too seriously, for after copulation she eats the male.

In a manner similar to Bates's thesis, Brobeck (*Rev. Prog. Hor. Res.*, **26**: 439, 1960) has compared food and temperature and makes the point that the two are so similar as to be almost identical. He reminds us of the relation between the temperature of food and its acceptability. Vegetable soup is eaten hot and vischyssoise cold, consommé either hot or cold, and fruit soup at room temperature. Vegetables are usually eaten hot unless they function as a salad, in which case they are served cold or at room temperature.

Extending this line of reasoning, I suggest that food and culture are so similar that they cannot be separated. It is for this reason that I should like to act as a poor substitute for an anthropologist at this symposium.

Food and eating are such obviously important factors in life that perhaps those of us in the basic sciences have failed to consider sufficiently their interactions with the development of culture. For example, it is a rare society without a religion, and a rare religion that does not include feasting and fasting as significant components. In Christianity much of the important symbolism centers around feeding—Adam and Eve ate of the forbidden fruit; the celebration of the Mass is eating the body and drinking the blood. It is the many food taboos imposed by religion that bring us closer to the context of this meeting on taste. There have been widespread prohibitions against the eating of animal flesh, but the prohibition against eating pork

is perhaps better known than any other. The genesis of these taboos is difficult to trace, but it appears that the prohibition against eating such meat was related more to economic factors than to anything else. This appears to be the case for the Jew. For the Moslem the general belief is that Mohammed probably banned pork in order to distinguish the Moslem religion from Christianity at a time when there was great competition between the two. In this vein, it is believed that alcoholic beverages were prohibited to Moslems to distinguish them from both Jews and Christians. However, for many, pork was not looked upon as a prohibited food. Galen taught Greek athletes that pork was a food more nutritious than others and that in order to perform their tasks better, they should partake of a pork meal before athletic events. (Simoons, *Eat Not This Flesh*, University of Wisconsin Press, Madison, 1961.)

An outstanding example of the role of foods, or more likely, the taste of a food, in the course of national events appeared in India during the Sepoy Rebellion of 1857–58. The Sepoys (Indian troops) rebelled against the British East India Company. The troops had been supplied new Enfield rifles, and the sealed caps of the cartridges were greased. Since the use of these cartridges necessitated biting off caps before the cartridge was inserted into the rifle, this seal took on great importance. A rumor spread among the troops that pork and beef grease had been used to seal the cartridges. The pork was an abomination to the Moslems and the beef an offense to the Hindus. As a consequence, this condition was significant in the precipitation of the rebellion, although there were other underlying factors. Many historians point to the time of this rebellion as the beginning of the rise of nationalism in India.

The homeopathic uses of foods have led to many aversions and preferences. For example, in Morocco, people eat the liver of wild boar to gain the animal's strength and also as a remedy for syphilis. The soldiers of Madagascar are forbidden to eat hedgehog because, when attacked and frightened, the animal curls up and becomes very timid. Thus, if the soldiers ate of this animal, they might develop timid characteristics in battle. Kidney is also a food not eaten by these soldiers for the word for kidney in the language is the same as that for "shot" (Frazer, *The Golden Bough* [abridged ed.], Macmillan, New York, 1958).

There are so many social aspects to eating that one might wonder if food is not enjoyed more and tastes better in a social context. The desire to eat alone on the part of some individuals may be as abnormal a response as is the alcoholic's desire to drink alone. The genesis of social eating probably can be traced to practices of primitive man. In some primitive cultures, an individual, after consuming an animal, made sure to bury the bones so that his enemies would not get hold of them. If one's enemy gathered the discarded bones, he could work a curse on the individual who had eaten the food. By eating together and partaking of the same food, primitive man could obviate this curse (Frazer, *op. cit.*).

It is a rare culture where partaking of the host's food is not related in some manner to indications of affection or at least of friendliness. Most of us learned as youngsters that the way to flatter "Aunt Minnie" was to eat as much of her proffered food as possible, regardless of its quality. Politicians have long known that the way to win votes is not only by kissing babies but also by eating all sorts of bland foods that may be presented. Sophisticated travelers know that they must be careful to accept the foods given to them by their foreign hosts;

otherwise, their behavior might prove offensive. Bates (*op. cit.*) poses the question that, while we talk about sexual perverts, what is to be said of the food pervert? Considering this, we might be concerned about the number of food perverts in our diplomatic corps who might offend their host's country by being unwilling to try new and exotic foods. Incidentally, this is a factor of which the Peace Corps is well aware.

In many cultures there are areas of food dislikes that have been learned because certain foods have been considered to be only for the poor. In America, the viscera of animals is one such food, and in the Far East, brown rice is another. Other foods are avoided because they are thought to be fit only for lower animals. Cottage cheese and buttermilk belong in this category. On the farm, these two products were fed to swine. Many a farm lad, coming to the city, has been surprised to find that these are acceptable foods for man.

Variety of the diet is also involved in feeding behavior and especially with food acceptance. This appears to present a paradox since the staples in the world, such as potatoes, wheat, and rice, are eaten almost daily and one never seems to tire of them. However, there are many different ways of preparing these staples, and generally, variety is superimposed on a particular food by its method of preparation. It is worth considering that variety may play a role within a single meal. For example, does a delicious steak taste as good after the first three-quarters of a pound have been eaten? In other words, does the last quarter-pound taste as good as the first? Le Magnen (Habit and food selection, in *Handbook of Physiology*, Cody and Brobeck [eds.], section on the Alimentary Canal [in press] has published data on rats showing that food intake is increased when different flavored diets are presented within a two-hour feeding session. This brings us to the question of the significance of taste in conditions of satiety. Very simply put, if, during the course of a meal, the taste of food becomes less and less reinforcing, perhaps this may be one of the factors that leads to a feeling of satiety.

All of these factors and many more must influence taste, at least as it relates to preference and aversion. Thus, regardless of the fundamentals of the taste receptors, their location, structure, or function, the real differentiation must take place centrally, and part of this central control must be acquired. These factors are of extreme importance when it comes to problems of feeding the burgeoning world populations. In many cases, problems of nutrition must be solved not by introducing new foods but by upgrading the conventional foods of a society. Thus, for a vegetarian group we will probably be less successful if we attempt to introduce meat products than if we combine vegetable products into a more nutritious as well as palatable mixture. Something like this is being done in Central America where corn meal and soybeans are combined in a flour called *incaparina*.

It is apparent that the contributions of psychologists, sociologists, and anthropologists will be as important in solving the world's food problems as are the roles of the nutritionists and agriculturists.

Fischer: Let me recall in this context our earlier finding of a relation between high taste thresholds for quinine and few food dislikes, as well as low taste thresholds for quinine—and, thus, for most "Gaussian" compounds—and many food dislikes (Fischer *et al., Nature,* **191**: 1328, 1961; Fischer *et al., Med. Exp.,* **9**: 151, 1963).

Harper: You mentioned that there was

very little evidence that taste has played a role in food taboos. You didn't discuss the possibility that toxic or adverse effects play a role in food taboos. The classic example is that of the Eskimos not eating polar bear liver, which is toxic because it contains excessive vitamin A.

Hamilton: I was thinking of taboos in the context of mysticism.

Pangborn: Did you come across any literature referring to the food taboos in our own puritanical culture, in which it is believed that if something doesn't taste good, it must be good for you. If you do eat it, you will be rewarded with some dessert or food that does taste good.

Hamilton: Yes, I remember it now.

De Ruiter: I am worried about this business of taste acting as a satiety signal. I think it may be a terminological problem. I just cannot see, in my terminology, how taste could possibly act as a satiety signal.

Hamilton: Taste may be involved in some manner with the satiety state. It would be a shift, during a meal, from acceptance to rejection.

Henkin: I cannot help wondering if we should not have a psychiatrist studying us. Here we are, fixated on the oral aspects of life!

REFERENCES

1. Beaudoin, R., and Mayer, J. Food intakes of obese and non-obese women. *J. Am. Diet. Assoc.,* **29**: 29–33, 1953.
2. Berg, H. W., Pangborn, R. M., Roessler, E. B., and Webb, A. D. Influence of hunger on olfactory acuity. *Nature* (London), **197**: 108, 1963.
3. Bruch, H. Role of the emotions in hunger and appetite, in R. W. Miner, The Regulation of Hunger and Appetite. *Ann. N.Y. Acad. Sc.,* **63**: 68–75, 1955.

4. Carlson, A. J. *The Control of Hunger in Health and Disease.* University of Chicago Press, Chicago, 319 pp., 1916.

5. Dobriakova, O. A. Concerning the parallel in changes in electrical sensitivity of organs of vision and taste under the influence of optical and taste stimuli. *Fiziol. Zhur. SSSR,* **26**: 192–99, 1939. (In Russian, French summary.)

6. Ekman, G., and Akesson, C. Saltiness, sweetness, and preference. A study of quantitative relations in individual subjects. Reports, Psychology Laboratory, University of Stockholm, **177**: 1–13, 1964.

7. Elsberg, C. A., and Levy, I. The sense of smell. I. A new and simple method of quantitative olfactometry. *Bull. Neur. Inst. N.Y.,* **4**: 5–19, 1935–36.

8. Engen, T., McBurney, D. H., and Pfaffmann, C. The sensory and motivating properties of the sense of taste, cited by C. Pfaffmann in *Nebraska Symposium on Motivation,* M. R. Jones (ed.). University of Nebraska Press, Lincoln, pp. 71–110, 1961.

9. Furchtgott, E., and Friedman, M. P. The effects of hunger on taste and odor RLs. *J. Comp. Physiol. Psychol.,* **53**: 576–81, 1960.

10. Goetzl, F. R., Abel, M. S., and Ahokas, A. J. Occurrence in normal individuals of diurnal variations in olfactory acuity. *J. Appl. Physiol.,* **2**: 553–62, 1950.

11. Goetzl, F. R., Ahokas, A. J., and Goldschmidt, M. Influence of sucrose in various concentrations upon olfactory acuity and sensations associated with food intake. *J. Appl. Physiol.,* **4**: 30–36, 1951.

12. Goetzl, F. R., Ahokas, A. J., and Payne, J. G. Occurrence in normal individuals of diurnal variations in acuity of the sense of taste for sucrose. *J. Appl. Physiol.,* **2**: 619–26, 1950.

13. Goetzl, F. R., Goldschmidt, M., Wheeler, P., and Stone, F. Influence of sugar upon olfactory acuity and upon the sensation complex of appetite and satiety. *Gastroenterology,* **12**: 252–57, 1949.

14. Goetzl, F. R., and Stone, F. Diurnal variations in acuity of olfaction and food intake. *Gastroenterol,* **9**: 444–53, 1947.

15. Gregson, R. A. M. Modification of perceived relative intensities of acid tastes by ambient illumination changes. *Aust. J. Psych.,* **16**: 190–99, 1964.

16. Gregson, R. A. M., and Wilson, G. D. Effects of illumination on the detection and perceived relative intensity of acid tastes. Research Project 10, Department of Psychology and Sociology, University of Canterbury, New Zealand, 28 pp., 1966.

17. Goudriaan, J. C. Influence de la temperature sur la sensation gustative. *Arch. Neerl. Physiol.,* **10**: 411–17, 1925.

18. Hall, R. L. Flavor study approaches at McCormick and Co., Inc., in *Flavor Research and Food Acceptance,* A. D. Little (ed.). Reinhold, New York, pp. 224–40, 1958.

19. Hammer, F. J. The relation of odor, taste, and flicker-fusion thresholds to food intake. *J. Comp. Physiol. Psychol.,* **44**: 403–11, 1951.

20. Hollander, F., Sober, H. A., and Bandes, J. A study of hunger and appetite in a young man with esophageal obstruction and jejunostomy, in R. W. Miner, The Regulation of Hunger and Appetite. *Ann. New York Acad. Sci.,* **63**: 107–20, 1955.

21. Hundley, J. M. Need for weight control program, in *Weight Control,* E. S. Eppright, P. Swanson, and C. A. Iverson (eds.). Iowa State College Press, Ames, Iowa, pp. 1–17, 1955.

22. Irvin, D. L., Ahokas, A. J., and Goetzl, F. R. The influence of ethyl alcohol in low concentrations upon olfactory acuity and the sensation complex of appetite and satiety. *Permanente Found. Med. Bull.,* **8**: 97–101, 1950.

23. Irvin, D. L., and Goetzl, F. R. The influence of tannic acid upon olfactory acuity and the sensation complex of appetite and satiety. *Permanente Found. Med. Bull.,* **9**: 119–24, 1951.

24. Janowitz, H. D., and Grossman, M. I. Gusto-olfactory thresholds in relation to appetite and hunger sensation. *J. Appl. Physiol.,* **2**: 217–22, 1949.

25. Janowitz, H. D., and Hollander, F. The time factor in the adjustment of food intake to varied caloric requirement in the dog, in R. W. Miner, The Regulation of Hunger and Appetite. *Ann. N.Y. Acad. Sci.,* **63**: 56–57, 1955.

26. Jones, F. N. A test of the validity of the Elsberg method of olfactometry. *Am. J. Psychol.,* **66**: 81–85, 1953.

27. Kanig, J. L. Mental impact of colors in food studied. *Food Field Reptr.,* **23**: 57, 1955.

28. Le Magnen, J. Le rôle des stimulations olfacto-gustatives dans le mécanismes de régulation de la prise alimentaire. *Ann. Nutr. et Aliment.,* **10**: 153–88, 1956.

29. Lepkovsky, S. The physiological basis of voluntary food intake (Appetite?), in *Advances in Food Research, I,* E. M. Mrak and G. F. Stewart (eds.). Academic Press, New York, 105–48, 1948.

30. Loeb, M. B. The social function of food habits. *J. Am. Acad. Appl. Nutrition,* **4**: 227–29, 1951.

31. Margulies, N. R., and Goetzl, F. R. The effect of alcohol upon the acuity of the sense of taste for sucrose and the sensation complex of appetite and satiety. *Permanente Found. Med. Bull.,* **8**: 102–6, 1950.

32. Margulies, N. R., Irvin, D. L., and Goetzl, F. R. The effect of alcohol upon olfactory acuity and the sensation complex of appetite and satiety. *Permanente Found. Med. Bull.,* **8**: 1–8, 1950.

33. Mayer-Gross, W., and Walker, J. W. Taste and selection of food in hypoglycaemia. *Brit. J. Exp. Path.,* **27**: 297–305, 1946.

34. McCleary, R. A. Taste and post-ingestion factors in specific-hunger behavior. *J. Comp. Physiol. Psychol.,* **46**: 411–21, 1953.

35. Meyer, D. R. The stability of human gustatory sensitivity during changes in time of food deprivation. *J. Comp. Physiol.,* **45**: 373–76, 1952.

36. Moir, H. C. Some observations on the appreciation of flavour in foodstuffs. *Chem. & Ind.* (London), **55**: 145–48, 1936.

37. Mook, D. G. Oral and postingestional determinants of the intake of various solutions in rats with esophageal fistulas. *J. Comp. Physiol. Psychol.,* **56**: 645–59, 1963.

38. Moore, H. B. The meaning of food. *Am. J. Clin. Nutrition,* **5**: 77–82, 1957.

39. Moore, M. E., Linker, E., and Purcell, M. Taste-sensitivity after eating: a signal-detection approach. *Amer. J. Psychol.,* **78**: 107–11, 1965.

40. Murskii, L. I. Recovery of analyzer function in resuscitated animals. (In Russian) *Sci. Rept.,* Ushinskii Pedagogic Institute Yaroslavl, U.S.S.R., **32**: 42–57, 1959.

41. Nutrition Reviews. Self-selection of diets. *Nutr. Rev.,* **2**: 199, 1944.

42. Pangborn, R. M. Influence of hunger on sweetness preferences and taste thresholds. *Am. J. Clin. Nutr.,* **7**: 280–87, 1959.

43. Pangborn, R. M. Influence of color on the discrimination of sweetness. *Am. J. Psychol.,* **73**: 229–38, 1960.

44. Pangborn, R. M., Berg, H. W., and Hansen, B. The influence of color on discrimination of sweetness in dry table wine. *Am. J. Psychol.,* **76**: 492–95, 1963.

45. Pangborn, R. M., and Simone, M. Body size and sweetness preference. *J. Am. Diet. Assoc.,* **34**: 924–28, 1958.

46. Pfaffmann, C., and Bare, J. K. Gustatory nerve discharges in normal and adrenalectomized rats. *J. Comp. Physiol. Psychol.,* **43**: 320–24, 1950.

47. Pfaffmann, C., and Hagstrom, E. C. Factors influencing taste sensitivity to sugar. *Am. J. Physiol.,* **183**: 651, 1955.

48. Pyke, M. Nutrition and a matter of taste. *Nature* (London), **154**: 229–31, 1944.

49. Roberts, Sir William. *Digestion and Diets.* 2nd ed. London, 1897 (Cited by Lepovsky, 1948).

50. Schneider, R. A., and Wolf, S. Olfactory perception thresholds for citral utilizing a new type olfactorium. *J. Appl. Physiol.,* **8**: 337–42, 1955.

51. Schutz, H. G., and Pilgrim, F. J. A field study of food monotony. *Psychol. Rep.,* **4**: 559–64, 1958.

52. Share, I., Martyniuk, E., and Grossman, M. I. Effect of prolonged intragastric feeding on oral food intake in dogs. *Am. J. Physiol.,* **169**: 229–35, 1952.

53. Yamashita, S., and Sato, M. The effects of temperature on gustatory response of rats. *J. Cell. Comp. Physiol.,* **66**: 1–17, 1965.

54. Yensen, R. Influence of salt deficiency on taste sensitivity in human subjects. *Nature* (London), **181**: 1472–74, 1958.

55. Yensen, R. Influence of water deprivation on taste sensitivity in man. *Nature* (London), **182**: 677–79, 1958.

56. Yensen, R. Some factors affecting taste sensitivity in man. II. Depletion of body salt. *Quart. J. Exp. Psychol.,* **11**: 230–38, 1959.

57. Yensen, R. Some factors affecting taste sensitivity in man. III. Water deprivation. *Quart. J. Exp. Psychol.,* **11**: 239–48, 1959.

58. Young, P. T. Psychologic factors regulating the feeding process, in *Symposium on Nutrition and Behavior,* Nutrition Symposium Series No. 14, The National Vitamin Foundation, Inc., New York, pp. 52–59, 1957.

59. Young, P. T. *Motivation and Emotion.* John Wiley & Sons, New York, 648 pp., 1961.

60. Zilstorff-Pedersen, K. Olfactory threshold determination in relation to food intake. *Acta Otolaryng.,* **45**: 86–90, 1955.

5: Genetics and Gustatory Chemoreception in Man and Other Primates *by Roland Fischer*

T HE TWO taste parameters in man to be dealt with in this essay are thresholds and just noticeable differences (jnds). A taste threshold denotes the minimum concentration of a compound in aqueous solution that can reproducibly be differentiated from distilled water. A jnd denotes the minimal magnitude increase in concentration of a compound in aqueous solution that can be detected.

GAUSSIAN AND BIMODAL DISTRIBUTION OF TASTE THRESHOLDS

Most of the pedigree and population studies of taste thresholds have been restricted to the bitter phenylthiourea (PTC) type antithyroid compounds that contain the characteristic H—N—C=S grouping. Taste thresholds for these approximately forty compounds [5,43,44], such as PTC, 6-n-propylthiouracil (PROP), 1-methyl-2-mercapto-imidazole, etc., follow a *bimodal distribution* in a Caucasian population differentiating it into tasters and "non-tasters." The classical hypothesis of "non-tasting" is based on homozygosity for simple Mendelian recessive alleles [63].

It should be emphasized, however, that taste sensitivity to PTC type compounds [36] is a special case since taste thresholds for most compounds do not follow a bimodal but a Gaussian or monomodal distribution. The importance of the latter general phenomenon is emphasized by our observation that men with low taste thresholds for compounds, such as quinine, the taste threshold of which follows a Gaussian distribution, also display low taste thresholds for a variety of other chemically unrelated compounds, irrespective of their taste quality [22,25]. Their only common characteristic is that of Gaussian distribution—with the exception of hydrochloric acid (HCl). However, a sensitive quinine taster, who therefore is also a sensitive taster of sucrose, urea, chlorpromazine, etc., i.e., of a large variety of "Gaussian" compounds (except HCl), *may or may not* be an insensitive "non-taster" of PTC type compounds. Similarly, a very insensitive quinine taster (also an insensitive taste responder to other "Gaussian" compounds) may or may not be a very sensitive taster or a very insensitive "non-taster" of PTC type compounds [20–22,25,54], as illustrated in Fig. 5–1. For these and other reasons [27] we classify the mediators of gustatory chemoreception as *"Gaussian" sensors,* i.e., sensors of chemicals with unrelated structures, and *bimodal receptors,* i.e., receptors of compounds with

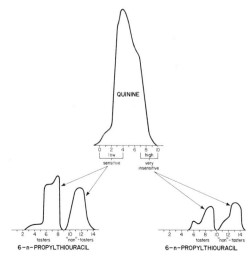

Fig. 5–1. Distribution of quinine taste thresholds in a population (N = 228) exemplifying the main class of taste sensitivity for "Gaussian" compounds— general phenomenon—and distribution of PROP taste thresholds in the same population exemplifying the subclasses of taste responsiveness toward bimodally distributed compounds—special phenomenon [23, 24]. Note that the position of the PROP antimode is influenced by the subjects' quinine thresholds [51, 53]. The PROP antimode is at threshold (solution number) 9 for subjects with low quinine thresholds; while it is at 10 for insensitive subjects with high quinine thresholds. A glance at the figure also reveals the total lack of very sensitive PROP tasters—with thresholds 2–5 —among the very insensitive quinine tasters. The influence of quinine taste sensitivity on the expression of PROP responsiveness may be regarded as an example of partial epistasis in humans.

specific chemical structure characterized by the presence of the H—N—C≡S molecular grouping.

Our methodology of macro taste threshold measurement is an adaptation of the Harris-Kalmus [44,45] double blind placebo procedure and involves geometric serial concentrations of compounds in aqueous solution ranging from $3.66 \times 10^{-7}M$ to $1.92 \times 10^{-1}M$. The Harris-Kalmus procedure is already an adaptation based on Sir Ronald A. Fisher's [32] forced choice design entitled "Mathematics of a Lady Tasting Tea." Our adaptations involve the use of *distilled water* for the serial dilutions and placebos, a *between-sampling mouth rinse* with distilled water, and the use of an *odorless phenylthiourea* (PTC) *type compound*, 6-n-phenylthiouracil (PROP) [54], the least toxic among the phenyl-thioureas [81]. Over a period of seven years, this method [19,22,24] has proved to be the most reliable for determining taste thresholds. Especially the use of PROP—the taste thresholds of which display a high positive correlation with those of PTC [26]—enabled us to test taste uncontaminated by smell.[1] PTC, the compound used in nearly all pedigree and population studies, displays a strong aromatic odor which may account for the clean but apparently artefactual separation of the tasting and "non-tasting" modes in a population. Our observations of the influence of PTC odor on its taste thresholds have been confirmed by Skude [73] who found that 65 per cent of his subjects displayed higher thresholds for PTC when their nostrils were plugged. In light of our own data, as well as that of the literature, the ability to taste odorless PTC type compounds is, therefore, neither an all-or-none phenomenon nor a typical continuous variable.

Attention should be called to our observation that sensitivity to "Gaussian" compounds is *not* meant to imply that an individual has *identical taste thresholds* for such compounds *but* it does imply *similar location* of the taste threshold within the range of distribution of each particular "Gaussian" compound.[2]

[1] For tabulations which compare our thresholds (solution numbers) with those of Harris and Kalmus [44,45] and express them in molarity [21,22].

[2] The solubility range of PROP extends between 3.66×10^{-7} M and 6.0×10^{-3} M concentra-

These ranges may differ as much as a thousand-fold concentration-wise, as exemplified by such a difference between the saturated aqueous solutions of quinine and sucrose.

The possibility that taste sensitivity for a compound may imply sensitivity to chemically unrelated compounds was uncovered because our solution numbers representing taste thresholds in doubling concentrations corresponded to certain molar concentrations (see Table 5–1). A solution number therefore stands for the same amount of molecules present in the solution, irrespective of the structure or molecular weight of the compound. If we contrast this procedure with that

TABLE 5–1: Concentration of Taste Solutions in Molarity

Taste Thresholds in Solution Numbers	Concentration in Molarity
21	7.6800×10^{-1}
20	3.8400×10^{-1}
19	1.9200×10^{-1}
18	9.6000×10^{-2}
17	4.8000×10^{-2}
16	2.4000×10^{-2}
15	1.2000×10^{-2}
14	6.0000×10^{-3}
13	3.0000×10^{-3}
12	1.5000×10^{-3}
11	7.5000×10^{-4}
10	3.7500×10^{-4}
9	1.8750×10^{-4}
8	9.3750×10^{-5}
7	4.6875×10^{-5}
6	2.3438×10^{-5}
5	1.1719×10^{-5}
4	5.8594×10^{-6}
3	2.9300×10^{-6}
2	1.4648×10^{-6}
1	7.3242×10^{-7}
0	3.6621×10^{-7}

tions, the latter representing a saturated aqueous solution of PROP at room temperature (denoted by solution number 14; the half-saturated solution is denoted by solution number 13, etc.); see Table 5–1. The range of the more soluble sucrose extends farther, i.e., between $3.66 \times 10^{-7} M$ (solution number 1) and $1.92 \times 10^{-1} M$ concentrations, the latter representing a saturated aqueous solution of sucrose at room temperature (denoted by solution number 19).

widely employed previously, namely, the use of solutions containing compounds on a weight per volume basis, it is easily understood that our observation of taste sensitivity to one "Gaussian" compound implying sensitivity to other chemically unrelated "Gaussian" compounds—with the exception of HCl—could not but be overlooked.

The exceptional status of HCl, itself a "Gaussian" compound, implies that a sensitive quinine taster may or may not be a sensitive taster of HCl [20–22,26]. Observations by Kalmus and Farnsworth [52] of the influence of irradiation in man on taste thresholds show the exceptional stability of the HCl threshold, as contrasted with the lability of thresholds for other compounds. This observation is in line with our finding that taste sensitivity to HCl is unrelated to a subject's sensitivity to other "Gaussian" compounds.

TWIN STUDIES

Pedigree and population studies of taste thresholds have been largely restricted to PTC type compounds [6,55]. There is general agreement that the inability to taste PTC type compounds appears to be inherited in a simple Mendelian recessive manner [53,60,63]. Stern [78] believes that a single pair of alleles T and t is responsible for the inheritance of taste responses to PTC. Ford [35] well illustrates (1) production of heterozygotes when both taster and "nontaster" parents are homozygous (tasting is the dominant character), (2) segregation among the children of a marriage between two heterozygotes, and (3) a backcross (heterozygote with recessive homozygote), showing that among the offspring, segregation takes place in a ratio of 1 : 1.

Taste thresholds for PTC type compounds follow a bimodal distribution in a population, and the trait is based on genetic factors at a single locus; the difference between tasting and "non-tasting" depends on a simple Mendelian alternative so that individuals of genotype TT or Tt are tasters while those of genotype tt are "non-tasters."

In a Caucasian population, using the odorous PTC with the original Harris-Kalmus procedure, and assuming that the population is at equilibrium under random mating for these alleles, the phenotypes and genotypes should be distributed as follows:

Phenotype Distribution	Tasters 0.7	Non-Tasters 0.3
Genotype Distribution[a]	TT + Tt 0.2 : 0.5	tt 0.3

[a] If p = frequency of T, q = frequency of t, and $p + q = 1$, the genotypes occur in a ratio: p^2TT : $2pq$ Tt : q^2tt [77], implying that homozygotes (TT) and heterozygotes (Tt) should occur in a ratio of 2 : 5.

We should bear in mind, however, that using PROP—the odorless PTC type compound—and repeated testing with our modified Harris-Kalmus procedure, the phenotypic distribution of tasters and "non-tasters" of PROP is 0.5 : 0.5 [21,22]. For a geographic distribution of the frequency of insensitive taste responders or "non-tasters," we should like to refer to the tabulations and charts of Allison and Blumberg [1,70] and Saldanha and Nacrur.[3] To the

[3] Both of these papers report only reliable data obtained with the Harris-Kalmus or "equivalent" sorting procedures and disregard the vast amount of studies employing the PTC paper test. We would like to discourage the use of PTC, the odorous compound, and especially the use of PTC paper, since we believe that studies with the latter are more relevant to the genetics of *paper* taste than to that of PTC type compounds. Our contention is supported by data (to be published with Kaplan) that show in 140 subjects that 25 per cent of them are misclassified, if the Harris-Kalmus procedure and PROP are substituted with the unreliable PTC paper test.

best of our knowledge, no twin studies have been conducted about genetic factors involved in taste thresholds for "Gaussian" compounds, such as quinine, where it is assumed that the trait is multifactorial in origin and cumulative in effect.

During the last three years, working with A. R. Kaplan of the Cleveland Psychiatric Institute and Hospital, we have developed a cooperative twin research project on the genetics of taste thresholds. Taste thresholds were determined in 45 dizygotic (DZ) and 26 monozygotic (MZ) twin pairs for HCl, and in 70 DZ and 75 MZ twin pairs for quinine and PROP (in that consecutive order). The latter 145 twin pairs were supplemented with 191 combinations on non-twin sibling (SIB) pairs from which 142 were also taste tested for HCl. For the sex distribution of twins and siblings, methodological details, and a complete two factor (kinship and sex) analysis of variance of the data, the reader is referred to the original study [55]. Here we restrict ourselves to extracting and reporting the information most relevant to this paper.

AVERAGE INTRAPAIR THRESHOLD DIFFERENCES

The distribution of average intrapair threshold differences in MZ and same-sex DZ twin pairs is illustrated in Fig. 5–2. Inspection reveals no difference for HCl between the pairs of genetically identical twins and the pairs of fraternal twins, a small but significant difference is observable for quinine, while PROP displays the largest intrapair difference. Therefore, genetic factors play a predominant role in determining taste sensitivity of individuals for PROP, a lesser role in determining sensitivity for quinine, and no role in HCl testing.

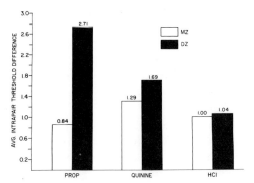

Fig. 5–2. Average intrapair threshold differences in monozygotic (MZ) and same-sex dizygotic (DZ) twin pairs for HCl, quinine, and PROP.

HOLZINGER INDEX

Since intrapair threshold differences do not lend themselves to a separation of environmental and genetic factors, the Holzinger index (H) [47] was chosen for a quantitative estimate of heritability. The index is based on concordance rates in MZ and DZ twin pairs:

$$H = \frac{\frac{\Sigma d^2 DZ}{2N DZ} - \frac{\Sigma d^2 MZ}{2N MZ}}{\frac{\Sigma d^2 DZ}{2N DZ}}$$

where $N MZ$ = the number of MZ twin pairs, $N DZ$ = the number of DZ twin pairs, $\frac{\Sigma d^2 DZ}{2N DZ}$ = the variance of mean difference in DZ twins, and $\frac{\Sigma d^2 MZ}{2N MZ}$ = the variance of mean difference in MZ twins. Inserting our respective data we obtain

$$H_{\text{quinine}} = \frac{\frac{260}{102} - \frac{257}{150}}{\frac{260}{102}}$$

$$= 0.33 \text{ and } H_{\text{PROP}} = \frac{\frac{646}{102} - \frac{125}{150}}{\frac{646}{102}} = 0.87$$

If 1.00 represents 100 per cent heritability, the values 0.33 for quinine and

0.87 for PROP express the extent of genetic control on the taste thresholds for these two compounds. Since, however, the environment influences the manifestations of the genotype, the Holzinger index would only be meaningful if "environment" could be defined and quantified. The Holzinger index is not, in fact, the measure of the proportion of a trait due to heredity but is only an index of the relative size of estimates of presumed components of variance due to hereditary and environmental factors [83]. Other difficulties are also inherent in the evaluation of genetic studies with the twin method [46,82].

FACTORIAL ANALYSIS OF VARIANCE

A preliminary factorial analysis of variance for each compound was performed on the threshold values obtained from the first of two testing sessions using each subject from each group. For the factors *kinship* and *sex*, no significant differences were found among the groups for quinine and PROP. There was a significant difference, however, between sexes for HCl at

$$F\left(\tfrac{2}{24}\right) = 18.84; \; P < 0.001.$$

Table 5–2 presents the number of individuals with their mean thresholds and variances for each compound.

Intrapair differences in taste thresholds from the first testing session were obtained for MZ, DZ, and SIB pairs of the same and opposite sexes [55]. To determine possible genetic effects, detailed comparisons of the within-pair variance among the three kinship levels and between the two sexes were considered. Evaluation of the various comparisons for a compound was made through factorial analysis of variance for each compound. An unweighted means solu-

TABLE 5–2: Means and Variances (σ^2) of Taste Thresholds for Hydrochloric Acid (HCl), 1-Quinine Sulfate (Quinine), and 6-N-Propyl-thiouracil (PROP).

	♀	♂	HCl[a]	Quinine[b] All Groups Combined	PROP[b] All Groups Combined
Number of Ss	124	108		446	446
Mean	9.85	10.55		5.28	9.55
σ^2	1.51	1.65		3.24	5.95

[a] Significant differences in threshold between ♀ and ♂ at $p < 0.001$.
[b] No significant differences in thresholds among groups at $p > 0.20$.

tion was used because unequal sample size did not reflect the proportions of the groups found in the population.

The results of the comparisons of the within-pair variance ($\sigma^2 w$) for *DZ and MZ twins* calculated by combining like-sex pairs, reveal the following:

for HCl, $F (25/25) = 0.90$; $p > 0.10$, i.e., no significant difference;

for quinine, $F (50/74) = 1.49$; $p < 0.05$, i.e., significant difference; and

for PROP, $F (50/74) = 1.49$; $p < 0.001$, i.e., highly significant difference.

The analysis of variance, with factorial design for each compound, shows a *kinship by sex interaction for hydrochloric acid* that is significant at the variance $p < 0.02$ ($F = 3.91$, $df = 2/86$). Individual comparisons are displayed in Table 5–3, revealing that male MZ pairs have smaller intrapair differences ($p < 0.01$) than male DZ and SIB pairs, which were not significantly different from each other and were therefore combined. It should be emphasized, however, that the above-mentioned significant sex difference may be due to the sequential order of the tasted compounds (HCl → quinine → PROP), a hypothesis which would only be tested by reversing the order of test compounds.

TABLE 5–3: Groupings of Ordered Means of Differences between Pairs for HCl (Italicized Means Are Not Different from Each Other)[a]

Sex	Kinship DZ	SIB	MZ[b]
♀ ♀[c]	*0.87*	*1.00*	*1.29*
♂ ♂[d]	1.27	1.32	0.44

[a] MS error in analysis of variance = 1.12.
[b] MZ ♂ ♂ smaller than MZ ♀ ♀ at $p < 0.02$. Other within-kinship differences are not significant at $p > 0.10$.
[c] Within ♀ ♀ group, none of the means differs from each other at $p > 0.10$.
[d] Within ♂ ♂ group, DZ and SIB do not differ from each other at $p > 0.20$. MZ is different from DZ and SIB combined at $p < 0.01$.

For quinine, neither the main factors nor the interaction was significant. For PROP, the kinship factor was significant at $p < 0.001$ ($F = 19.12$, $df = 2/179$). Individual comparisons are displayed in Table 5–4 revealing that MZ pairs

TABLE 5–4: Grouping of Ordered Means of Differences between Pairs for PROP (Italicized Means Are Not Different from Each Other)[a]

	MZ	SIB	DZ
Kinship with sexes combined	*0.84*[b]	*2.37*[c]	*2.70*

[a] MS error of analysis of variance = 3.48.
[b] MZ differs from DZ and SIB combined at $p < 0.001$.
[c] DZ and SIB do not differ from each other at $p > 0.20$.

have significantly smaller intrapair differences ($p < 0.001$) than DZ and SIB pairs, which are not significantly different from each other and therefore combined regardless of sex. The data on correlations between taste thresholds for PROP and quinine, quinine and HCl, as well as PROP and HCl, in 308 individuals, is presented in detail elsewhere [55].

Some of the inherent advantages and drawbacks of twin studies should be emphasized. For the study of normal variations, twin studies yield interesting information, and their elimination of the age factor is an added advantage. It is a drawback that, as in our own studies, concordance rates for dizygotic twins may be affected by environmental influences, e.g., by similar taste experiences through dietary routine; or in Rosenthal's [69] words, a very similar environment and routine may confound effects of "the genetic family and the behavioral family." We cannot achieve a separation of environmental and genetic factors either with heritability estimates or with an analysis of variance of intrapair threshold differences.

PHARMACOGENETIC ASPECTS OF TASTE THRESHOLDS

A general relationship prevailing between the taste thresholds of stereo specific drugs and their biological activity has been described [20,22]. For example, with l-quinine and d-quinine, as well as with D-amphetamine and L-amphetamine, the former of each drug pair is the biologically more potent compound, as indicated by its lower oral LD_{50} in the mouse. Correspondingly, humans can taste the more active compound in a lower concentration (i.e., they display lower taste thresholds). For these reasons we came to regard a subject's oral cavity as a pharmacological test preparation *in situ* and the taste response as a sensory expression of pharmacological activity.

It was from this vantage point that we found a statistically significant positive correlation for forty-eight acutely ill mental patients between *quinine taste thresholds* (i.e., thresholds three to six; see Table 5-1) and the cumulative *trifluoperazine dose* sufficient to induce extrapyramidal side effects [29]. After controlling for age, sex, and smoking, patients with high quinine taste thresholds (i.e., seven to nine; see Table 5-1) needed higher trifluoperazine dosage for the induction of extrapyramidal side

effects. It appears relevant to note that phenothiazine induced extrapyramidal reactions also appear to occur on a basis of hereditary predisposition [4,29]. We would like to emphasize, however, that extrapyramidal side effects were chosen only because they are a convenient and reliable parameter of systemic reactivity, and we do not want to postulate a specific mechanism linking extrapyramidal side effects with taste sensitivity. To the contrary, we regard the above relation as only one manifestation of a general relationship.

FURTHER GUSTATORY CHARACTERISTICS OF POSSIBLE GENETIC SIGNIFICANCE

Genetic involvement has been claimed to characterize either individuals with low thresholds, i.e., sensitive tasters, or individuals with high thresholds, i.e., insensitive tasters. In the following, we report observations enabling a further subclassification of sensitive tasters according to two criteria: *characteristic range of variability in the redetermination of taste thresholds* and *ability to lower taste thresholds in response to specified taste training*. Both of these are likely to be genetically influenced. Our point is illustrated by presenting the relevant data of two sensitive tasters.

The first subject, R. A., a twenty-one-year-old male, displayed the following macrothresholds two years ago: quinine = 3; PROP = 6. His characteristic variability during successive micro[4] taste

---

[4] The microprocedure is a modification of the macroprocedure, resulting in a fifty fold resolution, i.e., the concentration intervals of the microprocedure are 1 per cent of the next higher macroconcentration (solution number). Whereas the macroscale, i.e., the doubling of each subsequent concentration (solution number) is exponential, the microscale consists of fifty linear subdivisions of each exponential macrostep. The linear interpolation of the macrointervals results in a time-saving yet accurate procedure [41].

threshold determinations for a variety of over forty compounds was found to be ± 0.4 per cent of a macrostep (solution number). The same individual displayed another characteristic, namely, as a result of micro threshold practice in at least three hourly sessions per week, he lowered his taste thresholds three steps to quinine = zero and PROP = 3 within a few weeks.

The second subject, L. F., a twenty-year-old male, displayed the following macrothresholds one and one-half years ago: quinine = 5; PROP = 6. His characteristic variability during successive micro taste threshold determinations for the same forty-odd compounds was found to be ± 10.5 per cent of a macrostep. The same individual did not change his taste thresholds for quinine and PROP during the last one and one-half years in spite of constant exposure to the above-mentioned micro taste threshold practice.

The two parameters in our two sensitive taster subjects reveal characteristic differences that go undetected if we compare only their closely corresponding taste thresholds for various compounds (see Fig. 5–3 and Table 5–5). Small or

large variability in the redetermination of micro taste thresholds for various compounds and the ability or inability to lower taste thresholds in response to specified taste training may be characteristics with which one could further subclassify heterozygous tasters.

THE JUST NOTICEABLE GUSTATORY DIFFERENCE (JND)

In the previous section we have dealt with a fairly stable and reproducible taste parameter, namely, threshold, and we have mentioned that it varies with the chemical structure of the compound.

It should be added that thresholds also vary as a function of solution temperature. Research in our laboratory has shown that thresholds depend on the temperature of the tasted solution, specifically on a range of 5–42° C, with a minimum threshold at 22° C.[5] Specifically, the curves depicting temperature-threshold functions exhibit the following features: (1) a symmetrical, V-shaped pattern displaying a sharp threshold optimum at 22° C; (2) a symmetrical temperature inversion at 22° C, which indicates that the sign of the coefficient is negative below 22° C and positive above this temperature; and (3) a generally linear relation between temperature coefficient and threshold above and below 22° C [41]. This taste threshold-temperature dependence, however, is independent of the chemical structure of a compound. The above-mentioned characteristics of taste thresholds indicate an apparently close relationship to localized receptor phenomena. In contrast, with a gustatory indicator reflecting an individ-

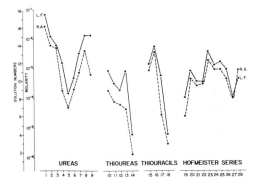

Fig. 5–3. Microtaste thresholds of two sensitive tasters, R. A. (quinine = 3; PROP = 6) and L. F. (quinine = 5; PROP = 6), for twenty-eight compounds. The data were combined with those of Griffin and replotted [41]. The chemical structure of the compounds and the subjects' taste thresholds in molarity are listed in Table 5–5.

[5] Incidentally, this temperature corresponds to the upper limit of the lower range of critical air temperature, that is, the lowest temperature at which man in the nude does not experience any discomfort. Twenty-three degrees Centigrade would be the start of the thermoneutrality zone at which metabolic rate is lowest and constant [76].

TABLE 5–5: Micro Taste Thresholds in Molarity of Two Sensitive Tasters for Twenty-eight Compounds Listed in the Same Consecutive Order as in Fig. 5–3

Compound Number	Compound	Taste Threshold in Molarity	
		Subject 1 R. A.	Subject 2 L. F.
	Urea Compounds		
1	Urea	2.5920×10^{-2}	6.7200×10^{-2}
2	Methylurea	5.9400×10^{-3}	1.2000×10^{-2}
3	Ethylurea	4.8000×10^{-3}	5.8800×10^{-3}
4	n-propylurea	1.6688×10^{-4}	1.5000×10^{-3}
5	Isopropylurea	4.6875×10^{-5}	1.4062×10^{-4}
6	n-butylurea	1.8750×10^{-4}	4.5000×10^{-4}
7	Allylurea	6.6750×10^{-4}	3.0000×10^{-3}
8	1,3-dimethylurea	3.6000×10^{-3}	1.2000×10^{-2}
9	1,3-diethylurea	5.6250×10^{-4}	1.1880×10^{-2}
	Thiourea Compounds		
10	Thiourea	1.5938×10^{-4}	7.5000×10^{-4}
11	Methylthiourea	7.0312×10^{-5}	2.8125×10^{-4}
12	1,3-dimethylthiourea	5.6250×10^{-5}	1.6688×10^{-4}
13	1,3-diethylthiourea	3.9844×10^{-5}	7.1250×10^{-4}
14	Phenylthiourea	1.2890×10^{-6}	5.8594×10^{-6}
	Thiouracil Compounds		
15	5-methyluracil	7.5000×10^{-4}	1.2000×10^{-3}
16	6-methyluracil	3.0000×10^{-3}	4.5600×10^{-3}
17	2-thiouracil	2.5781×10^{-5}	4.8750×10^{-4}
18	6-n-propyl-2-thiouracil	2.8128×10^{-6}	5.8594×10^{-6}
	Hofmeister Series		
19	Sulfuric acid	2.3438×10^{-5}	9.3750×10^{-5}
20	Sodium sulfate	3.7500×10^{-4}	6.9750×10^{-4}
21	Sodium phosphate	2.2500×10^{-4}	3.3375×10^{-4}
22	Hydrochloric acid	2.5875×10^{-4}	3.0000×10^{-4}
23	Lithium chloride	1.5000×10^{-3}	3.0000×10^{-3}
24	Sodium chloride	7.5000×10^{-4}	1.0500×10^{-3}
25	Potassium chloride	7.5000×10^{-4}	1.3200×10^{-3}
26	Ammonium chloride	3.7500×10^{-4}	7.5000×10^{-4}
27	Calcium chloride	9.1875×10^{-5}	9.2812×10^{-5}
28	Magnesium chloride	7.0500×10^{-4}	3.7500×10^{-4}

ual's metabolic-rate, dependent, systemic reactivity would be expected to be independent of the temperature of the taste solution, the chemical structure of the compound, its taste quality, and—in the middle range of sensitivity—its concentration. The just noticeable (taste) difference (jnd), we find, meets these requirements [23,28].

A micromethod has been developed [28,41] to determine the smallest concentration difference that can be distinguished—the just noticeable difference (ΔS)—by using comparison and reference concentrations as test solutions.

The reference concentration (S) is the lower limit of a jnd and is held constant while the comparison concentration is decreased in 1 per cent steps until the upper limit of a jnd is found. A jnd is conveniently expressed as a *Weber ratio*, i.e., a dimensionless ratio, $\frac{\Delta S}{S}$, with ΔS denoting the concentration difference between the lower and upper limits of a jnd in taste, and S denoting the lower limit. For the sake of convenience, we prefer to express Weber ratios in percentages.

With the above method, we were able

to reproduce and extend our initial observations [23], which showed that sympathetic stimulation—i.e., 8–12 mg psilocybin- and 6–10 mg D-amphetamine-produced excitation—decreases the size of a sucrose jnd; in other words, the systemic state of excitation is negatively correlated with the size of the Weber ratio. Systemic tranquilization, however, increases the size of the Weber ratio.

If successive jnds are determined under the influence of systemic D-amphetamine, concomitant with the excitation-produced decrease in *size* of the median Weber ratio, the *range* of the successive jnds is reduced approximately three and a half times in comparison with the control range.

The negative correlation between systemic state of excitation and size of Weber ratio is not specific for gustation since it seems to hold true also in vision. In cooperation with Dr. R. M. Hill (School of Optometry, Ohio State University), using neutral density filters, a reduction in brightness preference of over 50 percent was found under 5–10 mg psilocybin-produced excitation.

If taste thresholds could be characterized as being related to localized receptor phenomena, the size of a jnd might be interpreted as a reflection of the impulse relay that transmits information from gustatory receptors to higher nervous centers. Our results—based on more than 250 jnd determinations—indicate that tranquilizing drugs, which produce hypothermia and lower the metabolic rate, increase the size of a gustatory Weber ratio whereas drugs that produce an excitation syndrome and increase the metabolic rate [16] decrease the necessary stimulus intensity [28]. These findings may form the basis of a discussion about the possible modification of the Weber-Fechner and Stevens' [79] laws under systemic excitation and tranquilization. The classical Weber-Fechner psy-chophysical log law—valid in the middle range of intensities—can be reformulated since k, which has been taken as a constant for a particular sense in this law, is inversely proportional to the metabolic rate. The following reformulation deliberately disregards the individual intrahuman variables of age, sex, and other factors affecting individual levels of excitation and is an *interspecies* generalization.

$$S = \frac{k \log R}{kg^{3/4}} \tag{1}$$

where S stands for experienced intensity, R represents physical intensity, k is a proportionality constant peculiar to sensory modality, and $kg^{3/4}$ is the sign for the unit of metabolic body size.[6]

The same reformulation should apply to Stevens' log-log law according to which equal-stimulus ratios correspond to equal sensation ratios:

$$\Psi = k_1 \Phi^n \tag{2}$$

where Ψ stands for sensation magnitude, Φ for stimulus magnitude, the constant k depends on the units of measurement, and the value of the exponent n varies from one sensory continuum to another. Stevens' notation is meant to express that the intensity of sensation Ψ grows as the stimulus magnitude Φ is raised to a power of n. This notation, then, we propose to reformulate as:

$$\Psi = \frac{k_1}{kg^{3/4}} \Phi^n \tag{3}$$

[6] A linear correlation between the logarithm of metabolic rate and the logarithm of body weight shows that metabolic rate is proportional to a given power function of body weight. As an illustration, the metabolic level (under standard conditions) of adult homeotherms from mice to cattle averages 70 kcal per kg per day. It is therefore recommended that the three-fourth power of body weight be representative of metabolic body size and that $kg^{3/4}$ be chosen as the sign for the unit of metabolic body size [15,57].

We may go one step further and recall that body weight is correlated about 0.99 with basal metabolic rate [7] and that, therefore, a dimensional constant can be proposed:

$$\left(\frac{\tau_L}{kg^{3/4}}\right). \qquad (4)$$

Here τ_L stands for lifespan—denoting an inverse relationship between lifespan and metabolic rate [17].[7] Therefore, the relationship of intensity of sensation to lifespan and metabolic rate can be expressed on an interspecies level:

$$\Psi = k_1 \left(\frac{1}{kg^{3/4}}\right) \Phi^n. \qquad (5)$$

The resulting postulation is that smaller-sized, shorter-lived mammals should experience more intense sensations.

We can speculate on a further extension of our interspecies generalization. In every day life—i.e., in survival space [16]—and also in Aristotelian subject-object logic and ontology, we insist upon separation of motor from sensory functions since we are accustomed to experiencing only our *own* sensations while viewing the movements of *other* individuals. Gooddy [38], however, logically develops from the neurologist's point of view the postulate of the unity of sensorimotor performance: "movement is sensation." Witness the unity of a sensorimotor performance: there is no seeing without eye movements, no tasting without tongue movements, and there can be no "feeling" of touch without hand or finger movements toward the source of sensation. Therefore, it appears reasonable to attempt a reformulation of the psychophysical laws and to

replace sensation with sensorimotor performance.

The above speculations can be connected with Calhoun's [8] observations, who when measuring in rats the duration of sensorimotor performances, i.e., behavioral states such as drinking, walking, grooming, sex, etc., observed that no matter how long an effort has already lasted, there is a constant probability of its terminating within an additional specified amount of time. In any one rat's lifetime, for instance, an effort of more than seven minutes' duration is highly improbable [8]. Within the context of our interspecies generalization, expressed in eq. (5), we can now postulate that one implication of the above-mentioned relationship is that smaller-sized, shorter-lived mammals should experience more intense sensorimotor performances.

In summary, on an interspecies level, we have placed taste sensation within the context of sensorimotor performance, metabolic rate, and organismic lifespan. It is from this vantage point that we want to view genetic involvement in taste and to ask, what is a gene?

A gene is assumed to contain the information or code for a particular set of chemical reactions or a class of reactions; in short, a gene is the code of a function. However, chemical reactions cannot proceed in isolation; they occur only within an organismic context, that is, in relation to other chemical reactions and functions. It is within this organismic context that we dare to paraphrase John Donne: No gene "is an Iland intire of itselfe."

ORGANISMIC AND EVOLUTIONARY IMPLICATIONS OF PTC POLYMORPHISM

The tasting–"non-tasting" dimorphism of PTC type compounds apparently antedates the separation of the human

---

[7] It is a corollary of the relationship between metabolic rate and lifespan that inherited low metabolic rate favors longer life expectancy. This has been demonstrated for rats [86].

stock from the anthropoid apes [34] since tasters and "non-tasters" of PTC exist in proportions similar to that of man in the orangutan and chimpanzee [33]. Chiarelli [9] confirmed and extended these observations and found among other things that man and gorilla show a frequency of tasters that is about the same as that found in man and the African and Indian monkeys. Dr. G. L. Fisher's unpublished experiments with four *Saimiri sciureus* (squirrel monkeys), using the Richter [65] two-bottle preference testing procedure—each solution being paired with distilled water—reveal an indifference of the animals to concentrations of quinine up to $5 \times 10^{-4}M$, a range characteristic for *insensitive tasters* of quinine *in humans*. Another interesting result is that aversion to PTC in *Saimiri sciureus* starts at the $10^{-4}M$ concentration, i.e., at the antimode for PROP in humans ($1.8750 \times 10^{-4}M$). With respect to HCl and sodium chloride, the ranges preferred by the monkeys are similar to those of humans (personal communication). Another common feature of man and squirrel monkey is their taste preference for dulcin, whereas saccharin is preferred only by man [31]. During the last thirty years, Dr. Heinrich Klüver has repeatedly observed actual preference for quinine in certain rhesus monkeys. The animals apparently liked crystalline quinine since they consumed the offered quinine powder entirely (personal communication).[8]

Genetically a polymorphic system comprises two elements, the switching gene, or "supergene,"[9] on the segregation of which depends the determination of the

characteristic differences in the population; and the background genotype, on the balance of which depends the adjustment of the different phenotypes to the function they discharge. Like all systems, too, polymorphism has its inertia. The system may come into being as a result of forces other than heterozygous advantage—indeed, in many cases it obviously has done so—but once the system is in being, heterozygous advantage may arise merely as a by-product of the growth of the switching supergene. And once it has arisen it can hold the polymorphism in the population even after its initial cause has vanished. Ford speculates about the meaning of the heterozygous advantage of the gene already evolved in the common ancestors of man and the chimpanzee. In any case, at present, the PTC taster status of an individual may determine to some extent the type of thyroid disorder to which he is prone [10]. Kitchin and Howel-Evans [56] give an account of a detailed survey of 246 patients with adenomatous goiter, both toxic and nontoxic, characterized by a significantly high incidence of "non-tasters" (genotype tt), and report that this factor was greater in men than in women. Another study reports a very high proportion of "non-tasters" of PTC in athyreotic cretins, their parents and siblings [71,72].

The variation in PTC taste sensitivity is sometimes described as a cryptic human dimorphism since PTC is "quite outside ordinary experience, one that had not even been synthesized until this century" [34]. In fact, goitrin, L-5-vinyl-2-thiooxazolidone, isolated in 1949 from Brassica seeds as well as from crushed rutabaga, contains the same $H-N-C=$ | | S grouping as do PTC type compounds,

---

[8] It is well to remember that medial temporal lesions change preferences—and thereby the relative strength of rewards—without changing the sensory capacity to discriminate among the rewards [85].

[9] A "super-gene" is defined by Darlington and Mather [12], who introduced this important concept in 1949 as "a group of genes acting as a me-

chanical unit in particular allelic combinations." That is to say, the members of the group, though consisting of major genes, are so seldom separated by crossing-over that they can operate as a single genetic entity having diverse effects.

such as PROP, with which it shares an antithyroid activity of similar magnitude [84]. Other foods including cabbage, turnips, peas, beans, strawberries, milk, and the herbicide aminotriazole[10] display antithyroid activity, with turnips and rutabaga actually containing goitrin in quantities as high as 200 parts per million [50]. A related compound, barbarin phenylthiooxazolidone, has recently been isolated from various species of *Barbarea* and from *Reseda luteola,* present in the green parts of plants, consumed by livestock, and eaten in salads or as vegetables [40]. The influence on thyroid function of such and similar food is illustrated by the data of Langer and Kutka [59], who noted a significant decline in I[131] uptake by the thyroid, in eleven subjects, following the daily consumption of 500–600 g of cabbage for two weeks. For antithyroid effect, these authors have also synthesized and tested products assumed to be formed during cooking and digestion from naturally occurring isothiocyanates and amino-acids in plants. They found that derivatives of thiohydantoin without a side chain in position 5 were most effective, while non-cyclic disubstituted thioureas and cyclic thiohydantoins were also active [58]. It is appropriate, therefore, to say a few words about the possible selective aspects of the tasting–"non-tasting" dimorphism. Clements [11] describes the following general pattern of a sudden appearance and then a gradual disappearance of goiter in newly settled lands. The usual procedure, when new lands are settled, is for the cows and stock to first be grazed on the indigenous grasses. At the same time, land is cultivated for crops. Later, when this land is allowed to lie fallow, it quickly becomes infested with varieties of weeds, e.g., *Raphanus raphanistrum* and *Brassica campestris,*

which contain significant concentrations of bitter tasting goitrogenic compounds.

Epidemiological studies of seasonal thyroid enlargement in children seven to ten years of age have strongly suggested the etiologic involvement of goitrogens present in milk. In fact, Clements' data show seasonal peaks of incidence for visible goiter in Australia, each peak occurring in the months of August and September. Interestingly, the susceptible children develop goiter each year whereas others do not. It could well be that there is a relationship between taste thresholds, ingested goitrogens, and the development of visible goiter. This hypothesis, of course, has still to be tested. Meanwhile, further evidence has accumulated in support of the above hypothesis: (1) A fourfold prevalence of "non-tasters," in comparison to tasters, was found in 962 goitrous Israeli subjects. (2) In the endemic area of Brazil, *nodular* goiter proved to be significantly elevated among "non-tasters" of PTC, implying that goiter in "non-tasters" is more likely to evolve in the nodular form [26].

The frequency of "non-tasters" among school children in a Dutch non-urban area, however, is inversely proportional to the frequency of another type of goiter, the endemic variety, which is caused by iodine deficiency [13]. Since glaciation was shown to cause regional loss of iodine, Merke [62] believes that the geographic distribution of endemic goiter corresponds exactly to the extension of the glaciers during the last glaciation period.

It should be added that experimental evidence indicates that in animals, iodine deficiency or goitrogens may cause progressive changes in the thyroid gland, from diffuse to nodular hyperplasia to benign tumor and, sometimes, to malignant neoplasm [64].

At this point I should like to introduce a brief discussion of a few problems related to taste sensitivity to PTC

---

[10] Residues of which have been found in cranberries.

type compounds and to thyroid function in rats and mice.

It is well known that in a free-choice situation the albino rat can discriminate and obtain amounts of complete amino acid solutions sufficient to maintain normal body weight [42]. Domestication, however, may have produced an animal that is less sensitive to the nutritive value of food and more responsive to its "sensory" or "hedonic" qualities [61], even though domestic rats have about 18 per cent fewer fungiform papillae on their tongue than do wild Norway rats [30].

There is another difference between domesticated and wild Norway rats, namely, the greater susceptibility of the latter to the toxic action of certain thiourea derivatives. When Norway rats are first exposed to α-naphtylthiourea (ANTU)—the PTC type rodenticide— 90 per cent or more are killed. The relative species tolerance toward ANTU appears to coincide with dietary habits, vegetarian animals being much more resistant than carnivorous animals [66]. For a tabulation of the toxicity of ANTU to the Norway rat, dog, mouse, guinea pig, rabbit, cat, chicken, and Macaca mulata, see Williams [87]; he believes that differences in toxicity may be related to metabolic difference. It should be mentioned that Norway rats that survive sublethal doses of ANTU develop a high degree of tolerance, up to fifty times the ordinary fatal dose [67].

Genetically determined weight changes in C3H and C57 female and male mice following PROP administration, attributed to between-strain differences in taste sensitivity [49], cannot be evaluated since no taste threshold data nor weight changes in response to a PROP-free diet are included in the study. Studies of Hoshishima et al. [48], using the above strain of mice, clearly demonstrate that hypofunction of the thyroid, elicited by

the administration of I^{131}, raises the taste thresholds for saccharin, PTC, and acetic acid.

We have sketched the various disadvantages and the possible selective value of the dimorphism involving the bitter tasting PTC type antithyroid compounds; we turn now to other evolutionary aspects related to the phylogeny and ontogeny of the thyroid gland. The history of the thyroid gland, in phylogeny as in lamprey ontogeny, has been one in the course of which a feeding structure has been transformed into a gland of internal secretion. It is significant that clinically the thyroid hormone can be taken by mouth whereas other hormones, when introduced into the digestive tract in an unaltered state, are destroyed by gastric and intestinal juices. Early in chordate evolution, secretion of iodine compounds began in the endostyle while this was still a part of the feeding mechanism, the "hormone" being taken on into the gut with food materials. With the abandonment of filter feeding the endostyle lost its original function as a constituent of the pharynx; the thyroid gland has, as an endocrine structure, continued its glandular activity [68].

The basic property of thyroid tissue, the transport of iodine, is found, however, in other organs and tissues. These include the notochord, chloride cells of the gills, gastric glands, salivary glands, mammary glands, kidneys, as well as certain marine algae, and it is not too daring to postulate the idea that thyroxinogenesis preceded the thyroid gland in evolution. The thyroid gland is a relatively efficient and rapid producer (and storage organ) for thyroxine, but it would appear that invertebrates living in a high-iodine environment (sea water contains forty to sixty micrograms per liter) can slowly form this compound. Whether the thyroxine has any normal physiological role in most invertebrates, however, is highly questionable.

Does the wide phyletic distribution of the ability to form thyroid hormone and its precursors offer any suggestions with regard to evolution of thyroid function? This theory is based on the fact that at some point in time, thyroxine began to be utilized in metabolic processes of animals, to the benefit of those animals. The added "survival value," or adaptive value, of larger and more dependable sources of iodoprotein created the need for an organ like the thyroid, which can carry an animal through periods of iodine "famine" and release hormone as it is needed [39].

In view of the above, it is interesting to note the curious observation that an increase in the level of circulating thyroid hormone, in sticklebacks, induces a preference for fresh water, thus stimulating stickleback migration to fresh water in the spring when the thyroid gland shows signs of heightened activity. A lowering of the level of circulating thyroid hormone, however—or treatment with PTC type *antithyroid compounds* —results in the induction of *salt-water preference* thus stimulating stickleback migration seaward in the fall when the thyroid gland is less active.

Although the analogy may be fortuitous, it is tempting to compare the above observations with those obtained by Fregly [37] in rats in which *removal* of either the adrenal glands or the *thyroid* gland increased *spontaneous salt intake*.

Evolution in mammals made it possible to maintain a comparatively constant electrolyte pattern in the extracellular fluid, a pattern that closely resembles the ionic conditions under which life began [2]. The control of sodium balance, associated with aldosterone excretion—which again is a function of adrenal-thyroid relations—is the

subject of an informative review by Denton [14].

CONCLUSIONS

In summary, I have attempted to illustrate the extent of genetic control on the capacity of gustatory experience in man and primates.

Taste threshold studies in MZ and DZ twins and siblings reveal that genetic factors exert a weak control on man's ability to detect in water compounds the taste thresholds of which follow a Gaussian distribution in a population. Genetic control is stronger in case of the phenylthiourea (PTC) type compounds, the thresholds of which follow a bimodal distribution. Comparable observations are reported in other primates. Evolutionary and selective aspects of the PTC polymorphism were discussed and pharmacogenetic aspects of taste sketched.

Excitation, i.e., a rise in metabolic rate, diminishes the size of a just noticeable taste difference and hence reflects the systemic state of an individual. Therefore, on an interspecies level, one can view genetic control of the ability to experience sensation intensity within the wider context of sensorimotor performance, energy metabolism, and lifespan.

Discussion

De Ruiter: Fischer, would it be a permissible generalization from your findings to state that, statistically speaking, individuals whose metabolism is likely to be upset by certain harmful substances (which may be present in natural foods) also tend to have high taste sensitivity to such compounds? If so, this would have a direct bearing on some of the basic questions raised by our symposium.

Beidler: The pharmacological sensitivity

you related to the chemical senses could also be related to other sensory sensitivities. In your earlier work you related it to intelligence test scores.

Fischer: To behavioral characteristics, yes. We used a modified form of the Wechsler Adult Intelligence Scale and found that sensitive tasters—of "Gaussian" compounds—are sensitive people; they are introverts whereas the insensitive tasters may generally be classified as extroverts. Moreover, the extremely sensitive tasters of both quinine and PROP are often Kretschmerian leptosomes (Sheldonian ectomorphs) whereas the extremely insensitive tasters of both compounds conform mainly to the Kretschmerian pyknic (Sheldonian endomorph) body type. Indeed, tasters of PTC display a tendency to be taller (Jonston *et al., Amer. J. Physical Anthrop.,* **24:** 253, 1966).

Beidler: The introverts are probably more sensitive to any type of sensory input?

Fischer: It appears so, but we need more data, specifically in vision and hearing, before making such a generalization.

Henkin: Patients with untreated adrenal cortical insufficiency offer an interesting correlate to your observations. These patients can detect the taste of various solutions in concentrations one one-hundredth the strength of those detected by normal individuals. They can detect vapors in solutions one ten-thousandth as strong as those detected by normal individuals. Their thresholds for detection of sinosoidal tones are approximately fifteen decibels lower than those of normal individuals in the most sensitive range of hearing. Thus, their whole nervous system is keyed differently than ours. When these patients are treated with carbohydrate-active steroid, the heightened sensitivities return toward normal for all sensory stimuli. We have noted in these patients that neural impulses are conducted along the axon more quickly than normal when the patients are untreated but return toward normal after treatment with carbohydrate-active steroid. It might be better for all of us if we had some form of adrenal cortical insufficiency, for we could detect tastes and odors better and hear better. However, these patients have serious problems with respect to integration of information. Although there is an increase in peripheral axonal conduction velocity, there is a significant time lag across the myoneural junction and perhaps across synapses in the sensory system. Thus, even though these patients can detect sensory stimuli better than normal individuals, they are handicapped in their ability to recognize tastes or odors as well as to understand and interpret the meaning of words. It may well be that carbohydrate-active steroids act as an important set of chemical gain-control regulators in the nervous system.

In terms of teleology, the increased sensory sensitivity observed in these patients could have been interpreted in a quite different fashion. In these patients, detection sensitivity for sodium chloride was approximately 120 times better than normal, and they exhibited hyponatremia; therefore, teleologically they might have been expected to seek out sodium. Thus, their lowered detection threshold might have offered survival value in that they could select sodium chloride in substances in which its presence might not be noted in the normal state. This would be similar to the observations made in honeybees, who reject sucrose in concentrations of less than $1 M$ in their normal state but who will accept less concentrated sucrose as their need for carbohydrate increases and more concentrated sucrose is made unavailable to them. Just as the detection threshold for the taste of sodium chloride is decreased in untreated Addisonians, so are the detection thresholds for potassium chloride, sodium bicarbonate, sucrose, urea, and hydrochloric acid decreased. If salt-craving is an important correlate of decreased sodium concentration in the extracellular fluid, then it is surprising to observe that only 15–20 per cent of the patients with untreated adrenal cortical insufficiency exhibit this symptom. This method of thinking did lead investigators astray in the reporting that patients with hypertension exhibit increased salt taste thresholds (Fallis *et al.*, *Nature*, **196**: 74, 1962). It was reasoned that eating salt was an etiological factor in the development of hypertension. Thus, these patients eat more salt than normal because they cannot taste it as well as normotensive subjects and proceed to become hypertensive. I think this is specious reasoning. We have determined detection and recognition thresholds for representatives of each of the modalities of taste, including NaCl in patients with essential hypertension, hypertension secondary to renal artery stenosis, hypertension secondary to aldosteronomas, pheochromocytomas, etc., and have found them to be within normal limits. Furthermore, after correction of their hypertension, either by medical or surgical management, there was no alteration in these already normal thresholds. Although teleological reasoning may offer a preliminary clue as to etiology, it may also lead us down the garden path.

Fischer: The paper on hypertension can also be criticized on grounds of taste-testing methodology.

Bardach: Non-Gaussian compounds—how do they differ from the Gaussian compounds?

Fischer: It is their bimodal distribution which characterizes "non-Gaussian," PTC type compounds. They are bitter, display antithyroid activity, and also some forty of them have a common chemical structural feature.

Pfaffmann: The intriguing question is whether or not this is the only class of substances that shows this bimodality, because it really stands out as an isolated class of events. It would be important in terms of the chemistry of the stimulating receptor mechanisms, if there were other substances in the other chemical classes that were like this. I presume you have been looking, and perhaps you may have found some others.

Fischer: Up to now we have found only these two classes of compounds, "Gaussian" and bimodal. As to the latter, it could well be that the bimodal distribution of taste sensitivity for PTC type compounds is an evolutionary remnant.

Pfaffman: How about benzoate?

Fischer: Sodium benzoate apparently follows a Gaussian distribution. The various taste qualities of the compound, in certain concentration ranges, appear to correspond to different degrees of ionization.

Beidler: What about the unusual results obtained by using HCl; does one obtain this with all the acids?

Fischer: No, the previously mentioned behavior of sodium benzoate is characteristic for sodium salts.

Henkin: The phenomenon that you are describing is a very general one. Reports in the literature have indicated that there are groups of people from many different geographical locations whose taste thresholds are significantly below those which we consider normal. We measured detection and recognition thresholds for the tastes of various substances in normal volunteers from a number of homeogenous, stable populations. Many came from families who had lived in the same community for five or six generations. These populations appeared to be inbred. Two families exhibited markedly decreased thresholds for all taste modalities. Their adrenal cortical function was within normal limits. We concluded a genetic basis for certain individuals whose taste sensitivity was significantly better than that of others. These observations parallel your findings. Patients with adrenal cortical insufficiency exhibit increased detection thresholds for taste. Could patients with cystic fibrosis of the pancreas also exhibit this increased sensitivity? Patients with untreated adrenal cortical insufficiency cannot conserve sodium in the kidney or sweat gland. Patients with cystic fibrosis of the pancreas can conserve sodium in the kidney but not in the sweat gland. Thus, we wondered if the metabolic abnormality underlying cystic fibrosis were not somehow related to Addison's disease. We determined detection thresholds for various taste modalities in patients with cystic fibrosis and found them as decreased as in patients with Addison's disease. However, these decreased thresholds occurred mainly in males with this syndrome. Treatment with either desoxycorticosterone acetate (DOCA) or carbohydrate-active steroid did not alter decreased thresholds, a finding which is quite different from what we had observed in patients with Addison's disease. Further studies revealed that unaffected male siblings of patients with cystic fibrosis also exhibit this increased taste sensitivity, as do the unaffected mothers of these children. Thus, what we were observing

was not an alteration in taste threshold on the basis of a metabolic abnormality but a genetic trait of increased taste sensitivity.

Fischer: You are right. The proportion of tasters to non-tasters of PTC type compounds differs in various populations, as illustrated by Allison and Blumberg (*Hum. Biol.,* **31**: 352, 1959) in their world map of tasters. South American Indians and certain African Negro tribes have few, or practically no, insensitive tasters whereas Bombay Indians or Eskimos have over 40 per cent of them.

Snapper: Negroes less than Caucasians in our culture?

Fischer: Apparently most Negro tribes in Africa consist only of sensitive tasters; however, in this country, there seems to be a diminishing difference in the proportion of tasters to non-tasters between Caucasian and Negro populations. Specifically, we have found no difference at all in the Columbus, Ohio, area in an admittedly small sample of thirty Negro and thirty Caucasian youths.

Fregly: There are a number of classes of compounds which you used that are antithyroid agents in addition to the thiourea derivatives. Have you studied any of the thiocyanates or sulfonamides? Some of the latter are known to be goitrogenic agents. Have you also studied any of the thiazides? These are also sulfur-containing compounds and are used clinically in the treatment of hypertension. At proper doses these compounds are also goitrogenic.

Fischer: We have not pursued taste threshold distribution studies with sulfonamides such as chlorothiazide or hydrochlorothiazide, the chemical structure of which slightly deviates from that of a typical PTC type compound.

REFERENCES

1. Allison, A. C., and Blumberg, B. S. Ability to Taste Phenylthiocarbamide Among Alaskan Eskimos and Other Populations. *Hum. Biol.,* 31: 352–59, 1959.
2. Baldwin, E. *An Introduction to Comparative Biochemistry.* University Press, Cambridge, 164 pp., 1948.
3. Barbeau, A., and Raymond-Tremblay, D. Recent Biochemical Studies in Parkinson's Disease and Position of the Problem, in *Monographs Biol. and Med.,* Grune and Stratton, New York, pp. 79–94, 1965.
4. Barbeau, A., Tétreault, L., Oliva, L., Morazain, L., and Cardin, L. Pharmacology of Akinesia—Investigations on 3, 4-Dimethoxyphenylethylamine. *Nature* (London), 209: 719–21, 1966.
5. Barnicot, N. A., Harris, H., and Kalmus, H. Taste Thresholds of Further Eighteen Compounds and Their Correlation with PTC Thresholds. *Ann. Eugen.* (London), 16: 119–28, 1951.
6. Beidler, L. M. The Chemical Senses. *Ann. Rev. Psychol.,* 12: 363–88, 1961.
7. Brody, S. *Bioenergetics and Growth.* Hafner, New York, 1023 pp., 1964.
8. Calhoun, J. B. Ecological Factors in the Development of Behavioral Anomalies, in *Comparative Psychopathology.* Grune and Stratton, New York (in press).
9. Chiarelli, B. Sensitivity to P.T.C. (Phenylthio-carbamide) in Primates. *Folia primat.,* 1: 88–94, 1963.
10. Clarke, C. A. *Genetics for the Clinician.* Charles C Thomas, Springfield, Ill., 294 pp., 1962.
11. Clements, F. W. Naturally Occurring Goitrogens. *Brit. Med. Bull.,* 16: 133–37, 1960.
12. Darlington, C. D., and Mather, K. The Elements of Genetics. Macmillan, New York, 446 pp., 1950.
13. DeJong, W. W. W. Smaakproeven met phenylthiocarbamide (PTC) bij Nederlandse schoolkinderen; het verband met endemische krop. *Geneeskundige Bladen,* 12: 349–84, 1964.
14. Denton, D. A. Evolutionary Aspects of the Emergence of Aldosterone Secretion and Salt Appetite. *Physiol. Rev.,* 45: 245–95, 1965.
15. Fischer, R. Mitotic Rate in Organs and Tissues in Relation to Metabolic Body Size $(kg^{3/4})$. *Experientia,* 21: 349–50, 1965.
16. Fischer, R. Biological Time, in *The Voices of Time,* J. T. Fraser (ed.). George Braziller, New York, pp. 357–82, 1966.
17. Fischer, R. Sex, Lifespan and Smoking. *Experientia,* 22: 178–79, 1966.
18. Fischer, R. The Biological Fabric of Time. Paper presented at the "Interdisciplinary Perspectives of Time" Conference, January 17–20, 1966, New York. *Ann. N.Y. Acad. Sci.,* 1967 (in press).
19. Fischer, R., and Griffin, F. Biochemical Genetic Factors in Health and Mental Retardation. *Proceedings of the Third World Congress of Psychiatrty, Montreal,* University of Montreal Press, Montreal, 1: 542–47, 1962.
20. Fischer, R., and Griffin, F. Quinine Dimorphism, a Cardinal Determinant of Taste Sensitivity. *Nature* (London), 200: 343–47, 1963.
21. Fischer, R., and Griffin, F. Chemoreception and Gustatory Memory Formation. *Proceedings of the Sixth International Congress of Biochemistry,* 8: 651, 1964.
22. Fischer, R., and Griffin, F. Pharmacogenetic Aspects of Gustation. *Arzneim.-Forsch.* (Drug Research), 14: 673–86, 1964.
23. Fischer, R., Griffin, F., Archer, R. C., Zinsmeister, S. C., and Jastram, P. S. The Weber Ratio in Gustatory Chemoreception: An Indicator of Systemic (Drug) Reactivity. *Nature* (London), 207: 1049–53, 1965.
24. Fischer, R., Griffin, F., England, S., and Pasamanick, B. Biochemical Genetic Factors of Taste Polymorphism and Their Relation to Salivary Thyroid Metabolism in Health and Mental Retardation. *Med. exp.,* 4: 356–66, 1961.
25. Fischer, R., Griffin, F., and Mead, E. L. Two Characteristic Ranges of Taste Sensitivity. *Med. exp.,* 6: 177–82, 1962.
26. Fischer, R., Griffin, F., and Pasamanick, B. The Perception of Taste: Some Psychophysiological, Pharmacological and Clinical Aspects, in *Psychopathology of Perception,* P. Hoch and J. Zubin (eds.). Grune and Stratton, New York, pp. 129–64, 1965.
27. Fischer, R., Griffin, F., and Rockey, M. A. Gustatory Chemoreception in Man: Multidisciplinary Aspects and Perspectives. *Persp. Biol. Med.,* 9: 549–77, 1966.
28. Fischer, R., and Kaelbling, R. Increase in Taste Acuity with Sympathetic Stimulation: The Relation of a Just Noticeable Taste Difference to Systemic Psychotropic Drug Dose, in *Recent Advances in Biological Psychiatry 9.* Grune and Stratton, New York (in press).
29. Fischer, R., Knopp, W., and Griffin, F. Taste Sensitivity and the Appearance of Phenothiazine-Tranquilizer Induced Extrapyramidal Symptoms. *Arzneim.-Forsch.* (Drug Research), 15: 1379–82, 1965.
30. Fish, H. S., and Richter, C. P. Comparative Number of Fungiform and Foliate Papillae on Tongues of Domestic and Wild Norway Rats. *Proc. Soc. Exp. Biol.,* 63: 352–53, 1946.
31. Fisher, G. L., Pfaffmann, C., and Brown, E. Dulcin and Saccharin Taste in Squirrel Monkeys, Rats, and Men. *Science,* 150: 506–7, 1965.

32. Fisher, R. A. *The Design of Experiments.* Hafner, New York, p. 11, 1951.

33. Fisher, R. A., Ford, E. B., and Huxley J. Taste-testing the Anthropoid Apes. *Nature* (London), **144**: 750, 1939.

34. Ford, E. B. *Genetic Polymorphism.* Faber and Faber, London, p. 82, 1965.

35. Ford, E. B. *Genetics for Medical Students.* Methuen, London, pp. 11–14, 1965.

36. Fox, A. L. The Relation Between Chemical Constitution and Taste. *Proc. Nat. Acad. Sci.,* **18**: 115–20, 1932.

37. Fregly, M. J. Effect of Hypothroidism on Sodium Chloride Aversion of Renal Hypertensive Rats. *Endocrinology,* **71**: 683–92, 1962.

38. Gooddy, W. Time and the Nervous System. Part IV: The Human Hand as a Four-dimensional Scanner: Some Reflections on the "Function" of the Posterior Columns of the Spinal Cord. *Brain,* **88**: 753–62, 1965.

39. Gorbman, A., and Bern, H. A. *A Textbook of Comparative Endocrinology.* John Wiley & Sons, New York, p. 140, 1962.

40. Greer, M. A., and Whallon, J. Antithyroid Effect of Barbarin (Phenylthiooxazolidone), A Naturally-occurring Compound from Barbarea. *Proc. Soc. Exp. Biol. Med.,* **107**: 802–4, 1961.

41. Griffin, H. F. On the Interaction of Chemical Stimuli with Taste Receptors. Unpublished Ph.D. Thesis, Ohio State University, 1966.

42. Halstead, W. C., and Gallagher, B. B. Autoregulation of Amino Acids Intake in the Albino Rat. *J. Comp. Physiol.,* **55**: 107–11, 1962.

43. Harris, H. *An Introduction to Human Biochemical Genetics.* Cambridge University Press, London, pp. 69–75, 1955.

44. Harris, H., and Kalmus, H. Chemical Sensitivity in Genetical Differences of Taste Sensitivity. *Ann. Eugen.* (London), **15**: 32–45, 1949.

45. Harris, H., and Kalmus, H. The Measurement of Taste Sensitivity to Phenylthiourea (P.T.C.). *Ann. Eugen.* (London), **15**: 24–31, 1949.

46. Harvald, B., and Hauge, M., Hereditary Factors Elucidated by Twin Studies, in *Genetics and the Epidemiology of Chronic Diseases,* J. V. Neel, M. W. Shaw, and W. J. Schull, (eds.). U.S. Department of Health, Education, and Welfare, Public Health Service Publication, Washington, pp. 61–76, 1965.

47. Holzinger, K. J. The Relative Effect of Nature and Nurture Influences on Twin Differences. *J. Educat. Psychol.,* **20**: 241–48, 1929.

48. Hoshishima, K., Yokoyama, S., and Seto, K. Taste Sensitivity in Various Strains of Mice. *Amer. J. Physiol.,* **202**: 1200–4, 1962.

49. Jacobs, B. B. Propylthiouracil Taste Inheritance in Mice. *J. Hered.,* **53**: 183–86, 1962.

50. Jukes, T. H., and Shaffer, C. B. Antithyroid Effects of Aminotriazole. *Science,* **132**: 296–97, 1960.

51. Kalmus, H. Improvements in the Classification of the Taster Genotypes. *Ann. Hum. Gen.* (London), **22**: 222–30, 1958.

52. Kalmus, H., and Farnsworth, D. Impairment and Recovery of Taste Following Irradiation of the Oropharynx. *J. Laryn. Otol.,* **73**: 180–82, 1959.

53. Kalmus, H., and Smith, S. M. The Antimode and Lines of Optimal Separation in a Genetically Determined Bimodal Distribution, with Particular Reference to Phenylthiocarbamide Sensitivity. *Ann. Hum. Gen.* (London), **29**: 127–38, 1965.

54. Kaplan, A. R., and Fischer, R. Taste Sensitivity for Bitterness: Some Biological and Clinical Applications, in *Recent Advances in Biological Psychiatry. VII: Proceedings of the Nineteenth Annual Meeting of the Society of Biological Psychiatry,* J. Wortis (ed.). Plenum Press, New York, p. 320, 1965.

55. Kaplan, A. R., Fischer, R., Karras, A., Griffin, F., Powell, W., Marsters, R., and Glanville, E. Taste Thresholds in Twins and Siblings. *Ann. Hum. Gen.* (submitted for publication).

56. Kitchin, F. D., and Howel-Evans, W. Genetic Factors in Thyroid Diseases. *Brit. Med. Bull.,* **16**: 148–51, 1960.

57. Kleiber, M. *The Fire of Life.* John Wiley & Sons, New York, p. 215, 1961.

58. Langer, P., Drobnica, L., and Augustin, J. On the Possible Mechanism of the Antithyroidal Action of Some Natural Mustard Oils. *Physiol. Bohemoslov.,* **13**: 450–56, 1964.

59. Langer, P., and Kutka, M. Influence of Cabbage on the Thyroid Function in Man. *Endocr. Exp.,* **1**: 303–6, 1964.

60. Leguèbe, A. Génétique et anthropologie de la sensibilité à la phénylthiocarbamide. *Bull. Inst. Roy. Sci. Nat. Belgique,* **26**: 1–27, 1960.

61. Maller, O., and Kare, M. R. Selection and Intake of Carbohydrates by Wild and Domesticated Rats. *Proc. Soc. Exp. Biol. Med.,* **119**: 199–203, 1965.

62. Merke, V. F. Die Eiszeit als primordiale Ursache des endemischen Kropfes. *Schweiz. med. Wschr.,* **95**: 1183–92, 1965.

63. Merton, B. B. Taste Sensitivity to PTC in 60 Norwegian families with 176 children. *Acta. Genet.,* **8**: 114–28, 1958.

64. Pendergrast, W. J., Milmore, B. K., and Marcus, S. C. Thyroid Cancer and Thyrotoxicosis in the United States: Their Relation to Endemic Goiter. *J. Chron. Dis.,* **13**: 22–38, 1961.

65. Richter, C. P. Salt Taste Threshold of Normal and Adrenalectomized Rats. *Endocrinology,* **24**: 367–71, 1939.

66. Richter, C. P. The Development and Use of Alpha-naphthyl thiourea (ANTU) as a Rat Poison. *J. Amer. Med. Assoc.,* **129**: 927–31, 1945.

67. Richter, C. P. As quoted in T. Sollman, *A Manual of Pharmacology* (1951 ed.). W. B. Saunders Co., Philadelphia, 1946.

68. Romer, A. S. *The Vertebrate Body.* W. B. Saunders Co., Philadelphia, pp. 561–62, 1962.

69. Rosenthal, D. Discussion of Dr. Kallmann's paper, in *Recent Research in Schizophrenia, Psychiatric Research Reports of the American Psychiatric Association*, P. Solomon and B. C. Glueck, Jr. (eds.). **19**: 146–48, 1964.

70. Saldanha, P. H., and Nacrur, J. Taste Thresholds for Phenylthiourea among Chileans. *Amer. J. Phys. Anthro. N. S.,* **21**: 113–19, 1963.

71. Shepard, T. H. Phenylthiocarbamide Nontasting Among Congenital Athyrotic Cretins: Further Studies in an Attempt to Explain the Increased Incidence. *J. Clin. Inv.,* **40**: 1751–57, 1961.

72. Shepard, T. H., and Gartler, S. M. Increased Incidence of Non-tasters of Phenylthiocarbamide Among Congenital Athyrotic Cretins. *Science,* **131**: 929, 1960.

73. Skude, G. Some Factors Influencing Taste Perception for Phenylthiourea (P.T.C.). *Hereditas,* **50**: 203–10, 1963.

74. Smith, A., Farbman, A., and Dancis, J. Absence of Taste-bud papillae in Familial Dysautonomia. *Science,* **147**: 1040–41, 1965.

75. Snyder, L. H. Studies in Human Inheritance. IX: The Inheritance of Taste Deficiency in Man. *Ohio J. Sci.,* **32**: 436–40, 1932.

76. Spector, W. S. (ed.). *Handbook of Biological Data.* W. B. Saunders Co., Philadelphia, p. 437, 1956.

77. Srb, A. M., Owen, R. D., and Edgar, R. S. *General Genetics.* 2nd ed. W. H. Freeman and Co., San Francisco, 557 pp., 1965.

78. Stern, C. *Principles of Human Genetics.* W. H. Freeman and Co., San Francisco, p. 167, 1960.

79. Stevens, S. S. The Quantification of Sensation. *Daedalus,* **88**: 606–21, 1959.

80. Takewaki, K., (ed.). *Progress in Comparative Endocrinology.* Academic Press, New York, pp. 193–94, 1962.

81. Trotter, W. R. *Diseases of the Thyroid.* Blackwell Scientific Publications, Oxford, p. 195, 1962.

82. Vandenberg, S. G. Multivariate Analysis of Twin Differences, in *Methods and Goals in Human Behavior Genetics,* S. G. Vandenberg (ed.). Academic Press, New York, pp. 29–43, 1965.

83. Vandenberg, S. G., and Kelly, L. Hereditary Components in Vocational Preferences. *Acta. Gen. Med. Gemell,* **13**: 266–77, 1964.

84. Virtanen, A. I. Some Organic Sulfur Compounds in Vegetables and Fodder Plants and Their Significance in Human Nutrition. *Angew. Chem.* (International ed.), **1**: 299–306, 1962.

85. Weiskrantz, L. Effects of Medial Temporal Lesions on Taste Preference in the Monkey. *Nature* (London), **187**: 879–80, 1960.

86. Weiss, K. A. Resting Metabolic Rate and Longevity in the Rat. *Fed. Proc.,* **24**: 466, 1965.

87. Williams, R. T. *Detoxication Mechanisms.* Chapman & Hall, Ltd., London, 796 pp., 1959.

Parts of these studies were supported by U.S.P.H.S. grants M–2731, M–4694, MH–07679, and General Research Support Grants administered as Projects 236 and 372 of the College of Medicine of Ohio State University. The twin studies were supported by N.I.H. Grants HD–00591–2 and by The Council for Tobacco Research, U.S.A.

I am grateful to Drs. Ian Gregory, Athan Karras, Arnold R. Kaplan, and N. S. Fechheimer as well as to Robert C. Archer and Leonard Fendell, Columbus, for contributing to this research, and I would like to thank Drs. Heinrich Klüver, University of Chicago, and G. L. Fisher, University of Maryland, for permission to refer to their personal communications.

6: Critic's Comments

by Leendert de Ruiter

NUTRITIONAL HOMEOSTASIS depends on complex processes in a vast network of organs. Each of us in his own experiments can get a good view of only a small part of this complex. To my mind the main value of our present symposium lies in the fact that it brings together specialists dealing with many different aspects of chemoreception and nutrition. This gives us an unusual opportunity to bring the whole complex into perspective. If we want to make good use of this, as I am sure we all do, it may help if we can agree on a model on which to base our discussions. The following model (Fig. 6–1) may serve this purpose. Chemical stimuli (C) from the environment are encoded by the chemoreceptors (R) into a nervous message, which provides the nervous system with the gustatory and olfactory input signal (I). These incoming messages are decoded by an afferent analyzer (A), which distributes them (according to content) to the coordinating command stations for the various modes of behavior available to the individual. Of the latter, only one is of interest to our present symposium, the feeding behavior system (F). When triggered, this gives off commands to the neuromuscular machinery for the acquisition and ingestion of food. The subject, then, of our present symposium is the relation between

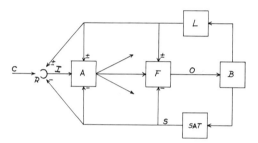

Fig. 6–1. Simplified diagram of the relation between chemosensory stimulation and feeding behavior. L = learning mechanism; SAT = mechanism integrating postingestional signals. For further explanation, see text. The effects of learning may either enhance or decrease the responsiveness of the I-O transmitting system to a given type of stimulation. On the motivational side (hunger and satiety) the possible existence of positive feedback loops is disregarded in this diagram, although these may well be functionally important.

that output (O) and the chemoreceptor input (I).

In the analysis of this relation we run into several complications. First, the actual ingestion of food has manifold effects on the state of the body (B), which result in a variety of postingestional signals feeding back into the nervous system. We are all familiar with the fact that many of these messages can be classed as satiety signals (S), i.e., they reduce the probability that the feeding behavior mechanism will respond to a given chemosensory input. There is at least some evidence that satiety signals may act not only at the level of the behavioral mechanism, but also at that of the afferent analyzer, and possibly even at the level of the receptor itself.

Secondly, the effects of the performance of food-directed behavior (of which ingestion itself is only the terminal stage) give rise to learning processes that modify the form of the feeding movements as well as the way in which the analyzer decodes and distributes the incoming messages, and that may even affect the stimulus transducing properties of the receptors themselves.

In this primitive form the model, of course, does not account for most of what is already known about the control of feeding behavior. For instance, this behavior is a sequential chain of activities, each link of which is elicited by special environmental cues, which may include, e.g., visual and auditory as well as chemical stimulation. Nor can the model do justice to the multiplicity of chemosensory inputs, the diversity of satiety signals (arising from digestive tract, circulation, and body reserves), or to the complexity of the mechanisms of learning. Further, even if the model were fully amended on all these points, it would still not be satisfactory. It is not enough to have a complete diagram such as the present one.

Nevertheless, even in this form the model may be used to bring out the threshold value of this line of approach. First, models provide a framework for scattered data, which, linked together, may provide explanations for phenomena that at first sight appear puzzling. Second, they are helpful in formulating meaningful problems for further research. Third, they provide a basis for exact operational definition of the concepts various experimenters use, and they may thereby reduce waste of energy on unnecessary controversies. To illustrate the first two aspects, I will briefly discuss the interaction in feeding behavior of taste and satiety, as illustrated by the "finickiness" noted in cases of hypothalamic hyperphagia; to exemplify the third aspect, the concept of motivation provides a case in point.

Ravenous ingestion of palatable food, combined with pronounced "finickiness," has been observed in subjects robbed of their ventromedial hypothalamic nuclei. This has appeared paradoxical to many workers because it is normally observed that hungry individuals will eat food they would scorn in times of plenty. Indeed, if one takes the plausible view that the effect of the hypothalamic lesion amounts to reduction of the satiety brakes on feeding, the phenomenon seems puzzling at first sight. Yet models of the type here presented indicate that there may be a straightforward explanation.

The probability that a food object perceived in the environment will elicit feeding behavior depends on the behavior-releasing (or incentive) value of the exteroceptor message set up by that object on the one hand, and on the strength of the satiety signals impinging on the mechanism for feeding behavior on the other. If a hungry individual is presented with a superabundance of food objects, all of the same kind, he will engage in a series of ingestive responses that continues until the resulting satiety signals come to match the releasing value of this type of food. As soon as this happens feeding will cease. The lower the releasing value of the food, the earlier, *ceteris paribus*, the termination of the "meal," and the smaller the quantity ingested (Fig. 6–2a).

Further data on the influence of palatability of the diet (keeping caloric density and other nutritional properties constant) on the pattern of intake, both as regards meal size and duration of pauses

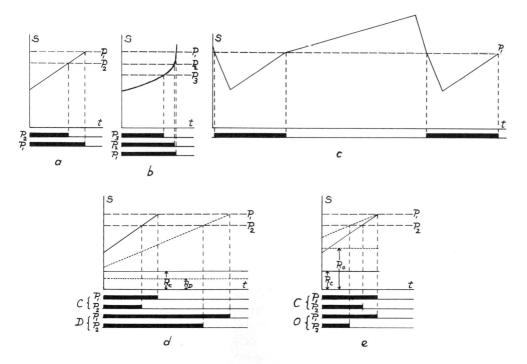

Fig. 6–2. *Taste, satiety, and the pattern of meals (hypothetical diagram). For lack of concrete data the linear time course of satiety has been assumed (except in Fig. 6–2b). The black bars below the graps indicate meal size. P = Palatability (identical nutrient content of foods of different palatability is assumed throughout); S = Satiety; t = time; (a) Starting from the same hunger level, the individual will take smaller meals of less palatable food; (b) If the time course of satiety is non-linear, a moderate change in palatability may barely affect meal size, though greater change can still be effective; (c) When the system is in a steady state (caloric equilibrium), the delay in the satiety feedbacks results in a cyclic pattern of intake; (d) Depression of the satiety signals by hypothalamic lesion results in increased meal size. R = contribution of reserves signal to total satiety; C = control subject; D = dynamic hyperphagic subject; solid line denotes course of satiety in control subject; broken line indicates course of satiety in lesioned subject; (e) As the reserves increase due to hyperphagia, the reserves signal goes up, and meal size decreases (until the latter returns to preoperative values), and static obesity is achieved. R_c, R_o, = reserves signal in control and static obese subject, respectively.*

between meals, would be of great interest. For instance, even if it is true that lower palatability results in reduction of meal size, it does not necessarily follow that daily intake of calories is similarly affected in individuals kept on such food for a longer time. There are several reasons why this may not be so. First, if the duration of between-meal intervals is directly proportional to meal size, palatability will not affect daily intake. Whether such proportionality exists

(from our data on mice and rats I do not think it does) will depend on the time course of the rise and fall of satiety after each meal. When ingestion ceases, satiety will continue to rise because of the delay of the feedbacks, part of which come into play only after absorption from the gut. Eventually, however, digestion and metabolism cause all satiation signals to wane, and once satiety falls below the threshold set by the incentive value of the food, a new meal will be initiated (Fig. 6–2c). Daily intake depends on the time course of this entire cycle.

Secondly, it is conceivable that, at least over a certain range, even the size of individual meals is independent of palatability (as assessed for instance in preference tests). This may be so, if the time course of satiety rather than being linear shows an abrupt rise at the termination of a meal (Fig. 6–2b), so that meals of foods of different palatability have much the same duration, or if learning processes adjust the palatability rating of a given kind of food to its caloric content.

Thus, thinking about caloric regulation in terms of a model of this kind makes us aware of the crucial importance of data on the time pattern of food intake, on the influence thereon of palatability, and on the time course of the various components of satiety. Surprisingly little work appears to have been done on these points so far. In this way a model may help us to detect gaps in our knowledge.

Now what about finickiness? The balance of available physiological evidence suggests that damage to the ventromedial nuclei of the hypothalamus reduces the satiety signals fed back into the mechanism for feeding behavior. Consequently, in the case of food of a given palatability, the lesioned animal will eat larger meals than will the intact control animal (Fig. 6–2d). It is well known that the animal's body weight goes up in consequence. At this point we must recall that satiety has several different components. Some of these (signals from the digestive tract and circulation) go up with each meal and wane before the next one takes place. In fact, as we have seen, the time course of these signals sets the period of the cyclic pattern of feeding behavior. In contrast, signals derived from the reserves will be

nearly constant over such brief lengths of time. When body weight goes up in consequence of hyperphagia, the latter signals will rise to a higher level. Hence, the contribution of the fluctuating signals to the total satiety required to terminate a meal, becomes smaller. If we assume that the number of meals per day remains constant throughout these changes (as, somewhat surprisingly, our data on goldthioglucose obesity in mice suggest), static obesity will be achieved when meal size has returned to preoperative values (Fig. 6–2e).

However, if we change the palatability of the food, the immediate effect on meal size will be greater in the lesioned animal than in the intact control animal because of the less steep rise of satiety in the former (Figs. 6–2d and 6–2e). Under the assumptions made here, both the intact control animal and the static obese animal will return to the original meal size (when put on a less palatable, but calorically equivalent, diet) when the reserves signal has decreased, as a result of temporary hypophagia, by an amount equal to the change in incentive value of the food. This will involve a greater change in the quantity of reserves (body weight) in the lesioned animal than in the control animal, if (and only if) the reserves signal has been affected by the lesion (less signal per calorie of reserves).

It seems, then, that in these terms we can account for several of the known features of hypothalamic hyperphagia. No paradox appears to be involved at all, and the somewhat mysterious overreactiveness of lesioned animals to the sensory qualities of food, often invoked to explain the results obtained, becomes more understandable in terms of the interaction between external messages releasing feeding behavior and satiety signals. All this does not mean that the explanation envisaged here is correct.

Most of the data necessary to decide that are not available. But the model is useful at least in that it clearly indicates what experiments we should undertake.

Finally, I want to comment briefly on the concept of motivation. This term appears to be used in a different sense by experimental and physiological psychologists, on the one hand, and by European ethologists on the other. This may lead to confusion, which is regrettable, particularly because I do not think that there is much basic disagreement between these schools as regards either the facts we are dealing with or the causal mechanisms behind them. Let me try, then, to elucidate the sense in which the ethologist uses this concept. His starting point is that to a very large extent the behavior of an individual can be analyzed into distinct patterns of movement that recur time and again. Some of these units of behavior, which together form the repertoire available to the individual at a given time of his life, may be independent of experience; others undoubtedly are learned. Irrespective of this, however, any one of these units can be considered a response to a set of external "releasing" stimuli that are specific for that unit. However, the probability that a given set of releasing stimuli will elicit the corresponding unit fluctuates in time. Now it is found that there are groups of units, within each of which these fluctuations are largely parallel. It is then concluded (1) that a common set of signals contributes to the occurrence of all units of such a group, and (2) (since the fluctuations in this set cannot be attributed to changes in the momentary environment) that the immediate source of these signals must lie in the internal state of the individual. The state of this common message set is termed the motivation for the group of units concerned. Such a group may be termed a "behavior system."

One such system consists of all patterns of behavior which may result in detection, acquisition, and ingestion of food. It seems appropriate to refer to the motivation for this behavior system as hunger. Satiety, in the sense in which I am using it, indicates the reverse of hunger, that is, its value is minimal when hunger is maximal, and vice versa; the two quantities are uniquely related mutually over their entire range. The hunger motivation, then, determines the probability that the individual will perform a given element of feeding behavior in response to the appropriate external stimuli. This is true both of learned responses and of those whose incorporation in the repertoire of the individual is independent of experience.

The model, which I took as the starting point of this discussion, brings out the respective roles of learning and motivation (in the sense in which I am using this term) in feeding behavior. Essentially, I think this (and any other) behavior can be approached, for the purpose of causal analysis, in terms of the operation of an input/output system that would translate the exteroceptor messages set up by the environment into the motor activities of the individual. The information-transmitting properties of this system are subject to modification in several different ways. At the present state of our knowledge it is convenient to divide these into two classes, called learning and motivational changes respectively. Both have in common the fact that they are being fed back into the various links of the system to modify its subsequent handling of information because of the effects of foregoing operations of the system. Motivational changes, however, tend to be relatively short lived and cyclical in nature, whereas the effects of learning are more lasting and persist over many cycles of the motivation.

It is not for me to say exactly in what sense psychologists, who invoke motivation as a factor in learning, use this term. I am inclined to think, on further analysis, that motivation in that sense may prove identical to what I have just been discussing. In other words, it is my working hypothesis that there is a set of signals, common to all units of a given behavior system, which not only governs the probability that any such unit will be performed in response to the appropriate external releasing situation, but which, in addition, provides a necessary condition for learning either on the efferent side (incorporation of new motor patterns as units of the system) or on the afferent side (rerouting of exteroceptor messages). I term this set of messages the motivation for that behavior system.

This view implies that there is a specific motivation for each separate behavior system (feeding, sexual behavior, etc.). The question of whether we must postulate in addition a general motivation, energizing all modes of behavior, is better left open, I think, until we know more about the specific motivations and their interaction.

To conclude, the results of ethology prove, at the present stage of behavioral research that the concept of specific motivation is a useful tool. However, it can be used with safety only if we give it a precise meaning. For that purpose, models that aim at a synthesis of the available data are a great help.

Part Two

7: Chairman's Remarks

by Samuel L. Lepkovsky

I WISH TO OPEN this session with a quotation from Adolph's paper (*Amer. J. Physiol.*, **151**: 110, 1947). "All animals that have been studied, those without alimentary tracts, as well as those which have, recognize food, spurn food when it is superabundant, and put forth extra efforts to get it when it is rare. Hence, whatever be the machinery that may fix the pattern of priorities in rats, comparable patterns seem to be endowments of all animals, whether or not they possess specialized neuromuscular or alimentary systems."

All animals, in particular the higher animals, in reality, do not live in the outside world. The living element of animals is the cell, which lives in "an internal liquid environment of its own ... with a controlled, unchanging atmosphere which made the organism independent of outside conditions" (Smith, *Sci. Amer.*, January 7, 1953). Bernard (*Lecons sur les proprietes physiologiques et les alterations pathologiques des liquides de l'organisme*. Bailliere, Paris, 1859) has pointed out that "all the vital mechanisms, however varied they be, have only one object; that of preserving constant the conditions of life in the internal environment." The fixed composition of the internal environment is made possible by the transfer from the outside world of the compounds needed to maintain "constant the conditions of life."

These compounds are present in food, which is selected by animals through specific alimentary behavior, not only for the maintenance of the internal environment, but also for growth and reproduction. Broadly, at this conference we are dealing with biochemistry (bodily chemistry) and behavior.

The scheduled papers deal with taste and its relationship to nutritional processes which in turn deal with dynamic interrelationships among neurophysiology, endocrinology, and biochemistry.

Animals cannot eat unless they find food in the external environment. Animals must select from the available food supply a nutritionally adequate diet in accordance with their bodily needs. Failure to choose foods correctly leads to malnutrition, nutritional disease, and death. To choose food correctly, animals must be able to recognize food that exists in the outside world. Hence they require:

1. *Information about food from the outside world.* This necessitates the use of the senses. Foods possess sensory stimuli, such as taste, odor, and texture, that are capable of exciting receptors in the mouths of animals. The receptors are connected with nerves that transmit the excitation to the central nervous system.

2. *Information about bodily needs.*

91

Such information is transmitted to the central nervous system through mechanisms that are not well understood, that are probably neural and humoral.

3. *Integration in the brain.* Information about food from the external environment is integrated with information on bodily needs in the central nervous system and leads to food-seeking behavior that is specific and directed to a choice of food which is best suited for the survival of the animal.

The excitation of the receptors by the sensory stimuli of foods is transformed in the brain to sensations that are characterized as taste and smell. Taste, smell, and other sensory stimuli of food determine the taste of food. Intrinsically, food tastes neither good nor bad; the taste of food is determined largely by the internal chemistry of the animal.

Taste and smell are sensations. What are sensations? "A person's sensations stand at the innermost portal of his soul and lead to a realm to which nobody but he himself can have access. . . . Just what a sensation actually is, nobody can reveal to others; it is a basic phenomenon of life, mysterious as life itself. . . . Everything in the world becomes known to us through our sensations alone. . . . we cannot make any statement about the sensations of animals. This does not mean that they do not exist, but simply that our knowledge reaches a barrier that we cannot cross" (Von Buddenbrock, *The Senses,* University of Michigan Press, Ann Arbor, 1958).

What is the nature of a sensory stimulus in food that makes it a flavor? The human being responds to a large number of compounds that have odors, but very few of these odors are related to food. Both perfume and onions have highly acceptable odors, but only the onion is associated with food. Other odors, some of them emanating from the

bodies of animals, alive and dead, are aversive. Human beings are also indifferent to many odors.

The chemical compounds of food that act as sensory stimuli probably serve as "markers" which enable many animals to choose foods in accordance with their bodily needs. Is this also true for human beings? It is generally accepted that animals can sense their physiological needs much better than can human beings. The sensory stimuli of food serve also as sources of pleasure which play an unsuspectedly important role in human life. There are two ways in which pleasure may be derived from food:

1. Hunger is a painful sensation, is accompanied by hyperirritability, ugly tempers, and the like, and is abolished by food. In this respect, "pleasure is an absence of pain" (Sherrington, *The Integrative Action of the Nervous System,* Yale University Press, New Haven, 1947), and probably functions similarly in both animals and human beings.

2. Human beings may continue to derive pleasure from eating after the abolition of hunger. This kind of pleasure is probably limited largely to human beings because of their more highly developed neocortex. Sherrington *(op. cit.),* working with decerebrate animals, pointed out that "pain centers seem to be lower than pleasure centers . . . no region of the cortex cerebri has been assigned to pain."

Evidence is accumulating to indicate that food sensory stimuli may compensate for the deprivation of other sensory stimuli. Young human beings, including college students, seem to be more or less indifferent to food sensory stimuli. A good restaurant is seldom found in a college town. This may be due to economic reasons. It may also be due to the availability of abundant sources of sensory stimuli that come from sports, debating, social contacts, dancing, movies, etc. In general, as human beings get older, they respond more and more positively to the sensory stimuli of food. This may be due to progressive deprivation of other sources of sensory stimuli; the sensory stimuli of the food may compensate for those of which they are deprived. It is also possible that as a consequence of changes in bodily biochemistry the sensory stimuli of food may elicit greater responses in adults than they do in younger people. It is not possible here to differentiate between cause and effect.

An extreme case of deprivation of sensory stimuli is that of the astronaut who is denied even the stimuli that come from gravity. With such severe deprivation the importance of food may be greatly exaggerated since his chief source of sensory stimuli is food.

Deprivation of sensory stimuli in human beings is currently receiving a great deal of attention. Schultz (*Sensory Restriction,* Academic Press, New York, 1965) introduces his book on sensory restriction thus: "A changing sensory environment seems essential for human beings. Without it, the brain ceases to function in an adequate way, and abnormalities of behavior develop. In fact, as Christopher Burney observed in his remarkable account of his stay in solitary confinement: 'Variety is not the spice of life; it is the very stuff of it.'"

8: Abnormalities of Taste and Olfaction in Various Disease States   by Robert I. Henkin

A T THE National Institutes of Health, we have been carrying out studies to evaluate the senses of taste and smell in various disease states. These studies were instructive in understanding more about the mechanisms of the diseases and the physiology of taste and smell.

The work of Richter demonstrated that preference thresholds for sodium chloride (NaCl) were significantly below normal in adrenalectomized rats [10]. With these studies in mind we compared detection and recognition thresholds for the taste of NaCl in a group of normal volunteers and in a group of patients with untreated adrenal cortical insufficiency (Fig. 8–1). These results demonstrate that the median detection threshold for NaCl in patients with untreated adrenal cortical insufficiency is about one one-hundredth of that observed in the normal volunteers [6]. This change in detection threshold is different from the change in preference threshold described by Richter [10]. The decreased detection threshold occurred in each patient with untreated adrenal cortical insufficiency tested whereas only 15–20 per cent of the patients with untreated adrenal cortical insufficiency craved salt [6,9].

Since detection thresholds for NaCl were significantly decreased in these untreated patients, it was of interest to determine their detection thresholds for other salts and other modalities of taste. Figure 8–2 illustrates that the median detection thresholds for the taste of potassium chloride (KCl), sodium bicarbonate ($NaHCO_3$) and NaCl (salt), sucrose (sweet), urea (bitter), and hydrochloric acid (HCl, sour) were significantly decreased in patients with untreated Addison's disease as compared to normal volunteers. Thus, untreated Addisonians can detect each of these compounds in about one one-hundredth the concentration detected by normal subjects. To investigate this phenomenon further, we treated patients with Addison's disease with a salt-retaining hormone (desoxycorticosterone acetate, DOCA) for two to nine days and once again determined detection thresholds for various modalities of taste. An example of such a study with NaCl is shown in Fig. 8–3; results were essentially the same for each of the other taste modalities. It is apparent that after treatment with DOCA there was no significant alteration in detection threshold; sensitivity remained as elevated as it was in the untreated state. However, after treatment of the Addisonian patients with various carbohydrate-active steroids by oral, intramuscular or intravenous routes of administration, detection thresholds for NaCl and for each of the

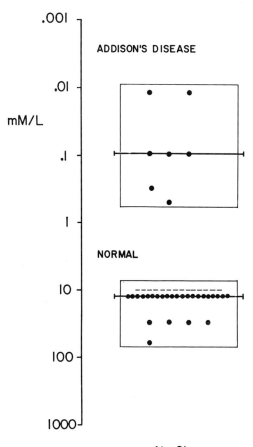

Na Cl

Fig. 8–1. The median and range of the detection threshold for the taste of NaCl in normal subjects and in patients with untreated Addison's disease. The black dots indicate individual detection thresholds, the lines enclosing the dots indicate the upper and lower limits of the range of response, and the lines extending through the boxes indicate the median detection threshold for both the normal subjects and the patients. The range of normal response is 6–60 mM/L; the median detection threshold is 12 mM/L. The dotted line within the box enclosing the normal range indicates the median detection threshold determined by several other investigators. The median detection threshold for the untreated patients is 0.1 mM/L.

other taste modalities returned to normal levels. Fig. 8–4 illustrates these results for thresholds for NaCl. Since this test is simple to carry out, and since the

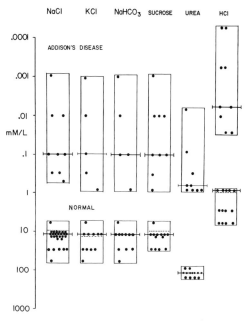

Fig. 8–2. The median and range of the detection threshold for the taste of NaCl, KCl, NaHCO₃, sucrose, urea, and HCl in normal subjects and in patients with untreated Addison's disease. The organization is similar to that of Fig. 8–1. There is no overlap between thresholds of the patients and those of the normal subjects.

phenomenon has been demonstrated in each patient tested, it is a relatively useful technique for evaluating adrenal cortical insufficiency.

Figure 8–5 illustrates a longitudinal study in which one patient, representative of many, was carefully studied over a twenty-seven day period, during which time serial determinations of serum sodium and potassium concentration, body weight, and NaCl detection threshold were carried out under various treatment conditions. After treatment with prednisolone and DOCA was discontinued, detection thresholds for NaCl decreased from the normal range (6–60 mM/L) to the values observed in patients with untreated adrenal cortical insufficiency (0.1 mM/L). This occurred over a period of four days after treatment was stopped. Maximum sensitivity

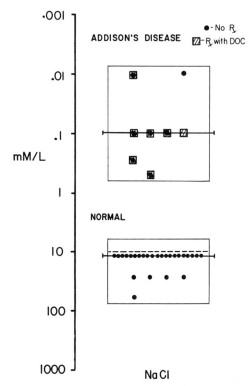

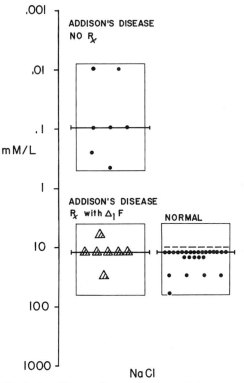

Fig. 8–3.   The median and range of the detection threshold for the taste of NaCl in normal subjects and in patients with Addison's disease treated with desoxycorticosterone acetate (DOCA). The small hatched squares *surrounding the individual thresholds of the Addisonian patients (the* black *dots) indicate that the detection thresholds determined after treatment with DOCA are the same as those in the untreated state.*

Fig. 8–4.   The median and range of the detection threshold for the taste of NaCl in normal subjects and in patients with Addison's disease before and after treatment with prednisolone (ΔlF). The hatched triangles *indicate the individual detection thresholds determined in the patients after treatment with* ΔlF.

seemed to persist as long as replacement therapy was withheld. During this time, the patient demonstrated hyperkalemia and hyponatremia. After treatment with DOCA there was no alteration in taste detection threshold although serum potassium concentration decreased to the normal range, serum sodium concentration rose to the normal range, and body weight increased. Only after treatment with carbohydrate-active steroid for twelve to thirty-six hours did taste sensitivity return to normal. This was apparent without any significant change in serum sodium or potassium concentra-

tion or change in body weight. Teleologically it may appear surprising that a salt-retaining hormone apparently has no effect on detection thresholds for the taste of NaCl. This same pattern of response occurred for each of the other taste modalities. The time over which the increase in taste sensitivity became maximal after treatment was discontinued appeared relatively constant, three to four days. However, the time over which taste sensitivity returned to normal was partially dependent upon the dosage of carbohydrate-active steroid administered. A large dose returned sensitivity to normal in as short a time as six to eight hours.

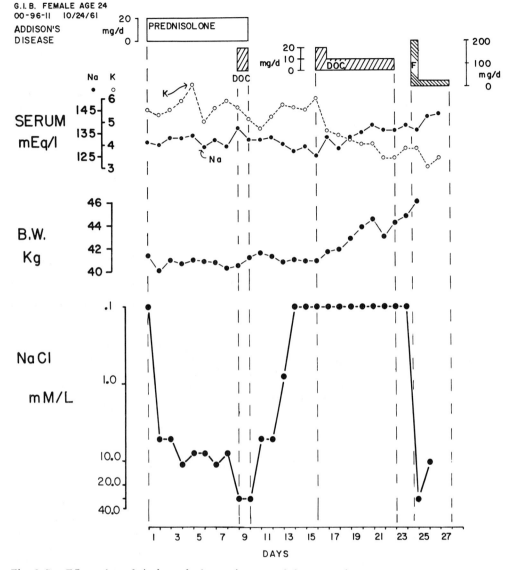

Fig. 8–5. *Effect of prednisolone, hydrocortisone, and desoxycorticosterone acetate
on serum Na and K concentrations, body weight, and taste threshold for NaCl. Threshold
values for NaCl ranging from 6–60 mM/L are within normal limits.*

Since taste sensitivity was altered in untreated adrenal cortical insufficiency, it seemed of interest to investigate detection and recognition thresholds for various vapors. A technique similar to the one used to measure taste thresholds was used to measure smell thresholds; i.e., the subjects were required to sniff the vapors from three bottles, two of which contained water and one of which contained a solution of some salt, sucrose, urea, or HCl. Subjects were required to state which one of the vapors from the three bottles was different from the other two. From these responses detection thresholds for the vapor of those same solutions were then used to determine taste thresholds in normal volunteers and in patients with adrenal cortical insufficiency (Fig. 8–6). Of the normal

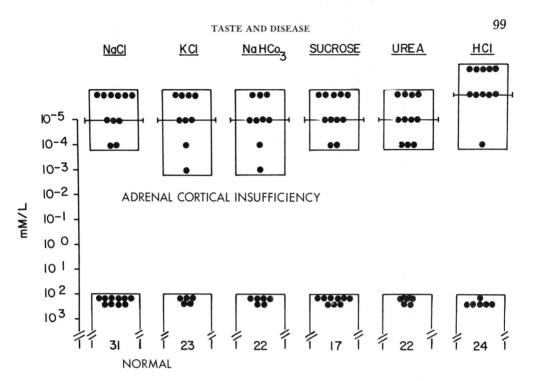

Fig. 8–6. *The median and range of the detection threshold for the vapor of NaCl,
KCl, NaHCO₃, sucrose, urea, and HCl in normal subjects and in patients with untreated
adrenal cortical insufficiency. The* lower *enclosures indicate the range of response
of the normal subjects; the* black dots, *the individual detection thresholds. The* numbers
*at the open end of these enclosures illustrate that this number of normal subjects
could not detect any difference between two solutions of water and a solution of NaCl,
KCl, NaHCO₃, sucrose, urea, or HCl as concentrated as 300 mM/L by smell. The*
upper boxes *indicate the range of response of the untreated patients with adrenal cortical
insufficiency, the* black dots, *the individual detection thresholds. There is no overlap
between the thresholds of the patients and those of the normal subjects.*

individuals tested, approximately 75 per cent could not distinguish by smell solutions of NaCl, KCl, NaHCO₃, sucrose, urea, or HCl (as concentrated as 300 mM/L) from the two solutions of water [4]. However, approximately 25 per cent of the normal volunteers tested were able to make detections between distilled water and solutions as dilute as 150 mM/L.

The reports of the subjects as to the sensations they perceived in carrying out this test were rather vague. They were required to state which one of the three solutions was different and also how it was different from the other two. However, they did not give any consistent response as to how the solution detected as different was perceived as such. I would press them for an answer but they did not report any consistent sensation. As you might expect, this is a very difficult question to answer, and it is not answered by saying that a given solution "smells" salty, bitter, sweet, or sour, for it does not. However, they consistently reported that one solution was different from the other two, the difference being perceived by olfaction. What type of olfaction occurred with these stimuli is an interesting question indeed. However, my major concern was to determine a difference in detection ability between normal volunteers and patients with untreated adrenal cortical insufficiency. Figure 8–6 illustrates the results obtained. The upper boxes indicate the range of the olfactory detection thresholds for various solutions in patients with untreated adrenal cortical insufficiency, the lower boxes, the range of similar thresholds in normal volunteers. The increase in sensitivity in the olfactory detection thresholds between the more sensitive Addisonians and the less sensitive normal subjects is approximately 10^7 times. This increase in sensitivity holds not only for NaCl but also for each of the solutions previously used to test taste thresholds.

How can normal subjects or patients with Addison's disease detect differences between water and substances which are supposedly non-volatile? We attempted to answer that question for one substance, NaCl. After a NaCl solution was labeled with $Na^{22}Cl$, significant radioactivity could not be obtained in the vapor phase above the solution. However, when $NaCl^{36}$ was used, a fourfold rise in radioactivity in the vapor phase was demonstrated within a period of a few hours. Our hypothesis is that both normal subjects and Addisonian patients detect the smell of chlorine gas over a solution of NaCl. This occurs through the action of light on the NaCl solution, which causes the oxidation of the chloride in solution to Cl_2 and its subsequent release into the atmosphere as chlorine gas. It is replaced in the solution by CO_2 from the air. If we had measured pH we might have been able to detect a microchange in the remaining solution. If the NaCl solutions stood for a few days or weeks in the laboratory in clear glass containers, detection of difference was made more easily than if the solutions were kept in colored glass containers and refrigerated. Similarly, if the solutions of NaCl were freshly prepared, these detections were made with greater difficulty. Although this hypothesis may explain the detection of NaCl, we have

no definitive answer as to how sucrose or other supposedly non-volatile solutions are detected [4].

The difference in olfactory sensitivity between normal volunteers and untreated patients with adrenal cortical insufficiency has also been demonstrated with substances that are considered to be volatile (Fig. 8–7). The difference in

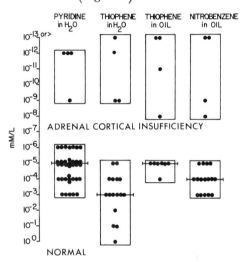

Fig. 8–7. The median and range of the detection threshold for the vapor of pyridine, thiophene, and nitrobenzene in normal subjects and in patients with untreated adrenal cortical insufficiency. The organization is similar to that of Fig. 8–6. There is no overlap between the thresholds determined in the patients and those of the normal subjects.

median olfactory detection sensitivity between normal subjects and untreated Addisonians for pyridine, thiophene, or nitrobenzene is approximately the same as that reported for the supposedly non-volatile substances noted previously.

As with the sense of taste, treatment with DOCA did not alter the already decreased olfactory thresholds (illustrated for NaCl, Fig. 8–8). However, treatment with carbohydrate-active steroids returned smell sensitivity to the normal range in each patient (illustrated for NaCl, Fig. 8–9). After replacement ther-

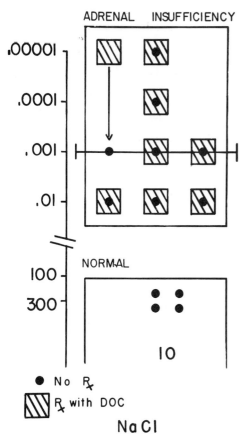

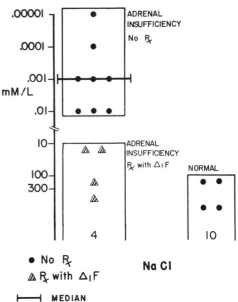

Fig. 8–9. *The median and range of the detection threshold for the vapor of NaCl in normal subjects and patients with adrenal cortical insufficiency before and after treatment with prednisolone (ΔlF). The* hatched triangles *indicate the individual detection thresholds determined in the patients after treatment with ΔlF.*

Fig. 8–8. *The median and range of the detection threshold for the vapor of NaCl in normal subjects and in patients with adrenal cortical insufficiency treated with desoxy-corticosterone acetate. The* small hatched squares *surrounding the individual thresholds determined in the Addisonians (the* black dots) *indicate that the detection thresholds determined after treatment with DOCA are the same as those determined in the untreated state.*

apy was instituted, four of these patients could no longer distinguish between a solution of NaCl as concentrated as 300 mM/L and the two solutions of distilled water.

In an effort to compare taste and smell responses in the same patient, we repeated the longitudinal studies previously carried out for taste alone. An example of the results for one of these studies is shown in Fig. 8–10. Results are

illustrated here for NaCl but are similar for responses to other vapors. After treatment with carbohydrate-active steroids was discontinued, taste sensitivity increased above the normal range within four days. At this time, sensitivity to smell was still normal. Three to four days later, smell sensitivity increased above the normal range. After treatment with carbohydrate-active steroids was resumed, smell sensitivity decreased to normal levels within twelve hours while taste sensitivity required twenty-four to thirty-six hours to return to normal. As noted previously, treatment with DOCA did not alter taste or smell sensitivity although serum sodium and potassium concentrations returned toward normal.

The preceding data illustrate increased sensitivity for taste and smell. This sensitivity is controlled by the pres-

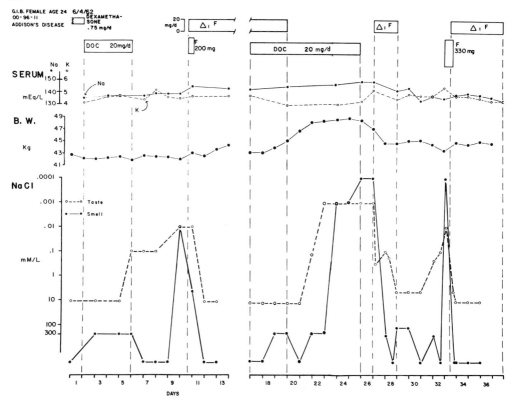

Fig. 8–10. Effect of prednisolone and desoxycorticosterone acetate on serum Na and potassium concentrations, body weight, and taste and smell thresholds for NaCl. Threshold values for the vapor of NaCl 150 mM/L and above are within normal limits.

ence or absence of carbohydrate-active steroid. Since there were patients who exhibited increased sensitivity, there might also be patients who would exhibit decreased sensitivity for the senses of taste and smell. We made a search for such a patient group, and Fig. 8–11 illustrates a comparison of median detection thresholds between normal volunteers and patients with familial dysautonomia [7]. Of these patients, four were unable to detect a concentrated solution of NaCl, sucrose, or urea as being different from water. A solution of HCl as concentrated as 300 mM/L could not be distinguished from two solutions of water by three of these patients. Figure 8–12 illustrates that these dysautonomic patients were totally unable to recognize saturated solutions of NaCl, sucrose, or

urea correctly. Similarly three of the patients could not recognize a solution of HCl 300 mM/L as sour.

Some of these patients demonstrated increased thresholds for the detection of various vapors; some demonstrated normal thresholds. This may be a useful tool in the classification of patients with familial dysautonomia, for those who exhibit increased thresholds for both taste and smell are usually more severely affected by the disease than those whose taste alone is involved.

The mechanism by which this decreased sensitivity occurs is most interesting but still not fully worked out. If we were to inspect the tongue of a patient and compare it with that of an unaffected mother we could observe that the tongue of the patient is smooth,

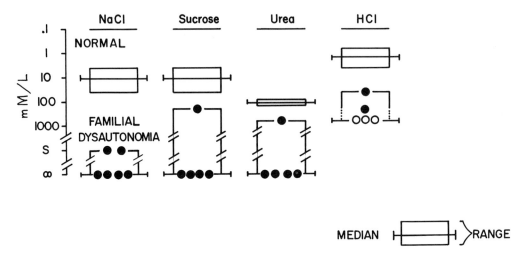

Fig. 8–11. *Median detection thresholds (MDT) for taste in normal subjects and in patients with familial dysautonomia. The* black and white dots *indicate the individual detection thresholds for the patients for each modality tested. The lines enclosing the dots* indicate the range of response of the patients. *The* enclosed boxes without dots *indicate the upper and lower limits of the range of response for normal subjects for each modality tested. The* lines through the enclosures *represent the MDT for all subjects. The letter S refers to a saturated aqueous solution. A black dot at this level indicates that the patient detected this concentration as different from water. A dot level with the infinity sign (∞) indicates that the patient could not detect a difference between a saturated solution of the substance and two comparison stimuli of water. The three white dots and dotted lines in the column under HCl indicate that these patients could not detect 0.3 N HCl as different from water.*

without either fungiform or circumvallate papillae (Fig. 8–13). The tongue of the mother shows fungiform and circumvallate papillae and a generally normal anatomical appearance. Light and electron microscopic studies of biopsy material from anterior and posterior areas of the tongue of two of these patients demonstrated that indeed there were no papillae on the tongue, but also no taste buds could be found. The only neural elements observed in the tongue biopsies from these patients have been unmyelinated nerve fibers which terminate as free nerve endings.

Since methacholine has been shown to produce tears in these patients, we injected methacholine, subcutaneously,

into two of these patients and noted that there was a consistent decrease in detection and recognition threshold for NaCl until thresholds fell within the normal range in both patients (Fig. 8–14). As the effect of the drug wore off, there was a gradual increase in threshold back to pretreatment level. For these patients, methacholine is somehow able to restore normal taste sensitivity both for detection and recognition.

In an effort to block the severe respiratory effects which methacholine produces in these patients, we pretreated them with atropine. The problem here is that they are inappropriately sensitive to atropine because this drug also produces marked respiratory spasm in these

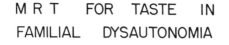

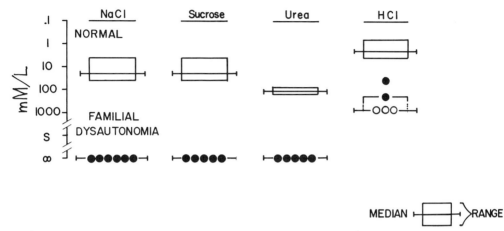

Fig. 8–12. *Median recognition thresholds (MRT) for taste in normal subjects and in*
patients with familial dysautonomia. The organization is similar to that in Fig. 8–11.

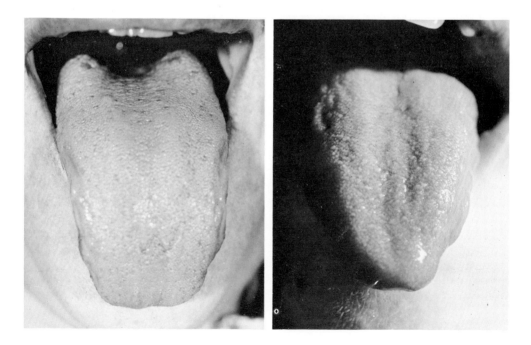

Fig. 8–13. *Comparison of photographs of the tongue of one patient with*
familial dysautonomia with that of an unaffected mother. On the right is the photograph
of the patient with familial dysautonomia. Notice that the tongue is smooth,
without the normal anatomical architecture and without fungiform and circumvallate
papillae. On the left is the photograph of the tongue of the unaffected mother.
Notice that papillae are readily observed.

DETECTION AND RECOGNITION THRESHOLDS
FOR TASTE

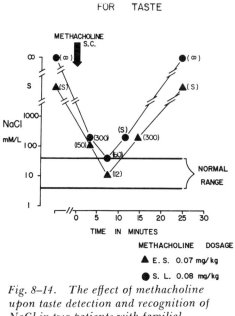

Fig. 8–14. The effect of methacholine upon taste detection and recognition of NaCl in two patients with familial dysautonomia. Detection thresholds for the patients are represented by the dot *and* triangle, *recognition thresholds by the* numbers in parenthesis *beside each symbol.*

patients. Thus pharmacological studies in these patients must be undertaken only with a great deal of caution. They are exquisitely sensitive to acetylcholine-like drugs and develop symptoms of respiratory distress quite easily.

We have just discussed two groups of patients, one group whose taste and smell thresholds are significantly decreased below normal, the other group whose thresholds are significantly greater than normal. There are groups of patients with various diseases whose taste and smell thresholds fall between these two extremes. We have recently described such a group [5]. The patients exhibit submucous clefts of the dorsal hard palate, facial hypoplasia, and physical growth retardation below the third percentile in addition to abnormalities of taste and smell. These patients exhibit normal detection thresholds for

each of the four taste modalities, but median recognition thresholds for them are significantly higher than normal (Fig. 8–15). Although these patients can detect differences between solutions of NaCl, sucrose, urea, and HCl, as well as can normal subjects, they have difficulty in recognizing whether these solutions are in fact salty, bitter, sweet, or sour. This difficulty in recognition, however, is not as severe as that noted for the dysautonomic patients. Because recognition thresholds for all taste is affected in these patients, they have a unique abnormality which we have labeled *recognition hypogeusia.*

All these patients exhibit hyposmia. Figure 8–16 demonstrates that olfactory detection thresholds for pyridine, thiophene, and nitrobenzene are approximately 10,000 times higher in these patients than in normal volunteers; however, these patients can detect and recognize pure solutions of all odorous solutions presented to them.

Since we were interested in the relationship between abnormalities of facial form and those of taste and smell, we determined taste and olfactory thresholds in patients with large clefts of the dorsal hard palate (Fig. 8–17). Thresholds for the taste of NaCl and the vapor of pyridine in water were normal in these patients. Thus, cleft palate alone is not sufficient to produce these abnormal sensory responses; rather there is some other characteristic of the patients with submucous cleft palates and growth retardation.

Figure 8–18 demonstrates the detection threshold for pyridine in these patients compared with that of their mothers and of normal volunteers. It is apparent that thresholds in the affected children and in their mothers are essentially the same. Thus, it appears that the hyposmia is familial. We are apparently dealing with a genetic abnormality, for

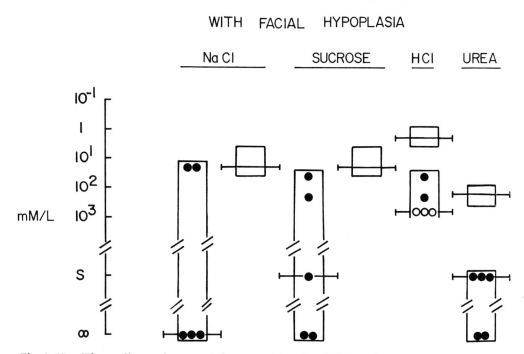

Fig. 8–15.   *The median and range of the recognition threshold for the taste of NaCl, sucrose, urea, and HCl in normal subjects and in patients with "facial hypoplasia." The organization is similar to that of previous figures.*

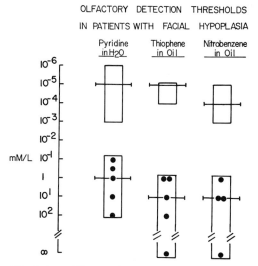

Fig. 8–16.   *The median and range of the detection threshold for the vapor of pyridine, thiophene, and nitrobenzene in normal subjects and in patients with "facial hypoplasia." The organization is similar to that of previous figures.*

we can trace the hyposmia through the mothers in each family that we have studied.

These examples in a number of disease states indicate that there is a spectrum of sensitivity of taste and smell responses extending from markedly increased to markedly decreased sensitivity. Figure 8–19 outlines this concept. Patients with untreated adrenal cortical insufficiency and the adrenogenital syndrome [2] exhibit taste and olfactory sensitivity that is increased above normal. Their thresholds return to normal after treatment with carbohydrate-active steroids. Some patients with cystic fibrosis of the pancreas [8] exhibit increased taste and smell sensitivity. This ability is probably a genetic trait for it occurs mainly in male siblings and in mothers of these patients. It may bear no metabolic relationship to the disease at all.

OLFACTORY DETECTION THRESHOLDS
FOR PYRIDINE IN WATER
IN PATIENTS WITH FACIAL HYPOPLASIA AND
WITH DORSAL CLEFTS OF THE HARD PALATE

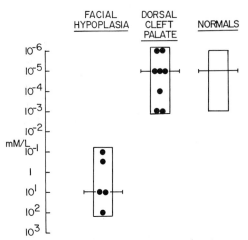

Fig. 8–17. *Median and range of the detection threshold for the vapor of pyridine in normal subjects, patients with dorsal clefts of the hard palate, and patients with "facial hypoplasia."*

There are other groups in the population at large that exhibit increased taste and smell sensitivity. We have examined the members of two such families at the National Institutes of Health, all of whom were apparently well and healthy but who exhibited decreased detection thresholds for various taste and smell modalities.

On the other hand, patients with familial dysautonomia exhibit taste sensitivity that is decreased below normal and some exhibit decreased olfactory sensitivity. Some patients with hypogonadism (Turner's Syndrome) exhibit hyposmia and a decreased ability to detect and recognize the tastes of urea and HCl [1]. Patients with submucous clefts of the dorsal palate and growth retardation (for convenience called "facial hypoplasia") exhibit recognition hypoageusia and hyposmia. There are probably groups within our population that

have decreased taste and smell sensitivity on the basis of some genetic characteristics. We have not observed these patients but we have not screened a large population in search of them. A partial example of this type of patient might be those athyreotic cretins who exhibit the inability to recognize phenylthiocarbamide as bitter.

The vast majority of the population falls within the broad category of "normal" sensitivity of taste and smell. However, as we obtain more information about taste and smell thresholds in various disease states and in the "normal" population, we will be better able to define normality and the mechanisms of deviation from it.

Discussion

Chauncey: Have you tested sensitivity to sodium chloride in persons having Cushing's syndrome? Have you found any changes that would be associated with higher sodium chloride levels in blood and in saliva?

Henkin: Theoretically, you might expect to observe the converse of increased sensitivity in patients with Cushing's syndrome. These patients had high excretion of urinary 17 hydroxycorticosteroids, but detection and recognition thresholds for various taste modalities and vapors were within normal limits. We have also treated a number of normal volunteers with high doses of carbohydrate-active steroid for as long as five days and could detect no difference in taste or smell thresholds.

Chauncey: Relative to your work with cystic fibrosis, where you have high sodium chloride levels in the sweat, we have also found extremely high sodium and chloride levels in saliva. Wotman and some of his colleagues (*Am. J. Dis.*

OLFACTORY DETECTION THRESHOLDS FOR PYRIDINE IN WATER
IN PATIENTS WITH FACIAL HYPOPLASIA

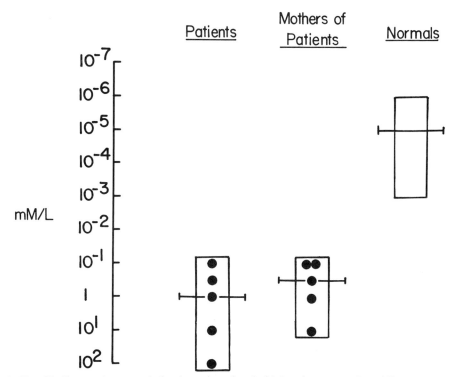

Fig. 8–18. Median and range of the detection threshold for the vapor of pyridine in normal subjects, patients with "facial hypoplasia," and mothers of patients with "facial hypoplasia."

Child., **108**: 372, 1964) have indicated that there is a decreased sensitivity to sodium chloride in these people, and it may well be that the composition of the saliva is the responsible factor. Furthermore, environment can alter taste threshold. In the Polaris submarine, for example, there is a high carbon dioxide concentration in the air—about ten times the normal. The Navy has indicated that under these conditions there is an increase in the sensitivity of the men to sour solutions.

Henkin: With respect to Wotman's work, it is important to point out that the threshold change we observed in

patients with cystic fibrosis was one of detection, not recognition. It is critical, when evaluating taste sensitivity, to differentiate detection from recognition thresholds. At best, working with small children is difficult, and in our studies it was necessary to make repeated observations to insure reproducibility of our results.

Pfaffmann: As I understand your work, these defects are not, at least in the Addisonian, specific to the particular change in electrolyte balance. In fact, these large electrolyte balances have very little to do with sensory function. They are hormonal.

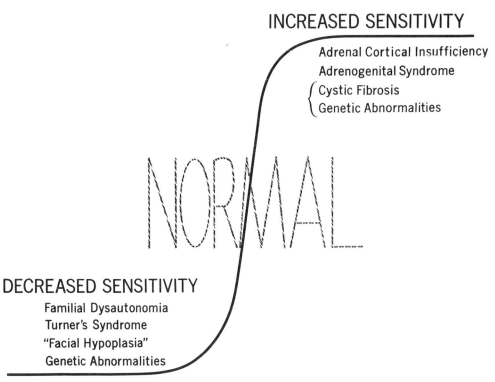

INCREASED SENSITIVITY

Adrenal Cortical Insufficiency
Adrenogenital Syndrome
{ Cystic Fibrosis
{ Genetic Abnormalities

NORMAL

DECREASED SENSITIVITY

Familial Dysautonomia
Turner's Syndrome
"Facial Hypoplasia"
Genetic Abnormalities

Fig. 8–19.   The sensitivity range of taste and olfaction in normal subjects and in patients with various diseases.

Henkin: It probably is related to circulating hormone level. However, I do not think we can say that there is no relationship between electrolyte changes and the observed sensory changes. We have measured only changes in the concentration of sodium and potassium in extracellular fluid and have found no correlation with changes in sensory sensitivity. What happens at the intracellular level is not clear. With respect to circulating levels of carbohydrate-active steroid, we have presented evidence demonstrating high concentrations of corticosteroids in various parts of the central and peripheral nervous system of the cat, which decrease significantly after adrenalectomy (Henkin and Bartter, *Prog. Endocr. Soc.*, **37**, 1966). Other investigators have demonstrated the presence of steroids in the brain of man (Touchstone *et al.*, *Steroids*, **7**: 205,

1966). Thus, some very close relationships might exist between increased sensory sensitivity and removal of carbohydrate-active steroids from the nervous system.

Pfaffmann: We have been trying to find a correlation between electrolyte balance in adrenalectomized or sodium deprived animals and receptor measures of sensitivity but have been unable to find anything conclusive.

Jacobs: Do patients suffering from dysautonomia and hypochondraisis have any other symptoms?

Henkin: Symptoms of familial dysautonomia include orthostatic hypotension without a corresponding orthostatic tachycardia, respiratory distress with repeated pulmonary infections, kyphosis and kyphoscoliosis, unexplained high fevers, poor appreciation of pain, and many other symptoms. Patients usually die from pulmonary infection with decreased pulmonary reserve, in spite of adequate treatment measures.

Jacobs: Do these people have other types of debilitating syndromes? Are there problems in diet, etc., which are related to taste?

Henkin: These patients are extremely finicky eaters. Almost all the children we have observed are from Jewish parents. Their mothers made every effort, with little success, to get them to eat adequately. They do not grow well and almost all of them are dwarfed to some extent. The relationship that the absence of taste has to this feeding phenomenon is not known. Some of these children did state that they preferred certain foods over others, but these were mainly children who exhibited normal smell thresholds. Decreased growth was more apparent in those children who exhibited decreased sensitivity of both taste and smell.

Fregly: Have you used any other doses of DOCA other than the 20 mg?

Henkin: We used two dosages, 10 mg and 20 mg.

Fregly: My question stems from the studies of Herxheimer and Woodbury (*J. Physiol.,* 151: 253, 1960). They showed that administration of large doses of DOCA to normal rats lowered their preference (taste) threshold for sodium chloride solution. If this phenomenon also exists in humans, it might explain why your patients with adrenal insufficiency failed to show an increase in NaCl taste threshold after administration of DOCA.

Henkin: We routinely used lower doses in children in order to obtain a more appropriate dose per kilogram of body weight. Our major concern was to obtain an adequate dosage of salt-retaining hormone so that we could be sure this hormone was adequately replaced. Since this hormone was injected intramuscularly in oil, it was always possible that it would not be maximally absorbed. However, we have made no systematic survey of doses of DOCA other than 10 and 20 mg per day.

Fischer: Why use urea to test bitterness? With another compound, such as quinine, you would not have to employ such high concentrations, and in addition, you would prevent partial denaturation of the proteinous parts of taste receptors.

I should like to bridge the two extreme conditions, genetic inability to taste and disease-induced increase in taste sensitivity, by showing the influence of extended taste practice on taste thresholds of an insensitive taster of both quinine (lower curve of Fig. 8–I) and 6-n-propylthiouracil (PROP) (upper curve of figure). The data confirm earlier observations and show that a genetically insensitive taster of PROP and quinine can lower his macrothreshold for quinine 256-fold from solution number *9* to solution number *1* (macrothresholds) under the influence of microthreshold practice. Here, as in our previously published case, the increase in taste acuity, i.e., lowering of taste threshold, does not occur gradually but stepwise. Such step functions with finite intervals of constancy, separated by instantaneous jumps, can be found in homeostatic systems (Ashby, *Design for a Brain,* John Wiley & Sons, New York, 1960). It is a matter of semantics whether we call this step function "adaptation" or "learning."

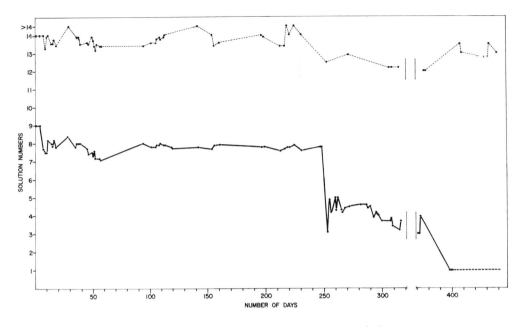

Fig. 8–1   The influence of extended taste practice on the taste thresholds of an insensitive taster of Quinine and 6-N-Propylthiouracil.

Hodgson: Pursuing Pfaffmann's question, and aiming at determining the site of the hormone action, have you seen any hormone effects in less than three or four days?

Henkin: Taste and smell thresholds in patients with adrenal cortical insufficiency, treated with as much as 300 mg of solucortef intravenously, have been observed to return to normal in as short a time as six hours. It appears to take time for this effect to occur. After treatment with carbohydrate-active steroid is discontinued, it takes three to four days for the increased taste sensitivity to appear. It takes an additional one to three days for increased olfactory detection sensitivity to appear.

Hodgson: Considering the rapid turnover of taste receptor cells, which Beidler has demonstrated, it is quite conceivable that the hormones could act during the differentiation of entirely new receptor cells in these cases. The kind of hor-

mone effects that we observed with insects occur within minutes and appear to be more the pharmacological type of effects. This seems quite different.

Henkin: The mechanism by which carbohydrate-active steroid affects the receptor is not at all clear.

Kare: You find dramatic changes, with adrenal insufficiency, in the threshold for sodium chloride. Nachman and Pfaffmann (*J. Comp. Physiol. Psychol.,* **56:** 343, 1963) reported that with adrenalectomized rats they obtained no differences in the electrophysiological threshold. Would you comment on what would appear to be a contradiction?

Henkin: I do not think that there is a contradiction. The rat and man differ greatly in their response to adrenalectomy. The adrenalectomized rat can be maintained indefinitely on salt water whereas the untreated Addisonian generally requires replacement with adrenal cortical steroids. Nerve conduction velocity is altered in adrenalectomized rats. Treatment with either DOCA or carbohydrate-active steroid changes this conduction velocity. Nerve conduction velocity is also altered in the untreated patient with adrenal cortical insufficiency. However, treatment with DOCA does not change nerve conduction velocity in the Addisonian. Only treatment with carbohydrate-active steroid can do this.

Pfaffmann: I don't follow the argument. I thought that what you were saying was somewhat in agreement with our findings.

Henkin: Yes, I think that is correct. There is no question that patients with adrenal cortical insufficiency treated with DOCA may exhibit normal concentrations of sodium and potassium in their extracellular fluid but still exhibit increased sensitivity of taste and smell and increased ulnar nerve conduction velocity. On the other hand, replacement of carbohydrate-active steroid in these patients may return sensory sensitivity to normal in spite of hyperkalemia and hyponatremia.

Beidler: It seems to me that many experimenters confuse taste and smell. Rats whose NaCl thresholds are lowered by conditioning with electric shock may actually use the odor of the solution as a cue rather than the taste of the NaCl. We know that if you place sodium chloride solution over the olfactory epithelium of the water turtle, you excite it tremendously. But if you prepare your sodium chloride solution and then add activated carbon to eliminate all the impurities, there will not be any excitement. You can smell the difference between sodium chloride solution and sucrose solution at high concentrations. I wonder how much we confound the taste of sodium chloride with the odor. An animal does not know what type of experiment we design but will use any cue he can.

Pfaffmann: The answer to this is a neurological dissociation made by knocking out the central representation of the taste system. It is true that the adrenalectomy has not been tested with a hypoageusic rate, but calcium hunger has. R. Emmers and M. R. Nocenti (*The Physiologist,* **6**: 176, 1963) put a lesion in the ventro-basal complex of the sensory thalamus, to which the taste system projects. An animal, made calcium hungry by the removal of the parathyroid, normally selects the calcium solution. With hypoageusia, from a lesion in the thalamus, the animal no longer made the selection. It was quite clear that it was depending upon that taste relay. Oakley (*J. Comp. Physiol. Psychol.,* **59**: 202, 1965) showed the same thing with regard to sugars. Even though sugars can be smelled, there is definite evidence that you can, by this method, set the controls on the question that you are raising. It is true that the experiment has never been done on the adrenalectomized animal; it might well be worth going back just to confirm this point.

Snapper: One cannot compare an animal whose adrenals have been taken out with a human who has hypocorticism because we know that hypocorticism in the human often exists when a piece of adrenal is present. We have no hypocorticism when both of the adrenals are destroyed by carcinoma or by amyloid. Therefore, rats and humans cannot be compared completely. If you see patients who have been adrenalectomized because they have certain diseases, then hypocorticism is not the same as Addison's disease. There are a number of different effects in these conditions.

Henkin: In our studies we have seen patients with adrenal cortical insufficiency of different etiologies. These would include hypopituitarism, idiopathic adrenal insufficiency, adrenal cortical insufficiency secondary to tuberculosis of the adrenal cortex, postsurgical adrenalectomy for Cushing's Syndrome, and adrenal cortical hyperplasia. Whatever the etiology of the adrenal cortical insufficiency, the patients all responded in the same manner, in terms of their taste and smell sensitivity, to discontinuation and replacement of carbohydrate-active steroid. In this sense, they are all the same, but in other characteristics they show a number of clinical and physiological differences.

REFERENCES

1. Henkin, R. I. Hypogonadism associated with familial hyposmia. *Clin. Res.,* 13: 244, 1965.
2. Henkin, R. I., and Bartter, F. C. Increased sensitivity of taste and smell in patients with congenital adrenal hyperplasia. *Clin. Res.,* 12: 270, 1964.
3. Henkin, R. I., and Bartter, F. C. The presence of corticosterone and cortisol in the central and peripheral nervous system of the cat. Program of the Endocrinology Society, Forty-eighth Meeting, p. 37, 1966.
4. Henkin, R. I., and Bartter, F. C. Studies on olfactory thresholds in normal man and in patients with adrenal cortical insufficiency: The role of adrenal cortical steroids and of serum sodium concentration. *J. Clin. Invest.,* 45: 1631, 1966.
5. Henkin, R. I., Christiansen, R. L., and Bosma, J. F. Impairment of recognition of oral sensation and familial hyposmia in patients with facial hypoplasia and growth retardation: A new syndrome. *Clin. Res.,* 14: 236, 1966.
6. Henkin, R. I., Gill, J. R., Jr, and Bartter, F. C. Studies on taste thresholds in normal man and in patients with adrenal cortical insufficiency: The role of adrenal cortical steroids and of serum sodium concentration. *J. Clin. Invest.,* 42: 727–35, 1963.
7. Henkin, R. I., and Kopin, I. J. Abnormalities of taste and smell thresholds in familial dysautonomia: Improvement with methacholine. *Life Sciences,* 3: 1319–25, 1964.
8. Henkin, R. I., and Powell, G. F. Increased sensitivity of taste and smell in cystic fibrosis. *Science,* 138: 1107–8, 1962.
9. Henkin, R. I., and Soloman, D. H. Salt-taste threshold in adrenal insufficiency in man. *J. Clin. Endocr. Metabl.,* 22: 856–58, 1962.
10. Richter, C. P. Increased salt appetite in adrenalectomized rats. *Amer. J. Physiol.,* 115: 155–61, 1936.
11. Touchstone, J. C., Kasparow, M., Hughes, P. A., and Horwitz, M. R. Corticosteroids in human brain. *Steroids,* 7: 205–11, 1966.

9: The Role of Hormones in the Regulation of Salt Intake in Rats[1] *by Melvin J. Fregly*

REMOVAL OF both adrenal glands from rats is accompanied by an increase in spontaneous sodium chloride (NaCl) intake [30]. The salt appetite is relatively specific for sodium-containing compounds and enhances survival of the adrenalectomized rats [34]. Although a number of factors is known to influence this NaCl appetite, the mechanism or mechanisms important in its genesis are unknown. Richter and Eckert contributed significantly to an understanding of the mechanism when they reported that transplantation of adrenal cortical tissue to adrenalectomized rats reduced their NaCl intake if the transplant grew [35]. Thus, the essential experiments were performed nearly thirty years ago to show that a hormonal factor produced by the adrenal cortex affected the spontaneous NaCl intake of rats given a choice between water and NaCl solution to drink. Richter provided additional evidence for hormonal regulation of NaCl intake by showing that administration of the synthetic mineralocorticoid hormone, desoxycorticosterone acetate (DOCA), at 0.5–1.0 mg/day returned the increased NaCl intake of adrenalectomized rats to normal [33]. The interpretation of these observations seemed quite clear until the studies carried out by Braun-Menendez and Brandt [5], Rice and Richter [29], and Tosteson *et al.* [39] in both normal

and renal hypertensive rats revealed that daily administration of 0.5–2.5 mg of DOCA *increased* their spontaneous NaCl intake. It seemed surprising that similar doses of DOCA produced opposite responses depending upon the presence or absence of the adrenal glands. The first studies reported here were performed in order to determine the dose-response relationship between the dose of DOCA administered and spontaneous intake of NaCl solution by adrenalectomized rats. The desire to perform these experiments was also stimulated by the fact that the naturally occurring mineralocorticoid, aldosterone, is now available and its effect on NaCl intake could be compared with that of DOCA. A further additional stimulus was the observation that rats made hypothyroid by either surgical thyroidectomy or administration of the antithyroid drugs, propylthiouracil (PTU), thiouracil, or methimazole, also manifested a spontaneous appetite for $0.15 M$ NaCl solution [14]. It seemed worthwhile to compare adrenalectomized rats with hypothyroid rats to determine whether similar mechanisms might account for their similar salt appetites.

METHODS AND RESULTS

All experiments used male albino rats of either the Holtzman or Carworth CFN strains. The rats were caged indi-

vidually and maintained in a window-
less room at $26\pm1^\circ$ C. The room was
illuminated from 8:00 A.M. to 6:00 P.M.
Fluid containers consisted of infant nursing bottles with cast aluminum spouts
as described by Lazarow [24]. Food containers were spill-proof and have been
described in detail [10].

Treatments were assigned at random
so that a randomized statistical design
and analysis of variance could be used to
aid in the interpretation of results [36].

*Effect of Desoxycorticosterone Acetate
on Spontaneous NaCl Intake of Adrenalectomized Rats* Three separate experiments were performed, the details of
which have been published elsewhere
[17]. The objective of the experiments
was to determine the dose-response relationship between spontaneous intake of
NaCl solution and dose of DOCA (Per-
corten, Ciba Pharm. Co.) administered.
A total of thirty-six animals ranging in
body weight from 340 to 427 g were
adrenalectomized at least two weeks
prior to the experiment. They were
maintained on a 0.15 M NaCl solution
and finely powdered Rockland Rat Diet
until the experiment began, at which
time all rats were randomly divided into
groups and given a choice between tap
water and 0.15 M NaCl solution to drink.
The same food was used during the experiment as prior to it. Each experiment
generally began with a control period of
four or five days during which body
weight and daily intakes of water, saline, and food were measured. Following
the control period, treatments were initiated and included daily subcutaneous
injections of either 0.2 ml peanut oil
or DOCA at graded doses dissolved
in 0.2 ml peanut oil. Treatment continued during the next four or five days,
after which the experiment was terminated. Intakes of water, saline, and food
were also measured daily during the

treatment period. Intakes of individual
rats during treatment were compared
with their intakes prior to treatment and
are expressed as percentage changes.

Figure 9–1 is a composite graph made
up of data from the three experiments.

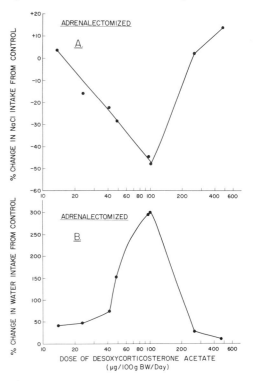

*Fig. 9–1.   A. Composite graph to summarize
data from three separate experiments. The
relationship between mean percentage
change in intake of 0.15 M NaCl solution
from the control group and the logarithm
of the dose of DOCA administered to
adrenalectomized rats is shown. B. Similar
data are graphed for percentage change in
simultaneous water intake.*

Percentage changes in both NaCl intake
(Fig. 9–1, *A*) and water intake (Fig. 9–1,
B) are plotted against the logarithm of
the daily dose of DOCA administered
(μg/100 g body weight per day). This
figure shows that a V-shaped dose-
response relationship exists between percentage changes in NaCl intake from the
control period and the logarithm of the
dose of DOCA administered. Adminis-

tration of increasing doses of DOCA to adrenalectomized rats was accompanied by a decrease in NaCl intake compared with oil-treated control rats until a dose of 100 μg/100 g body weight/day was reached. Further administration increased salt intake such that at the highest dose (470 μg/100 g body weight/day), the treated rats ingested more NaCl solution than controls. The percentage change in water intake (Fig. 9–1, B) was approximately a mirror image of the percentage change in NaCl intake shown in Fig. 9–1, A.

Effect of d-Aldosterone on Spontaneous NaCl Intake of Adrenalectomized Rats Three separate experiments were performed, the details of which have also been published elsewhere [17]. The objective of these experiments was to determine the dose-response relationship between spontaneous intake of NaCl solution and dose of aldosterone administered to adrenalectomized rats. A total of forty-five animals weighing approximately 300 g were adrenalectomized at least two weeks prior to the experiment and kept under conditions identical to those described above except that during the treatment period graded doses of d-aldosterone were used instead of DOCA.

Figure 9–2 combines data from all experiments. Percentage changes in both NaCl (Fig. 9–2, A) and water (Fig. 9–2, B) intake are plotted against the logarithm of daily dose of aldosterone administered (μg/100 g body weight/day). This figure shows a rough V-shaped dose-response relationship. Administration of increasing doses of aldosterone to adrenalectomized rats is accompanied by a decrease in NaCl intake compared with oil-treated control rats until a dose of 10.8 μg/100 g body weight/day is reached. Doses of aldosterone higher than this tend to return NaCl intake

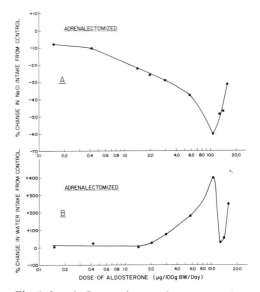

Fig. 9–2. A. Composite graph to summarize data from three separate experiments. The relationship between mean percentage change in intake of 0.15 M NaCl solution from the control group and the logarithm of the dose of d-aldosterone administered to adrenalectomized rats is shown. B. Similar data are graphed for percentage change in simultaneous water intake.

toward that of untreated, adrenalectomized rats. The percentage change in water intake (Fig. 9–2, B) is a rough mirror image of the percentage change in NaCl intake shown in Fig. 9–2, A.

Effect of 9-α-Fluorocortisol on Spontaneous NaCl Intake of Adrenalectomized Rats Twenty-five male rats weighing from 290 to 320 g were used. They were adrenalectomized two weeks prior to the experiment, as described above. After operation, they were caged individually and given finely powdered Rockland Rat Diet and were allowed to choose between tap water and 0.15 M NaCl solution to drink.

At the start of the experiment the rats were divided randomly into five equal groups. A five-day control period began, during which daily measurements of body weight and intakes of water and

NaCl solution were made. At the end of the five-day control period, a five-day experimental period began, during which the same intake measurements were made while the drug was injected. Group One received daily a subcutaneous injection of 0.2 ml peanut oil. Groups Two to Five, inclusive, received respectively 5, 10, 15, and 20 μg of 9-α-fluorocortisol/100 g body weight/day subcutaneously in 0.2 ml peanut oil. Intakes measured during the control period were compared with intakes measured during the treatment period for each individual rat and are expressed as percentage changes from the control period.

Administration of 9-α-fluorocortisol resulted in a V-shaped dose-response relationship between dose of hormone and percentage change in intake of NaCl solution that was similar in character to that observed for both DOCA and aldosterone (Fig. 9–3). Maximal reduction in NaCl intake occurred when 5 μg/100 g body weight/day were administered. The percentage change in water intake accompanying drug administration was a rough mirror image of NaCl intake.

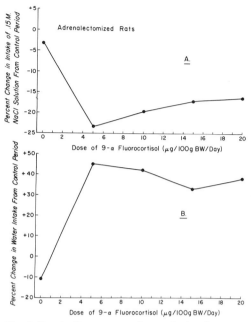

Fig. 9–3. A. *Percentage change in intake of 0.15 M NaCl solution from pretreatment control period is shown for each dose of 9-α-fluorocortisol administered to adrenalectomized rats. B. Similar data are graphed for percentage change in simultaneous water intake.*

Effect of Spironolactone on Spontaneous NaCl Intake of Adrenalectomized Rats Given Graded Doses of Desoxycorticosterone Acetate   This study was designed as a test of the specificity of the mineralocorticoid effect on NaCl intake of adrenalectomized rats. The mineralocorticoid inhibitor, spironolactone, which is known to inhibit the effect of DOCA on renal tubular reabsorption of sodium [21,37], was used and its efficacy in reversing the effect of DOCA on NaCl intake of adrenalectomized rats was tested.

Twenty-five rats weighing initially from 360 to 400 g were adrenalectomized. After operation all rats were given 0.15 M NaCl solution to drink and Rockland Rat Pellets to eat. Three weeks after operation the rats were placed in individual, round metabolism cages and given a choice between distilled water and 0.15 M NaCl solution to drink. The animals were divided randomly into five equal groups. The first group received 0.2 ml peanut oil subcutaneously daily. The second to fifth groups inclusive received subcutaneously daily 50, 100, 200, and 400 μg DOCA/100 g body weight dissolved in 0.2 ml peanut oil. Three days after initiation of the hormone treatment, a four-day control period began. During this time, body weight and individual daily intakes of water, 0.15 M NaCl solution, and food (finely powdered Rockland pellets) were measured. DOCA was administered daily throughout both control and treatment periods.

At the completion of this control period, all rats were given powdered Rockland diet into which were thoroughly mixed 400 mg spironolactone/kg food. Measurement of intake and body weight continued for another four-day period.

The effect of administration of DOCA at graded doses on the spontaneous intakes of 0.15 M NaCl solution and water by adrenalectomized rats is shown in Fig. 9–4. The reduction in intake of

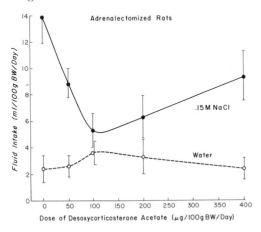

Fig. 9–4. Effect of administration of DOCA on intakes of water (○) and 0.15 M NaCl solution (●) by adrenalectomized rats. Mean ± 1 standard error is shown.

NaCl solution, reaching a minimum when approximately 100 μg DOCA/100 g body weight/day was administered, has been described above. Also described above is the tendency for NaCl intake to return toward the level of the untreated control rats when doses of DOCA greater than 100 μg/100 g body weight/day are administered. Water intake tends to be the mirror image of NaCl intake and is of less magnitude because the total fluid intake of adrenalectomized rats under these conditions consists mainly of NaCl solution.

A compound which successfully blocks the effects of all the doses of DOCA shown in Fig. 9–4 would be expected to yield intakes of NaCl solution similar to that of the untreated, adrenalectomized controls. Such a compound would thus be expected to reduce the U-shaped dose-response curve of Fig. 9–4 to a straight

line. Hence, a high dose of spironolactone was administered simultaneously with DOCA to achieve this effect.

An attempt was made to reduce experimental variability in the design of the experiment by comparing the intake of each rat during a control period with intake during the following treatment period. The difference is expressed as percentage change from the prespironolactone control period. This procedure is also consistent with the method of expression of change used in the studies described above and lends itself well to analysis of variance.

The curve in Fig. 9–5 was obtained

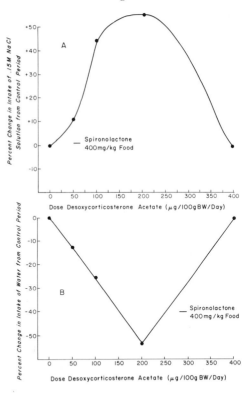

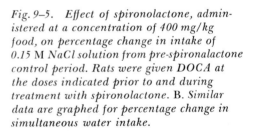

Fig. 9–5. Effect of spironolactone, administered at a concentration of 400 mg/kg food, on percentage change in intake of 0.15 M NaCl solution from pre-spironalactone control period. Rats were given DOCA at the doses indicated prior to and during treatment with spironolactone. B. Similar data are graphed for percentage change in simultaneous water intake.

by plotting the percentage change in intake of 0.15 M NaCl solution, induced by spironolactone, against the dose of DOCA administered simultaneously. The curve shows a maximum somewhere between 100 and 200 μg DOCA/100 g body weight/day. The shape of the curve obtained *during* simultaneous administration of graded doses of DOCA and 400 mg spironolactone/kg food can be explained on the basis of the fact that intake of NaCl solution (ml/100 g body weight/day) increased relative to controls at all doses of DOCA administered except at the highest dose. Administration of spironolactone tended to flatten the NaCl intake curve shown in Fig. 9–4. For this reason, the greatest percentage change in NaCl intake from the control level occurred at doses of DOCA ranging from 100 to 200 μg/100 g body weight/day. In contrast, the percentage change in water intake accompanying administration of spironolactone was V-shaped but otherwise corresponds to the curve for NaCl intake (Fig. 9–5, B).

Table 9–1 gives both mean intakes (ml or g/100 g body weight/day) and percentage changes in intakes of 0.15 M NaCl solution, water, and food for all groups during the period in which 400 mg spironolactone was mixed into each kilogram of food. There is a significant (P < 0.01) effect of treatment with 400 mg spironolactone/kg food on percentage change in intake of 0.15 M NaCl solution detectable by analysis of variance. The relationship between drug dose and percentage change in intake of 0.15 M NaCl solution can be expressed by a quadratic regression. Use of the pooled variance and "T" test reveals that only the 100 and 200 μg doses of DOCA differ significantly (P < 0.05) from control [36]. There is no significant effect of treatment on percentage change in either water or food intake. The amount of spironolactone ingested daily by the rats was calculated from their

food intake and was approximately 8 mg/100 g body weight.

Effect of Cortisone Acetate on Spontaneous NaCl Intake of Adrenalectomized Rats An objective of this experiment was to determine whether a glucocorticoid hormone, also produced by the adrenal cortex, would affect spontaneous NaCl intake in the same manner as observed for the mineralocorticoid hormones described above.

Fifteen male rats ranging in body weight from 280–350 g were used. They were adrenalectomized two weeks prior to the experiment and were divided randomly into five equal groups. The rats were caged individually and given a choice between tap water and 0.15 M NaCl solution to drink. Food was finely powdered Rockland Rat Diet. During a three-day control period, fluid and food intakes and body weights were measured daily. At the end of the control period, treatments were assigned randomly and included daily intraperitoneal injections of 0.2 ml saline, 50, 100, 500, or 1,000 μg cortisone acetate suspended in 0.2 ml saline. Treatments continued during the next three days after which the experiment was terminated. Intakes of NaCl solution, water, and food were measured daily during treatment. The mean percentage changes in intake of fluid and food from control to treatment periods were calculated for each rat and the data were clarified by analysis of variance.

Administration of cortisone acetate had no significant effect on intake of either 0.15 M NaCl solution or food but had a noticeable (P < 0.05) effect on water intake (Table 9–2). The relationship between dose of cortisone administered and water intake is not a linear one.

Effect of Antithyroid Drugs on Spontaneous NaCl Intake of Intact Rats During the early phases of studies with

TABLE 9–1: Effect of Dietary Administration of Spironolactone (400 mg/kg Food) on Spontaneous Intakes of 0.15 M NaCl Solution, Water, and Food by Adrenalectomized Rats Receiving Graded Dose Levels of Desoxycorticosterone Acetate

Daily Drug Dose	Number of Days Given Drug	Measurements Made	Control Period	Experimental Period	Percentage Mean Change from Control Period
			ml or g/100 g BW/Day		Period
Adrex + Oil	4	0.15 M NaCl Sol. Intake	13.9	11.9	−14.5
		Water Intake	2.4	3.8	+58.5
		Food Intake	6.8	6.5	− 4.9
		Δ Body Weight (g/4 days)			+ 3
Adrex + 50 μg DOCA/100 g BW	4	0.15 M NaCl Sol. Intake	8.9	8.5	− 4.4
		Water Intake	2.6	3.5	+35.7
		Food Intake	6.2	5.7	− 7.7
		Δ Body Weight (g/4 days)			+ 6
Adrex + 100 μg DOCA/100 g BW	4	0.15 M NaCl Sol. Intake	5.3	6.9	+30.0
		Water Intake	3.6	4.8	+32.9
		Food Intake	6.1	5.3	−12.3
		Δ Body Weight (g/4 days)			+ 5.0
Adrex + 200 μg DOCA/100 g BW	4	0.15 M NaCl Sol. Intake	6.3	8.9	+41.4
		Water Intake	3.3	3.5	+ 5.2
		Food Intake	5.8	5.7	− 1.8
		Δ Body Weight (g/4 days)			+ 2
Adrex + 400 μg DOCA/100 g BW	4	0.15 M NaCl Sol. Intake	9.4	8.0	−14.8
		Water Intake	2.4	3.8	+58.7
		Food Intake	5.9	5.8	− 1.3
		Δ Body Weight (g/4 days)			+ 2.0

Analysis of Variance (Mean Percentage Change)

Source	df	0.15 M NaCl Sol. MSS	F	P	Water MSS	F	P	Food MSS	F	P
Treatment	4	3,176.26	4.42	< 0.01	2,444.35	1.05	> 0.05	104.71	0.36	> 0.05
Linear	1	1,017.90	1.42	< 0.05						
Quadratic	1	7,381.05	10.27	< 0.01						
Error	20	718.86			2,323.88			287.36		
Total	24									

antithyroid drugs, it was observed that administration of propylthiouracil (PTU) to hypertensive rats abolished their characteristic spontaneous NaCl aversion [12]. Studies were then performed to determine whether normotensive rats treated with the antithyroid drugs, propylthiouracil, thiouracil, and methimazole, showed a spontaneous appetite for NaCl solution.

The studies were performed separately but were similar and will be described together. The rats were kept under the same conditions as described above for DOCA. The first study used ten rats, five of which had been given PTU (1.0 g/kg food) for eighteen weeks prior to the experiment. The second study also used ten rats, five of which had been given thiouracil (1.0 g/kg food) for eight weeks prior to the experiment while the third study used eight rats, four of which had been given methimazole (0.5 g/kg food) also for eight weeks prior to the experi-

TABLE 9–2: Effect of Cortisone Acetate on Spontaneous Intakes of 0.15 M NaCl Solution, Water, and Food by Adrenalectomized Rats

Daily Drug Dose	Number of Days Given Drug	Measurements Made	Control Period	Experimental Period	Percentage Mean Change from Pre-Drug Control Period
			ml or g/100 g BW/Day		
Adrex + Saline	3	0.15 M NaCl Sol. Intake	24.9	22.9	− 8.2
		Water Intake	2.1	2.9	+ 39.3
		Food Intake	8.4	8.8	+ 5.1
		Δ Body Weight (g/3 days)			+ 18
Adrex + 50 μg Cortisone	3	0.15 M NaCl Sol. Intake	19.4	16.8	− 13.5
		Water Intake	3.4	3.2	− 6.4
		Food Intake	8.4	8.0	− 4.6
		Δ Body Weight (g/3 days)			+ 12
Adrex + 100 μg Cortisone	3	0.15 M NaCl Sol. Intake	20.5	18.4	− 10.9
		Water Intake	1.8	4.3	+139.9
		Food Intake	8.0	8.5	+ 5.8
		Δ Body Weight (g/3 days)			+ 17
Adrex + 500 μg Cortisone	3	0.15 M NaCl Sol. Intake	12.0	8.0	− 33.5
		Water Intake	5.2	7.8	+ 49.8
		Food Intake	8.1	7.2	− 10.8
		Δ Body Weight (g/3 days)			+ 14
Adrex + 1000 μg Cortisone	3	0.15 M NaCl Sol. Intake	16.9	19.2	+ 13.3
		Water Intake	2.6	1.7	− 3.6
		Food Intake	7.8	8.1	+ 4.3
		Δ Body Weight (g/3 days)			+ 11

Analysis of Variance (Mean Percentage Change)

Source	df	0.15 M NaCl Sol. MSS	F	P	Water MSS	F	P	Food MSS	F	P
Treatment	4	836.04	2.54	> 0.05	10,543.91	3.55	< 0.05	93.79	0.08	> 0.05
Linear	1	159.16	0.48	> 0.05	262.28	0.08	> 0.05	104.90	0.90	> 0.05
Error	10	328.89			2,962.63			116.85		
Total	14									

ment. All rats were caged individually, given finely powdered Purina Laboratory Chow as food and a choice between distilled water and 0.15 M NaCl solution to drink. The rats given drugs prior to the experiment were maintained on them during the experiment. Intakes were measured daily for one week in the first experiment and two weeks in the second and third.

The combined results are shown in Table 9–3. Rats treated with antithyroid drugs had significantly greater NaCl intakes relative to body weight than did control rats. Water intakes were not affected significantly by drug treatment, but total intake (water plus NaCl solution) was significantly greater than that of the control rats. Food intakes of PTU-treated rats were significantly reduced from control level but food intakes of thiouracil- and methimazole-treated groups were not.

Effect of Administration of Thyroxine on Spontaneous Sodium Chloride Intake

TABLE 9–3: The Effect of Antithyroid Drugs on Spontaneous Fluid and Food Intakes of Rats

Treatment Group	Number of Rats	Mean Body Weight (g)	Intake (ml or g/100 g BW/Day)		
			Water	0.15 M NaCl Sol.	Food
Study 1					
Control	5	458	6.0 ± 1.5[a]	1.8 ± 0.4	4.4 ± 0.3
PTU-Treated	5	406	6.5 ± 0.6	8.7 ± 1.0[b]	3.0 ± 0.2[b]
Study 2					
Control	5	440	9.2 ± 0.8	2.6 ± 0.5	4.8 ± 0.1
Thiouracil-Treated	5	305	10.4 ± 0.6	6.8 ± 0.9[b]	4.6 ± 0.2
Study 3					
Control	4	515	5.1 ± 0.5	3.2 ± 0.5	3.7 ± 0.1
Methimazole-Treated	4	427	3.3 ± 0.5	9.2 ± 0.8[b]	3.8 ± 0.3

[a] One standard error of mean.
[b] Significantly different from control (P < 0.01).

of Propylthiouracil-Treated Rats This study was performed to determine whether administration of thyroxine to rats treated with PTU would depress their spontaneous NaCl appetite. Twenty-eight rats were used. They were divided into four equal groups. Three of the four groups were given PTU in the diet (1.0 g/kg food) for three weeks preceding the experiment. Thyroxine administration began three days prior to beginning daily measurement of water, 0.15 M NaCl solution and food intakes. Measurement was made for ten days. Two of the three PTU-treated groups were given thyroxine intraperitoneally daily. One group was given 7.5 μg/day while the second group received 15.0 μg/day. The third group of PTU-treated rats received a daily injection of the vehicle only.

The results are shown in Table 9–4. These studies show again that PTU treatment increases spontaneous NaCl intake and decreases food intake significantly (P < 0.05). Water intake was not changed. Administration of the lower dose of thyroxine returned intakes of NaCl solution and food to control level.

The higher dose of thyroxine had no further influence on NaCl intake but tended to increase water and food intake. Apparently the spontaneous NaCl appetite of propylthiouracil-treated rats is the result of a specific deficiency of thyroxine.

Effect of Propylthiouracil on Preference Threshold of Rats for NaCl Solutions The salt appetite of PTU-treated rats is reminiscent of that commonly observed in adrenalectomized rats by a number of investigators [1,30]. Since adrenalectomized rats are known to have a reduced preference ("taste") threshold for NaCl solutions [1,31], this experiment was carried out to determine whether preference threshold is also reduced in PTU-treated rats.

Six control and six PTU-treated rats were used. The PTU-treated rats received the drug in finely powdered Rockland Rat Diet (1.0 g/kg food) for eight weeks prior to the experiment and were continued on the drug during the experiment. During the first two weeks of the experiment, both bottles contained distilled water. Intakes were measured

TABLE 9–4: Effect of Thyroxine Administration on Spontaneous Sodium Chloride Intake of Propylthiouracil-Treated Rats

| | | Initial Mean Body Weight (g) | Final Mean Body Weight (g) | Intake (ml or g/100 g BW/Day) | | |
| | | | | Water | 0.15 M NaCl Solution | Food |
Group	Number of Rats					
Control	7	393	418	7.7 ± 0.6^a	5.3 ± 1.3	5.9 ± 0.2
PTU-Treated (0.1% in diet)	7	320	303	8.3 ± 1.3	8.9 ± 1.2^b	4.3 ± 0.1^b
PTU-Treated +7.5 µg Thyroxine	7	353	372	7.2 ± 0.3	5.0 ± 1.2	5.4 ± 0.2
PTU-Treated +15.0 µg Thyroxine	7	352	370	9.1 ± 0.4	5.2 ± 1.7	5.8 ± 0.2

[a] Plus or minus 1 standard error of mean.
[b] Significantly different from controls ($P < 0.05$).

daily to ascertain that each rat drank roughly equal amounts of water from each bottle. Positions of the bottles on each cage were changed daily to avoid habit formation in the selection of drinking fluid. During this period, about 20 per cent of the rats were rejected as position drinkers and were replaced by other rats. At the end of the two-week period, two-day test periods were begun. During the first period, each rat was offered a choice between distilled water (bottle A) and 0.0001 M NaCl solution (bottle B). All NaCl solutions used were made from a concentrated stock NaCl solution by serial dilution. Each dilution was checked for accuracy by determination of chloride concentration. During subsequent two-day periods, each rat was given a choice between distilled water and the following molar NaCl solutions in chronological sequence: 0.0003, 0.0004, 0.0008, 0.001, 0.010, 0.020, 0.050, 0.100, 0.150, and 0.300. Daily intakes of water and NaCl solution were measured and expressed as ml/100 g body weight/day to correct for differences in body weight.

The criterion of preference threshold used was the same as that used by Richter [31], namely, the concentration of NaCl solution at and above which simultaneous volumes taken from the test bottle exceeded that from the reference (water) bottle and differed significantly from it ($P < 0.05$). Statistical comparison of the results obtained from the two groups was made by the "T" test [36].

Figure 9–6, A shows simultaneous intakes of distilled water and NaCl solution for control rats. When both bottles contained distilled water, total fluid intake was 7.9 ml/100 g body weight/day. As concentration of NaCl increased in bottle B, control rats gave the first indication of preference for it at 0.01 M but differences between simultaneous intakes of water and NaCl solution were not significant until 0.050 M was given. Differences between intakes of water and NaCl solution remained significant thereafter. In the range of concentrations between 0.150 M and 0.300 M, NaCl solution was rejected in favor of water offered simultaneously.

When both bottles contained distilled water, total fluid intake of PTU-treated rats was 10.6 ml/100 g body weight/ day (Fig. 9–6, B). The increased total fluid intake of PTU-treated rats has been described [11]. The first apparent differ-

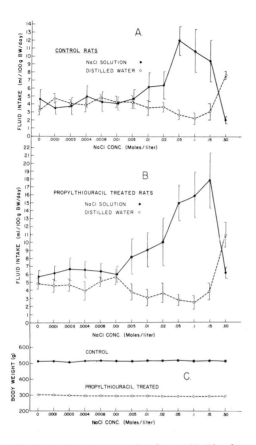

Fig. 9–6. Spontaneous intakes of NaCl solution (●) and distilled water (○) are shown for control rats (A) and propylthiouracil-treated rats (B). Body weight of each group is shown in C. Means ± 1 standard error are shown.

of NaCl solution by PTU-treated rats is readily apparent by comparison with intakes of control rats in panel A. Control rats ingested maximal amounts of NaCl solution when the concentration was 0.05–0.10 M while PTU-treated rats ingested maximal amounts of NaCl solution when the concentration was 0.15 M.

Although all rats were the same age initially, mean body weight of PTU-treated rats was less than that of the control rats (Fig. 9–6, C). The growth-depressing effect of PTU is well known. Changes in the concentration of NaCl solution had little effect on mean body weight of either group.

Effect of Administration of Propylthiouracil on Sodium and Potassium Loss by Rats on a Diet Deficient in Sodium and Potassium The similarities between adrenalectomized and PTU-treated rats with respect to spontaneous NaCl appetite and preference threshold for NaCl solution are so striking that this study was designed to assess the ability of the PTU-treated rat to retain sodium under conditions of dietary sodium deprivation. Adrenalectomized rats are unable to retain sodium because of lack of the mineral-retaining hormone, aldosterone, and die within seven to fifteen days under these conditions [7,34].

Ten rats were used in this study, five of which received PTU in their diets for thirteen weeks prior to the experiment. The remaining five were untreated control rats. During a four-day control period, both groups of rats received a synthetic sodium deficient diet (obtained from Nutritional Biochemicals Corp.) into which 20 g NaCl was mixed per kilogram of food. This amount of NaCl was used to ensure that the PTU-treated rats would be able to maintain a sodium balance. During three days following the control period, both PTU-treated and control rats were given the same syn-

ence between simultaneous intakes of distilled water and NaCl solution occurred when 0.005 M was given. However, the difference was not significant (P > 0.05). When a choice was offered between 0.010 M NaCl solution and water, the difference between intakes was significant (P < 0.05). Differences between the two fluid intakes were significant thereafter (P < 0.01) for all concentrations of NaCl solution offered. When 0.30 M NaCl solution was offered, the PTU-treated rats preferred water to the salt solution. The exaggerated intake

thetic diet but one deficient in both sodium and potassium. The diet was analyzed by flame photometry for sodium and potassium content and was found to be virtually free of both. During the period of sodium and potassium deficiency, individual intakes of food and fluid were measured daily, as were urinary volume, fecal output, and body weight. Both urine and feces were analyzed for sodium and potassium content by flame photometry.

During the three-day period in which the diet was deficient in both sodium and potassium, the PTU-treated rats excreted significantly more (P < 0.01) sodium than did the control rats (Table 9–5). The fecal sodium to total sodium

aged 0.21 while the Na/K ratio of the PTU-treated rats averaged 2.09 (P < 0.01). The high urinary Na/K ratio of PTU-treated rats observed under these conditions is characteristically observed in animals with an adrenocortical deficiency of aldosterone.

Secretion of Aldosterone by Adrenal Glands of Propylthiouracil-Treated Rats Since PTU-treated rats have both a spontaneous appetite and a reduced preference threshold for NaCl solution, as well as an inability to conserve sodium during dietary sodium deprivation, it appeared likely that these animals were unable to secrete the mineral-retaining hormone, aldosterone, at a normal rate.

TABLE 9–5: Effect of Propylthiouracil on Sodium and Potassium Loss of Rats on a Diet Deficient in Sodium and Potassium[a]

Group	Number of Rats	Initial Body Weight (g)	Final Body Weight (g)	Total Na Output (mEq/3 days)	*Fecal Na* (%) Total Na	Total K Output (mEq/3 days)	*Fecal K* (%) Total K	Urinary Na/K Ratio
Control	5	462	463	0.88 ± 0.07[b]	16 ± 2	1.05 ± 0.05	9 ± 1	0.21 ± 0.08
PTU-Treated	5	329	322	1.63 ± 0.22[c]	3 ± 1[c]	0.70 ± 0.06[c]	11 ± 1	2.09 ± 0.23[c]

[a] Rats on deficient diet for three days.
[b] Plus or minus the standard error of mean.
[c] Significantly different from controls (P < 0.01).

ratio was significantly lower for the PTU-treated rats than for the control rats. Apparently the major route for sodium excretion in the PTU-treated rat was the urinary one. The total potassium output during the period of dietary sodium and potassium deficiency was significantly less (P < 0.01) for the PTU-treated rats than for the control rats. The ratio of fecal potassium to total potassium was similar for the two groups. The control rats gained an average of 1 g in weight during the three days on the deficiency diet while the PTU-treated rats lost 7 g. The urinary Na/K ratio of the control rats for the last day of the three-day deficiency period aver-

This experiment was carried out to determine the rate of secretion of aldosterone by the adrenal glands of PTU-treated rats [13].

Twelve male euthyroid rats weighing from 425 to 500 g and twenty-seven PTU-treated rats of the same age and strain weighing from 160 to 200 g were used to test the effect of administration of PTU, with and without thyroxine, on rate of secretion of aldosterone by the adrenal gland. The PTU-treated groups had been given the drug at a dose of 1.0 g/kg food for twenty weeks prior to the experiment in finely powdered Rockland Rat Diet. During two weeks prior to the experiment, three groups of PTU-treated rats (five rats per group) received daily injections of crystalline L-thyroxine i.p. at doses of 6.7, 13.4, and 26.8 μg/100 g body weight. PTU-treated, control rats were injected with the vehicle in which thyroxine was dissolved.

On the day of the experiment each rat was anesthetized with ether and given 50 USP units of sodium heparin intravenously. The left adrenal vein was then cannulated with a twenty gauge needle, which stretches the adrenal vein and thereby prevents leakage from occurring around the needle. The needle was positioned so that it lay within 0.5 mm of the adrenal gland. This allowed collection of only adrenal venous blood. The time required for collection of 1.0 ml of blood was measured by stopwatch in order to calculate adrenal blood flow. The double isotope, dilution derivative procedure of Peterson [27], as modified by Cade and Perenich [6], was used to assay aldosterone concentration in the adrenal blood samples.

The results are given in Table 9–6. Difficulties arising from cannulation of the adrenal vein required elimination of one PTU-treated rat given 6.7 μg thyroxine. The containers of adrenal blood samples from two other rats (one PTU-treated control rat and one PTU-treated rat given 13.4 μg thyroxine) were inadvertently broken. Analysis of the results of the first experiment indicates that both adrenal blood flow and aldosterone secretion rate, calculated either as mμg/minute/adrenal/100 g body weight or as mμg/minute/adrenal, are reduced significantly by treatment with PTU. A significant ($P < 0.05$) linear regression exists between dose of thyroxine administered and either aldosterone secretion rate or adrenal blood flow. Graphic analysis of the data for aldosterone secretion rate suggests that 8.0 μg thyroxine/100 g body weight/day returns secretion rate (mμg/minute/adrenal/100 g body weight) to that of euthyroid control rats while 10.2 μg thyroxine/100 g body

TABLE 9–6: Effect of PTU plus Thyroxine on Rate of Secretion of Aldosterone by the Adrenal Gland

Treatment	Number of Rats	Aldosterone Secretion Rate		Adrenal Blood Flow (ml/min)
		mμg/min/ Adrenal	mμg/min/ Adrenal/100 g BW	
Control	12	17.8	3.4	0.35
PTU-Treated	11	5.6	2.5	0.12
PTU-Treated + 6.7 μg T₄/100 g Body Wt.	4	9.3	2.8	0.24
PTU-Treated + 13.4 μg T₄/100 g Body Wt.	4	19.4	5.8	0.30
PTU-Treated + 26.8 μg T₄/100 g Body Wt.	5	23.7	6.1	0.31
Pᵃ (Treatment)		<0.005	<0.01	<0.005
P (Control vs. PTU)		<0.005	<0.05	<0.005
P (Linearity)		<0.005	<0.005	<0.05

ᵃProbability value, analysis of variance.

weight/day is required if secretion rate is not based on body weight.

Effect of Desoxycorticosterone Acetate on Spontaneous NaCl Intake of PTU-Treated Rats Since PTU-treated rats may now be considered to be not only hypothyroid but also hypoadrenal with respect to aldosterone secretion, it seemed appropriate that the effect of DOCA on spontaneous NaCl appetite be tested. Therefore, this experiment was performed to determine the dose-response relationship between dose of DOCA administered and spontaneous intake of 0.15 M NaCl solution.

Twenty-four rats weighing initially from 190 to 224 g were used. The rats received PTU at a concentration of 1.0 g/kg food for eight weeks prior to the experiment. They were caged individually and given a choice between distilled water and 0.15 M NaCl solution to drink for four days prior to the experiment. Treatments were then assigned at random. The six treatment groups (four rats per group) were as follows: 50, 100, 200, 500, and 1,000 μg DOCA per day for five days. The steroid was given in 0.2 ml peanut oil subcutaneously, and the control rats were given peanut oil only. Daily measurements of water, 0.15 M NaCl solution, food, and body weight were made for an additional five days.

Figure 9–7 shows the relationship between logarithm of the dose of DOCA administered and both mean percentage change in NaCl intake (Fig. 9–7, *A*) and mean percentage change in water intake (Fig. 9–7, *B*) from the control group. The percentage change in NaCl intake was minimal when 180–200 μg DOCA/day (approximately 70–100 μg/100 g body weight/day) were administered. Either higher or lower doses increased the percentage change in NaCl intake. The mean percentage change in water intake from the control group is the approxi-

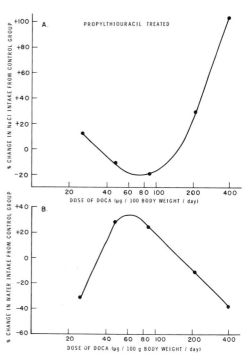

Fig. 9–7. A. *Relationship between mean percentage change in intake of 0.15* M *NaCl solution from the control group and the logarithm of the dose of DOCA administered to propylthiouracil-treated rats.* B. *Similar data are graphed for percentage change in simultaneous water intake.*

mate mirror image of NaCl intake. Apparently, 180–200 μg DOCA/day both reduces NaCl intake and increases water intake maximally.

Effect of Corticosterone Acetate on Spontaneous NaCl Intake of Propylthiouracil-Treated Rats To study further the specificity of the mineralocorticoid effect on spontaneous NaCl intake of propylthiouracil-treated rats, the naturally occurring glucocorticoid secreted by the rat adrenal cortex, corticosterone, was administered as the ester acetate. The objective was to determine whether corticosterone acetate would induce the dose-response curve typical of DOCA as described above.

Twenty-four rats weighing from 280

to 320 g were used. They were maintained in individual cages and given a choice between 0.15 M NaCl solution and distilled water to drink, as described above. The rats received PTU in food at a concentration of 1.0 g/kg for six weeks prior to the experiment. The animals were divided randomly into four groups with six rats per group. During a four-day control period, daily intakes of water, 0.15 M NaCl solution, and food were measured. Body weight was also measured daily. At the end of the control period, the rats of Group One received 0.2 ml peanut oil subcutaneously daily for the next four days while the rats of Groups Two, Three, and Four received respectively 64, 128, and 256 μg corticosterone in 0.2 ml peanut oil sub-

cutaneously daily. Measurement of intake and body weight continued during the experimental period. The percentage change in intakes from the control period was calculated by analysis of variance (Table 9–7).

Corticosterone acetate had no significant effect on percentage change in intakes of either NaCl solution, water, or food as compared to the control period.

The results of these studies, viewed as a whole, strongly suggest that rats regulate their spontaneous NaCl intake and that intake is regulated by blood level of mineralocorticoid hormone. Experimental evidence for this statement has been presented above and will be summarized here.

A U- or V-shaped dose-response rela-

TABLE 9–7: Effect of Corticosterone Acetate on Percentage Changes in Spontaneous Intakes of 0.15 M NaCl Solution, Water, and Food by Propylthiouracil-Treated Rats

Daily Drug Dose	Number of Days Given Drug	Measurements Made	Percentage Mean Change from Control Period
PTU + OIL	4	0.15 M NaCl Sol. Intake	+24.0
		Water Intake	− 6.7
		Food Intake	− 4.6
		Δ Body Weight (g/4 days)	+ 1.0
PTU + 64 μg Corticosterone Acetate	4	0.15 M NaCl Sol. Intake	+18.6
		Water Intake	−36.3
		Food Intake	− 8.0
		Δ Body Weight (g/4 days)	+ 3
PTU + 128 μg Corticosterone Acetate	4	0.15 M NaCl Sol. Intake	+66.9
		Water Intake	−18.6
		Food Intake	− 1.7
		Δ Body Weight (g/4 days)	+ 4.0
PTU + 256 μg Corticosterone Acetate	4	0.15 M NaCl Sol. Intake	+14.8
		Water Intake	− 6.4
		Food Intake	− 5.6
		Δ Body Weight (g/4 days)	+ 1.0

Analysis of Variance (Mean Percentage Change)

| Source | df | 0.15 M NaCl Sol. | | | Water | | | Food | | |
		MSS	F	P	MSS	F	P	MSS	F	P
Treatment	3	3,513.38	1.89	> 0.05	1,191.06	0.84	> 0.05	43.40	0.39	> 0.05
Error	20	1,859.40			1,409.16			110.06		
Total	23									

tionship exists between intake of NaCl solution and dose of mineralocorticoid hormone administered to either adrenalectomized or PTU-treated rats (Figs. 9–1, 9–2, and 9–4). This relationship is of interest from several points of view. In the case of DOCA, the greatest reduction in intake of NaCl solution occurred when approximately 100 μg/100 g body weight/day was administered to either adrenalectomized or PTU-treated rats. In the case of aldosterone, approximately 11 μg/100 g body weight/day, administered to adrenalectomized rats, reduced NaCl intake maximally. Doses greater than these returned percentage change in NaCl intake toward that of the untreated control rats. An interesting aspect of this dose-response relationship is that the daily dose of aldosterone producing maximal reduction in NaCl intake (11.0 μg/100 g body weight/day) is very similar to the rate of aldosterone secretion in normal rats measured experimentally and shown in Table 9–6 (9.8 μg/2 adrenals/100 g body weight/day). Indeed, experiments similar to these, but using intact rats, show that the dose-response curve begins near the bottom and contains only an ascending limb [41]. Under normal conditions the homeostatic mechanisms of the rat appear to regulate intake of 0.15 M NaCl solution near its lowest level. Thus, either an increase or a decrease in blood level of mineralocorticoid from the normal would be expected to increase intake of NaCl solution. Adrenalectomy, with its abrupt cessation of aldosterone secretion, increases NaCl intake. This movement up the *descending* limb of the curve has survival value. Similarly, increased secretion of aldosterone induced by sodium deficiency also increases NaCl intake. Thus, Cade and Perenich [6] reported that maintenance of normal rats on a sodium deficient diet for one week increased the aldosterone secretion rate

from 9.8 to 25.1 μg/100 g body weight per day. This is higher than the highest dose administered to the adrenalectomized rats shown in Fig. 9–2. The possibility exists that movement up the *ascending* limb of the curve as a result of a continued, unremitting hypersecretion of aldosterone may have pathological consequences. Administration of excess DOCA to rats given only NaCl solution to drink has been for many years a standard laboratory procedure for production of cardiovascular hypertension [38].

The shape of the dose-response curve also provides an answer to the dilemma posed at the beginning of these studies, viz., why does the same dose of DOCA reduce NaCl intake of adrenalectomized rats while increasing NaCl intake of intact rats? The same dose of DOCA could conceivably bring the adrenalectomized rat down the descending limb of the curve to the vicinity of the lowest point on the curve, thereby reducing NaCl intake. Since the NaCl intake of the normal rat is regulated near the bottom of the curve, administration of the same dose of DOCA would be expected to move this rat up the ascending limb of the curve and to increase NaCl intake. Thus, for the first time, an explanation is possible for the disparate reports of the effects of DOCA on spontaneous NaCl intake of normal and adrenalectomized rats.

The specificity of the salt intake response to mineralocorticoids was tested by administration of other hormones. It appears at present that only those hormones with mineralocorticoid-like activity influence the spontaneous NaCl intake of adrenalectomized rats. Graded doses of cortisone acetate (Table 9–2), testosterone propionate [17], estrone [17], and thyroxine [18] were tested and shown to be without effect. Furthermore, spironolactone, the mineralocorticoid antagonist [21,37], blocked the effect of simultaneous administration of DOCA on NaCl intake. This is considered to be a further suggestion that the mineralocorticoid effect on NaCl intake is specific.

A similar specificity of the salt intake response to mineralocorticoids also appears to exist for PTU-treated rats. Administration of either corticosterone acetate (Table 9-7) or estrone [19], in graded doses, failed to produce significant effects on the NaCl intake of PTU-treated rats.

The fact that the NaCl appetite of the PTU-treated rat is associated with an aldosterone secretion rate approximately one-third that of normal rats is striking. Also striking is the fact that administration of thyroxine to PTU-treated rats increased aldosterone secretion rate and also reduced NaCl intake. When thyroxine was administered to adrenalectomized rats, no significant effect on NaCl intake was observed [18]. Thus, the reduction in NaCl intake of PTU-treated rats cannot be attributed to thyroxine administration per se. The results strongly suggest a relationship between NaCl intake and aldosterone secretion rate.

The mechanism by which intake of NaCl solution is affected by mineralocorticoids may be related to changes in either salivary sodium concentration or the concentration ratio of sodium to potassium. Blair-West et al. [3] showed that graded increases in rate of infusion of aldosterone into sheep reduced the Na/K ratio of saliva in a graded fashion whereas the glucocorticoids, cortisol and corticosterone, were without effect in physiological doses. In addition, several investigators report a reduction of salivary Na/K concentration ratio in patients treated with mineralocorticoids [23,9]. McBurney and Pfaffmann [26] and Bartoshuk et al. [2] recently showed

that adaptation of the human tongue to certain concentrations of NaCl solutions resulted in either a salty or sweet taste of test concentrations of NaCl solution above the adaptation concentration and sour or bitter tastes of test concentrations below that of the adaptation concentration. Tests using the adaptation concentration showed it to be tasteless. Thus, the tastes of both water and NaCl solution are specific and apparently depend on the concentration of sodium in the saliva bathing the taste receptors.

After adaptation of the tongue for 15 minutes to a certain concentration of NaCl solution, subjective estimation of the taste intensity of test NaCl concentrations higher and lower than the adapting concentration yielded a V-shaped curve relating concentration to the logarithm of taste intensity when taste modality was disregarded [25]. The lowest intensity of taste, or the apex of the curve, was at the concentration of NaCl to which the tongue was adapted. A family of curves was found, one for each concentration of the adapting solution, the minimal intensity of which was always at the adapting concentration. The possibility that the V-shaped curves of humans and those of rats are related was intriguing and suggested that the common denominator for "taste" of NaCl in both humans and rats is either the concentration of sodium bathing taste receptors or the ratio of the concentrations of sodium and potassium in saliva. In the case of the humans described by McBurney [25] and McBurney and Pfaffmann [26], alterations in salt taste were accomplished by bathing the tongue with NaCl solutions of varying concentration. In the experiments described here, the blood level of mineralocorticoid altered the sodium and potassium concentrations of saliva by its effect on salivary secretion of these ions and thereby produced a condition similar to bathing the tongue with a salt solution. In spite of this rationalization, it is recognized that the V-shaped curve observed here applies to hormone-treated rats given a choice between water and only one concentration of NaCl solution, viz., 0.15 M. This contrasts with the wide range of NaCl concentrations used by McBurney [25]. However, if certain assumptions are made, the V- or U-shaped curve of the adrenalectomized or PTU-treated rats can be derived from McBurney's [25] family of curves. If it is assumed (1) that the intensity of "taste" in humans, as given by McBurney, can be equated to the volume of NaCl solution ingested each day by rats, and (2) that compounds containing mineralocorticoid activity, e.g., DOCA, bear an inverse linear relationship to salivary sodium concentration in rats [3], then by drawing a vertical line at the 0.15 M concentration on the family of curves in Fig. 9–8, A, the intersections with the family of curves will form a U-shaped dose-response curve (Fig. 9–8, B). It is also assumed in this figure that each dose of DOCA is represented by one curve since each dose of DOCA would be expected to change the salivary sodium concentration to a new and constant level thereby adapting the taste receptors to that concentration. The shape of the family of curves shown in Fig. 9–8, A has been idealized but is based on the curves described originally by McBurney. If the rats in the studies described earlier had been given either very high or very low concentrations of NaCl solution instead of the 0.15 M con-

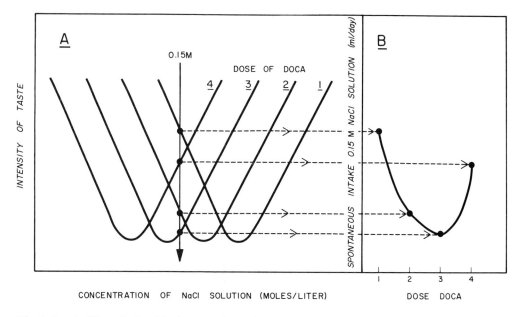

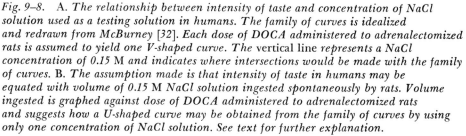

Fig. 9–8. A. *The relationship between intensity of taste and concentration of NaCl solution used as a testing solution in humans. The family of curves is idealized and redrawn from McBurney [32]. Each dose of DOCA administered to adrenalectomized rats is assumed to yield one V-shaped curve. The vertical line represents a NaCl concentration of 0.15 M and indicates where intersections would be made with the family of curves.* B. *The assumption made is that intensity of taste in humans may be equated with volume of 0.15 M NaCl solution ingested spontaneously by rats. Volume ingested is graphed against dose of DOCA administered to adrenalectomized rats and suggests how a U-shaped curve may be obtained from the family of curves by using only one concentration of NaCl solution. See text for further explanation.*

centration used, the curves predict that a U- or V-shaped dose-response curve would *not* result when volume of NaCl solution ingested daily is plotted against dose of DOCA administered. Studies have recently been performed in rats that indicate that this is the case for very low concentrations of NaCl solutions (unpublished observations). Thus, the results are strongly suggestive that the human and the rat are similar with respect to the effect of change in sodium concentration of saliva on taste and preference, respectively, for NaCl solutions.

Other factors undoubtedly affect the preference of the rat for NaCl solution. Some of these are shown in Fig. 9–9. A

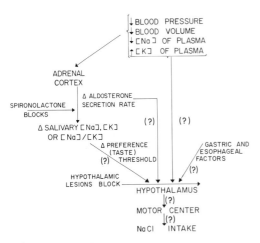

Fig. 9–9. A schema is presented to suggest interactions that may be important in initiating the spontaneous NaCl intake of the rat. See text for further explanation.

decrease in blood pressure or blood volume, a decrease in plasma sodium concentration or an increase in plasma potassium concentration probably stimulates the adrenal cortex of the rat to increase its rate of secretion of aldosterone by way of the renin-angiotensin system [4,6,8,13]. The increase in sodium intake by either normal rats or sheep made sodium deficient is well documented [4,15]. It is assumed that the increase in

aldosterone secretion occurring under these conditions affects spontaneous NaCl intake by altering salivary concentrations of sodium, potassium, or the ratio of the two. Aldosterone may act directly on the hypothalamus to initiate NaCl intake. Although evidence is lacking, it is also possible that those factors initiating an increase in aldosterone secretion rate may affect the hypothalamus directly. It is postulated that alteration in salivary ionic composition alters the preference or "taste" threshold for NaCl. At least three procedures initiating an increased spontaneous NaCl intake, viz., adrenalectomy, hypothyroidism, and administration of large doses of DOCA to normal rats, are known to be accompanied by a reduced preference threshold for NaCl solution [1,16,20,31]. These data suggest at least that there may be an inverted V-shaped dose-response relationship between preference threshold and blood level of mineralocorticoid, with normal rats positioned near the apex of the curve. Whether the change in threshold is transmitted to the hypothalamus, in terms of a change in impulse traffic in the nerves mediating taste, is unknown. The suggestion must be tempered by the fact that abolition of an estimated 85 to 90 per cent of the total gustatory afferent input by peripheral nerve section alters very little the normal preference of rats for NaCl solution [28,32]. Hypothalamic lesions are reported to block the spontaneous NaCl appetite of adrenalectomized rats and to prevent the increased NaCl intake attendant upon either administration of large doses of DOCA or intraperitoneal dialysis against isotonic glucose solution [22,40]. As with thirst, a factor must be postulated to turn off sodium ingestion as well as to turn it on. From studies recently performed to determine the ability of rats to regulate their sodium intake [15], it is suggested that this factor resides in the mouth, pharynx, and esophagus or possibly in the stomach.

The schema presented here must be considered only tentative. It is hoped that it will serve as a guide to others to prove or disprove it and thereby add to our understanding of the regulation of sodium intake.

SUMMARY

Both adrenalectomized and hypothyroid (propylthiouracil-treated) rats manifest a spontaneous salt appetite when given a choice between water and 0.15 M NaCl solution to drink. The appetites are relatively specific for sodium solutions, and preference (taste) thresholds for NaCl are reduced. In addition to these similarities, both groups of rats are unable to conserve sodium during dietary sodium deprivation and die (50 per cent) within seven and twenty-one days respectively. The mineralocorticoid hormone secreted by the adrenal cortex, aldosterone, is absent in the adrenalectomized rats and reduced in the hypothyroid rats. When graded doses of aldosterone and other homones containing mineralocorticoid activity were administered to either adrenalectomized or hypothyroid rats also given a choice between water and 0.15 M NaCl solution to drink, a V-shaped dose-response relationship was observed between the logarithm of the dose and intake of NaCl solution. The dose of desoxycorticosterone acetate (DOCA) that induced the greatest reduction of NaCl intake was 100–120 $\mu g/100\ g$ body weight/day in the adrenalectomized rats and 85–100 $\mu g/100\ g$ body weight/day in the hypothyroid rats. In the case of aldosterone, it was 8–11 $\mu g/100\ g$ body weight/day for adrenalectomized rats. Doses of the hormones greater than these returned NaCl intake toward that of the untreated control rats. The simultaneous water intake tended generally to be the mirror image of NaCl intake. The effect of graded doses of mineralocorticoids on spontaneous NaCl intake appeared to be relatively specific in that graded doses of other hormones, including cortisone acetate, estrone, or testosterone proprionate, were without effect. As an additional test of specificity of the mineralocorticoid effect on salt intake, it was shown that administration of the mineralocorticoid blocker, spironolactone, prevented the effect of DOCA on spontaneous NaCl intake of adrenalectomized rats. The results suggest that the blood level of mineralocorticoid influences spontaneous intake of NaCl solution in the rat. The physiological significance of the V-shaped curve may be that normal rats regulate NaCl intake near the apex; i.e., either a reduction or an increase in aldosterone secretion rate increases NaCl intake. The increase in NaCl intake resulting in decreased aldosterone secretion rate has survival value whereas the increase in NaCl intake resulting in increased aldosterone secretion rate may have pathological consequences. Some physiological mechanisms that may interact to produce the ultimate behavioral change initiating NaCl intake have been described.

Discussion

Epstein: I would like to challenge the conception of sodium intake as a regulated intake. This implies that a constancy is maintained that in some way represents the animal's need for the electrolyte. The literature on sodium intake in rats shows that intake is not constant and that they consume more than they need. The rats are offered the saline solutions while eating a diet that is replete with sodium. The major determinant of the volume intake of a sodium chloride solution is its concentration, and as the concentration varies, intake varies, with no indication of constancy either of volume or of gram intake of salt (Weiner and Stellar, *J. Comp. Physiol. Psychol.*, 44: 394, 1951). There is no doubt that changes in the animal's hormonal and electrolyte status will influence its volume intake, but this is not the same as a situation in which intake is held constant, as in the ingestion of other nutrients. I believe in sodium appetite, but I don't see any reason to think of the intake as regulated.

Fregly: Whether a rat ingests more sodium chloride than it "needs" is a point that cannot be resolved until one can define "need" for each experimental situation. We showed (*Am. J. Physiol.*, 209: 287, 1965) that intake of sodium by way of sodium chloride solution was maintained at a relatively constant level when we allowed rats to choose between a NaCl solution (either 0.15, 0.20, or 0.25 M) and water to drink. Rats detect NaCl in food very poorly and "regulation," if it occurs, depends on detection of NaCl in solution. The mechanism regulating NaCl intake was separate from that regulating water intake and was located somewhere within either the mouth or the pharyngeal region, or both. Our view of the problem is similar to Adolph's original approach to the problem of thirst, viz., that water intake appears to be closely related to water deficit in a number of animal species. We have made rats sodium deficient by giving them a sodium-deficient diet and distilled water for varying periods of time. We measured excretion of sodium in urine and feces during the deficiency period. At the end of this period we allowed the rats to choose between distilled water and NaCl solution to drink. Not only did the rats choose the NaCl solution in preference to water, as one would predict from the U-shaped curve I presented, but the amount of NaCl ingested was directly related to prior sodium deficit. Furthermore, Denton and

Sabine (*J. Physiol.*, 157: 97, 1961) have performed a similar experiment using sheep with a unilateral parotid fistula, which results in continuous loss of alkaline saliva. When these animals were made sodium deficient for twenty-three hours and then allowed a choice between water and $NaHCO_3$ solution for only one hour, roughly 50 per cent of the sodium deficit was ingested in the first five minutes. The animals generally returned to sodium balance by the end of the hour. These results certainly suggest a regulation to me.

Epstein: Did you vary the concentration?

Fregly: Not in the last study I mentioned. We gave all rats a choice between 0.15 M NaCl solution and water after the period of deficiency.

Epstein: You made a very poor choice of concentration for the regulation question. Isotonic solutions are very close to the peak of the sodium chloride preference-aversion curve. My prediction is that if you had moved away in either direction from that concentration, the rats' intake would have declined.

Brobeck: It seems to me that Epstein has said oxygen intake is not constant. But the amount of oxygen available to the tissue does not vary because there are other things in the body that adjust this. As long as there is a controlled output at the other end, the animal doesn't really have to control intake. Energy balance turns around the other way. There is very little control of energy output, so if there is to be an energy balance, it will have to be controlled by way of energy intake.

Epstein: Thank you for rescuing me from the complexities of my thinking.

Fregly: Are you saying, Brobeck, that

there is no regulation of water intake because antidiuretic hormone regulates output?

Brobeck: We will probably argue as to what the term "regulation" means, as Epstein was using it. You can talk about the regulation of the salt content of the body or the salt concentration of the body fluids, but we ought to know if there is a constancy of intake of salt.

Lát: Regarding your recent publication, in which you reported that thyroidectomy resulted in an increased salt intake, for how long a period did you increase salt intake? Some experiments that we have done show the opposite of what we had expected. When studying the interactions between carbohydrates and salt appetite, we have seen that a diet increased in carbohydrate intake is followed by an increase in salt intake. It has been shown that thyroxine increases carbohydrate intake; therefore, after thyroidectomy, a decrease in carbohydrate intake, and then a decrease in salt intake, occurs. Maybe the difference lies in the time period of your observation.

Fregly: We find that administration of antithyroid compounds to rats given a choice between water and NaCl solution to drink is accompanied by an increase in NaCl intake within two weeks (*Endocrinology,* **69**: 1060, 1961). We have maintained rats on the drug for as long as thirty weeks and the appetite persists. We have not altered dietary composition to determine its effect on NaCl intake. I believe that the salt appetite of the hypothyroid rat is related to the fact that aldosterone secretion rate is reduced to approximately one-third that of normal rats (*Endocrinology,* **77**: 777, 1965). Administration of graded doses of thyroxine to the hypothyroid rats progressively reduced NaCl intake and progressively increased aldosterone secretion rate.

Epstein: There is no question that there is a sodium appetite that may be exaggerated by sodium deficiency. The question is whether or not there is a regulation of the intake of sodium.

Henkin: It is difficult and dangerous to equate the rat and man. Among patients with untreated Addison's disease only 15–20 per cent crave salt. The apochryphal story of the patient who presents himself at the hospital with a block of salt in his arms, thereby establishing the diagnosis of adrenal cortical insufficiency, may have just such a condition. There are significant procedural and physiological differences between detection, recognition, and preference thresholds. In the rat, you have used preference thresholds for your physiological response, but this preferential type of response is not uniformly present in patients with adrenal cortical insufficiency.

Fregly: I am sorry if I implied I was equating the two.

Henkin: Denton's studies (*Physiol. Rev.,* **45**: 245, 1965) with sheep offer information about this problem from another viewpoint. These sheep possess parotid gland fistulas and, therefore, lose a significant amount of salt and water through them. They are presented with a choice of various concentrations of salt-water solutions to drink. Initially they make their choice of solution by smell. This is particularly impressive in the motion pictures Denton has prepared. After making their preference by olfaction, they drink a specific amount of the chosen salt-water solution, which essentially replaces the amount of salt lost through the fistula. They will take in this amount of salt regardless of the concentration of salt in the prepared solution. However, if an esophageal fistula is made in addition to the parotid gland fistula, the salt water solution imbibed can be made to run out into a pail rather than proceed into the gut. Nevertheless, these sheep will continue to replace the amount of salt they have lost through their parotid fistulas. This significant phenomenon has not been adequately explained.

Fregly: I agree. Another interesting thing about Denton's studies is that he has been able to show that intake of sodium is constant, whether or not he alters the concentration presented to his animals. This again is suggestive of something that may be called regulation.

Henkin: One answer to the apparent quandry is that the multiplier for maintaining salt and water balance is in the brain; once the signals are carried out, there is significant drive reduction.

REFERENCES

1. Bare, J. K. The specific hunger for sodium chloride in normal and adrenalectomized white rats. *J. Comp. Physiol. Psychol.,* 42: 242–53, 1949.
2. Bartoshuk, L. M., McBurney, D. H., and Pfaffmann, C. Taste of sodium chloride after adaptation to sodium chloride: implications for the "water taste." *Science,* 143: 967–68, 1964.
3. Blair-West, J. R., Coghlan, J. P., Denton, D. A., Goding, J. R., and Wright, R. D. The effect of aldosterone, cortisol and corticosterone upon the sodium and potassium content of sheep's parotid saliva. *J. Clin. Invest.,* 42: 484–95, 1963.
4 Blair-West, J. R. Coghlan, J. P. Denton, D. A., Goding, J. R., Wintour, M., and Wright, R. D. The control of aldosterone secretion. *Recent Progr. Hormone Res.,* 19: 311–83, 1963.
5. Braun-Menendez, E., and Brandt, P. Aumento del apetito especifico para la sal provocade por la desoxicorticosterona. I: Characteristicas. *Rev. Soc. Argent. Biol.,* 28: 15–23, 1952.
6. Cade, J. E., and Perenich, T. Secretion of

aldosterone by rats. *Amer. J. Physiol.,* 208: 1026–30, 1965.
7. Dorfman, R. I., Shipley, R. A., Schiller, S., and Horwitt, B. N. Studies on the "cold test" as a method for the assay of adrenal cortical steroids. *Endocrinology,* 38: 165–77, 1946.
8. Eilers, E. A., and Peterson, R. E. Aldosterone secretion in rats, in *Aldosterone: A Symposium,* E. E. Baulieu and P. Robel (eds.). Davis, Philadelphia, pp. 251–64, 1964.
9. Frawley, P. F., and Thorn, G. W. The relation of the salivary Na/K ratio to adrenal cortical activity, in *Proceedings of the Second Clinical ACTH Conference. I: Research,* J. R. Mote (ed.). Blakiston, New York, pp. 115–22, 1951.
10. Fregly, M. J. A simple and accurate feeding device for rats. *J. Appl. Physiol.,* 15: 539, 1960.
11. Fregly, M. J. Increased water exchange in rats treated with antithyroid drugs. *J. Pharm. Exp. Therap.,* 134: 69–76, 1961.
12. Fregly, M. J. Effect of hypothyroidism on sodium chloride aversion of renal hypertensive rats. *Endocrinology,* 71: 683–92, 1962.
13. Fregly, M. J., Cade, J. R., Waters, I. W., Straw, J. A., and Taylor, R. E., Jr. Secretion of aldosterone by adrenal glands of propylthiouracil-treated rats. *Endocrinology,* 77: 777–84, 1965.
14. Fregly, M. J., Galindo, O., and Cook, K. M. Spontaneous sodium chloride appetite of goitrogen-treated rats: Effect of hypophysectomy and adrenalectomy. *Endocrinology,* 69: 1060–67, 1961.
15. Fregly, M. J., Harper, J. M., Jr., and Radford, E. P., Jr. Regulation of sodium chloride intake by rats. *Amer. J. Physiol.,* 209: 287–92, 1965.
16. Fregly, M. J., and Waters, I. W. Effect of propylthiouracil on preference threshold of rats for NaCl solutions. *Proc. Soc. Exp. Biol. Med.,* 120: 637–40, 1965.
17. Fregly, M. J., and Waters, I. W. Effect of mineralocorticoids on spontaneous sodium chloride appetite of adrenalectomized rats. *Physiol. Behavior,* 1: 65–74, 1966.
18. Fregly, M. J., and Waters, I. W. Hormonal regulation of the spontaneous sodium chloride appetite of rats, in *Olfaction and Taste, II,* T. Hayashi (ed.). Pergamon Press, New York (in press).
19. Fregly, M. J., and Waters, I. W. Effect of desoxycorticosterone acetate on NaCl appetite of propylthiouracil-treated rats. *Physiol. Behavior,* 1: 133–38, 1966.
20. Herxheimer, A., and Woodbury, D. M. The effect of desoxycorticosterone on salt and sucrose taste preference thresholds and drinking behavior in rats. *J. Physiol.* (London), 151: 253–60, 1960.
21. Kagawa, C. M. Blocking the renal electrolyte effect of mineralocorticoids with an orally

active steroidal spirolactone. *Endocrinology*, **67**: 125–32, 1960.

22. Kissileff, R. H., and Epstein, A. N. Loss of salt preference in rats with lateral hypothalamic damage. *Amer. Zool.*, **2**: 116, 1962.

23. Lauler, D. P., Hickler, R. B., and Thorn, G. W. The salivary sodium-potassium ratio. *New Eng. J. Med.*, **267**: 1136–37, 1962.

24. Lazarow, A. Methods for quantitative measurement of water intake. *Methods Med. Res.*, **6**: 225–29, 1954.

25. McBurney, D. H. Magnitude estimation of NaCl intensity after NaCl adaptation. Proceedings of the Fourth Annual Meeting, Psychonomic Society, Philadelphia, August, 1963.

26. McBurney, D. H., and Pfaffmann, C. Gustatory adaptation to saliva and sodium chloride. *J. Exp. Psychol.*, **65**: 523–29, 1963.

27. Peterson, R. E. *Proceedings of the Symposium on Advances in Tracer Applications of Tritium.* New England Nuclear Corporation; Boston, p. 16, 1958.

28. Pfaffmann, C. Taste preference and aversion following lingual denervation. *J. Comp. Physiol. Psychol.*, **45**: 393–400, 1952.

29. Rice, K. K., and Richter, C. P. Increased sodium chloride and water intake of normal rats treated with desoxycorticosterone acetate. *Endocrinology*, **33**: 106–15, 1943.

30. Richter, C. P. Increased salt appetite in adrenalectomized rats. *Amer. J. Physiol.*, **115**: 155–61, 1936.

31. Richter, C. P. Salt taste thresholds of normal and adrenalectomized rats. *Endocrinology*, **24**: 367–71, 1939.

32. Richter, C. P. Transmission of taste sensation in animals. *Trans. Amer. Neurol. Assoc.*, **65**: 49–50, 1939.

33. Richter, C. P. Sodium chloride and dextrose appetite of untreated and treated adrenalectomized rats. *Endocrinology*, **29**: 115–25, 1941.

34. Richter, C. P. Total self regulatory functions in animals and human beings. *The Harvey Lectures*, **38**: 63–103, 1942–43.

35. Richter, C. P., and Eckert, J. F. Mineral metabolism of adrenalectomized rats studied by the appetite method. *Endocrinology*, **22**: 214–24, 1938.

36. Snedecor, G. W. *Statistical Methods.* 5th ed. Iowa State University Press, Ames, p. 237, 1956.

37. Streeten, D. H. P. Symposium on the experimental pharmacology and clinical use of antimetabolites. Part VII: The spirolactones. *Clin. Pharmacol. Therap.*, **2**: 359–73, 1961.

38. Sturtevant, F. M. The biology of metacorticoid hypertension. *Ann. Int. Med.*, **49**: 1281–93, 1958.

39. Tosteson, D. C., DeFriez, A. I. C., Abrams, M., Gottschalk, C. W., and Landis, E. M. Effects of adrenalectomy, desoxycorticosterone acetate and increased fluid intake on intake of sodium chloride and bicarbonate by hypertensive and normal rats. *Amer. J. Physiol.*, **164**: 369–79, 1951.

40. Wolf, G. Effect of dorsolateral hypothalamic lesions on sodium appetite elicited by desoxycorticosterone and by acute hyponatremia. *J. Comp. Physiol. Psychol.*, **58**: 396–402, 1964.

41. Wolf, G. Effect of desoxycorticosterone on sodium appetite of intact and adrenalectomized rats. *Amer. J. Physiol.*, **208**: 1281–85, 1965.

This work was supported by Grant HE03503–09 from the National Heart Institute, National Institutes of Health.

10: Endocrines and Taste

by Keiichiro Hoshishima

THE PIONEERING works of Richter [64,65,67] described the mechanisms that control the interaction between the taste response for sweet and salty substances and the internal milieu. The mechanism for the taste of bitter has received limited investigation [21,33].

The author would like to speculate on a mechanism that might control the effects of certain hormones on bitter taste, in particular, on the local mechanism of tasting propylthiouracil (PROP). The bitter taste of PROP, phenylthiocarbamide, quinine, etc., is different from the other three taste modalities. Representatives of each of the other taste modalities, such as glucose, sodium chloride, or hydrochloric acid, are easily found in the body, but this is not the case for bitter substances. The effects of local anesthesia [75,76] and temperature [84] on the response to bitter suggest that this modality is different from the other three. Further, this taste modality seems rather stable in the face of changes in the internal milieu [40,76, 85,86].

SEX HORMONES AND THE TASTE RESPONSE FOR PROP

Observations differ concerning sex differences in perception of bitter taste among human beings. In a well-controlled study, the existence of a sex difference was questioned [43]. In our laboratory, preference thresholds of mice for PROP, using Richter's two-bottle method [64], were determined. Our data indicated that the taste threshold for PROP reached a plateau at seven to eight weeks of age. Histochemical findings, such as PAS reaction [58], SH-group staining [53], phospholipids staining [2], and the enzymatic activities of acid phosphatase [30], alkaline phosphatase [31], peroxidase [54], and esterase [9] of the tongue and the salivary glands, showed no change after this age was reached. Thus, the author selected mice seven to eight weeks of age for the experiment.

Female mice were more sensitive than male mice to the taste of PROP. When mice were subjected to castration after weaning, both sexes became less sensitive. Administration of estradiol benzoate to these mice at dosages of 20 μg every two days for two weeks brought about the decrease of threshold for PROP (Table 10–1).

Taste buds are covered with a mucous membrane similar to one found in the oral cavity [6]. The author performed chloroform-methanol extracts on the surface tissue of the tongue of mice and extracted phospholipids. The adsorption of PROP into this phospholipid fraction was then tested in vitro. The phospho-

TABLE 10–1: The Changes of the Taste Thresholds for PROP Associated with the Administration of Sex Hormones and Related Compounds

Treatments	Male	Female
Untreated	No. 14[b]	No. 13
Castrated	> No. 14[c]	> No. 14
Testosterone (C)[a]	No. 14[d]	> No. 13
Stanozolol (C)	> No. 13	> No. 14
Estrogen (C)	No. 13	No. 13
SC-6924 (C)	> No. 13	No. 14
"Vasolastine"	> No. 13	> No. 13

[a] C indicates the castrated animal.

[b] The number is the solution number of PROP used by Fischer [22] and is used through all the tables in this paper.

[c] The *broken underline* indicates increased threshold compared with control.

[d] The *solid underline* indicates decreased threshold compared with control.

These underlines are used in all the tables in this paper.

lipid fraction was dissolved in ligroin and shaken with water containing PROP. The amount of PROP left in the water layer was determined UV-spectrophotometrically [33]. The phospholipid fraction obtained from the tongue of female mice adsorbed significantly more PROP when compared with the fractions of male mice. It has been suggested that the first step in taste might be the adsorption of the substances into the surface of taste buds and into the cellular membrane that contains phospholipids. The "oily" nature of the surface of the tongue was confirmed by Von Békésy [7]. If the phospholipid derived from the tongue of an animal has a higher affinity for PROP, it is possible that the animal might be more sensitive in its response to this substance. To a certain extent, this relationship was observed following hormonal treatments, but the author found exceptions to this rule. Hence, other mechanisms were investigated.

To understand the phenomena that occur on the tongue surface or at the taste buds, the in vitro system that the author used initially proved to be too simple. There are easily detectable discrepancies, which can occur in the oral cavity, between this simple system and a more complicated one. The time during which taste stimula make contact with the receptors might be very short [7]. In the author's procedure, it takes at least thirty minutes for the shaking and separation of the two layers. In 1964 Wilkins and Hartman [82] reported an electrical analog for the olfactory processes. They demonstrated the processes of adsorption and de-adsorption as did Friedman *et al.* [28]. Baradi [3] noted the space between taste buds and its surrounding tissue. He concluded that this space had an important role in washing away the substances that evoke the taste sensation. In the author's system, there was no process of de-adsorption.

It is well established that saliva is one of the most important factors for taste perception [12,33,57]. Data indicate that physiological state or hormonal treatment influences the composition of saliva [21,25,41].

It was reported that certain local anesthetics inhibit the taste sensation [75]. Feinstein *et al.* [20] showed that local anesthetics react with phosphodiester groups occurring in phospholipids, phosphoproteins, and ribonucleic acids, such as cephaline, photovitin, and soluble liver RNA, but do not react with phosphomonoesters or pyrophosphate-containing compounds such as lacithin, sphingomyelin, and ATP. The chloroform-methanol extracts from the tongues of mice were analyzed chromatographically on thin-layer plates of silicic acid [80]. No detectable differences were observed in staining with Rhodamin-6G [56] or other reagents or in [32] P-autoradiograms following hormonal treatment of animals.

These results indicate the following possibilities: (1) A different mechanism may operate between the inhibition of taste sensitivity following the application of certain local anesthetics and the changes of taste threshold for PROP after hormonal treatment; (2) thin-layer chromatography used for the analysis of chloroform-methanol extracts was not sensitive in detecting the chemical component or components that might have a role in the mechanism of change in the taste threshold; (3) a phosphate-containing substance or substances other than phospholipids in nature may be responsible for the changes in threshold after the application of local anesthetics. The third possibility is most plausible since the turnover ratio of nucleic acids or nucleoproteins in taste buds is known to be very high [5].

When castrated male mice were injected with testosterone propionate at dosages of 150 μg every two days for two weeks, the taste threshold of treated mice increased, but the administration of hormones that have high anabolic activity and lower androgenic effects such as MAS (1-methyl-Δ'-androstenolone acetate "Primobolan"), HMD (2-hydroxymethylene 4, 5-dihydromethyl testosterone "Anadrol"), Δ'-17MT (Δ'-17 γ-methyl-17β-hydroxyandrosta-1, 4-dien-3-one "Dianabol"), and Δ'-Testololactone, Stanozolol (17β-hydroxy-17α-methylandrostano-[3.2-C] pyrazole "Winstrol"), or its derivative (WIN-16568), did not show any effect upon the taste threshold for PROP (Table 10–1). This indicates that the testosterone effect on the taste threshold is not due to its anabolic action. The mechanism of action in testosterone and in other anabolic steroids suggests that these compounds stimulate the formation of messenger RNA and then accelerate protein biosynthesis [26]. This result apparently contradicts the reported higher metabolic activity of nucleic acids or nucleoproteins of taste buds [5]. It is particularly true if the anabolic action of testosterone and its derivatives has a

direct stimulative effect upon the biosynthesis of nucleic acids or nucleoproteins in taste buds, and the elevated metabolic state facilitates the sensitivity of taste perception.

There are several ways to explain this discrepancy: (1) the elevated metabolic ratio of nucleic acids or nucleoproteins in taste buds does not necessarily mean the acceleration of taste sensitivity—this seems quite unlikely; (2) the nucleic acids or nucleoproteins in taste buds are not affected by anabolic action of steroids; (3) the so-called androgenic action of testosterone is responsible for taste threshold; (4) the action of testosterone might not be local; it might be more involved in the general function of the taste mechanism.

Although the role of acetylcholine or acetylcholine esterase in the taste mechanism is not yet defined [15,69,70,74], the fact that androgen apparently depresses the synthesis of acetylcholine is [78] suggestive of a fourth possibility. During the course of study of chemoreception among the patients of adrenal insufficiency, Henkin et al. [36], suggested that the action of ACTH might be a generalized one, and Pfaffmann [60] similarly concluded a generalized control of insulin on perception of sweetness. From these facts, it is plausible to conclude that the effect of testosterone on the taste threshold might be a general one, not a local one.

When estradiol benzoate was injected into castrated mice at doses of 20 g every two days for two weeks, taste threshold for PROP decreased markedly. Administration of its derivatives, such as SC-6924 (3-methoxy-16γ-methyl-1, 3, 5 [10]-estratriene-16β, 17β-diol "Anvene") [13], and Vallestrill (2, 2-dimethyl-3-[6-methoxy-2-naphthyl] pentanoic acid) [17], which are known to have low feminizing effects and greater effects on shifting the cholesterolphospholipid ratio of plasma and certain tissues, did not show any effects on taste threshold. These results indicate that the effect of estrogen on tasting PROP dissociates it from its lipid-shifting action. The administration of large doses of "Vasolastine" [48], -Enzy-pharm-(0.2–0.4 ml every day for adult mice for two months and 0.1 ml per day from birth to the age of seven weeks), did not show any effect on the taste threshold for PROP in mice. This drug is known to have a more potent effect on decreasing the cholesterolphospholipid ratio of plasma and certain tissues than that of estrogen or its derivatives (see Table 10–1). This result confirms the suggestion mentioned above.

There might be a complicated mechanism involved in the action of estrogen on the taste of bitter. The suggestion that estrogen stimulates the synthesis of acetylcholine and the observations concerning the effect of estrogen upon the nasal mucosa of monkey [59], as well as clinical findings about the effects of administration of estrogen and androgen upon olfactory perception threshold [71] and the report [63] on the effects of sex hormones upon oral mucosa must all be considered.

The PAS reaction in the submaxillary and sublingual gland of less sensitive mice was more distinct than that of more sensitive animals, and in some cases, under the microscope the author could detect the taste buds covered with a PAS-positive substance. Ellis [18] discussed the function of Ebner's gland in the taste mechanism and concluded that this gland might perform the major flushing action for the surface of taste buds. In some cases that showed less sensitivity for PROP, the author found that the PAS-positive substance came from this gland and covered the taste buds.

The chemical nature of PAS-positive substances in the salivary gland [79] and the mechanism of its secretion [73] have been discussed previously. The protective role of mucin or mucin-like substances for mucous membrane or epithelium [8] has also been reported. It is plausible that the PAS-positive substance, to a certain degree, obstructs the contact of PROP with the surface of the taste receptors.

The activity of peroxidase, histochemically demonstrated, did not show any correlation with taste threshold. This apparently contradicts the postulated concept of destruction of PROP by a salivary enzyme [33]. The existence of a certain amount of enzyme in the salivary glands does not necessarily mean that the enzyme is secreted into saliva. The mechanism of secretion of large molecular substances in the salivary glands is complicated [72]; this might explain the discrepancy between the histochemical data and Griffin's and Fischer's [33] results.

The nucleotide fraction was obtained from the acid soluble fraction of the surface tissue of the tongue of mice by barium and ethanol precipitation [11]. With thin-layer chromatograms or with DEAE-cellulose [55,61] chromotography, the author could detect spots under UV light and with [32] P-radioautographs. In the fraction obtained from untreated mice, two spots, which corresponded to ATP and ADP, were detectable (Table 10–2).

The chromatograms changed after treatment with certain hormones; e.g., estrogen treatments of castrated mice showed decreased thresholds for PROP. ADP could not be detected in their nucleotide fraction. Caldwell et al. [10] indicated in their study on active transport of sodium in giant axons of the squid that an elevated ATP/ADP ratio was favorable for the active transport of sodium. If the absence of ADP can be interpreted as the elevated ATP/ADP

TABLE 10–2: The Effects of the Treatments on the Chromatographic Patterns of Nucleotides Obtained from the Tongue of Mice

Sample	Treatments		M^a	D^b	T^c
	Untreated (M,F)			⊕	⊕
A	TP^d (M) "Vasolastine" (M)		⊕	⊕	⊕
	Radiothyroidectomy; at the time of weaning (F)		⊕	⊕	+
B	MAS ("Primobolan") (C^eM)		+		
	HMD ("Anadrol") (CM)		+		O^f
	Radiothyroidectomy; within 24 hours after birth (M)			⊕	
C	Radiothyroidectomy; at the 5th day (M) Mo-diet (F)				
	Radiothyroidectomy; within 24 hours after birth (F)			⊕	+
	SC-6924 (CM)				
D	Estrogen (CM)	Estrogen (CF)			⊕
	Testosterone (CF)	Win-16568 (CM)			

[a] Mononucleotides.
[b] Dinucleotides.
[c] Trinucleotides.
[d] Testosterone propionate was injected within 24 hours after birth.
[e] C indicates the castrated animal.
[f] *Circle* indicates the positive spot on [32] P-radioautogram.

ratio, the condition that is favorable for sodium transport is also favorable for the promotion of taste sensitivity for PROP. But the other samples, which also showed decreased thresholds, showed reverse changes in the chromatograms; i.e., ATP was absent and ADP was present.

The author's data concerning the local effects of vasopressin and amphotericin-B upon taste sensitivity, shown later, suggest that taste sensitivity is not coupled with sodium transport. The findings from these chromatographic patterns must be interpreted from another standpoint.

Duncan's experiment [14] concerning the transducer mechanism of taste buds indicated that the ATP-ase that is concerned with this mechanism is not the ATP-ase that works during the process of active transport of sodium. Although he used sodium chloride as the taste stimuli [16], his results might support this interpretation.

The effects of constant illumination or darkness on the synthesis of melatonin revealed that illumination decreased the melatonin content of the pineal gland while darkness increased the content [83]. When female mice were maintained under constant illumination for two weeks, a decrease of taste thresholds for PROP was noted. This was not the case with male animals. The effect of constant illumination was more marked in the case of non-oöphorectomized mice than that of oöphorectomized ones. Furthermore, the effect of light on the biosynthesis of melatonin does not require gonads [83]. Thus, it might be assumed that the effect of melatonin upon taste thresholds was directly expressed in the case of oöphorectomized mice and that the combined effects of melatonin and an ovarian hormone, probably estrogen, were expressed in the case of non-oöphorectomized animals.

When male mice were injected with testosterone within twenty-four hours after birth at dosages of 50 μg [4], they became sterile and taste thresholds decreased; if two million thymus cells were injected simultaneously with testosterone into the neonatal mice, taste thresholds increased. Kincl et al. [45] showed the preventive effect of the administration of thymic cell suspension against steroid-induced sterility, and the effect was rather specific for thymus cells.

Considering the author's results and Kincl's report, it is probable that a common mechanism might cause both sterilization of the mice and altered taste thresholds.

Administration of dydrogesterone (9-β, 10-γ-pregnane-4, 6-diene-3, 20-dione "Duphaston") and gonadtropins (HCG and PMS) did not show any applicable effects upon taste thresholds.

PROP dissolved in water containing vasopressin (30 μg/ml) was used for taste threshold determination. The local application of vasopressin did not show any effect upon the thresholds of mice while that of amphotericin-B (14 μg/ml) made mice more sensitive to PROP (Table 10–3). Leaf and his co-workers

TABLE 10–3: The Local Application of Vasopressin, Amphotericin-B, Guanidine, and the Thresholds for PROP in Mice

Treatments	Male	Female
Untreated	No. 14	No. 13
Vasopressin	> No. 13	No. 13
Amphotericin-B	No. 13	No. 12
Sodium desoxycholate	> No. 13	No. 13
Guanidine HCl	No. 12	No. 13

[50,52] showed that both amphotericin-B and vasopressin stimulated the active transport of sodium at the mucosal surface of the toad bladder and that the former compound stimulated the penetration of the small molecular solute at the same site while the latter did not. If the characteristics of the mucous membrane of the toad bladder and that of the chemoreceptor are similar, it is unlikely that PROP evoked a bitter sensation coupled with the stimulation of the active transport of sodium. Frazier [24] demonstrated competitive interference with the entry of sodium by guanidine. When guanidine HCl was applied locally, the taste sensitivity for PROP increased markedly; this might be due to the unmasking effect of SH groups, as suggested by Yur'eva [87]. This effect of

guanidine also suggests that increasing active sodium transport does not couple directly with the increasing sensitivity of taste for PROP.

It is thought that amphotericin-B exerts its effect as an antibiotic by combining with lipid [49], particularly with sterols in the cell membranes, and one might speculate that a similar drug-sterol interaction is responsible for the taste threshold changes associated with amphotericin administration.

THYROID AND PARATHYROID FUNCTION AND THE TASTE RESPONSE FOR PROP

Phenylthiocarbamide, a substance commonly used for the threshold determination of bitter is known as a potent goitrogen. The inability to taste this substance, taste-blindness, is controlled by a recessive gene. Thyroid disorders occur more commonly among families of patients with thyroid dysfunction as compared with other families [39]. Thus, the ability to taste bitter and its relation to thyroid function is important in genetic and pathogenetical studies of thyroid diseases [23]. Kitchin et al. [46] showed that the percentage of taste-blindness among patients with thyroid disorders was different from that of a healthy control group.

Taste thresholds in females with thyroid disorders were compared with the thresholds of a matched, normal control group. Subjects in both groups did not smoke [42] and were not menstruating at the time of the study [29]. The following items were checked in each patient: the clinical course of disease, the basic metabolic rate, plasma protein-bound iodide, forty-eight-hour PB ^{131}I test, ^{131}I-thyroidal uptake, and ^{131}I-T$_3$-resin sponge uptake test, scintillation scanning, and the histopathological findings of thyroid tissues in the surgically operated cases. The author could not detect any significant difference in taste thresholds for PROP among patient groups and the healthy control group.

If the ability to taste PROP was compared among patients before and after operation, i.e., in the hyperthyroid and hypothyroid states, a decrease in threshold was noted after the operation (Table 10–4). This result suggests that thyroid

mouse) at the time of weaning, the threshold for PROP decreased in males and increased in females. This was the same pattern of changes in thresholds associated with the injection of dimethylglyoxime into mice (0.1 ml containing 0.06 mg of this reagent every two days for two weeks) (Table 10–5). Dimethylglyoxime is a well-known nickel chelating agent, and our data [87] suggested

TABLE 10–4: The Effects of Thyroidectomy upon the Changes of the Taste Thresholds for PROP

Changes of Thresholds	Toxic Diffuse Goitre (111 Cases)	Adenoma (38 Cases)	Total (149 Cases)
Unaltered	42	18	60
	$(38\% \pm 4.6\%)$	$(48\% \pm 8.1\%)$	$(40\% \pm 4\%)$
Decreased			
2 steps or less	41	12	53
	$(37\% \pm 4.6\%)$	$(32\% \pm 7.5\%)$	$(36\% \pm 3.9\%)$
3 steps or more	16	3	19
	$(14\% \pm 3.2\%)$	$(8\% \pm 4.7\%)$	$(13\% \pm 2.7\%)$
Total	57	15	72
	$(51\% \pm 4.8\%)$	$(39\% \pm 7.9\%)$	$(48\% \pm 4.1\%)$
Increased			
2 steps or less	11	4	15
	$(10\% \pm 2.8\%)$	$(11\% \pm 5\%)$	$(10\% \pm 2.4\%)$
3 steps or more	1	1	2

state is related to taste threshold in some fashion.

Our previous data [38] concerning thresholds in radiothyroidectomized mice also suggested that thyroidal function was related to bitter (PTC) sensitivity. Fischer et al. [21] suggested that the saliva derived from taste-blind cases showed higher activity of an enzyme that decomposed PROP than did the saliva derived from PROP-sensitive cases. The difference of enzymatic activity indicates the clue for understanding the biochemical mechanism of taste-blindness. However, the author could not find any significant difference in taste threshold using PROP alone or using PROP plus DIT as stimuli as Fischer and Griffin [21] suggested. The author could not explain this discrepancy.

When mice were subjected to radiothyroidectomy (200 μc of ^{131}I for each

that after the radiothyroidectomy of mice, the disappearance of nickel metal from the homogenate of the whole body and from certain tissues could be detected chromatographically. These two facts indicate that nickel has some bearing upon the taste for PROP.

When a mixture of PROP and dimethylglyoxime was used to measure thresholds, taste thresholds decreased in both sexes, and the pattern of thresholds and histochemical findings (Table 10–5) was different from that observed after radiothyroidectomy or after dimethylglyoxime injection. The data shown in Table 10–5 indicate that there is no systematic correlation between taste thresholds and histochemical findings.

Frieden et al. [27] suggested the possibility that copper (II) forms a chelated complex with thyroxine. Although they did not deal with the reaction of nickel

TABLE 10–5: The Effects of the Radiothyroidectomy, the Administration of Dimethylglyoxime, and Feeding Molybdenum-Containing Diet upon the Histochemical Findings in the Submaxillary Gland of Mice

Effect	Untreated		Radiothyroidectomy		Dimethylglyoxime				Mo-Diet	
					Injection		Local			
	M	F	M	F	M	F	M	F	M	F
	14[a]	13[a]	13[a]	> 13[a]	13[a]	> 13[a]	13[a]	12[a]	12[a]	11[a]
Alkaline Phosphatase	+	+	+	+	+	+	+	+	++	++
PAS-Reaction	++	++	+	++	++	+++	++	++	++	++
Phospholipids[b]	+	++	++	–	+++	±	+++	±	++	–

NOTE: These treatments did not show any distinct effects upon the activity of acid phosphatase, esterase, peroxidase, and SH groups.
[a] Histochemical test or threshold number.
[b] Granules in the duct cells.

metal and thyroxine, both copper (II) and nickel are divalent ions. Considering these facts, the possibility of complex formation of nickel with thyroxine, and the effect of the complex formation upon the taste thresholds for PROP may be useful areas for investigation.

In the study of the influence of thyroxine and sex hormones upon optically evoked potentials in gold fish, Hara et al. [34] suggested that the stimulative action of thyroxine might not take place on the periphery but at a central site, e.g., the optic tectum. Wase et al. [81] reported an extremely low rate of turnover for nickel metal in the brain as compared with the rate in other tissues.

Considering the author's results, the reports mentioned above, and other suggestions [32,37], the effects of radiothyroidectomy or nickel deficiency upon taste thresholds might be a central, rather than a local, effect.

In thyrotoxicosis, the copper content of serum decreased in some patients [44]. When mice were fed a diet containing molybdenum (40 mg percentage) for five weeks [1], the animals showed apparent symptoms of copper deficiency, and their taste thresholds for PROP decreased markedly. Mice treated with the larger doses of thyroid extract did not show any appreciable change in thresholds for bitter. These results indicate that copper deficiency may have a certain bearing upon the changes of taste thresholds. It is unlikely that the mild copper deficiency in the case of thyrotoxicosis has a specific role in the taste of bitter.

When mice were fed a diet containing 2, 4-dinitrophenol (7 mg percentage), an elevated metabolic ratio was observed. Changes in taste thresholds could not be detected. These results suggest that the factor or factors working for the elevation of basic metabolic rate do not have any direct effect upon the changes of taste thresholds for PROP. This was con-

firmed by the author's data that indicated that there is no correlation between the taste thresholds for PROP and the value of basic metabolic rate among thyroid patients.

Mice that received distilled water containing sodium fluoride (400 p.p.m.) ad libitum for four weeks exhibited decreased thresholds for the taste of PROP (Table 10–6). Faccini et al. [19] reported

TABLE 10–6: The Effects of the Radiothyroidectomy, Feeding DNP[a]-Containing Diet, and Giving Fluoride-Containing Water[b] on the Thresholds for PROP in Mice

Treatments	Male	Female
Untreated	No. 14	No. 13
Radiothyroidectomy; at the time of weaning	No. 13	> No. 13
Radiothyroidectomy; within 24 hours after birth	No. 13	No. 12
Radiothyroidectomy; at the time of weaning—thyroid extract[c]	> No. 13	> No. 13
DNP-diet	> No. 13	No. 13
Fluoride	No. 13	No. 12

[a] Feeding the basal diet containing 7 mg percentage DNP for 3.5 weeks.
[b] Giving the water containing 400 p.p.m. fluoride for 4 weeks.
[c] Injection was started from the time of weaning.

elevated parathyroid activity when they fed sheep fluoride-containing water. The effects of drinking water containing fluoride upon thresholds might relate to the effects of parathyroid hormone on the taste of bitter. Richter [65,66] and others [51] suggested altered taste thresholds for calcium and other salts, but as far as the author is aware, there is no report dealing with the interaction between this hormone and the taste of bitter. Riggs [68], reviewing the works of Rasmussen and his co-workers [62], suggested that parathyroid hormones may have "a rather general action on membranes." If the effect of this hormone is to change the dynamic state of membranes, it might also change the taste thresholds for PROP.

Research concerning the relationship between endocrinological state and taste threshold is an attractive subject for further study. It may also serve as one of the most potent tools in clarifying the complicated mechanism of this sensation.

Discussion

Beidler: Are you familiar with the work of Allara (*Rev. Biol.*, 44: 209, 1952), who observed that castrated animals showed a change in the number of taste buds?

Pfaffmann: We repeated Allara's experiments to determine if there was a change in taste preference thresholds. There was no change in the behavioral measures, following either castration or ovariectomy.

Henkin: We measured the thresholds for taste and olfaction of various substances in postmenopausal and ovariectomized women and observed no significant alterations from normal in these thresholds. Thresholds for various taste modalities in patients with malignancy who were receiving estrogen or testosterone were not different from normal.

Kare: We used massive doses of testosterone as well as diethylstilbesterol in birds and measured their response to a variety of compounds. We observed no change in their behavior toward taste stimuli.

Henkin: There are various types of hypogonadal states in which we have observed taste abnormalities, for example, Turner's syndrome. These patients have elevated sour and bitter thresholds. They also demonstrate a characteristic type of hyposmia, abnormalities of facial form, high arched palates, and decreased palatal perception. How these observations relate to one another is not yet clear.

However, it may well be a genetic phenomenon that we are observing since a similar type of hyposmia has been demonstrated in the mothers of each of these patients.

Pfaffmann: It seems to me that there is emerging a general observation that the sensitivity of the receptors is very difficult to budge. That is the way I interpret the earlier work that Henkin reported, these experiments, which show that local changes in the receptors are hard to demonstrate, and our own earlier work on adrenalectomy. I wonder if Hodgson, in view of his observations that hormones will modify receptors, would make a comment in regard to this evidence for stability of the receptor.

Hodgson: The hormone effects described may turn out to be among those exceptions that merely make the general rule stand out. However, I am not sure that the two experimental systems can be properly compared. For one thing, the speed with which epinephrine acts, via the open circulatory system of an insect, upon the tactile and chemical receptors is much faster than the other hormone effects which have been discussed. The problem is our ignorance of the site of the effects. This extends to other interpretations as well. For example, I wonder about Hoshishima's conclusion that taste sensitivity is not coupled with sodium transport in the taste receptors. Taste sensitivity may not be affected by hormone treatments that are known to affect sodium transport in other membranes, such as the toad bladder preparation, but despite local surface application, the hormone molecules might not pass intact to the actual taste receptor membranes in the mouse tongue. Certainly they would not be doing so via a normal route. Consequently, I would prefer to leave the site of hormone actions an open question and to exercise corresponding caution in making deductions concerning receptor membrane mechanisms.

Bardach: Gorbman is working on hormonal effects on the sensitivity of various sensory systems in fish. I believe he speculated that the site of action was removed from the receptors; at what level, he doesn't know.

Hoshishima: He suggested that in the case of optic-evoked potential it is at the site of the optic tectum.

Bardach: Well, in any case, it is not the receptors.

Hoshishima: No.

Pangborn: Recently we studied the effect of the menstrual cycle, over a seven-month period, on taste thresholds for sodium chloride, sucrose, glucose, and citric acid, as well as on odor thresholds for vanillin and butanol. We noted as much variability among the eight females as between the two male controls, with no consistent pattern of response that could be related to the monthly cycle. In a second study, using three female subjects, over six cycles, odor thresholds as well as magnitude estimations of suprathreshold levels were measured, using Le Magnen's compound, "exaltolide" (15-hydroxypentadecanoic acid lactone). One woman showed an increased sensitivity during menstruation, one showed a decrease, and the third was unaffected.

Pfaffmann: We ran this same experiment over only three cycles several years ago. The first cycle gave us a change in sensitivity; in the second one it disappeared; and in the third there was no sign of it.

Henkin: There is another major factor in taste variation that we have not yet considered, that of circadian variation. Detection thresholds for NaCl determined in normal volunteers have varied from as high as 60.0 mM/L in the morning hours to as low as 0.5 mM/L in some female patients in the evening. This extremely wide variation may well exist in the rat as it does in man.

Brobeck: In thinking about this question of the control of sensitivity for olfaction and taste, it might be well to point out that in the case of olfaction we have more pathways in the central nervous system than anybody knows what to do with. This is true especially of those pathways that come back out into the olfactory system. A neuroanatomist is not going to be surprised to have modulation at all stages along this line. A long time ago when Ruch was trying to work out the cortical projection of taste, we also tried to abolish taste, with Brobeck making the lesions in the mesencephalon, and missing, and accidentally we got fat monkeys. We didn't destroy the taste pathways, but these were interesting obese monkeys because they became obese without hypothalamic lesions. I have not done much about these taste pathways since that time, but it is my impression that for taste one simply has to assume that the pathways are there; at least, I do not know of anyone who has described them.

Moulton: It seems an implicit assumption in these discussions that agents altering the sensitivity of the receptors must act at the receptor level or within the central nervous system. This may be a serious oversight. There is a third possibility: a change in access of stimulus molecules to the receptors. For example, there is some evidence that olfactory sensitivity is favored by a moist and somewhat swollen mucosa. Subjects with a dry, shrunken mucosa, and those with an exceptionally swollen and moist mucosa, tended to have lower thresholds to citral than those with the intermediate condition (Schneider and Wolf, *J. Appl. Physiol.*, **8**: 337, 1955). Even if hormones or drugs that change the degree of mucosal swelling and secretion rate are administered, the effect on olfaction might depend on the initial condition of the mucosa. In those subjects with normally dry and shrunken mucosa, olfaction would be improved. In subjects already having the optimal degree of swelling and secretion, there should be a decline in sensitivity due to increased obstruction of air flow. It is interesting that when estrogen was administered to three hypogonadal women there was a significant lowering of thresholds for citral associated with a slight reduction in nasal swellings and secretions (Schneider *et al., J. Clin. Endocrinol.*, **18**: 379, 1958). Such considerations may explain, in part, why highly inconsistent results have been reported in the past concerning, for example, the effects of the menstrual cycle on olfactory sensitivity.

Beidler: If that is true, then anything affecting the sympathetic system will affect olfaction.

Lepkovsky: I would like to raise a question here. Should we carefully separate taste and olfaction? Since olfaction goes over the first cranial nerve and taste passes over the fifth, seventh, and ninth cranial nerves, I am not sure that we should be so careful when it comes to actually separating taste from olfaction.

Moulton: This would depend on what aspect you are looking at. Olfaction differs from other sensory systems in that it does not project initially to the thalamus but to rhinencephalic centers. This may help to explain why odors can, for example, block pregnancy in mice while

taste substances apparently cannot. Taste and olfaction are probably quite distinct in this sense.

Henkin: We have shown that after total excision of the olfactory epithelium and cutting of the olfactory nerves, a step taken in some operative procedures for removal of maxillary sinus tumors, patients can respond to vapors through the use of the fifth, ninth, and tenth cranial nerves. We have observed responses to vapors over a number of different pathways and by different receptors. It is unlikely there are specialized receptors that respond to vapors in the anatomical areas innervated by these nerves. However, it is possible to train these patients to differentiate between various odors using only the fifth, ninth, and tenth cranial nerves. A painter who had undergone this surgical procedure was unable to immediately recognize various solvents postoperatively, but with training he was able to do so on the basis of the irritation or sensation he felt in his nose and pharynx. Anatomically, the receptors involved in this process and how they function to perform these tasks is not yet clear. It is also of interest that a loss of the ability to recognize the taste of various foods was associated with this acquired hyposmia.

Lepkovsky: I am glad to hear you bring the trigeminal nerve into olfaction. We have that very problem in the brain of the chicks.

Fischer: Another point. It doesn't suffice to use the best available procedure such as a double blind taste testing technique with forced choice; it is recommended that a second test also be administered, especially with patient populations. For example, a population of migraine outpatients (N = 42), studied with the cooperation of Hunt at Ohio State University, did not display an antimode for PROP with the first testing. The bimodal distribution of PROP thresholds became evident only after the second testing. In other populations a third testing may be necessary for obtaining true threshold values.

REFERENCES

1. Arthur, D. Interrelationships of molybdenum and copper in the diet of the guinea pig. *J. Nutr.*, **87**: 69–76, 1965.
2. Baker, J. R. The histochemical recognition of lipine. *Quart. J. Microscop. Sci.*, **87**: 441–70, 1946.
3. Baradi, A. F. Intragemmal spaces in taste buds. *Z. Zellforsch.*, **65**: 313–18, 1965.
4. Barraclough, C. A. Production of anovulatory sterile rats by single injections of testosterone propionate. *Endocrinology*, **68**: 62–67, 1961.
5. Beidler, L. M. Taste receptor stimulation. *Progress in Biophysics and Biophysical Chemistry*. Pergamon Press, New York, 1961.
6. Beidler, L. M. Dynamics of taste cells, in *Olfaction and Taste*, Y. Zotterman (ed.). Pergamon Press, New York, pp. 133–48, 1963.
7. Békésy, G. von. Taste theories and the chemical stimulation of single papillae. *J. Appl. Physiol.*, **21**: 1–9, 1966.
8. Blumberger, W., and Glatzel, H. Beiträge zur Physiologie der Gewürze und Würzstoffe. IV: Die Speichelwirksamkeit der "Genusssauren." *Nutr. Dieta.*, **6**: 296–312, 1964.
9. Burstone, M. S. Esterase of the salivary glands. *J. Histochem. Cytochem.*, **4**: 130–39, 1956.
10. Caldwell, P. C., Hodgkin, A. L., Keynes, R. D., and Shaw, T. I. The effects of injecting "energy-rich" phosphate compounds on the active transport of ions in the giant axons of Loligo. *J. Physiol.* (London), **152**: 561–90, 1960.
11. Cardini, C. E., and Leloir, L. F. General procedure for isolating and analyzing tissue organic phosphates, in *Method in Enzymology, III*, S. P. Colowich and N. O. Kaplan (eds.). Academic Press, New York, 835–40, 1957.
12. Cohen, J., and Ogdon, D. P. Taste blindness to phenylthiocarbamide and related compounds. *Psychol. Bull.*, **46**: 490–98, 1949.
13. Cook, D. L., Calhoun, D. W., and Edgren, R. A. Lipodiactic and antiatherogenic properties of mytatrienediol and various estrogenic substances. *Arch. Intern. Pharmacodynamie*, **135**: 91–104, 1962.
14. Duncan, C. J. The transducer mechanism of sense organs. *Naturwiss.*, **51**: 172–73, 1963.

15. Duncan, C. J. Synaptic transmission at taste buds. *Nature*, **203**: 875–76, 1964.
16. Duncan, C. J. Personal communication, 1966.
17. Edgren, R. A. Notes on impeded estrogens. *Proc. Soc. Exp. Biol. Med.*, **92**: 569–71, 1956.
18. Ellis, R. A. Circulatory patterns in the papillae of the mammalian tongue. *Anat. Rec.*, **133**: 579–91, 1959.
19. Faccini, J. M., and Care, A. D. Effect of sodium floride on the ultrastructure of the parathyroid glands of the sheep. *Nature*, **207**: 1399–1401, 1965.
20. Feinstein, M. B., and Paimre, M. Specific reaction of local anesthetics with phophodiester groups. *Biochem. Biophys. Acta,* **115**: 33–45, 1966.
21. Fischer, R., and Griffin, F. "Taste-blindness" and variations in taste-threshold in relation to thyroid metabolism. *J. Neuropsychiat.*, **3**: 98–104, 1961.
22. Fischer, R., and Griffin, F. Pharmacogenetic aspects of gustation. *Drug Research*, **14**: 673–86, 1964.
23. Fraser, G. R. Genetical aspects of thyroid disease, in *The Thyroid Gland, II*, R. Pitt-Rivers and W. R. Trotter (eds.). Butterworths, London, 271–97, 1964.
24. Frazier, H. S. Specificity of sodium transport and the biologically active form of sodium ion. *J. Clin. Invest.*, **43**: 1265–66, 1964.
25. Fregly, M. J., and Waters, I. W. Effect of desoxycorticosterone acetate on NaCl appetite of propylthiouracil treated rats. *Physiol. Behav.*, **1**: 65–74, 1966.
26. Frieden, E. H. Sex hormones and the metabolism of amino acids and proteins, in *Actions of Hormones on Molecular Processes*, G. Litwack and D. Kritchevsky (eds.). John Wiley & Sons, New York, pp. 509–59, 1964.
27. Frieden, E. H., Forsblad, K., and Ezell, A. L. Reduction of Cu(II) by throxine, thyronine analogs and other phenols. *Arch. Biochem. Biophys.*, **96**: 423–29, 1962.
28. Friedman, H. H., Mackay, D. A., and Rosano, H. L. Odor measurement possibilities via energy changes in cephalin monolayers. *Ann. N.Y. Acad. Sci.*, **116**: 602–7, 1964.
29. Glanville, E. V., and Kaplan, A. R. The menstrual cycle and sensitivity of taste perception. *Amer. J. Obst. Gynec.*, **92**: 189–94, 1965.
30. Gomori, G. Distribution of acid phosphatase in tissues under normal and under pathologic conditions. *Arch. Pathol.*, **32**: 189–99, 1941.
31. Gomori, G. The distribution of phosphatase in normal organs and tissues. *J. Cellular Comp. Physiol.*, **17**: 71–83, 1941.
32. Gorbman, A., Oshima, K., and Hara, T. Olfaction in fishes and its responsiveness to endocrine state. *Abstracts of the Twenty-third International Congress of Physiological Science* (Tokyo, Japan), p. 244 only, 1965.

33. Griffin, F., and Fischer, R. Differential reactivity of saliva from "tasters" and "nontasters" of 6-n-propylthiouracil. *Nature*, **187**: 417–19, 1960.

34. Hara, T., Ueda, K., and Gorbman, A. Influences of thyroxine and sex hormones upon optically evoked potentials in the optic tectum of goldfish. *Gen. Comp. Endocr.*, **5**: 313–19, 1965.

35. Hashimoto, Y., Tsuiki, S., Quintarelli, G., and Pigman, W. A comparison of submaxillary glands of humans, cattle, dogs and rats. *Biochem. Biophys. Acta*, **48**: 404–6, 1961.

36. Henkin, R. I., Gill, J. R., and Bartter, F. C. Studies on taste thresholds in normal man and in patients with adrenal cortical insufficiency: The role of adrenal cortical steroids and of serum sodium concentration. *J. Clin. Invest.*, **42**: 727–35, 1963.

37. Henkin, R. I., and Solomon, D. H. Salt-taste threshold in adrenal insufficiency in man. *Clin. Endocr. Metab.*, **22**: 856–58, 1962.

38. Hoshishima, K., Yokoyama, S., and Seto, K. Taste sensitivity in various strains of mice. *Amer. J. Physiol.*, **202**: 1200–4, 1962.

39. Ito, K. Personal communication, 1966.

40. Jorgesen, M. B., and Buch, N. H. Sense of smell and taste in pregnant diabetics; clinical studies. *Pract. Oto-rhino-laryng.*, **23**: 390–96, 1961.

41. Junqueira, L. C. U., Toledo, A. M. S., and DeJorge, F. B. Studies on the physiology of rat and mouse submaxillary glands. II: The action of testosterone on sodium and potassium content of submaxillary saliva in castrate rats and mice, in *Salivary Glands and Their Secretions*, L. M. Screebny and J. Meyer (eds.). Pergamon Press, New York, 119–22, 1964.

42. Kaplan, A. R., Glanville, E. V. and Fischer, R. Taste thresholds for bitterness and cigarette smoking. *Nature*, **202**: 1366 only, 1964.

43. Kaplan, A. R., Glanville, E. V., and Fischer, R. Cumulative effect of age and smoking on taste sensitivity in males and females. *J. Gerontol.*, **20**: 334–37, 1965.

44. Kasanen, A., and Viltanen, I. On the copper content of the thyroid tissue and serum in thyrotoxicosis. *Acta Med. Scand.*, **153**: 467–72, 1956.

45. Kincl, F. A., Oriol, A., Folchi Pi, A., and Maqueo, M. Prevention of steroid-induced sterility in neonatal rats with thymic cell suspension. *Proc. Soc. Exp. Biol. Med.*, **120**: 252–55, 1965.

46. Kitchin, F. D., and Evans, W. H. Genetic factors in thyroid diseases. *Brit. Med. Bull.*, **16**: 148–51, 1960.

47. Klucik, I. Biologicky a hygienicky vyznam niklu. *Pracovni legarstvi*, **13**: 243–54, 1961.

48. Kruskemper, H. L., and Schulze, G. Versuche zur Verhinderung det unter Cholinmangel entsehenden Fettleber durch Behandlung mit frementen des Fettstoffwechsels. *Arch. Exp. Path. Pharm.* **229**: 34–40, 1956.

49. Lampen, J. O., Arnow, P. M., Borowska, Z., and Laskin, A. L. Location and role of sterol at nystatin binding sites. *J. Bact.*, **84**: 1152–60, 1962.

50. Leaf, A. Transepitherial transport and its hormonal control in toad bladder. *Ergeb. Physiol.*, **56**: 216–63, 1965.

51. Lewis, M. Behavior resulting from calcium deprivation in parathyroidectomized rats. *J. Comp. Physiol. Psychol.*, **57**: 348–52, 1964.

52. Lichtenstein, N. S., and Leaf, A. Effect of amphotericin B on the permeability of the toad bladder. *J. Clin. Invest.*, **44**: 1328–42, 1965.

53. Lillie, R. D., and Burtner, H. J. The ferric ferricyanide reduction test in histochemistry. *J. Histochem.*, **1**: 87–92, 1953.

54. Lison, L. Zur Frage de Ausscheidung und Speicherung des Hamoglobins in der Amphibienniere. *Beitr. Path. Anat.*, **101**: 94–108, 1938.

55. Mangold, H. K., Schmid, H. H. O., and Stahl, E. Thin-layer chromatography (TLC), in *Method of Biochemical Analysis, XII*, D. Glick (ed.). Interscience Publishers, New York, 393–451, 1964.

56. Marinetti, G. V., Erbland, J., and Stotz, E. Phosphatides of pig heart cell fractions. *J. Biol. Chem.*, **233**: 562–65, 1961.

57. McBurney, D. H., and Pfaffmann, C. Gustatory adaptation to saliva and sodium chloride. *J. Exp. Psychol.*, **65**: 523–29, 1963.

58. McManus, J. F. A. Histological and histochemical uses of periodic acid. *Stain Technol.*, **23**: 99–108, 1948.

59. Mortimer, H., Wright, R. P., Bachman, C., and Collip, J. B. Effect of estrogenic hormone administration upon nasal mucous membrane of the monkey (*Macaca mulatta*). *Proc. Soc. Exp. Biol. Med.*, **34**: 535–38, 1936.

60. Pfaffmann, C. Taste mechanisms in preference behavior. *Amer. J. Clin. Nutr.*, **5**: 142–47, 1957.

61. Randerath, K., and Struck, H. Thin-layer chromatographic separation of nucleic acid derivatives on cellulose layers. *J. Chromatog.*, **6**: 365, cited in *Chem. Abstr.*, **56**: 10479, 1962.

62. Rasmussen, H., Sallis, J., Fang, M., DeLuca, H. F., and Young, R. Parathyroid hormone and anion uptake in isolated mitochondria. *Endocrinology*, **74**: 388–94, 1964.

63. Richman, M. J., and Abarbanel, A. R. Effects of estradiol, testosterone, diethylstibesterol and several of their derivatives upon the human oral mucous membrane. *J. Amer. Dental Assoc.*, **30**: 913–23, 1943.

64. Richter, C. P. Increased salt appetite in adrenalectomized rats. *Amer. J. Physiol.*, **115**: 155–61, 1936.

65. Richter, C. P., and Eckert, J. F. Increased

calcium appetite of parathyroidectomized rats. *Endocrinology,* 21: 50–54, 1937.

66. Richter, C. P., and Eckert, J. F. Mineral appetite of parathyroidectomized rats. *Amer. J. Med. Sci.,* 198: 9–16, 1939.

67. Richter, C. P., and Schmidt, E. Increased fat and decreased carbohydrate appetite of pancreatomized rats. *Endocrinology,* 28: 179–92, 1941.

68. Riggs, T. R. Hormones and the transport of nutrients across cell membranes, in *Actions of Hormones on Molecular Processes,* G. Litwack and D. Kritchevsky (eds.). John Wiley & Sons, New York, pp. 1–57, 1964.

69. Sakai, K. Studies on the chemical transmission in taste fiber endings. I: The action of acetylcholinesterase on bitter taste. *Chem. Pharm. Bull.,* 12: 1159, 1163, 1964.

70. Sakai, K., and Ozawa, H. Studies on chemical transmission in taste fiber endings. *Chem. Pharm. Bull.,* 13: 1440–44, 1965.

71. Schneider, R. A., Costiloe, J. P., Howard, R. P., and Wolf, S. Olfactory perception thresholds in hypogonadal women; changes accompanying administration of androgen and estrogen. *J. Clin. Endocrinol. Metab.,* 13: 379–90, 1958.

72. Schramm, M., and Bdolah, A. The mechanism of enzyme secretion by the cell. III: Intermediate stages in amylase transport as revealed by pulse labelling slices of parotid gland. *Arch. Biochem. Biophys.,* 104: 67–72, 1964.

73. Shackleford, J. M. Histochemical comparison of mucous secretions in rodent, carnivore, ungulate, and primate major salivary glands. *Ann. N.Y. Acad. Sci.,* 106: 572–82, 1963.

74. Skouby, A. P., and Zilstroff-Pedersen, K. The influence of acetylcholine, menthol, and strychnine on taste receptors in man. *Acta physiol. Scand.,* 34: 250–56, 1955.

75. Skramlik, E. von. The fundamental substrates of taste, in *Olfaction and Taste,* Y. Zotterman (ed.). Pergamon Press, New York, pp. 125–32, 1963.

76. Skude, G. Some factors influencing taste perception for phenylthiourea (P.T.C.). *Hereditas,* 50: 203–10, 1963.

77. Timiras, P. S., and Woodbury, D. M. The effect of thyroid activity on brain function and brain electrolyte distribution in rats. *Endocrinology,* 58: 181–92, 1956.

78. Torda, C., and Wolff, H. G. Effect of steroid substances on the synthesis of acetylcholine. *Proc. Soc. Exp. Biol. Med.,* 57: 327–30, 1944.

79. Tsuiki, S., Hashimoto, Y., and Pigman, W. Comparison of procedures for the isolation of bovine submaxillary mucin. *J. Biol. Chem.,* 236: 2172–78, 1961.

80. Wagner, H., Horhammer, L., and Wolff, P. Dunnschichtchromatographic von Phosphatiden und Glykolipiden. *Biochem. Z.,* 334: 175–84, 1961.

81. Wase, A. W., Goss, D. M., and Boyd, M. J. The metabolism of nickel: Spatial and temporal distribution of nickel in the mouse. *Arch. Biochem. Biophys.,* 51: 1–4, 1954.

82. Wilkins, W. F., and Hartman, J. D. An electrical analog for the olfactory processes. *Ann. N.Y. Acad. Sci.,* 116: 608–12, 1964.

83. Wurtman, R. J., Axelrod, J., and Fischer, J. F. Melatonin synthesis in the pineal gland: Effect of light mediated by the sympathetic nervous system. *Science,* 143: 1328–30, 1964.

84. Yamashita, S., and Sato, M. The effects of temperature on gustatory response of rats. *J. Cellular Comp. Physiol.,* 66: 1–17, 1965.

85. Yensen, R. Some factors affecting taste sensitivity in man. II: Depletion of body salt. *Quart. J. Exp. Psychol.,* 11: 230–38, 1959.

85. Yensen, R. Some factors affecting taste sensitivity in man. III: Water deprivation. *Quart. J. Exp. Psychol.,* 11: 239–48, 1959.

87. Yur'eva, G. Yu. New data on the role of protein sulfhydryl groups in taste sensitivity. *Biophysics* (an English translation of *Biofizika*), 6: 29–32, 1961.

Special appreciation is due Dr. M. Hoshino, Mr. M. Kudo, Mr. K. Izumi, Dr. S. Narita, Mr. N. Takase, Mr. H. Suzuki, Mr. Y. Saito, Miss Y. Yasuda, and Mr. H. Ochiai in our department for their collaboration in this work.

A part of this experiment was supported by funds from Tahoku Yaguruto Co., Ltd., Fukushima, Japan.

11: Dietary Protein and Amino Acids in Food Intake Regulation   *by Alfred E. Harper*

REDUCED FOOD intake is usually the earliest and most common sign of a dietary deficiency. Deficiencies of indispensable amino acids depress food intake particularly rapidly. Also, animals will make distinct selections between various deficient and adequate diets, particularly between diets containing and diets devoid of protein. Despite these intriguing observations, the problems of regulation of food intake and the chemical basis for food preferences have received only scanty attention from biochemists and nutritionists.

Food intake is affected by the quantity of protein in the diet and by the dietary pattern of amino acids. Food intake of animals fed a very low or a very high protein diet is depressed. The low food intake of animals fed a low protein diet is usually attributed to the inability of such a diet to support normal growth. Yet, if rats fed a low protein diet are exposed to a cold environment or are exercised—treatments that greatly increase energy expenditure—their food intake is enhanced, their protein intake is increased, and their growth rate is improved [14]. This implies that the depressed food intake of rats fed a low protein diet is the result of their limited ability to dissipate energy. It should be acknowledged, of course, that energy intake is limited by the inability of the low protein diet to support a rapid rate of growth and that there is something of the proverbial "vicious circle" in this situation.

Food intake is also depressed by a high protein intake. One question that arises here is whether the high specific dynamic action associated with ingestion of a high protein diet results in a large heat increment, which, according to the thermostatic hypothesis of food intake regulation, can inhibit food intake [2]. Although this may be important it does not seem to be the complete answer, for rats that are fed a high protein diet ad libitum show only a transitory depression of food intake [8]; then, after a few days, their food intake increases and their growth rate approaches that of a control group receiving a standard diet. During the few days required for food intake to rise, many of the enzymes of amino acid catabolism increase in activity. Although there is no direct evidence of a cause and effect relationship between these two phenomena, the association suggests that food intake may be depressed because of the accumulation of amino acids themselves or some products of amino acid catabolism. The increased activity of enzymes of amino acid catabolism may contribute to the maintenance of homeostasis by facilitating the removal of these substances. This in turn could increase the capacity of the animal to ingest protein.

The food intake of rats can also be markedly affected by the dietary pattern of amino acids. This problem has attracted our attention and is the one that I shall discuss in somewhat more detail. It is an outgrowth of studies of nutritional and biochemical effects of dietary amino acid balance begun about twenty years ago by Elvehjem and associates [3]. I shall not review the early investigations but shall depend on the first few slides to summarize the basic observations from which our work arose [7,9, 10].[1]

The general composition of the diets used in most of these studies is illustrated in Table 11–1. The basic diet is

TABLE 11–1: The Typical Purified Diet

Composition	g/kg
Protein (Casein or Fibrin)	60 to 120
Carbohydrate (Sucrose or Dextrin)[a]	to make 1000
Fat (Corn Oil)	50 to 100
Mineral Mixture	50
Vitamin Mixture	2.5

[a] Carbohydrate content adjusted to compensate for changes in fat, protein, or amino acid content.

a highly purified diet containing usually between 6 per cent and 12 per cent protein. It is a high carbohydrate, low fat diet containing adequate quantities of minerals and vitamins but not enough protein to satisfy the amino acid requirements of the rat.

Figure 11–1 illustrates some terms that I shall use. The basal diets for the experiments to be discussed have amino acid patterns resembling in general the pattern portrayed at the top of Fig. 11–1. The basal diets have balanced amino acid patterns, are low in protein, and

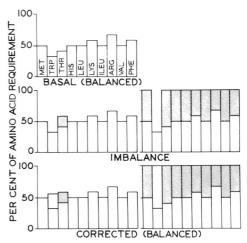

Fig. 11–1. Amino acid patterns of basal, imbalanced, and corrected diets. The open bars represent the proportions of indispensable amino acids, expressed as a percentage of the requirement of the rat, in the basal diet. The heavily crosshatched bars represent amino acids added to create an imbalance, the lightly crosshatched are those added to correct the imbalance.

usually meet about 50 per cent of the amino acid requirements of the rat. Diets that we refer to as imbalanced with respect to amino acids are of two types. The first type is prepared by adding to the basal diet a small amount of the one or more amino acids that are second limiting for growth. In the early experiments an amino acid imbalance of this type was created by adding a small excess of threonine to a 9 per cent casein diet supplemented with methionine and deficient in nicotinic acid. The growth of animals fed this diet was depressed, and the growth depression was accompanied by a depression of food intake. The other type of imbalanced diet, illustrated on the right of Fig. 11–1, results in a more severe condition and is the one we have used most extensively in our studies because the responses produced with it are larger and more reproducible. This type of imbalance is created by adding to the basal diet a mixture of all but one of the indispens-

[1] References [3], [7], [9], and [10] are review articles. They summarize much of the earlier literature on this subject and include references to the articles on which this paper is based.

able amino acids. We use the term "corrected diet" for the imbalanced diet supplemented with the amino acid or acids required to increase food intake and stimulate growth. The two corrected diets shown at the bottom of Fig. 11–1 provide nutritionally balanced patterns of amino acids. The basal and imbalanced diets have exactly the same concentration of the amino acid that is present in least amount; so, at least theoretically, they should be nutritionally equivalent. The amino acids added to create an imbalance represent merely a surplus that should be oxidized and used as a source of energy.

Typical effects of amino acid imbalances on the growth rate of rats are shown in Table 11–2. The basal diet

Figure 11–2 shows the relationship between the growth and food intake of

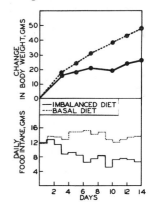

Fig. 11–2. *Average change in body weight and average daily food intake of protein-depleted rats fed 6 per cent fibrin basal or imbalanced (basal plus amino acid mixture devoid of histidine) diet ad libitum.*

TABLE 11–2: Weight Gain of Rats Fed on Diets in Which Amino Acid Imbalances Have Been Created

| Diet | Composition | | Weight Gain (g/2 wks.) |
	Fibrin (%)	Amino Acids	
Control	6	None	32
Imbalanced A	6	0.4% DL-met + 0.6% DL-phe	19
Corrected A	6	As for imbalanced A + 0.1% each of L-his, L-leu, DL-ileu, DL-val	40
Imbalanced B	6	Amino acid mix minus his	2
Corrected B	6	As for imbalanced B + 0.05% L-his	33

contained 6 per cent fibrin as the source of protein. Addition to the basal diet of 1 per cent of a mixture of methionine and phenylalanine, together with the second limiting amino acids, caused a growth depression which was prevented by further supplementation with a mixture of the four amino acids that are equally most limiting (imbalanced diet *A* versus corrected diet *A*). The effect of the imbalance created by addition of a mixture of amino acids devoid of histidine to the basal diet was more severe (imbalanced diet *B*). The adverse effect was completely prevented by a further supplement of histidine (corrected diet *B*).

protein-depleted rats fed the diet in which an amino acid imbalance was created by addition of a mixture of amino acids lacking histidine. A depression in food intake occurs within one day in non-depleted rats previously fed the basal diet. Rapid occurrence of the effect is shown in Fig. 11–3. The animals for this study were depleted of protein for four days, then were kept without food overnight so that they would eat quite avidly a diet containing protein. They were then allowed to eat ad libitum and food intake measurements were made at intervals over a twenty-four-hour period.

Observations on the preferences of

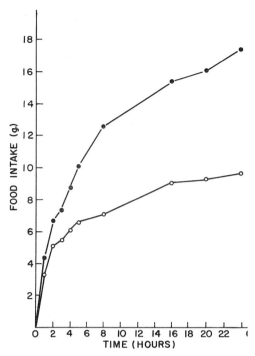

Fig. 11–3.   Twenty-four-hour food intake pattern of rats fed 6 per cent casein basal or imbalanced (basal plus amino acid mixture devoid of threonine) diet.

protein-depleted rats offered the basal diet (6 per cent fibrin) and a protein-free diet or the imbalanced diet (6 per cent fibrin plus amino acid mixture devoid of histidine) and a protein-free diet are shown in Fig. 11–4. Those offered the

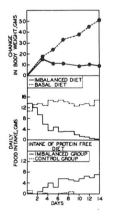

Fig. 11–4.   Average change in body weight and average daily food intake of protein-depleted rats offered a free choice between inbalanced diet (fibrin basal diet plus amino acid mixture devoid of histidine) and protein-free diet.

basal diet ate very little of the protein-free diet and their intake of the basal diet remained quite constant throughout

the experimental period. Those offered the imbalanced diet ate gradually increasing amounts of the protein-free diet and their intake of the imbalanced diet fell until, toward the end of the experiment, they were eating almost exclusively the protein-free diet, which will not support life, and were rejecting the imbalanced diet, which will support a moderate rate of growth.

Some further studies of food preferences of rats offered other choices are illustrated in the next few figures. The basal diet for the study summarized in Fig. 11–5 contained 6 per cent casein

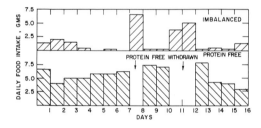

Fig. 11–5.   Average daily food intake of rats offered a free choice of imbalanced diet (casein basal diet plus amino acid mixture devoid of tryptophan) or protein-free diet.

supplemented with methionine to make it limiting in tryptophan. The imbalanced diet contained in addition a mixture of amino acids lacking tryptophan. The two diets were offered ad libitum. For seven days the rats ate primarily the protein-free diet and relatively little of the imbalanced diet. After the seventh day the protein-free diet was withdrawn for one day so that they had access only to the imbalanced diet; they ate it quite well. The next day when they were again offered a choice they ate almost exclusively the protein-free diet. Then the protein-free diet was withdrawn for two days, and again when they were offered a choice they selected the protein-free diet.

The food selection pattern for a single rat offered a protein-free diet and a 6 per cent fibrin diet to which an amino acid mixture devoid of histidine was added to create an imbalance is shown in Fig. 11–6. By the end of a week this

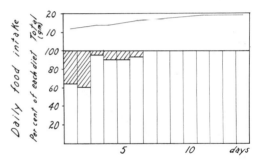

Fig. 11–7. Daily food intake of protein-depleted rats offered a choice between 6 per cent fibrin basal and imbalanced (basal plus amino acid mixture devoid of histidine) diets.

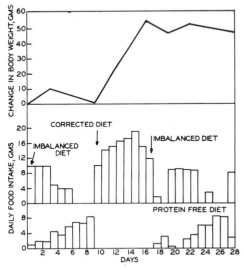

Fig. 11–6. Weight change and daily food intake of an individual rat offered im-balanced (fibrin basal plus amino acid mix-ture devoid of histidine) and protein-free diets simultaneously. Imbalance corrected by addition of histidine from days 10 to 17.

rat was selecting the protein-free diet exclusively. Histidine was then added to correct the imbalance and immediately the rat stopped eating the protein-free diet and ate only the corrected diet. Then the histidine was withdrawn. The food intake pattern was initially some-what erratic but after a few days the animal was eating more of the protein-free diet than of the imbalanced diet that will support growth. The results of an experiment in which protein-depleted rats were offered the basal diet contain-ing 6 per cent fibrin and the imbalanced diet containing an amino acid mixture lacking histidine are shown in Fig. 11–7. During the first two days the rats ate both diets nearly equally but after the third day they ate very little of the im-balanced diet. After six days they ate only the balanced basal diet and com-

pletely rejected the imbalanced diet. When rats were offered the corrected diet, which is well balanced together with a protein-free diet, they ate very little of the protein-free diet and selected almost exclusively the corrected diet throughout the fourteen-day period (Fig. 11–8). Rats offered two balanced diets—

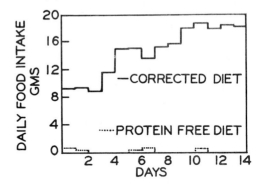

Fig. 11–8. Daily food intake of rats offered a choice between corrected (imbalanced diet of Fig. 11–7 plus histidine) and protein-free diets.

the basal, which is a low-protein diet (6 per cent fibrin), and the corrected diet, which is a balanced diet with essentially a somewhat higher protein level (6 per cent fibrin plus a complete amino acid mixture)—showed no uniform prefer-ence (Table 11–3); some rats selected exclusively one diet and some the other.

TABLE 11–3: Food Intake of Protein-Depleted Rats Offered a Choice between Basal and "Corrected" Diets

Rat Number	Food Intake (g/2 wks.)	
	Basal	Corrected
1	200	3
2	196	8
3	4	210
4	2	199
5	1	213
6	206	3

Figure 11–9 summarizes results obtained when rats were offered a choice

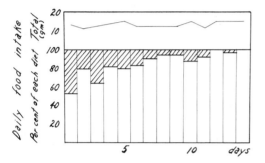

Fig. 11–9. Daily food intake of protein-depleted rats offered a choice between imbalanced (as for Fig. 11–7) and corrected (as for Fig. 11–8) diets.

between an imbalanced and a corrected diet. The pairs of diets used in the selection studies discussed so far have differed considerably in appearance, texture, or taste because of the presence or absence of protein or additional free amino acids in one diet of each pair. The two diets used in this experiment contained exactly the same amount of protein, exactly the same amount of free amino acids to create the imbalance, and differed only in that the corrected diet contained an additional 0.1 per cent of histidine·HCl in a mixture of 6 per cent amino acids containing more than 1 per cent arginine·HCl and lysine·HCl. These animals were a little slower to make a clear selection, but by the seventh day they showed a distinct preference for the

corrected diet, with the imbalanced diet making up only about 10 per cent of their total food intake. Apparently the rat can distinguish between two diets differing only in the 0.1 per cent histidine·HCl content in the presence of two other amino acid hydrochlorides.

The probability that the rat distinguishes among these diets by taste rather than smell is indicated by the results shown in Fig. 11–10. An amino acid mix-

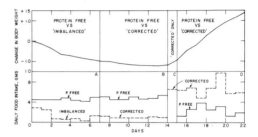

Fig. 11–10. Average weight change and average daily food intake of rats offered a choice between: (A) imbalanced (casein basal plus amino acid mixture devoid of tryptophan) and protein-free diets; (B) corrected (imbalanced plus tryptophan) and protein-free diets; (C) corrected diet; no choice; (D) as for B.

ture lacking tryptophan was used to create the amino acid imbalance used in this experiment. The basal diet contained 6 per cent of casein supplemented with methionine and threonine. After the animals had been selecting the protein-free diet in preference to the imbalanced diet for a week, the imbalance was corrected by the addition of tryptophan. Nevertheless, the rats continued to eat the protein-free diet for another week, until it was withdrawn for one day and they were forced to eat the corrected diet. When they were again offered a choice between the protein-free and the corrected diet their preference changed and they took about 80 per cent of their food from the corrected diet and grew well.

Figure 11–11 summarizes a series of

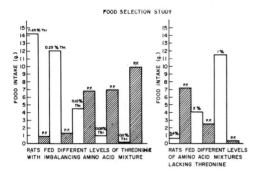

FOOD SELECTION STUDY

Fig. 11–11. Average daily food intake of rats. Right. *Offered a choice between protein-free diet and imbalanced diet containing different amounts of amino acid mixture devoid of threonine.* Left. *Offered a choice between protein-free diet and imbalanced diet containing different amounts of threonine to correct the imbalance.*

observations made with a basal diet that contained 6 per cent casein supplemented with methionine. The amino acid imbalance was created by adding to it 6 per cent of a mixture of amino acids lacking threonine. In one experiment different quantities of the amino acid mixture lacking threonine were added to the basal diet to create imbalances differing in severity; rats were offered a choice between one of these and a protein-free diet. With 1.0 per cent of the amino acid mixture lacking threonine in the diet, the animals selected that diet and rejected the protein-free diet. When the quantity of amino acid mixture lacking threonine was increased to 2.0 per cent, the animals ate almost as much of the protein-free as of the imbalanced diet. When the quantity of amino acid mixture was increased further to 5.4 per cent, the animals selected the protein-free diet and almost completely rejected the imbalanced diet. Then, increments of threonine were added to this diet which the animals rejected to give a series of corrected diets that differed in threonine content. As the increments of threonine in the diet were increased from 0.05, to 0.1, to 0.25 per cent the

amount of protein-free diet selected fell and the amount of corrected diet selected increased more or less proportionately to the amount of threonine added to correct the imbalance.

The next two figures show some of the changes observed in plasma amino acid concentrations of rats fed a diet (6 per cent fibrin) in which an amino acid imbalance was created by addition of an amino acid mixture lacking histidine. The plasma histidine concentration of rats fed the basal diet was constant over a period of several days; a slight fall occurred in the concentration of lysine (Fig. 11–12). The plasma histidine con-

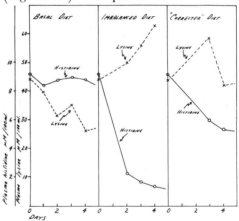

Fig. 11–12. Plasma concentrations of lysine and histidine of rats fed fibrin basal diet, imbalanced diet (basal plus amino acid mixture devoid of histidine), or corrected diet (imbalanced diet plus histidine).

centration of rats fed the imbalanced diet fell sharply; the concentration of lysine which was added in the mixture used to create the imbalance rose substantially. In rats fed the corrected diet histidine concentration fell a little but not nearly as much as in animals fed the imbalanced diet. Lysine concentration rose only temporarily. Fig. 11–13 shows how the ratios of lysine and certain other amino acids to histidine changed in the plasma of rats fed the imbalanced diet.

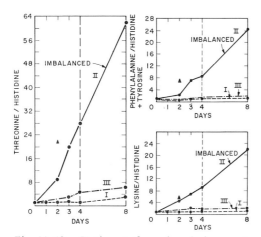

Fig. 11–13. Ratios of threonine, lysine, and phenylalanine to histidine in plasma of rats fed diets as for Fig. 11–12.

The ratios for both the basal and the corrected groups remained quite constant throughout the experiment. These groups ate well and grew well whereas the food intake and rate of growth of those fed the imbalanced diet were depressed.

The change in threonine concentration in plasma with time, after ingestion of a single meal of the imbalanced diet, is shown in Fig. 11–14. Rats for

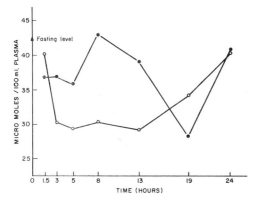

Fig. 11–14. Plasma concentrations of threonine of rats fed casein basal diet or imbalanced diet (basal plus amino acid mixture devoid of threonine).

this study were trained to eat for only two hours daily and were then fed a

5 g meal of the imbalanced diet containing the amino acid mixture lacking threonine. In animals fed the imbalanced diet, threonine concentration was low during the interval of from two to twelve hours, the same period during which depression of food intake occurs. Animals fed the basal diet did not show a comparable fall until the postabsorptive period and this is not regularly observed. Both groups consumed the same amount of threonine.

The results of an experiment in which isotopically labeled threonine was included in the basal and imbalanced diets to determine the fate of the limiting amino acid are shown in Table 11–4.

TABLE 11–4: Distribution of Radioactivity after Feeding Rats Basal or Imbalanced Diets Containing U-C^{14}-Threonine

	% of Ingested C^{14}	
Distribution	Control Diet (6% Casein)	Imbalanced Diet (6% Casein + 10% A.A. Mix.-Thr.)
Expired CO_2	18.4	14.3
Urine	2.1	2.2
Feces	1.6	1.2
Carcass	70.1	74.6
Liver	5.9	7.2
Total	98.1	99.5

NOTE: Each rat was fed 7 g of diet containing 8.5 μc of C^{14}-threonine at the beginning of the experiment and the same amount of the same diet without C^{14}-threonine twenty-four hours later. The experiment lasted forty-eight hours.

We had originally thought that the amino acids added to create an amino acid imbalance might stimulate the oxidation of amino acids generally and that this might result in some wasting of the amino acid that was already limiting growth. Such an effect would be equivalent to making the diet more deficient and could account for the growth and food intake depressions observed and for the fall in the plasma concentration of the limiting amino acid. The results of the isotope study provided no evidence that an amino acid imbalance enhanced either oxidation or excretion of the limiting amino acid. It appeared, however, that there was enhanced incorporation of radioactivity from the limiting amino acid threonine in the carcass and the liver. The results provided no evidence that an amino acid imbalance caused a metabolic defect that could account for the growth and food intake depressions observed.

At this time we were struck by certain analogies between animals fed a diet having an amino acid imbalance and animals fed a diet that was completely deficient in a single amino acid. It was well known that the food intake of rats fed a diet that was deficient in a single indispensable amino acid fell rapidly [4], that the plasma concentration of the amino acid missing from the diet fell drastically [12], and that such animals would eat more of a protein-free diet than of the amino acid–deficient diet. Sidransky and associates [15] had observed that if rats were force-fed a diet devoid of a single indispensable amino acid, they developed pathologic lesions such as fatty infiltration of the liver and atrophy of pancreatic and intestinal cells, and their lifespan was shorter than that of rats fed the same diet ad libitum. This suggested that the reduced food intake of rats fed ad libitum protected them for some time from the adverse effects associated with ingestion of a large amount of an amino acid–deficient diet and that the same might be true of rats fed an imbalanced diet.

In an effort to magnify the adverse effects of an amino acid imbalance, rats fed an imbalanced diet were injected with insulin to stimulate their food intake. In contrast to the observations on rats force-fed an amino acid–deficient diet, stimulation of the food intake of rats fed the imbalanced diet caused no adverse effects; in fact, the insulin-injected animals grew well and appeared as healthy as the control animals. Similar observations were made by Klain and associates [11], who stimulated the food intake of rats fed an imbalanced diet by exposing them to a cold environment. Growth curves for animals so treated are shown in Fig. 11–15. These results

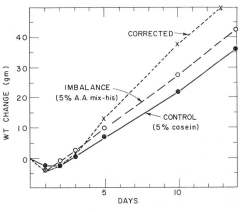

EFFECT OF A.A. IMBALANCE ON GROWTH AT 7°C

Fig. 11–15. Weight change of rats fed basal, imbalanced, and corrected diets at 7°C.

indicated that the adverse effects of amino acid imbalance were the result of food intake depression, not the cause of it.

In some further studies we have observed that the food intake of rats exposed to a cold environment can be depressed if the amino acid imbalance is made very severe (Fig. 11–16). We have also observed that rats exposed to cold will select a protein-free diet in preference to the imbalanced diet, which they eat avidly if they are given no choice (Fig. 11–17). Presumably, then, the same factors operate to depress the food intake of rats in a cold or a warm environment, but sensitivity to these factors is much less in the cold because of the overriding need for energy.

We do not know the biochemical basis

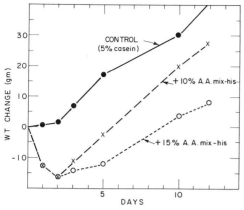

EFFECT OF A.A. IMBALANCE ON GROWTH AT 7°C

Fig. 11–16. Weight change of rats fed severely imbalanced diets at 7°C.

for the depressed food intake and aberrant food preference of rats fed a diet in which there is an amino acid imbalance. There are, however, some interesting associations that invite speculation. The metabolic studies suggest that an amino acid imbalance does not stimulate oxidation or excretion of the limiting amino acid but probably enhances its incorpo-

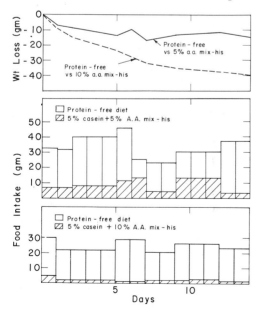

Fig. 11–17. Weight change and food intake of rats offered a choice between imbalanced and protein-free diets at 7°C.

ration into liver proteins and possibly into intestinal proteins. Initially, at least, incorporation of the growth-limiting amino acid into muscle is not depressed. Elevated incorporation into the liver with no decrease in incorporation in the rest of the body would tend to reduce the amount of the limiting amino acid circulating in body fluids and could account for the fall in its concentration in blood and muscle plasma. The end result, as was mentioned, would be a change in the plasma amino acid pattern resembling that which occurs in animals fed a diet that is completely deficient in one of the indispensable amino acids.

Since pathologic lesions develop in rats force-fed a diet that is deficient in one of the indispensable amino acids but not in those fed such a diet ad libitum [15], the sharp fall in the food intake of the animals fed ad libitum can be interpreted as a homeostatic response which tends to prevent a drastic and deleterious change in the internal environment. Others have suggested [1,4,13] that the altered plasma amino acid pattern may be the stimulus that triggers the response. Reduced food intake would tend to prevent excessive accumulation of amino acids that cannot be used for protein synthesis and ingestion of a protein-free diet, would tend to restore the plasma amino acid pattern toward normal.

To account for the depressed intake of an imbalanced diet that will support growth and the preference of rats offered such a diet for a protein-free diet, we must assume that a signal indicating some generally adverse condition in the internal environment is monitored, and further, that this signal does not indicate the true state of affairs. This might be compared to holding an ice cube by the thermostat in a hot room with the result that the furnace is activated. If it is assumed that the plasma amino acid pattern is monitored, and that changes in the pattern of the type that occur in rats fed an amino acid–deficient diet result in depressed food intake, the similarly altered plasma amino acid pattern of rats fed an imbalanced diet should also result in depressed food intake. How and where such changes are monitored is unknown. In fact, it is difficult to accept the idea that the variety of changes that can occur with over twenty different amino acids are distinguished. It seems more likely that changes of a certain type result in a lack of well-being that, once sensed, causes a loss of appetite.

The ability of the rat to distinguish among diets that differ by only a small amount of one amino acid also deserves comment. That the rat can distinguish between imbalanced and corrected diets, both of which contain free amino acids and differ by only 0.1 per cent of one amino acid, is clear. The need, in some experiments, to force the animal to eat the corrected diet before it will distinguish between the corrected and imbalanced diets certainly suggests that taste rather than smell is the sense involved, and this would be anticipated with such non-volatile substances as amino acids. There is evidence that individual amino acids elicit responses from nerves involved in taste [5] and there is some evidence of individual amino acid preferences [6]. Again, it is not necessary to assume that all of the individual amino acids can be distinguished, only that the animal can distinguish between two diets, one of which is associated with well-being and one of which is not.

Although this research has raised many questions and has answered few, it provides an interesting example of a situation in which an animal will show almost absolute preference for a nutritionally inadequate diet and rejection of a diet that will support life. Apparently the response to some chemical change in the internal environment overrides the response to a nutritional need.

Discussion

Lepkovsky: What do amino acids have to do with taste?

Harper: I did point out that animals are in some way able to distinguish between two diets that differ only in relatively small amounts of a single amino acid in the presence of others that from an anthropomorphic viewpoint we would expect to taste similar to the amino acid omitted.

Beidler: Am I correct in assuming that if you take one amino acid out of the diet, proteins needing this amino acid are not made?

Harper: Right.

Beidler: Is there not some evidence, in insects, that there is a protein receptor?

Epstein: In the female fly *Phormia regina,* protein intake increases before each batch of eggs is laid (Dethier, *Biol. Bull.,* **121**: 456, 1961).

Beidler: There is evidence of self-regulation of amino acids in rats (Halstead and Gallagher, *J. Comp. Physiol. Psychol.,* **55**: 107, 1962).

Harper: Kare's work and that of others indicate that preferences exist for certain amino acids even in rats that are not deficient. Halstead used animals that had been fed a completely deficient diet. That is quite different from what we are doing and is an extension of work that Cannon initiated quite a number of years ago. Threonine was lacking in Cannon's diet and the animals selected the threonine over glycine.

Jacobs: What is the earliest you've seen this avoidance?

Harper: For the most part it has been overnight, probably sixteen hours. We are now beginning to look at shorter intervals.

Jacobs: Although you've not used the term "taste" operationally, the animals discriminate some signal in the diet. Would you accept the possibility that these animals are learning a short-time avoidance?

Harper: I think one could phrase it in those terms if we assume that a homeostatic mechanism tends to maintain a relatively constant pattern of plasma amino acids, and that the animal is avoiding a diet that will bring about an alteration of the normal plasma pattern. The protein-free diet, which will not support life, will tend to restore the plasma amino acid pattern to normal. We have no evidence of a cause and effect relationship between the plasma pattern and food intake, just an association between them under several conditions.

Barnes: One of your graphs showed a free-choice study in which you were comparing rats given two containers, one with the imbalanced diet and the other with a corrected diet. You fooled the rats even though the amino acid composition was balanced.

Harper: That was one in which tryptophan was low. The response was different from that observed with histidine and threonine low. We haven't done enough work to show whether this happens by chance occasionally or whether it is characteristic of amino acids. When we replaced the tryptophan, apparently the animals didn't recognize, during the course of a week, that there was any difference between the corrected and the imbalanced diet, and they continued to eat the protein-free diet. When the protein-free diet was withdrawn for one day and they were forced to eat the corrected diet, they continued to eat it at a level of about 80 per cent of their total food intake for the duration of the experiment. I think that the animals recognize the protein-free diet as being completely different from a diet containing the mixture of amino acids, that they do not even taste the corrected diet during this period of time. After they are once forced to take it, I suggest that they experience a feeling of well-being which they can associate with the improved diet; then they continue to take it.

Kare: Working with birds, we offered an adequate diet, save for methionine, and then set up a preference situation where these birds could correct their diet with a methionine solution. They failed to select the methionine. Also, where we had birds on very low-protein diets (5 per cent protein) and gave them an opportunity to have an adequate protein intake from fluid in a two-choice situation, they died of protein insufficiency rather than drink dilute casein solution. The casein was amino acid supplemented. For some reason casein is highly offensive to birds and is not particularly palatable for rats.

In work with Halpern and Bernard (*J. Gen. Physiol.,* **45**: 681, 1962), preferences for both the essential and nonessential amino acids in rats on an adequate diet, were studied. The electrophysiological response magnitude and the behavioral response for the nonessential amino acids were more impressive than were those for the so-called essential amino acids. Rats selected glycine and alanine while all the essential amino acids tested—threonine, tryptophan, methionine, and valine—had a low response magnitude and were rejected in behavioral trials.

Stevenson: Have you tried insulin in these animals that are hypophagic?

Harper: We could stimulate their food intake with insulin when the imbalance was not severe; they ate well and grew normally. When we tried insulin with the more severe imbalance, the animals died, mainly from hypoglycemia, before they would eat enough to prevent hypoglycemia.

Stevenson: They grew well, did they? Beaton and I gave insulin to animals that were hypoglycemic because of a low-protein diet. They ate well, but their growth rate was only half that of normals; it was halfway between the protein-deficient diet without insulin and the complete diet.

Harper: These diets were almost the same as our low-protein control diet, but insulin at the level we used (1 unit/100 g body weight) did not stimulate the food intake of the controls.

REFERENCES

1. Almquist, H. J. Utilization of amino acids by chicks. *Arch. Biochem. Biophys.,* **52**: 197–202, 1954.
2. Brobeck, J. R. Hormones and metabolism. *Recent Progr. Hormone Res.,* **16**: 439–59, 1960.
3. Elvehjem, C. A., and Krehl, W. A. Dietary interrelationships and imbalance in nutrition. *Borden Rev. Nutr. Res.,* **16**: 69–84, 1955.
4. Frazier, L. E., Wissler, R. W., Steffee, C. H., Woolridge, F. L., and Cannon, P. R. Studies in amino acid utilization. I: The dietary utilization of mixtures of purified amino acids in protein-depleted adult albino rats. *J. Nutr.,* **33**: 65–83, 1947.
5. Halpern, B. P., Bernard, R. A., and Kare, M. R. Amino acids as gustatory stimuli in the rat. *J. Gen. Physiol.,* **45**: 681–702, 1962.
6. Halstead, W. C., and Gallagher, B. B. Autoregulation of amino acids intake in the albino rat. *J. Comp. Physiol. Psychol.,* **55**: 107–11, 1962.
7. Harper, A. E. Amino acid toxicities and imbalances, in *Mammalian Protein Metabolism, II,* H. N. Munro and J. B. Allison (eds.). Academic Press, New York, 87–134, 1964.
8. Harper, A. E. Effect of variations in protein intake on enzymes of amino acid metabolism. *Can. J. Biochem.,* **43**: 1589–1603, 1965.
9. Harper, A. E., Leung, P., Yoshida, A., and Rogers, Q. R. Some new thoughts on amino acid imbalance. *Fed. Proc.,* **23**: 1087–92, 1964.
10. Harper, A. E., and Rogers, Q. R. Amino acid imbalance. *Proc. Nutr. Soc.,* **24**: 173–90, 1965.
11. Klain, G. J., Vaughan, D. A., and Vaughan, L. N. Interrelationships of cold exposure and amino acid imbalance. *J. Nutr.,* **78**: 359–64, 1962.
12. Longenecker, J. B., and Hause, N. L. Relationship between plasma amino acids and composition of the ingested protein. *Arch. Biochem. Biophys.,* **84**: 46–59, 1959.
13. Mellinkoff, S. Digestive system. *Ann. Rev. Physiol.,* **19**: 193–96, 1957.
14. Meyer, J. H., and Hargus, W. A. Factors influencing food intake of rats fed low-protein rations. *Amer. J. Physiol.,* **197**: 1350–52, 1959.
15. Sidransky, H., and Baba, T. Chemical pathology of acute amino acid deficiencies. III: Morphologic and biochemical changes in young rats fed valine- or lysine-devoid diets. *J. Nutr.,* **70**: 463–71, 1960.

12: Nutrition, Learning, and Adaptive Capacity *by J. Lát*

THIS PAPER will deal with the effect of different diets on behavior and with the question of whether it is possible for the functional state of the central nervous system (CNS) to be regulated by means of self-selection of dietary components. In reviewing the literature, two important characteristics become apparent. In the past, experimental workers have concentrated on pathological consequences rather than on the question of how CNS-functions can be regulated by means of nutrition. Therefore, the conspicuous effects of depletion of food components rather than the effects of overnutrition were investigated [3,4,5,9].

In considering the more fruitful problem of the regulation of CNS-functions, one is struck with the following paradox: Most of the theorists (Carpenter, Liebig, Boyd-Orr, Carrel, Williams) emphasize the role of nutrition in determining the individual and national character [32]—"The man is what he eats." On the other hand, clinical and experimental experience lend poor support to such speculations. Is this discrepancy due to the limited effect of the diet? Perhaps it is a consequence of the highly effective homeostasis of the CNS? On the other hand, this paradox might be an expression of methodological errors and difficulties. Another group of problems concerns the possible ways of enhancing the effects of nutrition on the CNS.

Evidence for the above-mentioned discrepancy between the theoretically expected and actually observed effects of nutrition is to be found within the following three methodological problems:

1. Part of the contradictory findings stem from semantic and logical causes. For example, there may be only a 15 per cent spread between the protein content of diets, designated in the literature as high-protein and low-protein diets containing 27–80 and 0–12 per cent protein respectively. This absence of standardization camouflages a number of undefined conditions, e.g., changes in source of proteins and, especially, different quantitative proportions of other food components.

2. A far more serious source of contradictions, however, is the uncertainty of what is actually measured by numerous methods of assessing behavior. Which psychic or nervous function is considered to be the basic one? The so-called Non-Specific Excitability Level (NEL) seems to fulfill the requirements [17]. It belongs in the category of motivational factors, related in some respect to concepts such as strength of excitation process (Pavlov), emotionality (Hall), general drive state, vigilance, level of arousal (Hebb), and perhaps even to Spearman's general intelligence factor.

Constitutional differences in NEL can be measured under standardized conditions by means of the frequency of spontaneous reactions [18], the average re-action time, or by the intensity of the reaction. NEL is a measure of the sensitivity of the organism to external stimuli. Figure 12–1 gives evidence of one

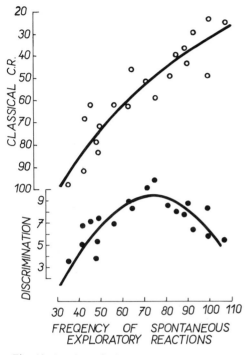

Fig. 12–1. *Correlations of the frequency of exploratory reactions with the speed of formation of a conditioned reflex (upper curve) and the speed of discrimination (lower curve). Male rats (N = 20) had learned to bar press a light stimulus. The speed of learning is expressed in the number of trials to reach a stable latency of response (ordinate of the upper graph). The same rats had to differentiate between the conditioned stimulus (continuous light) and interrupted light as an unreinforced stimulus. The speed of discrimination is expressed in average latency (ordinate of the lower graph) and is plotted against the intensity of exploratory reactions (the frequency of rearing reaction consists of four tests in the habituation period, abscissae).*

of its basic characteristics. NEL non-linearly determines the rate of both associative and discriminative types of learning. Similar relationships can be ob-

tained if constitutional differences in NEL are plotted against the speed of habituation—the rate of adaptation to physical, pharmacological, and nutritional trauma [2,8,17]. Some evidence exists that NEL plays a positive role in the longevity of lifespan [19]. Two of the most important lines for further investigation are the relation of NEL to other psychic functions, e.g., memory and mental illness, and the refinement of the methods of its quantitative and more direct measurement [22].

3. The inverted U-shape relationship between NEL and discrimination-learning (Fig. 12–1) explains some contradictory findings in the effect of diets on rate of learning. In individuals of low excitability level, a diet that increases NEL will increase the rate of learning. However, the same effect on learning in highly excitable individuals can be achieved by a diet that decreases NEL. If we take another rule into account, i.e., the qualitatively different effects of small, medium, and large doses of biologically active substances, one can understand the main sources of contradictory or negative conclusions concerning the effect of diet on learning [18,21].

If systematic attention is paid to biological variability, it can be used to show the close relationship between NEL and metabolic processes. It can be seen in Fig. 12–2 that with respect to inter- and intra-individual variability, a high correlation exists between the metabolic rate (caloric intake, oxygen consumption, body temperature, and weight increments) and NEL. Young or adult animals with an inherited high level of excitability possess a higher metabolic rate than do older rats of a lower excitability level.

The third type of evidence is provided by the direct influence of increased intake of certain food components. The depletion of specific substances (Table

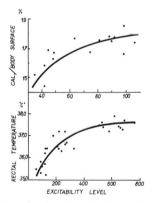

Fig. 12–2. Lower: *Correlation between individual differences in NEL and rectal temperature. Thirty-one females, genetically selected for NEL (F6 plus F7 generations) were used. NEL is defined in terms of the frequency of rearing reactions (sum of six tests). The individual values of rectal temperature are averages of from eighteen to twenty measurements performed during four days [11].*
Upper: *Correlation between calories per body surface and excitability level.*

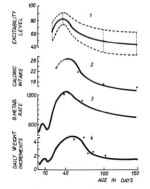

Above: *Ontogenetic changes: (1) in NEL; (2) in average food intake per body surface; in basal metabolic rate; (3) constructed from data obtained by Kibler and Brody [15]; and (4) in absolute weight increments.*

12–1) results in a general depressive effect upon NEL. The increased intake of carbohydrates, fats, and salt augmented the NEL whereas proteins and potassium decreased the NEL [7,21]. Thus, there exists a possibility of controlling NEL by means of nutrition.

The depletion of a food constituent does not depress NEL linearly but leads

TABLE 12–1: Effect of Food Components on CNS-Excitability Level (NEL)

Component	Over Feeding		Under Feeding
Calories	A ↑	B ↓	↓
Proteins	↓		↓
Carbohydrates	↑		↓
Fats	↑		↓
NaCl	↑		↓
KCl	↓		↓

in diminishing oscillations of excitatory and inhibitory phases. A permanently increased caloric intake during the period of body growth exerts only positive effects on NEL and other functions. On the other hand, during the second half of the lifespan, normally a period of fat deposition, a 25–30 per cent reduction in food intake increases the NEL [19,24].

The excitative or depressive effect of nutrition is not as dramatic when compared with the effects of some psychotropic drugs. Nutrition has, however, two great advantages:

1. The excitatory or depressive effect of a particular diet can be maintained for greater periods of time, with minimal changes, at a given level.

2. It removes the well-known dangers of side effects and resistance to the prolonged administration of drugs.

Let us attempt to analyze the problem of how to increase the effect of nutrition on NEL. There are several possibilities that include combining nutritive components, each of which exerts an effect in the same direction. In general, the law of summation and compensation applies here. In concrete situations, however, a number of interesting problems arise. Fraňková [8] gradually increased the amounts of salt added to a carbohydrate as well as to a high-protein diet. She obtained first an increase, then a depression, of the NEL (Fig. 12–3). She also depressed the excitatory effect of high-carbohydrate and high-fat diets by adding increased amounts of KCl. Fran-

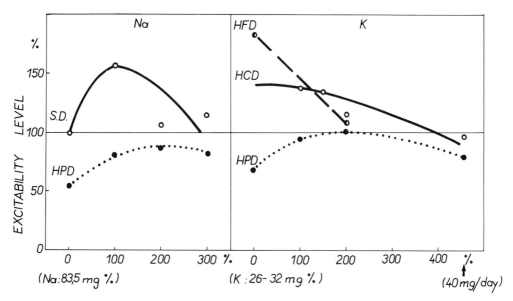

Fig. 12–3.   Changes in NEL obtained by increasing the amount of NaCl and KCl in experimental diets obtained by Fraňková [8]. Frequency of rearing reactions was used (as an indicator of NEL). Changes in NEL are expressed in percentages of parallel control values. Abscissae = increased amount of NaCl (left graph) or KCl (right graph) added to a standard diet (SD), high-protein diet (HPD), high-fat diet (HFD), and high-carbohydrate diet (HCD).

ková, however, observed a very interesting effect; the inhibitory influence of a protein diet was eliminated by the addition of increased doses of another inhibitory substance, KCl. I would like to suggest the following interpretation. In another experiment [16,20] it was found that the spontaneous intake of casein correlates positively with the intake of KCl whereas starch intake correlates with NaCl. Rats are "aware" that potassium is important for protein utilization. In an extreme diet such as that used by Fraňková (a 73 calorie percentage of proteins) a normal potassium content could constitute a relative lack of potassium, thus leading to depressed NEL, for other reasons than the addition of considerable doses of KCl to the diet. When combining excitatory or inhibitory substances, it is thus necessary to bear in mind that, in order to attain the summation effect, one cannot simply increase the amounts of one substance without taking into account its relations

to the quantitative pattern of other food components.

This stage of constructing a maximally excitatory or maximally inhibitory diet opens up wide perspectives for experimental work. The isolated effect of only a small number of food components on the NEL is known. The large number of possible combinations awaits discovery. This is one of the types of biological research in which the cooperation of a large number of behaviorists and biochemists would be effective. Probably the use of synthetic diets would be much more fruitful than diets originating from natural sources.

Let us now assume for a moment that we have these maximally excitatory, inhibitory diets, which meet all nutritional requirements. Can we expect the effects of these diets to be equally as strong as the effect of psychotropic drugs? Will it be possible to shift an individual from one extreme end of the Gaussian curve of excitability to the other? The simple fact that constitutional differences in the NEL of a standard diet are not eliminated indicates that the next step of the study should be aimed at understanding individual differences in the utilization processes. An important role is played here by individual differences in endocrinological processes. Relations between emotional–non-emotional or active-inactive strains of rats and endocrinological activity have been reported [13,23]. In a preliminary experiment we have seen that after adrenalectomy, nutritional needs change markedly in animals with low excitability, namely toward the selection of an excitatory (high-salt and high-carbohydrate) diet [20,23]. Andik and Donhoffer [1] showed that thyroxine administration increases the preference for starch, which has been shown to exert an excitatory effect.

From these assumptions and other findings concerning the long-term effects of a short-term nutritional treatment during early ontogeny [8,24,26], the following experiment on the effects of combined nutritional and endocrinological treatment upon NEL was designed. The time schedule of thyroxine and dietary treatment, as well as the average growth curves of six groups of rats, can be seen in Fig. 12–4. It was found in previous pilot experiments by Gollová that thyroxine given in a dose of 30 μg on the second, third, and fourth days of life has a slight but detectable effect upon NEL and body temperature in adulthood. As can be seen in Fig. 12–5, neither a 22 per cent increase in the carbohydrate content of the diet nor the administration of thyroxine increased the NEL markedly, but the combination of both increased the NEL to a level that comes close to the value of the genetically selected, excitable strain of rats. If an increased need for carbohydrates was induced by thyroxine, but the rats received a high-protein diet, the markedly inhibitory effect of this diet was re-

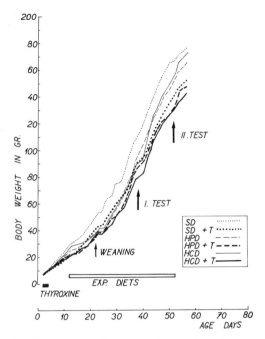

Fig. 12–4. Growth curves of experimental and control groups of female rats (N = 21 per group) treated in early ontogeny with thyroxine (ep.) and later fed experimental diets. Doses of thyroxine were 30 γ per rat on the second, third and fourth days of life. Experimental diets were given from the twelfth to the fifty-second day. The NEL was obtained on the fortieth and fifty-second day (see arrows). Experimental groups: SD = standard diet without thyroxine treatment; SD + T = standard diet and thyroxine treatment; HPD = high-protein diet only; HPD + T = high-protein diet and thyroxine treatment; HCD = high-carbohydrate diet only; HCD + T = high-carbohydrate diet and thyroxine treatment. The ratio of calorie percentage of proteins, carbohydrates, and fats was 27 : 52 : 21 in the standard diet, 60 : 27 : 13 in the high-protein diet, and 13 : 74 : 13 in the high-carbohydrate diet.

moved. Thus the combination of diet and thyroxine treatment exerts an additive effect upon NEL. The summation effect of the factors involved was tested by the analysis of variance performed by Roth (Table 12–2).

In Fig. 12–6 the quantitative effect of a high-protein diet and a high-carbohydrate diet with thyroxine treatment is

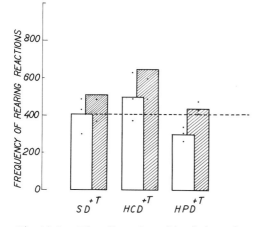

Fig. 12–5. The effect of combined thyroxine and dietary treatment on NEL. Results of the first test (forty days) are presented. The test was performed in 126 rats during two days in order not to interfere with the ontogenetic changes in the NEL. Rats were transferred in groups of seven animals from the home cage into one experimental box where the frequency of spontaneous rearing reactions was obtained [18]. Eight trials separated by 50-minute intervals were given. White columns represent the average activity scores of rats fed (1) a standard diet (SD), (2) a high-carbohydrate diet (HCD), and (3) a high-protein diet (HPD). Values of thyroxine-treated animals are depicted by hatched columns. Each point represents the sum of rearing reactions produced by a group of seven animals in the last four trials. Further tests of NEL on animals at a later age are in progress.

compared with the effect of the genetic selection of rats held on a standard diet.

It should be stressed that treated rats are litter mates from an unselected population. Even though genetic selection is still more effective in the separation of two populations according to NEL, the conclusion can be drawn that genuine possibilities exist for changing inherited psychosomatic constitution, including learning and adaptive capacity, by nutritional and endocrinological treatment.

This effort to alter nutritional needs represents the third important line of research.

Direct hormonal interference with the endocrine system is not the only way of altering nutritional needs. Some possibilities, at present not sufficiently elaborated, have appeared. In self-selection experiments we have often observed [20] reciprocal relationships among spontaneous intakes of specific food components; e.g., a higher intake of proteins leads to an increased intake of KCl and vice versa. This means that by forced intake of substances needed for utilization of proteins (potassium, B-vitamins), an increase in *spontaneous* intake of proteins can be stimulated. Long and lasting changes in appetite appear if the rat is first made to experience a severe deficiency of some disliked nutrient, e.g., casein, and then is forced for a short time to ingest in increased amounts substances needed for casein utilization. An-

TABLE 12–2: Analysis of Variance in the Effect of Combined Dietary and Thyroxine Treatment on NEL

Source of Variance	Sum of Squares	D.F.	Mean Square	F-Test	Critical Value
Thyroxine Treatment	75,531	1	75,531.0	5.204	1/12–5%–4.750
Dietary Treatment	118,888	2	59,444.0	4.096	2/12–5%–3.880
Interaction	1,427	2	713.5	0.049	2/12–5%–3.880
Error	174,144	12	14,512.0		
Total	369,990	17			

			Duncan Test			
Group	HPD	SD	HPD + T	HCD	SD + T	HCD + T
Average	303.33	404.66	442.00	498.33	509.33	643.66

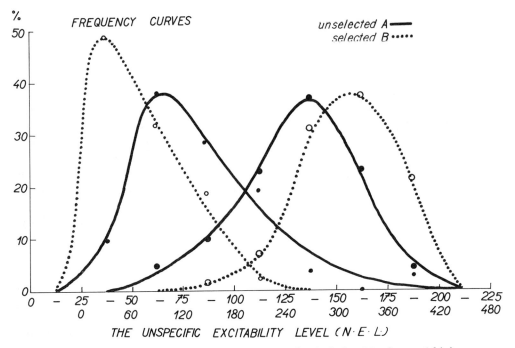

Fig. 12–6.   Comparison of distribution curves of rats selectively bred for low and high NEL (dotted lines, B; N = 67 + 59; ♂ + ♀; F₆ ± F₇) with distribution curves of two unselected populations of littermates (full lines, A), one of which was treated in early ontogeny with thyroxine and a high-carbohydrate diet (N = 21 ♀), the other one with a high-protein diet only (N = 22 ♀ + 10 ♂). In all animals the frequency of rearing reactions evoked by repeated exposure of rats to a standard new environment was taken as a indicator of NEL. Experimental conditions differed, however, in the number of trials. Six trials with 24-hour intervals between trials were applied for the selective breeding experiments; for the treated populations three trials (second test at the age of fifty-two days, cf. Fig. 12–5) were performed in individual rats with 50-minute intervals between trials. In both groups the range of variability scale was, therefore, divided into seven classes.

other method of creating new appetites was described in the pioneer work of Harris *et al.* [14] and of Richter [28]. Now, if this "educational" procedure is performed during early ontogenesis, it is probable that we will produce permanent appetites for various specific diets.

From the point of view of some mechanisms of dietary effect upon NEL, the following data seem to be highly interesting. We have often observed that the excitatory or inhibitory effect of the diet does not manifest itself until several days or even weeks after ingestion. Similarly, the effects do not disappear immediately but perseverate for approximately the

same amount of time. The earlier in ontogenesis one induces the nutritive change, the longer the duration of dietary aftereffects. This can perhaps be designated as "dietary imprinting." But it means that the absolute amount of ingested foodstuffs within a certain range cannot be the critical factor of the dietary effect and that altered utilization initiated by the increased consumption of specific foodstuffs is more important. This "education" of the endocrine and utilizing system might be associated with considerable morphological changes. It is known, for example, that a high-protein diet increases the weight of adre-

nals, which are involved in the gluco-
neogenic processes [27,30]. This explains
why the dietary effect upon NEL neither
manifests itself before a certain period of
time nor displays long-lasting aftereffects.

From the above analysis one can obtain a more concrete idea of the possibilities and limitations that may exist
in regard to regulation of the functional
state of CNS by means of dietary self-
selection. This possibility is demonstrated by the observed reciprocal relationship between the state of internal
environment and NEL shown schematically in Fig. 12–7. Both internal environ-

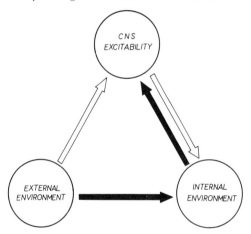

*Fig. 12–7.   The relationship between the
effects of internal and external environment
on NEL.*

ment and the NEL may be modified by
two kinds of external influences: First,
by those that affect internal environment
directly, i.e., nutritive and other substances, affecting NEL only secondarily;
second, by those that change the NEL
primarily, i.e., increased number and intensity of both intero- and exteroceptive
stimuli, changing the internal environment secondarily. This reciprocity of
functions may help to elucidate some
apparently paradoxical phenomena, for
example, why there should be any relationship between "intelligence" (learning ability) and the rate of bodily

growth [16,24,29]. Why is it possible simply by increased external stimulation
(handling) to alter not only the rate of
growth but also the resistance to stress
[25,31]? Why does the retirement of old
people with reduced stimulation and responsibility hasten the process of aging?

As far as the effect of self-selection in
regulating NEL is concerned, one must
realize that changes in qualitative food
intake need not be included in regulatory mechanisms. This holds as long as
the deviated functional state can be com-
pensated for by changes in the utilization pattern.

Let us first consider the question of
whether rats are able to regulate the
functional state of NEL under normal
variations of external conditions; e.g.,
are they capable by aid of self-selection
of diet to compensate for the less effective (too high or too low) NEL associated with a lower learning and adaptive
capacity? We have seen that such a possibility does exist. Experimental results
indicate that excitable rats selected excitative (high-carbohydrate and high-salt)
diets whereas those of low excitability
level selected a depressive (high-protein
and high-potassium) diet, i.e., their
choice was in accordance with their genetic constitution (Fig. 12–8) [16,20].

A chance observation [17] provided
some evidence that under moderately increased external stimulation, which ele-
vates the NEL, rats prefer carbohydrates
and fats, while in the period of decreased
stimulation, a small increase in protein
intake was observed. Under stress stimulation, which unfortunately also affects
the ability of adequate selection, the
preference for a high-protein diet should
be expected. The protective effect of a
high-protein diet under strong stimulation has been demonstrated [6]. In agreement with the known protective effect of
B_1 in neurosis, the higher spontaneous
intake of thiamine has been observed in

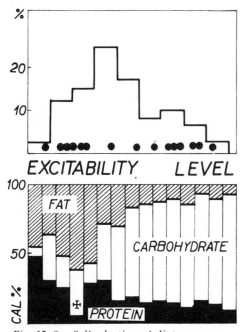

Fig. 12–8. Self-selection of dietary components in low and highly excitable rats. Upper graph: Frequency distribution in individual levels of NEL. The black circles represent fifteen male rats out of fifty-nine chosen for the self-selection experiment. Lower graph: Average caloric intake of protein, carbohydrate, and fat in fifteen rats (individual columns) in the same rank-order as in the upper graph (from low to high levels of NEL). The daily intake of casein, corn-starch, margarine, bone-flour, 1 per cent KCl, 3 per cent NaCl, vitamin B-complex solutions, and distilled water was studied for four months. Only measurements from periods of stable weight gain were used. One rat out of fifteen failed to grow and died. A significant negative correlation (r = −0.650) between individual differences in NEL and KCl intake and a positive correlation with NaCl intake (r = +0.779) were found. No significant correlation was obtained with the B-vitamin solution or with total water intake. (For details see [16] and [20].)

rats under stress stimulation [12]. The reciprocity of the relations given in Fig. 12–7. was clearly demonstrated by the experiments of Brožek [3] and Gantt [10]. A *primary* thiamine deficiency leads to neurotic symptoms in man and impairs conditional reflexes in dogs. On the other hand, a neurotic state produced *primarily* by external stress situations leads to an increased need for thiamine. The spontaneous intake of B-vitamins is at present the best example of the individual's ability to modify the functional state of the CNS by means of self-selection of dietary components. When the methodological difficulties of self-selection experiments are mastered [20] more information will be available on the true limitations of this regulatory function.

Discussion

Barnes: Was the experimental diet fed to the mother?

Lát: Yes, when the offspring were between twelve and fifteen days old. They probably ate small amounts of this diet, but from the time of weaning the only source of food was the experimental diets.

Barnes: Was the different supply of mother's milk in both groups of rats achieved by controlling litter size?

Lát: Yes, one mother fed three babies, the other one about eighteen. From the time of weaning, that is, at the age of twenty-one days, all the animals were put on the standard diet.

Barnes: On the last slide you showed the reciprocal relationship between the selection of proteins and the excitatory state. How old were these animals, and how long were they fed these diets?

Lát: The animals were approximately one hundred days old, and the self-selection experiment lasted about three months.

Barnes: Have you ever done the alternate experiment of feeding rats a low-protein diet?

Lát: Yes. We have done these experiments and have shown that the high-protein diet decreases the excitability level and the low-protein/high-carbohydrate diet increases the excitability level. This means that the free selection of diet in the animals of low excitability level was in accord with the effect of the low-protein diet.

Barnes: In studies that we have made, the animals with a severely low-protein diet, did not grow at all for a period of eight weeks. The animals were much more excitable. This is a nutritional effect upon the excitatory state. In your self-selection studies, is it necessarily the effect of a nutritional condition, or is it related to a genetic condition of the animal?

Brobeck: Did you select your animals for excitability before you gave them free-selection diets?

Lát: Yes. After the excitability level was defined, the animals were given free access to the following food components: casein, starch, margarine, 3 per cent solution of salt, 1 per cent solution of KCl, a solution of B vitamins, distilled water, and bone meal. In separate experiments the effects of high-protein and high-carbohydrate diets on animals of the same average excitability level were studied.

Fischer: If specific diet can speed up metabolic rate, it also may shorten lifespan. Another corollary of this relation would be that inherited low metabolic rate favors longer life expectancy, as demonstrated by Weiss for rats (*Fed. Proc.,* **24**: 466, 1965).

Lát: We have also made some studies on the relations between inherited excitability level and longevity. In the first series of experiments, we obtained a positive correlation, that is, excitable animals lived longer under standard nutritional conditions. In the second series of experiments, the correlation was not statistically significant, although in the same direction. The reason for this low correlation appears to be in the tendency of excitable rats to become fatter in later ages compared to animals with low excitability levels. If we reduce the overweight in old animals by reducing the food intake (20–30 per cent), the excitability level increases. This means that overeating was notably responsible for the low correlation coefficients in longevity experiments. It is interesting to note that increased caloric intake during the period of growth has only positive effects, not only on excitability level, but also on speed of maturation. On the other hand, decreased caloric intake at a later age has the same positive effect on excitability level.

To come back to your first question, if we compare the metabolic rate and the lifespan between different phylogenetic species, the reverse relationship is observed. That is, the lower the metabolic rate, the longer the lifespan. But within ontogeny of the same species this relationship does not necessarily hold.

Fischer: What is the taste threshold of your more excitable animals?

Lát: I do not know. I would like to know that too.

Hamilton: When you set up environmental conditions that appear to increase the excitability level of rats, viz., avoidance or escape conditioning, do you find differences in preference?

Lát: We have made the following chance observation. Weight increments were usually smaller on Saturday and Sunday than during the working days. So, we have controlled what is going on in our animal room. The only difference we have found is that the number of external stimuli produced by research workers, such as in the handling of animals, switching lights on and off, the sound of telephones, weighing of the animals, etc., was increased on working days. Direct evidence was obtained by Weininger and Levine (*J. Comp. Physiol. Psychol.*, 49: 1, 1956; *Science*, 126: 405, 1957) in the well-known experiments with the handling of rats. Under the condition of self-selection of diet, a small increase in carbohydrate intake during working days and an increase in protein intake on Saturday and Sunday were observed. The increased excitability level caused by the external stimulation thus leads to the same changes in selection of food components as we have seen in the food selection of excitable animals.

Hamilton: Isn't this in accordance with the experiments of Donhoffer (*Amer. J. Physiol.*, 150: 329, 1947) and his group, in which they exposed mice to cold ambient temperatures and found an increase in food intake from high-carbohydrate foods and no change in intake from the high-protein and high-fat diets?

Lát: Yes, this could probably apply in that respect. Thyroxine, as well as cold, increases the excitability level, and both conditions lead to a preference of carbohydrates.

REFERENCES

1. Andik, I., and Donhoffer, Sz. Die Wirkung des Thyroxins und der Thyreidektomie, sowie niedriger Umgebungstemperaturen auf die Nahrungaufnahme and Nahrungswahl der Ratte. *Plug. Arch.*, 264: 585–92, 1957.
2. Baigarová, L., Gollová, E., and Lát, J. Differences in the adaptation rate of rectal temperature to amphetamine in animals with a high and low excitability level. *Activitas nerv. sup.*, 7: 262–63, 1965.
3. Brožek, J. (ed.). Symposium on Nutrition and Behavior, Nutrition Symposium Series No 14 *Amer. J. Clin. Nutr.*, 5: 103–211, 1957.
4. Brožek, J. Experimental Investigations on the Effects of Dietary Deficiencies on Animal and Human Behavior. *Vitamins and Hormones*, 19: 43–94, 1961.
5. Brožek, J. Soviet Studies on Nutrition and Higher Nervous Activity. *Ann. N.Y. Acad. Sc.*, 93: 665–714, 1962.
6. Faltová, E., Poupa, O., Servít, Z. Vliv vzájemného poměru bílkovin a glycidů v potravě na křečovou pohotovost myší. (Effect of protein and carbohydrate in diets on susceptibility to audiogenic seizures in mice.) *Čs. fysiol.*, 4: 10, 1956.
7. Franková, S. C. Relationship between dietary fat intake and higher nervous activity in rats. *Activitas nerv. sup.*, 4: 471–75, 1962.
8. Franková, S. C. Effect of Nutrition on Behavior. Unpublished thesis, Prague, 1965.
9. Fritz, M. F. A Classified Bibliography on Psychodietetics. *Psychol. Monographs*, 46: 1–46, 1934.
10. Gantt, H. W. Effect of B-Complex Vitamins on Conditional Reflexes in Dogs, in Symposium on Nutrition and Behavior. *Amer. J. Clin. Nutr.*, 5: 19–38, 1957.
11. Gollová, E., Lát, J., and Franková, S. O vztahu mezi dráždivostí CNS a rektalní teplotou. (Relations between excitability of CNS and rectal temperature.) *Čs. fysiol.*, 13: 492, 1964.
12. Griffiths, W. J. Diet selections of rats subjected to stress. *Ann. N.Y. Acad. Sci.*, 67: 1–10, 1956.
13. Hall, C. S. Temperament: A survey of animal studies. *Psychol. Bull.*, 38: 909–43, 1941.
14. Harris, L. J., Clay, J., Hargreaves, F. J., and Ward, A. Appetite and choice of diet. The ability of the vitamin B-deficient rat to discriminate between diets containing and lacking the vitamin. *Proc. Roy. Soc.* [*Biol.*] (London), 113: 161–90, 1933.
15. Kibler, H. H., and Brody, S. Metabolism and growth rate of rats. *J. Nutr.*, 24: 461–68, 1942.
16. Lát, J. The relationship of individual differences in regulation of food intake, growth and excitability level of CNS. *Physiol. Bohemosl.*, 5: 38–42, 1956 (Supplement).
17. Lát, J. Factors affecting the basic nonspecific tonus of the nervous system, in *Central and Peripheral Mechanisms of Motor Functions: Proceedings of the Conference of the Czechoslovakian Academy of Science*, A. Gutmann and P. Hnik (eds.). Prague, pp. 255–63, 1963.
18. Lát, J. The spontaneous exploratory reactions as a tool for psychopharmacological studies, in *Pharmacology of Conditioning, Learning and Retention: Proceedings of*

the Second International Pharmacological Meeting, Prague. Pergamon Press, New York, pp. 47–66, 1963.

19. Lát, J. Konstitutionsproblematik and Langlebigkeit: Proceedings of the International Conference of Gerontology. Akad. Kiado, Budapest, p. 137, 1965.

20. Lát, J. Self-selection of dietary components. (Review in preparation.)

21. Lát, J., and Faltová, E. Vliv různého podilu živočišných bílkovin na vyšší nervovou činnost krys. (Effect of different amount of animal proteins on higher nervous activity of rats.) Čs. fysiol., 4: 171–80, 1955.

22. Lát, J., Gollová, E. O vztahu mezi mozkovou, rektální teplotou a dráždivosti CNS. Relations between brain and rectal temperature and CNS excitability.) Čs. fysiol., 1966 (in press).

23. Lát, J., Weisz, P. O vztahu mezi individualními rozdíly v dráždivosti CNS a činností nadledvinek. (Relation between individual differences in CNS excitability level and adrenal gland activity.) Čs. fysiol., 7: 293–94, 1958.

24. Lát, J., Widdowson, E. M., and McCance, R. A. Some effects of accelerating growth. III: Behaviour and nervous activity. Proc. Roy. Soc. [Biol.] (London), 153: 347–56, 1960.

25. Levine, S. Infantile experience and resistance to physiological stress. Science, 126: 405–6, 1957.

26. Nováková, V., Faltin, J., Flandera, V., Hahn, P., and Koldovský, O. Effect of early and late weaning on learning in adult rats. Nature, 193: 280, 1962.

27. Pařízek, J. Vliv nadbytku bílkovin v potravě na žlázy produkující steroidní hormony. (Effect of high-protein diet on glands producing steroid hormones.) Čs. gastroent. a výživa, 10: 236–39, 1956.

28. Richter, C. P., Holt, L. E., and Barelare, B. Nutritional requirements for normal growth and reproduction in rats studied by the self-selection method. Amer. J. Physiol., 122: 734–44, 1938.

29. Tanner, J. M. Growth at adolescence. Blackwell, Oxford, 1955.

30. Tepperman, J., Engels, F. L., and Long, C. N. H. Review of adrenal cortical hypertrophy. Endocrinology, 32: 373–402, 1943.

31. Weininger, O. The effects of early experience on behavior and growth characteristics. J. Comp. Physiol. Psychol., 49: 1–9, 1956.

32. William, R. J. Biochemical Individuality: The basis for the genetotrophic concept. John Wiley & Sons, New York, 1956.

13: Critic's Comments

by E. F. Adolph

I WOULD LIKE to play the role of commentator, though I am not experienced in that role. I have been concerned that few physiologists try to fit various pieces of investigation into a general setting. Annual reviews, for instance, could serve to ascertain directions in which currents of endeavor and new concepts are moving. Often our efforts diffuse in all directions at once, and to allow them to do so is our privilege as individuals. When we leave such a conference as this, each of us takes with him a certain sieveful of items that his mind is prepared to appreciate.

One can consider an animal to be a converter of environmental materials into an internal metabolic pool. All persons here have talked about this conversion, translation, and transformation. All were concerned with the animal's selection of materials. In an environment in which these materials are unevenly distributed, the animal seeks places (foods) where they are more concentrated than normal. Intake is always selective. If the animal loaded itself with everything in its environment, the alimentary processes and the metabolic pool would be clogged to an impossible degree. The ideal food selection would possibly be that made by cannibals, because cannibals get exactly the proportions of materials fitted to their nourishment.

When we speak of nutrition, we talk about what the animal ingests. But equally important, I believe, is what it rejects. Many rejected substances are non-metabolizable; others are metabolizable, for, as Harper emphasized, if some rejected diets are force-fed, the animal utilizes them and grows accordingly.

We cannot help stressing the role of exteroceptive senses in determining what is taken into the metabolic pool; but I think some of the rejection depends not on taste and smell but upon mechanical and non-specific chemical factors of alimentation. Lát's emphasis upon metabolic adaptation to diet touched upon the modifications in chemical processes of utilization, constitution, and pool size. These factors are changing from day to day and from meal to meal, so that we cannot expect an animal after it has been on diet A to react to diet B initially with a steady response. Although we know this, we often tend to neglect the adaptations, enzymic and others, that occur in all tissues. Long-term adaptation is ever-present, for much adaptation occurs without our recognition of the adaptive conditions. We assume that we controlled all variables when actually the shift of diet was only one of many shifts. When we impose temperature effects, electrolyte effects, and other circumstances, we are usually influencing metabolic processes.

I can remember the days when measurement of food intake was considered of no significance. Yet many of the same physiologists who thought that eating was a fickle behavior on the part of animals did measure body weights. Anyone could have seen, however, that change of body weight reflects a number of factors of which food intake is a big one. In those days it was said that a loss of body weight was due to a loss of appetite, so we had to determine what appetite was. Then we found that some deficient diets did not interfere with appetite, that other deficient diets did interfere. Thereupon we had to define deficiency. By hindsight, I conclude that we got along fairly well when we stuck to specific experiments but failed when we talked generally about appetite, deficiency, well-being, and non-nutrients.

My next comment poses a question: Are animals, as we find them, provided with as much information about available foods as they can use? We often speak of a coelenterate as lacking sensations when compared to a fish, or of a fish as being sensory-poor compared to a rat. I find great difficulty in saying that one species lives with sensory devices inferior to those of another. Perhaps we just know a bit more about the ways in which the sensory information comes to the rat. Would we be fooling ourselves less by thinking that one species has as much information about its metabolic supplies as have the other species? I see no way of judging each species' use of appropriate information; I hope one day some investigator will devise a scale by which we can measure the fitness of the animal's use of the information it gets. Information always undergoes selection, whether in the nervous system or in supposedly undifferentiated protoplasm.

There is dire need of more theories about food selection. For instance, the view is not satisfactory that every sort of substance which an animal ingests is taken in response to some particular "stat" that is a little off balance. If an animal could recognize all the substances that the biochemist can recognize, such an animal still could not manage to live on the mixtures in which food always comes, mixtures that have not been anticipated by a stat. It seems to me there is so much overlap among nutrients that only a human device leads us to the view that distinct stats activate intakes. We do have to recognize that bodily deficits of many substances induce responses of food-getting, but I suspect that few of the responses manage to recognize specific foods.

Another related comment concerns a general topic: Can the regulation of some constituent of the body be represented by a general pattern applicable to any constituent? We have discussed the kind of regulatory model we may hold before ourselves and the question of whether food is ingested in response to some disturbance of bodily regulation. Regulation, like other words, entitles each person to his own meaning. Several of us have tried to put into words the concepts that we think might help when regulations are discussed. But actual analysis of data requires some specific correlation in order to represent regulatory relations, for example, a graph containing ordinates and abscissae. I prefer to put on the abscissae the amounts of some measured substance contained in the organism or the concentrations of something in a specified body fluid; only then are we ready to talk about this particular item in the animal's economy. Until we define the item in such a manner, we cannot speak of a measured disturbance in the animal's economy. If we decide to correlate, say, the intakes of substance A that we have measured in the animal, with the amounts of substance A previously present in the animal, then we deal with a direct and unique relation since intake of A supplies content of A (negative feedback). This is a usual regulatory correlation, such as that noted by Fregly between the sodium intake and the sodium content of the body. But if we do not know the sodium content, we have difficulty in making any sense of the sodium intake as a regulatory adjustment. We can find other correlations of sodium intake, such as with potassium content or glucose concentration in blood plasma. Each of these explores a system other than that in which sodium content was ascertained. Lát pointed out that the amount of sodium intake may be correlated with varied characteristics of the animal, and his correlations were partly found in the nervous system. He would like to know whether nervous activities are modified by a deficit of sodium or of protein or of glucose. However, most nerve cells of mammals are bathed not by ordinary extracellular fluid but by cerebrospinal fluid. The composition of this fluid may be preserved in spite of a deficit in the body as a whole.

I have mentioned a few abstract notions with which we can profitably feel dissatisfied, but which we can use, I believe, as we climb to a concrete understanding of food intakes.

Part Three

14: Taste and the Role of Experience in the Regulation of Food Intake *by Harry L. Jacobs**

THIS PAPER will outline the problem of experiential factors in food intake, using the "sweet tooth" as a major example. We will focus on the following aspects of the problem. All meals contain nutrient and taste cues. What is the relationship between taste and nutrient properties of food in determining food acceptance? Is it learned? Is it innate? Is it both?

The term "taste" will be used to include all of the sensory complex usually subsumed under the rubric "flavor," including taste, smell, texture, viscosity, stickiness, etc. The discussion will be limited to laboratory studies on the rat and to the work of physiologists and psychologists interested in food intake.

Investigators in physiology and nutrition interested in the maintenance of energy balance have analyzed food intake in terms of neurophysiological and biochemical mechanisms. This approach usually assumes that organisms eat when they need food and that the relation between the need for nutrients and the acceptability of foodstuffs is innate and relatively independent of past experience.

Psychologists working on learning theory have also been interested in food intake, but from a different point of view. Their interest in hunger has been in the energizing properties of behavior. Hunger drive makes the organism highly active; once behavior is started, all changes in its direction are investigated as problems in trial-and-error learning. Thus, in the case of food intake, the search for and ingestion of foodstuffs is assumed to be learned. All food is presumed originally neutral in incentive value; the relation between need for nutrients and the acceptability of foodstuffs is learned and is fully dependent on past experiences.

We will not refer to the literature on human subjects in this paper, nor will we review the general work on incentive motivation in animals. Reference to the latter will be limited to selected cases where the interest has been in consummatory responses rather than in instrumental behavior.

TASTE AND INTAKE— THREE INTERPRETATIONS

There are at least five items present in any particular instance of feeding behavior. The *ingesta* contains *taste* and *nutrients* which can act as potential modulators of *intake*. When organic needs or *deficits* are present, the ingestion of nutrients acts to correct them. Psychologists have referred to this relationship as need reduction.

Figure 14–1 presents three views of

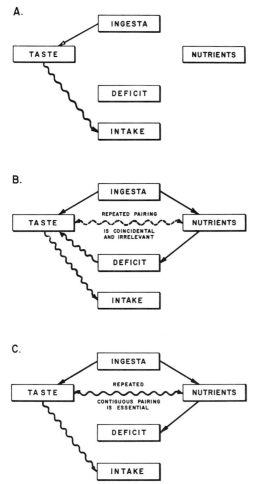

Fig. 14–1. Three interpretations of the role of taste in the control of food intake. A. Innate Incentives; *acceptability as a function of chemoreceptor stimulation.* B. Behavioral Regulation; *acceptability as a function of innate needs and homeostatic mechanisms.* C. Learning; *acceptability as a function of the association of taste with organic need reduction.*

the relationship between these five aspects of feeding. Inspection of the left side of each schema shows that they are similar in assuming that all ingesta produce taste cues *(solid lines),* and that taste acts to modulate further intake *(wiggly lines).* These diagrams differ in the role assigned to the necessity for occurrence of a deficit and its reduction by ingested nutrients.

The first approach, in the upper part

of Fig. 14–1, assumes that *innate* incentives regulate intake, irrespective of the nutrient content of a diet or the occurrence of a deficit. Young uses the term "palatability" to describe this approach, limiting it to cases where food acceptability is determined by stimulation of head receptors by characteristics of the food itself [29]. Troland postulates two general types of receptors, "beneceptors," and "nocioceptors," which, when stimulated, give rise to pleasantness and unpleasantness, respectively [26]. The major evidence for this approach comes from observations of preference for specific foodstuffs in satiated animals, where nutrient values of the food choices are identical and the choice is apparently independent of past experience. For example, Scott and Verney gave rats a choice between diets containing various carbohydrates in granulated form. Since the nutritive value of the choices was considered equal, these authors concluded that "it is impossible, therefore, that selection . . . was based on any nutritional qualities of the choices, and probable that the appetites shown for these substances were trivial in origin (a function of innate incentives, in our terms)" ([21], p. 406).

The second approach to the role of taste in food intake, in the center of Fig. 14–1, is labeled *behavioral regulation.* It is similar to the first in assuming that the role of taste is innate, but it extends the assumption by asserting that the occurrence of a deficit is the critical factor because it potentiates taste in modulating intake *(wiggly line between deficit and taste).* The fact that nutrients are present and relieve the deficit is considered irrelevant *(wiggly dashed line).* The best example of evidence for this approach comes from observations on the specific appetite for salt in adrenalectomized rats (see Fregly paper, this symposium). As Richter points out in his classic analysis of this case, "The results indicate that the adrenalectomized rats ingest salt, not because they learn that salt relieves their deficiency discomfort, but because of chemical changes in the taste mechanisms in the oral cavity, giving rise to enhanced salt discrimination" ([18], p. 370).

Richter may well be wrong about the specific sensory mechanisms mediating this shift in preference. The critical point is that the choice itself is mediated by innate physiological mechanisms. As Katz points out in his "avidity" theory of specific hungers, which assumes that need alters perceptual bias so that the animal seeks out and ingests the needed food, that learning may well be necessary in acquiring the instrumental responses involved in the *finding* of food [12]. However, the actual *choice* is determined by the increased acceptability of a particular set of taste qualities. As Fig. 14–1 points out, the fact that nutrients are also present is coincidental. The animal could be fooled by a substitute food identical in taste but containing no nutrients.

The third approach to the role of taste in food intake, at the bottom of Fig. 14–1, is labeled *learning*. In this view, both nutrients and the occurrence and relief of a deficit are critical. This approach assumes that taste cues are initially neutral stimuli. They gradually acquire the ability to modulate intake by conditioning, through repeated association of the taste of food with the deficit relieving effect of the nutrient. The first use of this approach in animal studies was in the classic work of Harris *et al.*, who described it in subjective terms: "... It depends not on a vague instinct but on an association between the distinctive character of the diet (smell, taste, appearance) and an experience of the prompt beneficial effects ..." ([6], p. 187).

Hull [7], attacking the same problem in the context of modern learning theory, is more objective, preferring to speak of effector responses (e.g., eating) as being conditioned to specific afferent discharges (in this instance, taste) contiguous with tissue need reduction (deficit relief). This approach has the advantage of allowing reference to a large body of independently derived principles available in learning theory. Thus, more precise predictions can be made in designing and carrying out experiments to evaluate this approach.

The rest of this paper will outline several studies designed to evaluate the role of taste in food intake from these three viewpoints.

THE ONTOGENY OF SACCHARINE PREFERENCE

Why does an adult rat have an appetite for saccharine? Although saccharine may have some physiological effects [27], it is non-nutritive. If this is so, saccharine may be an innate incentive (Fig. 14–1, *A*). In agreement with this possibility, Nachman [13] has shown that it is possible to breed rats with appetites and aversions for saccharine. However, the specificity of the genetic effect is still an open question, e.g., Nachman may merely be breeding for the ability to *acquire* saccharine preference.

The conditions of nurturance in the newborn rat are ideal for the application of the learning model (Fig. 14–1, *C*) to the ontogeny of saccharine preference. The argument, for any mammal, would run somewhat as follows. "Since taste buds in the babies' mouth are stimulated by milk sugar a little before the milk reaches the stomach, the argument that our liking for sweets is acquired by conditioning has some plausibility ..." ([28], p. 684).

Since the neonate rat is completely dependent on its mother for food and presumably eats when hungry, the mild sweetness of mother's milk provided by its 2.8 per cent lactose content [14] would have ample opportunity for contiguous pairing with deficit relief following each meal. Thus, the originally neutral sweetness of milk should become a conditioned incentive, establishing a stimulus generalization gradient so that sweet substances of greater or less concentration than the original conditioned stimulus should also be acceptable, though less so than the starting point, a 2.8 per cent lactose solution.

This argument generated some simple predictions. Neonate rats should show a gradual increase in appetite for 2.8 per cent lactose solution, and this learning curve of acquired preference value should be steeper than a very sweet 0.1 per cent saccharine solution, known to be palatable to the adult rat.

In order to test these predictions, we developed a reliable method for measuring acceptability of single drops of solution presented to neonate rats [10]. All subjects were raised with their mother and were removed for testing four times per day, at four-hour intervals. Figure

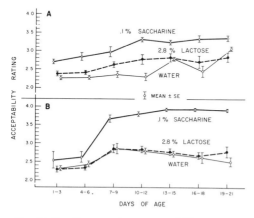

Fig. 14–2. Preweaning acceptability of lactose and saccharine solutions and water. A. Independent litters containing five pups each. B. Single four-pup litter tested on all solutions [10].

14–2 shows the results of our first series of experiments on this problem. In both

series of tests, the sweet 0.1 per cent saccharine showed increasing acceptability during the weaning period, while the 2.8 per cent lactose solution, which should have been more acceptable on the basis of our learning model, was not differentiable from water. In other experiments we increased the lactose percentage to 4 per cent (discriminable by adult rats) without effect. The only way we could make lactose palatable to the neonate rat was to make it sweeter. A 17 per cent lactose solution, far sweeter than the presumed original point of conditioning, finally produced an acceptability curve equal to the 0.1 per cent saccharine solution.

The acceptability curve for lactose was directly contrary to the predictions from the learning model outlined above. What about the increased intake of saccharine? Could this be learning, even though the reinforcement was unknown? Control experiments showed that this was not the case. Rats tested with 0.1 per cent saccharine for the first time at fifteen days of age required only one day to reach the asymptote of acceptability. We have taken this to indicate that the saccharine curve in Fig. 14–2 is due to the maturation of the indicator responses used in our tests, sucking and reaching out for a drop of solution, licking lips and face after swallowing, etc.

The above studies allow us to reject a simple learning model in interpreting the ontogeny of sweet preferences in neonate rats. We can now assume that saccharine preference in adult rats is not simply a case of stimulus generalization from early lactose conditioning.

SWEET PREFERENCE IN ADULT RATS

The problem of the relationship between deficit and taste still raises the question of learning in adult animals.

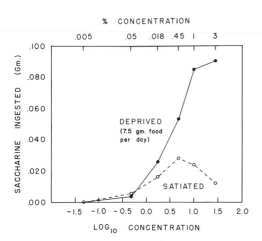

Fig. 14–3. The relative preference for sodium saccharine as a function of concentration in food-deprived (N = 18) or satiated (N = 18) rats. (Modified from [1].)

Magnen [15] attacked this question directly by comparing the effects of hunger on sucrose (taste and nutrients) with its effect on saccharine (taste). Figure 14–4

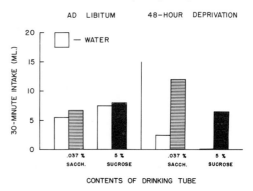

Fig. 14–4. The effect of food deprivation on the relative preference of sucrose or saccharine over water in two-choice tests. (Modified from [15].)

Figure 14–3 shows the results of a study by Bacon et al. [1] of relative saccharine preference in adult rats and its relation to a rather severe energy deficit. Using daily thirty-minute tests with single bottles, satiated rats show maximum preference for a mildly sweet 0.45 per cent solution. Food deprivation increases maximum preference to an extremely sweet, 3 per cent solution. These results are analogous to the kind of acceptability shifts demonstrable in specific hungers and raise the same questions.

Is it possible that energy deficit potentiates taste in regulating food intake in general, in the same way that adrenalectomy potentiates taste in salt preference? If so, does this operate on the basis of behavioral regulation, as Richter assumed in the case of specific hungers [20], or does the adult animal learn to like the taste because of deficit relief? Figure 14–3 suggests that the former may indeed apply, for hunger is potentiating the taste of saccharine (which lacks nutrients). What would happen if nutrients were added to the solution, i.e., if sugar were compared to saccharine? Le

shows that food deprivation increases the intake of both solutions but that the relative change in preference is even greater in the case of saccharine. These results are in agreement with Richter's [20] and Katz's [12] assumption that deficit potentiates taste regardless of nutrients or deficit relief.

However, these are very short-term tests. What happens to the saccharine effect if the tests are repeated daily? How long will the animal be fooled?

Sheffield and Roby [22] carried out a series of eighteen daily tests in which hungry rats were given brief drinking trials in which saccharine was available. Figure 14–5 shows the results of this study. Deprivation continues to increase intake throughout the testing period. The authors use these results to argue against a learning interpretation of the data. If the drinking response had been learned in the first place, it would have shown signs of extinction during the test series.

Smith and Capretta [23] disagreed with the conclusions of this study, arguing that optimal conditions for produc-

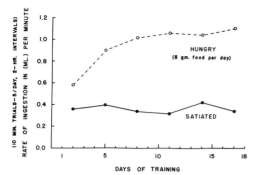

Fig. 14–5. The effect of food deprivation on the acquisition of drinking of 0.13 per cent saccharine solution in response to a specific cue-pattern accompanying availability of the solution. (Modified from [22].)

ing extinction had not been met. They designed a series of studies with rats adapted to a twenty-one-hour food deprivation schedule, precisely varying the opportunity for the animals to associate the ingestion of saccharine with contiguous nutrient ingestion and assimilation. The findings were quite consistent, showing that hungry rats did not continue to be fooled by saccharine if the drinking test was clearly and consistently separated from their daily meal [3,4,23].

Thus, as in Fig. 14–6, hungry rats that

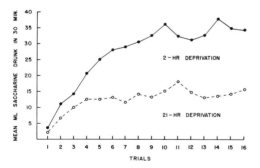

Fig. 14–6.   The effect of hunger at the time of testing on saccharine intake. (N = 8 in each group.) Upper group, twenty-one-hour food deprived, fed two hours before test; lower groups, twenty-one-hour food and water deprived, fed thirty minutes after test. (Modified from [4].)

were fed two hours before the saccharine test (top curve) continued to ingest large

amounts of solution, presumably because of the continued opportunity to associate its taste with deficit relief. Hungry animals denied this opportunity ingested less saccharine (lower curve). Capretta interprets the latter case as extinction.

However, Capretta does recognize an alternative interpretation, i.e., that the animals that are fed while hungry may be developing a learned avoidance for saccharine because of its association with this unpleasant state of affairs. He tried to test this in the experiment shown in Fig. 14–6 by using hungry and thirsty animals (lower curve). He argues that adding water deficit to food deficit should increase unpleasantness. Thus, if this were a learned avoidance, these animals would show less intake (more avoidance) than the groups in his previous studies, who only had hunger to contend with. He reports that this did not occur and thus he rejects the learned-avoidance hypothesis.

Although Capretta's argument is reasonable, it may be premature. First, due to the well-known correlation between food and water intake [11], the addition of thirst to hunger may not increase total deficit as much as he assumed. Further studies, adding other avoidance drives, e.g., shock, to food deprivation, are needed to answer the question he raises. Second, it is possible to show learned avoidance for saccharine in rats. Garcia and his colleagues have repeatedly demonstrated a learned avoidance after drinking saccharine in the presence of low-level gamma radiation (e.g., [5]). This is clearly shown in Fig. 14–7, where twenty-four-hour tests of saccharine solution and water intake produce a relative avoidance of saccharine for several weeks.

In summary, more work is needed to clearly evaluate the extent to which the learning model applies to the changes in saccharine preference induced by food deprivation in adult rats.

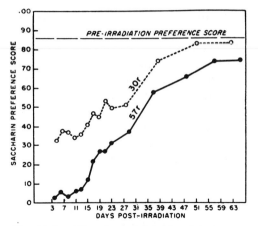

Fig. 14–7. The effect of drinking 0.1 per cent solution of saccharine during six hours of either 30r (upper curve) or 57r (lower curve) gamma radiation, on subsequent avoidance and recovery in a series of daily, two-choice tests between 0.1 per cent saccharine and water. (Modified from [5].)

LONG-TERM EFFECTS AND A TWO-FACTOR SYSTEM

The studies of food deprivation reviewed above were limited to intake tests of less than an hour's duration; long-term effects were measured by repeated daily measurements. What of the effects of deprivation on longer intake tests? I have studied this using insulin injections to induce hunger.

It has long been known that insulin hypoglycemia increases the intake of dry-stock diet or of glucose solutions (e.g., [19]). Soulairac [25] extended this technique by offering single-bottle choices of 10 per cent sucrose, glucose, or maltose. He found that the increase in intake was in direct proportion to sweetness. We verified this result using a choice test [8]. We found that insulin increased the intake of the sweeter solution over a three-day test period. At this point we became interested in the following question, quite like those presented above in our discussion of saccharine. Does this shift in appetite occur because the animal learns to like the sweeter solution, since it provides the

greater caloric density per unit of intake, or because of behavioral regulation making the sweeter solution taste better regardless of its caloric content?

We decided to attempt to answer this question by giving the rat a direct choice between a mildly sweet solution highly capable of relieving the deficit, and a much sweeter solution, less capable of relieving the deficit. Since insulin hypoglycemia produces a specific deficit for glucose [24], we chose this as our basal sugar. Our other choice was fructose, which is sweeter than glucose and much less efficient in relieving symptoms of hypoglycemia [2].

Rats were given two days of choice between water and 30 per cent solutions of glucose or fructose. Subcutaneous injections of insulin (PZI) or physiological saline were administered at twelve-hour intervals, at which time intake was measured. The insulin group received 2.0 units on the first day and 3.0 units on the second day. Table 14–1 shows the

TABLE 14–1: Number of Subjects Preferring Each Sugar Solution[a]

Group	Insulin		Control	
Preference	Glucose	Fructose	Glucose	Fructose
First day	1	10	6	5
Second Day	8	3	9	2

[a] Preference defined in terms of relative total volume consumed during the 24-hour interval.

frequency of subjects preferring either solution during the two-day test. On day *1*, insulin produced a significantly greater number of animals preferring the fructose solution ($p = 0.0119$). The insulin effect disappeared by the second day, on which both groups preferred the glucose solution. Figure 14–8 shows the average intake scores during the two-day test. Again, insulin produced a significant fructose preference for day *1* totals, which was sharply reversed in that significant preferences for glucose were

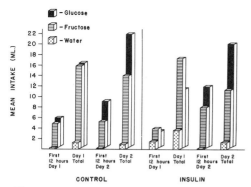

Fig. 14–8. The effect of insulin injections on the relative intake of 30 per cent solutions of glucose and fructose and water in a three-choice intake test. (N = 11 in each group.)

demonstrated during the first twelve hours on through the totals for day 2. The control group failed to show a preference for fructose during the two-day test. The glucose preference was clear but had not reached significance by the end of day 2.

In summary, insulin produced a significant preference for the sweeter fructose solution, apparently regardless of its inefficiency in relieving the insulin-induced deficit. If our observations were limited to day 1, we would conclude that behavioral regulation was potentiating sweet tastes, as in the saccharine cases described above. During the second day, however, the insulin-treated rats reversed their preference, now choosing the less sweet solution, which was very helpful in relieving the deficit. If our observations were limited to the second day, we would conclude that our learning model applied—the rats associating the taste of glucose with the deficit relief that followed its ingestion.

This is a very confusing situation. Apparently the rats took what they liked, presumably on an innate basis, on day 1, and took what they needed, presumably on a learned basis, on day 2. Although this explanation seemed quite *ad hoc* and overcomplicated to us, it would seem that it is not completely unreasonable.

Figure 14–9 shows a study by Le Magnen [15] of sucrose and saccharine intake in rats on five days of total food

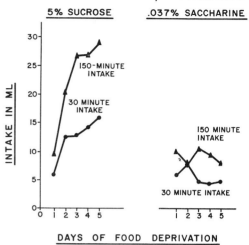

Fig. 14–9. The effect of food deprivation on the relative intake of sucrose and saccharine in daily three-hour single-bottle tests. (Modified from [15].)

deprivation. The rats were given a daily three-hour test. The intake was measured at "short-term," thirty minutes, and at "long-term," three hours. For the first day the thirty-minute intake showed saccharine to be higher than sucrose as in the work discussed in Fig. 14–4 above. This would be in agreement with a behavioral regulation view, as in the first day of our insulin studies. Following Fig. 14–9 again, the intake of sucrose kept increasing over the five-day deprivation period, while that of saccharine was variable and even tended to decrease. The latter result would be in agreement with a learning interpretation of the data, as in the case of the second day of our insulin studies.

I would like to paraphrase Le Magnen's interpretation of this type of study [15,17]. He distinguishes between two distinct and successive mechanisms regulating food acceptance. The *primary response* acts on a short-term basis, and the animal responds immediately by using flavor or other sensory qualities as a cue for ingestion, regardless of whether it corrects the nutritional disequilibrium. As the animal is allowed a series of trials lasting long enough for the ingesta to be assimilated, a *secondary response* develops, which is no longer specific to the sensory qualities of the food, but depends upon its capacity to repair the nutritional disequilibrium. In summary, Le Magnen's interpretation of his data is made in terms of a two-factor system combining the properties of what we have called behavioral regulation and learning in Fig. 14–1 above.

LEARNING AND THE ROLE OF SENSORY STIMULI IN SATIETY

Most of us tend to analyze the problem of satiety by assuming that nutrients supply the cues for the cessation of eating [9]. Thus, theories of food intake have really been theories of satiety, in which a particular metabolic change carries the burden of explanation, e.g., the "glucostatic" theory, "thermostatic" theory, "lipostatic" theory, and in recent discussions, an "aminostatic" theory. Le Magnen [17], in a thorough analysis of the role of sensory qualities (taste, in our terms) in the control of food intake, points out that metabolic cues are not very useful in precise control of adult food intake. He argues that animals learn to make use of sensory cues and that these cues can be equal to or even more important than metabolic cues in controlling rate of intake.

I shall briefly outline two examples of his work along these lines. In both cases he varied the sensory qualities of the diet by adding olfactory cues. First, he considered the case of satiety induced by associating the diet with insulin-induced hunger [16]. Rats were given a thirty-minute meal of a diet flavored with either citral or eucalyptal. Six intake tests were run each week, each rat alternating between diets. Two groups of rats were tested, each over a twenty-day period. In one group the citral was followed by injections of insulin; in the other group, the eucalyptal diet was followed by insulin. After twenty days of testing were completed, both groups were given a free choice between the two diets without insulin injections. Figure 14–10 shows the results of this study. During the twenty-day test period, the intake of the diet that was followed by insulin injections showed a sharp decrease. Unlike the ambiguous changes in Capretta's experiments discussed above, this is almost certainly another example of a

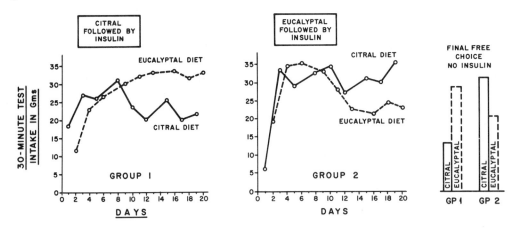

Fig. 14–10. The effect of subcutaneous insulin injections (0.05 U/kg), following twenty daily meals containing a specific olfactory cue pattern, on its subsequent intake in a free-choice test. (Modified from [16].)

clear-cut conditioned aversion, which carries over to the free-choice test, where the intake of the diet previously followed by insulin was depressed in proportion to the insulin effect.

The same kind of change can be shown by allowing the animal to associate an olfactory stimulus with satiety signals from an intragastric load of glucose [17]. Rats were given two one-hour meals per day, each with a discriminable olfactory cue added, as in the experiment just discussed. A constant pattern of feeding was established in which one meal was followed by a glucose load, the other by saline. Figure 14–11 shows the

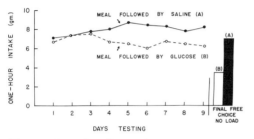

Fig. 14–11. The effect of intragastric glucose loads, following nine daily one-hour meals containing a specific olfactory cue pattern, on its subsequent intake in a free-choice test. (Modified from [17].)

results of this study. The meal followed by glucose showed a decreased intake, thereby reflecting the satiety value of the intragastric load. The final free choice again showed that conditioned satiety can be demonstrated. Le Magnen reports that the same effect can be obtained with D-amphetamine to induce satiety [17].

In summary, both of these examples clearly show the ease with which metabolic signals (changes in blood sugar level in these cases) can use sensory cues (via conditioning) as a vehicle to regulate intake. Le Magnen speculates that this is perhaps a dominant way of controlling intake in adult, "sophisticated" animals living in an environment where many food choices are available.

SUMMARY

This paper has outlined the problem of the roles of taste and nutrients as cues controlling food intake with special emphasis being placed on experimental factors. Studies of saccharine and sugar preference, or the appetite for flavored diets, in neonate and adult animals were reviewed. The effect of deficits induced by food deprivation or insulin injections in these studies was evaluated, leading to the over-all conclusion that deficits potentiate taste in the control of intake, and that these changes have both innate and learned components, the former on a short-term basis, the latter on long-term basis.

Discussion

Grossman: You are assuming temporal contiguity between taste and the nutritive effects of the ingested foods. Such contiguity certainly does not exist, and the delay of reinforcement is much greater than anything shown to be effective in any laboratory situation. How can you assume that learning or conditioning will take place under those conditions?

If this type of an association is, in fact, possible, I fail to see how your saccharine data rule out the possibility that the saccharine preference may be learned through an association of the sweet taste with nutrient effects of other sweet substances.

Jacobs: It is quite true that contiguity is seldom present. In Hull's famous footnote on the status of food as a reinforcer, he assumes that the temporal gap between mastication and need reduction is filled by a chain of secondarily reinforced associations, and that primary reinforcement may not operate at all (Hull, *Principles of Behavior*, Appleton-Century, New York, p. 98, 1943). Hull's analysis of this problem was developed in a rather artificial laboratory situation, of course.

As to the second question, I purposely chose the nurtural situation as one in which maximum opportunity was allowed for the association of the sweet taste with nutrient effects. If this association did take place, the maximum point of reinforcement should have been the 2.8 per cent lactose solution contained in rats' milk. The sweeter saccharine solution should have been farther out on the gradient of secondary reinforcement. Thus, it should have been less palatable. This did not happen, a fact which is not in agreement with the learning hypothesis.

I am not insisting that this is the only approach to the problem of learning. I once tried some experiments with chicks, depriving them of the opportunity to taste sweets from birth by putting them on a carbohydrate-free diet. As adults, the sweetness "deprived" chicks preferred sucrose as much as a group maintained on a high sucrose diet. Thus, early experience made no difference, which is also against the learning hypothesis.

Epstein: The interesting experiments of Le Magnen could be interpreted in the following way. After the treatment with insulin and glucose, the rat in a subsequent choice situation chooses the diet in which he has experienced the least anorexia. This is confirmed by the fact that Le Magnen has also used amphetamine with essentially similar results. Moreover, all of these differential appetites disappear if the choice is made after overnight deprivation. The animal becomes less discriminating.

Jacobs: I have seen secondary sources on this point; if this is a reliable effect, your interpretation may well apply.

Pfaffmann: Garcia (*Science*, **122**: 157,

1955) essentially reproduced what was demonstrated by M. Nachman (*Amer. J. Physiol.*, **205** [2]: 219–21, 1963) in my lab, i.e., the effect of long, slow poisoning or radiation, acting slowly to make the animal feel sick, which is attached to the taste of a particular food. That same treatment is specific to the spot where the poisoning took place. There appears to be a differential connection between tastes of foods and poisoning effects and the place where the poisoning has occurred. It is not just a homogeneous situation. There is a relevance between the stomach changes and the taste which produces that which obviates the delayed reinforcement problem. You cannot get the animal to show bait shyness for the place where the poisoning is taking place. This seems to follow the reinforcement difficulty. There is a whole area here which has not been investigated from a naturalistic point of view and which may point out that learning conceptions are, in fact, arbitrary.

Jacobs: I agree. Psychologists have been very proficient in designing simple, artificial techniques that give standard measures of learning and precise, reliable, and occasionally irrelevant results, at least in complicated situations such as these.

De Ruiter: With respect to Grossman's comment that there may be too long a delay for learning to be possible from the effects of ingestion, this may not be so in the case of sugars. We find that when a fasting rat starts a meal, its blood glucose concentration rises to satiated levels within some fifteen minutes. This is surprisingly rapid, and we are not sure what is behind it yet, but the delay may not be so very long.

Kare: Jacobs implied that "sweetness" is of consequence to chicks. We have measured the response to sugar solutions of thousands of birds, including chickens, gulls, blackbirds, starlings, robins, quail, and many others. We have yet to observe a preference for sucrose solutions when such birds are on an adequate diet (Kare, in Sturkie, *Avian Physiology,* Cornell University Press, Ithaca, 1965).

A commonly repeated suggestion that animals share man's "sweet tooth" receives limited support from experimental evidence. The failure to respond to so-called sweet solutions by many members of the class *Aves* is not unique. For example, the cat (Frings, *Experientia,* **7**: 424, 1951), the armadillo (Maller and Kare, *Anim. Behav.,* 1967 [in press]), and some species of fish do not display an avidity for sugars. On the basis of results available, one could similarly argue for the universal appeal of short-chain fatty acids. A generalization on the response to sweetness in animals would be premature since this sense has been studied in only a few of the millions of species.

An appraisal of the evidence on sugar preference among animals reveals that the specific sugar under study is often undefined. Consideration of specific sugars further weakens an argument for the universality of sweet perception. For example, maltose is one of the sugars that rats prefer most, but man derives little or no sweet sensation from it. The calf, which responds to sucrose solutions even at concentrations insipid to man, is indifferent to maltose while the armadillo is offended by this sugar. Obviously, the criterion of sweetness, as defined by man for specific sugars, does not freely transcend species boundaries.

A limited effort has been made in taste studies to ascertain if the response to a sugar is based upon nutritive value. The polysaccharides, starch and glycogen, which do not share the common sugar's sweetness, have not been compared in regard to acceptability. In fact, in the literature, equimolar solutions rather than isocaloric solutions are often compared, confounding these two parameters. We have demonstrated that the nutritive state will modify preference behavior for sucrose; therefore, it would be desirable in a taste study to divorce taste from nutritive value. The use of synthetic sweeteners—saccharine, dulcin, and sodium cyclamate—provides this opportunity. Unfortunately, however, the majority of animals tested with these chemicals are indifferent to or offended by their taste.

In our preference studies on sugar we have searched for physiological, chemical, or physical variables of sugar solutions that might be associated with their selection. We considered circulating blood glucose level (Kare and Ficken, in *Olfaction and Taste,* Y. Zotterman [ed.], Pergamon Press, New York, 1963) and milk sugar level. However, no physiological variable can be offered to explain the collective comparative results. We have examined preference data in terms of osmotic pressure, viscosity, melting point, configuration, and conformation, but could find no common denominator that might explain the difference in taste preference of sugars between species.

A second but minor point is that your slides seem to show a comparison between the responses to sugar and saccharine. Are these substances supposed to be near equal in sweetness? If we use the rule of thumb as applied to man, that saccharine is approximately 200 to 400 times as sweet as sucrose, there is a substantial difference in taste intensity between your choices.

Jacobs: That is a pretty broad rule. As to your point on whether chicks discriminate "sweetness," I agree that these data are unclear (Kare and Halpern [eds.], *The Physiological and Behavioral As-*

pects of Taste, University of Chicago Press, Chicago, 1961, p. 30.)

Kare: In the case of Le Magnen's data, he used 5 per cent sucrose and saccharin equivalents of 3.7 or 7.4 per cent, but yours were all the way up to 26–52 per cent. At these two levels, I do not think saccharin can be freely compared with the sugar solutions. I don't know of any animal that responds to 2.8 per cent lactose. I don't know how to interpret your conjectures on learning, if you are using a stimulus that may be meaningless to the rat.

Jacobs: I agree that conjectures on absolute sweetness levels may be meaningless. In my case I merely had to assume that 0.1 per cent saccharin was sweeter for the rat than a 2.8 per cent lactose solution.

Kare: It is difficult to get a substantial response from the rat to 2.8 per cent lactose; the opossum is unique in that it responds very well to lactose.

Jacobs: The lactose problem is complicated, even in rats. For one thing, lactose is toxic to adult rats. Adult rats can discriminate lactose from water at 4 per cent concentration (Richter and Campbell, *J. Nutr.,* **20:** 31, 1940). The learning hypothesis would have run into logical difficulty even if I had not carried out my experiments on neonates. If the neonate rat presumably learns to like sweets on the basis of mildly sweet 2.8 per cent lactose solution as a conditioned stimulus, why does the adult rat avoid *all* lactose solutions it can discriminate, while still liking low concentrations of other sweet substances? One would have to add all sorts of complicated *ad hoc* hypotheses about learned avoidance, gradients of secondary approach and avoidance, to explain this.

As to the discriminability of a 2.8 per cent lactose solution, it is possible that the neonate is more sensitive than the adult animal. In any event, I have also tried 4 per cent lactose in the neonate and it responds to it as to the 2.8 per cent solution. I had to increase sweetness to 17 per cent to change acceptability in my neonate subjects.

Kare: We can marshal examples to support the contention that animals will avoid harmful compounds, but the basis for avoidance is not necessarily taste. Further, the response to a toxic compound is unpredictable and is not uniform across species.

Under some circumstances, lactose is toxic. However, the fowl and the cat accept a 5 per cent solution indifferently. While the rat does not strongly prefer lactose solutions, it avidly selects galactose, the constituent monosaccharide to which is ascribed the lactose toxicity (Perry *et al., Acta Paedia.,* **45:** 228, 1956). Lactose is not the only sugar for which harmful aspects have been recognized. Xylose is recognized to have a deleterious action on the visual apparatus. Despite this, man finds it sweet and pleasant, the cat is indifferent, while the fowl actively rejects it in a choice situation.

REFERENCES

1. Bacon, W. E., Snyder, H. L., and Hulse, S. H. Saccharine preference in satiated and deprived rats. *J. Comp. Physiol. Psychol.,* **55:** 112–14, 1952.
2. Bhattacharya, B. K., Brdacha, S. B., and De'Lima, T. The metabolic fate of invert sugar. I: Absorption, excretion, and the effect of insulin on the utilization of sugar. *Ind. J. Med. Res.,* **39:** 377–90, 1951.
3. Capretta, P. J. Saccharin consumption under varied conditions of hunger drive. *J. Comp. Physiol. Psychol.,* **55:** 656–60, 1962.
4. Capretta, P. J. Saccharin consumption and the reinforcement issue. *J. Comp. Physiol. Psychol.,* **57:** 448–50, 1964.
5. Garcia, J., Kimeldorf, D. J., and Hovling, R. A. Conditioned aversion to saccharin re-

sulting from exposure to gamma radiation. *Science,* **122:** 157–58, 1955.

6. Harris, L. J., Clay, J., Hargreaves, F. J., and Ward, A. Appetite and choice of diet. The ability of the vitamin B deficient rat to discriminate between diets containing and lacking vitamin. *Proc. Roy. Soc. [Biol.]* (London), **113:** 161–89, 1933.

7. Hull, C. L. *Principles of Behavior.* Appleton-Century, New York, 1943.

8. Jacobs, H. L. Studies on sugar preference. I: The preference for glucose solutions and its modification by injections of insulin. *J. Comp. Physiol. Psychol.,* **51:** 304–10, 1958.

9. Jacobs, H. L. Some physical, metabolic, and sensory components in the appetite for glucose. *Amer. J. Physiol.,* **203:** 1043–54, 1962.

10. Jacobs, H. L. Observations on the ontogeny of saccharine preference in the neonate rat. *Psychonom. Sci.,* **1:** 105–6, 1964.

11. Jacobs, H. L. The interaction of hunger and thirst: Experimental separation of osmotic and oral-gastric factors in the regulation of caloric intake, in *Thirst Symposium,* M. Wayner (ed.). Pergamon, New York, pp. 117–37, 1964.

12. Katz, D. *Animals and Men.* Translated from the 1948 revised edition. Pelican, London, 1953.

13. Nachman, M. The inheritance of saccharin preference. *J. Comp. Physiol. Psychol.,* **52:** 451–57, 1959.

14. Nelson, W. L., Kaye, A., Moore, M., Williams, A. H., and Herrington, B. L. Milking techniques and the composition of guinea pig milk. *J. Nutr.* **44:** 585–94, 1951.

15. Le Magnen, J. Le processus de discrimination par le rat blanc des stimuli sucrés alimentaires et non alimentaires. *J. de Physiol.,* **46:** 414–18, 1954.

16. Le Magnen, J. Sur le mécanisme d'établissement des appétits caloriques. *Comp. Rend. Acad. Sci.,* **240:** 2436–38, 1955.

17. Le Magnen, J. Le control sensorial dans la regulation de l'apport alimentaire. Extrait de "L'Obesite," *Expansion Scientifique,* J. Le Magnen (ed.). Paris, pp. 147–71, 1963.

18. Richter, C. P. Salt-taste thresholds of normal and adrenalectomized rats. *Endocrinology,* **24:** 367–71, 1939.

19. Richter, C. P. Increased dextrose appetite of normal rats treated with insulin. *Amer. J. Physiol.,* **135:** 781–87, 1942.

20. Richter, C. P. Biology of drives. *J. Comp. Physiol. Psychol.,* **40:** 129–34, 1947.

21. Scott, E. M., and Verney, E. Self-selection of diet. V: Appetites for carbohydrates. *J. Nutr.* **34:** 401–7, 1947.

22. Sheffield, F. D., and Roby, T. B. Reward value of a non-nutritive sweet taste. *J. Comp. Physiol. Psychol.,* **43:** 471–81, 1950.

23. Smith, M. P., and Capretta, P. J. Effective drive level and experience on the reward value of saccharine solutions. *J. Comp. Physiol. Psychol.,* **49:** 553–57, 1956.

24. Soskin, S., and Levine, R. *Carbohydrate Metabolism.* University of Chicago Press, Chicago, 1952.

25. Soulairac, A. Action de l'insuline sur le consummation de différents glucides chez la souris. *Comp. Rend. Soc. Biol.,* **138:** 119–20, 1944.

26. Troland, L. T. *Fundamentals of Human Motivations.* Van Nostrand, New York, 1928.

27. Valenstein, E., and Weber, M. L. Potentiation of insulin coma by saccharin. *J. Comp. Physiol. Psychol.,* **60:** 443–46, 1965.

28. Woodworth, R. S., and Schlosberg, H. *Experimental Psychology.* Rev. ed. Henry Holt, New York, 1954.

29. Young, P. T. Appetite, palatability, and feeding habit: A critical review. *Psychol. Bull.,* **45:** 289–320, 1948.

*The University of Illinois and the U.S. Army Natick Laboratory, Natick, Massachusetts.

This work was supported by the following grants: MH 05754 from the Public Health Service (NIMH), 65–252 from the Foundations Fund for Research in Psychiatry, and a Grant-in-aid from the Corn Products Institute of Nutrition and the University of Illinois Research Board. The assistance of R. P. Kesner and L. J. Goldsmith, who worked as experimenters with the neonate rats, and of Dr. L. Bartashuk, who helped with the manuscript, is acknowledged.

15: Specific Appetite

by Owen Maller

T HE EXISTENCE of approximately 1,463 genera of mammalian species [47] supports the generalization that under natural conditions a substantial number obtain adequate nutrients for survival. Mammals consume a wide variety of materials categorized as food, although qualitatively their requirements for proteins, minerals, etc., are similar. Problems of obtaining sufficient quantities of nutrients, rather than of finding nutritionally adequate materials, are more likely encountered by wild animals.

Information regarding the food habits of wild mammals is anecdotal and indirect [7]. In a field study, Goodall directly observed wild chimpanzees, supposedly herbivores, feeding upon eighty-one varieties of food, including meals of Red Colobus monkeys, bush-pigs, and the larva of termites [16]. However, there are no direct observations of animals in their natural habitat developing nutritional deficiencies similar to those produced in the laboratory. Natural foods are mixtures of essential nutrients. Single components of nutrients, for example, vitamins, used in laboratory studies are rarely found in the natural environment.

The observations that domesticated animals are able to grow by selecting single food components as well as to correct nutritional deficiencies requiring microgram quantities [10,11,13,30,34,42] argue for the existence of a similar ability in wild mammals. The natural conditions under which this ability functions remain to be uncovered. A number of review articles dealing with various aspects of specific appetite in domestic animals are available [1,23,26, 50,51].

Related to the problem of locating adequate food is the question of how animals are able to identify nutrients. What information do they use to determine which nutrients and what quantities are adequate for survival? Is information regarding the value of a nutrient acquired through a trial and error process of learning to consume materials that are nutritious? Or, have mammals evolved an internal value system that controls the acceptance of certain nutrients available in their ecological niche? An innate value system for the acceptance of items classified as food would have greater survival potential than the risk involved in a trial and error process of learning.

Mammals are generally altricial and the young are dependent upon their parents to provide nourishment. The extensive nursing period and maternal care of offspring provide many opportunities for parental guidance and other forms of learning to occur in regard to the foraging and selecting of food. The complex interactions between innate and experiential factors in the ontogeny of appetite has been demonstrated by Kuo in studies of the development of predator-prey relationships in the domestic cat [24,25].

Ben Shaul [6] has compiled data on the composition of milk of a large number of species. Although there are similarities in the composition of milk, there are distinct differences that are often emphasized at certain stages of lactation. These changes in milk composition may be of importance in establishing food preferences.

EXPLANATIONS OF SPECIFIC APPETITE

Specific appetite encompasses detective as well as corrective functions. The detectional components involve an animal's ability to recognize a change in the internal state associated with the depletion of a specific nutrient or nutrients and the locating and selecting of adequate nutrients in the environment. Correctional aspects involve consuming sufficient quantities of the nutrient, associating relief from a need state with the ingestion of some discriminable components of the food, and the storage of this information for future use.

Three general types of explanations have been offered to explain specific appetites. The first proposes that specific appetite is learned. That is, an animal associates some discriminable component of a nutrient or adequate diet (taste, odor, texture, etc.) with a sensation signifying "well-being" that is the result of a postingestional feedback of signals evoked by repletion [17,21]. An animal learns to identify and select those food items that make it feel better after

ingesting them. This explanation has been used to account for the gradual time course observed in the correctional phase of certain deficiencies [19]. However, the time course of correction can be reduced by increasing the deficiency period [12]. Also, the taste or flavor of a diet has been shown to function as a learned cue for an animal in the recognition of a nutritionally adequate diet [21, 43].

Richter proposes that specific appetite functions as a "regulator of homeostasis," assisting in maintaining steady states in the internal chemical environment of the organism [34,36]. The nutritional or metabolic needs of an animal somehow alter the animal's sensory or perceptual threshold for a specific nutrient thereby modulating ingestion until the deficit is corrected. The selective and rapid increase in intake of sodium chloride by the adrenalectomized rat has been explained by such a mechanism [15,31,37].

The third explanation attempts to account for data indicating that animals sometimes avoid ingesting a needed nutrient when it is offered as a choice, or they consume greater quantities of nutrients than are required for growth or survival and display addictions to sugar that interfere with the correction of a nutritional deficiency. Young suggests that acceptance of nutrients is determined primarily by the quality and intensity of emotional arousal evoked by oropharyngeal contact with them. Food items vary in their arousal value or "palatability" and can be ranked in terms of their acceptance by an individual or a species. However, need states and dietary habits of an animal may override the palatability of a nutrient [54,55]. Some of the difficulties encountered in the explanations of specific appetite stem from the problems involved in defining nutritional needs.

NUTRITIONAL NEEDS

Need is defined as a deficit or absence of a nutrient or nutrients from the dietary regimen, which, unless corrected, eventually results in the death of an organism. Needs are demonstrated by omitting some vitamin, mineral, etc., from the diet of an animal and comparing its growth, behavior, survival, with an animal having the nutrient in its diet. Nutritional requirements of most domestic animals have been well established. McCoy [28] has provided a summary of known dietary requirements for the laboratory rat. There are, however, large variations in the dietary requirements of an animal as a consequence of age [18,45]; large individual and species differences also exist [33,48]. These differences in requirements reflect differences in the absorption, utilization, and storage of various nutrients.

There are two limitations to the concept of nutritional need. A particular nutrient is sometimes essential only if some other nutrient is lacking. For example, the calcium need of an animal is dependent upon the level of phosphorous available. Therefore, it is difficult to create a simple nutritional need. Also, the intake of some nutrients, at least in the case of the laboratory rat, seems to be affected by factors other than nutritional needs. For example, rats with nutritionally adequate quantities of sodium chloride and carbohydrate in their diets will consume large quantities of these substances when they are made available to them in solutions at certain concentrations [36,56]. The observation that animals consume quantitatively greater amounts than they "need" can be argued to have adaptive value. However, rats, for example, may consume many materials that are of questionable nutritive value, e.g., artificial sweeteners such as sodium saccharin [22]. Also, rats

nutritionally deficient in the mineral magnesium will avoid diets containing magnesium in a choice situation [44]. An unexplained preference by rats for thiamine-containing diets in the absence of a deficiency has been observed [40,46]. Finally, rats may develop such strong preferences for sucrose that these may interfere with the correction of a nutritional deficiency and result in death [4,20,52].

These kinds of observations introduce difficulties for the available explanations of specific appetite. Consequently, investigators have invoked concepts such as emotional responses, maladaptive habits, and palatability as *post hoc* explanations. Others have argued that the concept of nutritional need is useless and should be discarded. However, some of the contradictory data on specific appetite may be peculiar to the type of animal that has become the prototype for this area of research.

DOMESTICATION

Relatively little consideration has been given to the possible changes in metabolic and sensorimotor functions that may have resulted in the laboratory rat as an inadvertent consequence of selection for traits of tameness, growth, and reproductive capacity. Selection for these characteristics has proceeded for almost sixty years. A recent study has demonstrated feeding and metabolic differences between strains of rats selectively bred for maze brightness [49]. Saccharin preference also has been altered by selective breeding [30]. Multiple differences resulting from selective breeding are commonly observed [9].

Several workers have enumerated the distinct differences that exist between the wild Norway rat and its domesticated counterpart in respect to their anatomy, physiology, and behavior [8,35]. Studies of the responses of the wild Norway rat to complex foodstuffs presented to it in both its natural habitat and in the laboratory have been reported [2]. One of the more striking differences was observed in feeding behavior; wild rats display extreme caution when confronted by any changes made in the feeding situation. Food intake may be terminated temporarily by a change in the type or location of feeding containers [3].

Differences between wild and domesticated rats are not limited to feeding habits. Domesticated rats have been shown to possess a smaller number of fungiform and foliate papillae on the tongue [14], a lower basal metabolic rate [5], and decreased locomotor activity in response to starvation [39]. Wild rats are less able to tolerate high levels of salt in their diet but are better able to conserve it [38]. Mosier and Richter have described some histochemical and morphological differences between the adrenal glands of wild and laboratory rats that are correlated with their responses to salt [29].

Our interest in the issue of domestication stemmed from the general question of what function or functions taste serves an animal in the feeding process. Intuitively, under natural conditions it would seem to be advantageous for animals to be able to decide rapidly whether or not a food is nutritious. The wild animal cannot risk being guided solely by the palatability of a food. The selective breeding that has taken place during the process of domestication may have changed the function or functions that taste serves an animal in the detection, selection, and ingestion of nutrients. We have collected data that suggest that domestication has substantially changed the regulatory mechanisms of the laboratory rat, including both de-

tectional and correctional components involved in nutrient selection and intake.

In each of these experiments to be briefly described, different samples of wild and domesticated (Holtzman strain) rats were used. The wild rats were trapped locally and acclimated to the laboratory for one and half to two months.

The first study we conducted compared the two groups of rats in regard to their selection and intake of several common sugars in solution. Although the qualitative preferences were similar in both groups, with a few exceptions— for example, the preferences for lactose and xylose differed (they were less for the wild rat)—the quantities of sugar consumed were different [27]. An examination of the caloric intake indicated that the wild rats ingested less calories from the sugar solutions than did their domesticated counterparts. Furthermore, the domestic rat increased its total fluid intake, compared with the days when only water was available, from 24 per cent in the case of lactose to 197 per cent with maltose. In contrast, the maximum increased intake in the wild rats was 53 per cent for maltose. The over-all average increase in fluid intake amounted to 12 per cent for the wild rats as opposed to 87 per cent for the laboratory rats.

We then examined the responses of these animals to a more complex food. We noted the changes in caloric intake and body weight that occurred when these animals were switched from a diet low in fat content (10 per cent) to one high in fat content (60 per cent). Figure 15–1 shows the slight increase, but rapid return to baseline levels, of the caloric intake by the wild Norway rat and the sluggish response of the domestic rat. The changes in body weight were significant when statistically adjusted for initial dif-

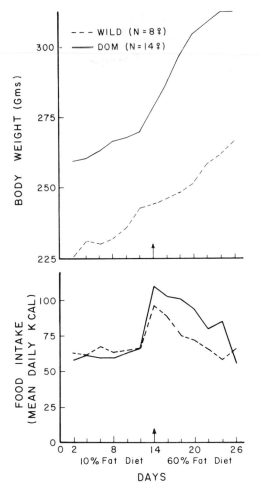

Fig. 15–1. Body weight and caloric intake of wild and domesticated rats maintained ad lib on a diet containing 10 per cent fat, then changed to a diet containing 60 per cent fat.

ferences (p < 0.01). A similar experiment was conducted on two additional groups of animals. In this experiment we added 25 per cent fat (by weight) to a commercial diet containing 4 per cent fat. The results were the same. The wild rats reduced their caloric intake more rapidly and showed a relatively smaller weight gain.

Since only positive-tasting nutrients were used, we attempted to determine whether similar responses would be obtained when the diet was negatively

flavored. Quinine sulfate was added (0.25 per cent by weight) to the base diet for a five-day period. We observed a temporary but significant (p < 0.05) decrease in the volume intake of food by the domestic rat, but no change in the intake of the wild rat.

We then repeated our experiments with the sugar solutions. In this set of experiments, varying concentrations (ranging from less than 1 per cent to 75 per cent w/v) of two sugars, glucose and sucrose, were presented in random order. Two groups of wild and domesticated rats were presented with the glucose and two different groups received the sucrose solutions. Again we observed that the domesticated rats showed a greater increase in their caloric intake and weight gain with both kinds of sugar solutions. However, the increases in caloric intake were greater with the sucrose solution, which is "sweeter" in taste quality to humans.

Since all of the studies described employed captive wild rats, the question was raised regarding the possible effects of differences in dietary adaptations and experience. The dietary background of the captive rats was unknown and might have been of consequence in their responses to the sugar. We repeated the sucrose study with first generation laboratory-reared wild rats (four litters). Figure 15–2 describes these results. In this situation the laboratory-reared wild rats showed less alteration in their caloric intake in response to the sucrose solutions than did the domesticated rats. In addition, the body weights of the wild rats fluctuated slightly as compared with the large weight gains observed in the laboratory rats. Whatever physiological and behavioral mechanisms were responsible for the difference in the wild rat's response to the sugar solutions, experience in its natural habitat does not seem to have been a prerequisite.

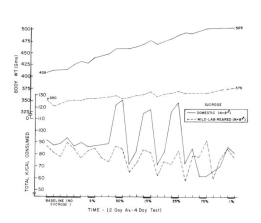

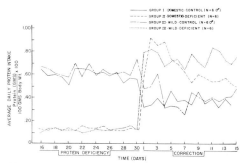

Fig. 15–3. Grams of protein intake/100 g
body weight × 100 of the wild and
domesticated rats deficient in protein. The
correction period offered a choice between
an adequate protein diet and a deficient diet.

Fig. 15–2. Body weight and caloric intake of
laboratory-reared wild and domesticated rats
maintained on an ad lib regimen, then
presented with a choice of a sucrose solution
and distilled water. The choices were
presented for four-day periods followed by
four days of water alone.

If the wild Norway rat is less responsive to the sensory qualities of nutrients,
then it should respond more efficiently
in the correction of a nutritional deficiency where nutritive value and sensory
qualities are opposed to one another. A
protein-deficient (2 per cent protein)
diet was prepared and made "palatable"
by using sucrose as the major source of
carbohydrate. Groups of rats were maintained on the protein-deficient diet for
approximately one month, at the end of
which time they showed a considerable
loss in body weight and other symptoms
of deficiency. The rats were then given
a choice between the deficient diet and
a protein-adequate diet (12 per cent protein) containing starch as the major carbohydrate source. Figure 15–3 shows the
protein intake of the two experimental
and control groups. Although the laboratory rat, for the first few days, consumed more of the adequate diet during
the correction period, it soon reverted
to consuming more of the palatable but

less adequate diet. The protein intake of
the wild rat remained at a high and
relatively constant level. That the level
of sucrose in the diet was not simply
aversive for the wild rat was shown by
the temporary preference for the deficient diet by the control group.

Thus, a tentative conclusion from our
data is that the process of domestication
has produced an animal that is more
responsive to the sensory qualities of
food than to nutritive value. Further,
our data, as well as the data available in
the literature, suggest that the responses
by the rat to certain nutrients are in-
nately determined. Innate responses to
nutrients exist within a species as well
as between species. However, learning
has been shown to be of consequence
in identifying nutrients where several
choices are available [21,43,52], but the
precise role it plays in the correction of
a specific appetite is not clear.

SUMMARY

The exclusive study of domesticated
species of mammals may result in a
focusing upon behavioral and physiological parameters of feeding produced
inadvertently by selection for characteristics of tameness, growth, and reproduc-

tive capacity. Food selection and the control of intake by the laboratory rat are quantitatively different from those of its wild counterpart. These differences are evident in the response to so-called sweet solutions, diets high in fat content, and a negatively flavored food. With these foods, the caloric intake of the wild rat was influenced less by the sensory qualities or the palatability. Also, body weight was more rigorously controlled by the wild rat through a more precise monitoring of intake and probably through a greater expenditure of energy. The physiological and behavioral changes produced during domestication of the Norway rat are reflected in the selection, intake, and metabolism of nutrients.

Discussion

Pearson: Is this a genetic characteristic of the wild rat? Is there less capacity for weight gain or for utilizing food, or is it a taste mechanism?

Maller: We have not determined whether there are differences in detection or recognition thresholds with sugar solutions between these groups. However, preliminary work with sodium saccharine solutions indicates that the domesticated rats show a lower preferential threshold for these solutions and are more tolerant of higher concentrations. The differences between these two groups of animals would most likely include sensorimotor as well as metabolic differences, i.e., they would include differences in growth capacity as well as in food utilization. (King, *Amer. Anat. Mem.,* 14: 11, 1929) and (Benedict and Fox, *Amer. J. Physiol.,* 108: 285, 1934).

Pearson: You might be working with two different strains that have completely different characteristics. This may not be

related to taste at all. It may be a capacity for growth or for utilizing nutrients.

Epstein: Have you had a chance yet to raise the wild pups with a domesticated mother? Your interpretation that experience in natural environments does not produce this difference is quite proper. But we should be cautious in assuming that this is a genetic difference. We know that considerable differences in excitability can be produced in rats by their early experience. Rasmussen (*Acta Psychol.,* 4: 295, 1939) gave wild pups to domesticated mothers shortly after birth. As adults, they were conspicuously less emotional and less active than wild pups raised by wild mothers in the laboratory.

Maller: Experiments similar to those of Rasmussen were performed by King (*Amer. Anat. Mem.,* 17: 1, 1939) and others (Stone *et al.,* in *Studies in the Dynamics of Behavior,* University of Chicago Press, Chicago, 1930), who found that unless gentling experiences were continued through adulthood, the wild rats reverted to their "wild state." Further, the nature of the relationship that exists between the emotional state of an animal and its intake of a particular nutrient remains to be established.

Epstein: Maller has shown us wild rats that are not ingesting carbohydrate as vigorously as tame rats. We know that the wild rat is notoriously more excitable than his tame cousin. Lát, is this consistent with what you were discussing yesterday?

Lát: Experience with a mother's milk may influence the metabolic pathways when the animal is given conventional feed.

Epstein: What about the difference in

carbohydrate intake? The wild animals have less preference for carbohydrate than the tame ones.

Lát: True, the results would not be consistent with our findings, but carbohydrates are not the only source of excitability which can be changed by factors involved in the utilization of carbohydrate.

Henkin: If we can extrapolate your data to man, who must be the most domesticated of all the animals, this kind of phenomenon certainly seems to hold to a great extent in various diseases. Children with phenylketonuria or galactosemia will eat diets rich in phenylalanine or galactose, respectively, and become increasingly ill. The doctor must decrease the amount of phenylalanine or galactose in their diets in order to get the children, at least metabolically, on the road to some kind of recovery. It is only with a great deal of effort that he can do this. On the other hand we have the alcoholic, who is missing many essential nutrients from his diet. It is only with great effort that we can get him to take these essential nutrients. Man seems to be the example par excellence of what you are talking about.

Maller: Richter has written a very interesting paper comparing man with the wild Norway rat in terms of various pathological symptoms that have developed in both species as a possible consequence of domestication (Richter, *Amer. Psychologist,* 14: 18, 1959).

De Ruiter: Did I understand correctly that you find that when you add quinine to the diet the domesticated form will lower its intake?

Maller: Yes, the intake was lowered temporarily for a few days.

De Ruiter: We find in CBA mice that if we give only a quinine-containing diet, i.e., if there is no choice, the animals will eat less and lose weight. But if we use sucrose octa acetate as a bitter substance, the mice will maintain their intake and will not lose body weight. Thus, the decrease of intake by animals on the quinine diets may well be due to the pharmacological effects of the drug and not to its bitter taste. The difference you found might be due to the fact that the wild-born are better buffered against the pharmacological effects of quinine than the domesticated strains.

Maller: This is a possible explanation of the quinine data. Although quinine is offensive to all the domestic animals tested, sucrose octa acetate is accepted indifferently by most of them (Kare, in *Physiology of Domestic Animals,* ed. H. H.. Dukes *et al.* Cornell University Press, Ithaca, 1967).

Barnes: As a biochemist I feel that there hasn't been any serious attention given to metabolic factors that may be involved in two different strains of animals. In addition, nothing at all has been said about the effect of intestinal microflora. It has been found that the rate of gain in rats fed the low-protein diet is greatly influenced by the kind of carbohydrate used.

We believe that intestinal microflora are involved in the relative growth responses to two forms of carbohydrate. It seems to me that such factors are being left out of the discussion. Metabolic factors may be influencing the level of food intake.

Harper: Two problems come to mind; one is with regard to the preference an animal shows for a diet that provides the nutrient to remedy a deficiency. Such a preference has a great deal to do with the rapidity of physiological response of the animal to the nutrient. There is a very clear selection for thiamine by thiamine-deficient animals and for protein by animals that are severly protein deficient. The other problem is in regard to choices between various levels of a nutrient. Meyer and Hargus mentioned (*Amer. J. Physiol.*, **197**: 1350, 1959), and we have had some similar experiences, that there seems to be no specific selection, over the range of dietary protein levels, from an amount that will support about half-maximum growth to an amount that is adequate. Does this occur regularly in studies of diet preferences with a wide range of nutrient levels? In relation to this, what were the protein levels?

Maller: In studies of nutritional deficiencies, animals are generally better able to correct qualitatively than quantitatively. The replete diet contained 12 per cent protein, the deficient one only 2 per cent.

Harper: You would expect some clear selections with that large a difference.

Jacobs: There are two factors that could raise difficulty here. Extreme deprivation provides a good cue, i.e., the fact that the animal is suffering "malaise." Also the choices allowed the animal may be limiting, raising problems of whether the rat can discriminate differences in each case. Thus, you may have trouble in showing repletion to a deficiency, either because the nutritional need is not sharp enough to discriminate or because the choice is too difficult.

Harper: There have been some studies of vitamin A–deficient animals who show preferences for diets containing vitamin A. These were not successful. This is a deficiency that responds relatively slowly compared with thiamine deficiency.

Maller: There is one study demonstrating that rats can successfully correct a deficiency with provitamin A (Harriman, *J. Genet. Psychol.*, **86**: 45, 1955), but, as I recall, the animals were vitamin deprived for a long period of time. Vitamin D is another type of deficiency that develops slowly and has not been found to be correctable by the rat (Wilder, *J. Comp. Psychol.*, **24**: 597, 1937; Young and Wittenborn, *J. Comp. Psychol.*, **37**: 327, 1944).

Hamilton: Isn't there a problem here related to the duration of the deficiency? As the deficiency develops there may be metabolic alterations (changes in enzyme systems, for example) that obviate against any changes in diet selection when the animals are given a choice.

Maller: This might explain instances in which correction was unsuccessful.

Barnes: But don't forget that when you are talking about a deficiency, it doesn't have to be a deficiency that you have imposed intentionally. It may be a deficiency that is there because you did not know enough to put all of the necessary nutrients into the diet.

Pearson: We do know that in domestic animals within the same species there are many strains, some of which have the genetic capability of growing much faster than others, even though they are on the same diet, and of course these consume more to make them grow.

Epstein: In the Harris experiment (Harris *et al.*, *Proc. Roy. Soc.* [*Biol.*] [London], **113**: 161, 1933) in which the B_1 hunger of B_1-deficient rats was first described, the deficient animals chose the vitamin diet only if the choice was easy. Each of the diets was distinctively marked with a flavor cue, and most of the rats did well if they had to choose from only two or three. When the number of diets was increased to six or ten they failed to choose the diet containing thiamine. Harris then ran the education experiment that Harper showed us the other day. He restricted the deficient rat to a single diet containing thiamine and marked with some flavor cue. After the period of education, which lasted about a week, the animal was able to select the vitamin diet in preference to all the others. Harris went further and did what he called the deception experiment. He switched the thiamine from the diet, say the one marked with bovril, to the one marked with lard. The animal, having been educated to eat the bovril diet, continued to do so and died in the presence of the diet containing the thiamine, now the lard diet. In some cases Harris saved their lives by re-educating them. It is quite clear from this unsurpassed experiment and from the emphasis of Harris' discussion that the B_1-deficient rat does not choose the diet containing thiamine; it chooses the diet on which it experiences well-being, the beneficial diet. It chooses the diet on the basis of olfactory and taste cues, and the significance of these cues is learned. Even under those circumstances, I think only two-thirds of his animals succeeded in choosing the thiamine diet.

Maller: The level of the B vitamin in the adequate diet and the vigor of physiological response it produces are critical parameters for the education experiment ([21], p. 185). Incidentally, olfactory cues appear dispensable, for the rat, in regard to correcting a thiamine deficiency (Tribe and Gordon, *Brit. J. Nutr.,* **9**: 11, 1955) or a sodium deficiency (Richter, in *L'Instinct dans le Comportement des Animaux et de l'Homme,* Masson et Cie, Paris, 1956).

Harper: Evidence of this kind may provide the basis for the type of generalizations that Adolph was requesting yesterday. We probably do not need to postulate a whole series of receptors to enable animals to distinguish between an adequate and inadequate diet. We only need the animal to distinguish between well-being and a lack of well-being and to have a clue that it can use to identify the diet that is associated with well-being. This gets around a great many complications.

Maller: We are still faced with the problem of describing physiologically what we mean by a feeling of well-being and the characteristics of the vital nutrient the animal associates with the sensation of well-being.

REFERENCES

1. Anonymous. Self-selection of diets. *Nutr. Rev.,* **2**: 199–203, 1944.
2. Barnett, S. A. *A Study in Behaviour: Principles of ethology and behavioural physiology displayed mainly in the rat.* Methuen, London, 1963.
3. Barnett, S. A. Experiments on 'neophobia' in wild and laboratory rats. *Brit. J. Psychol.,* 49: 195–201, 1958.
4. Behrman, H., and Maller, O. Appetite for sugar and fat in the thiamine deficient rat. *Psychonomic Sci.,* 3: 523–24, 1965.
5. Benedict, F. G., and Petrick, J. M. Metabolism studies on the wild rat. *Am. J. Physiol.,* 94: 662–85, 1930.
6. Ben Shaul, D. M. The composition of the milk of wild animals, in *International Zoological Yearbook,* C. Jarvis and D. Morris (eds.), 4: 333–42, 1962.
7. Bourliere, F. *The Natural History of Mammals.* 3rd ed. rev. New York, p. 387, 1964.
8. Castle, W. E. The domestication of the rat. *Proc. Nat. Acad. Sci. U.S.A.,* 33: 109–17, 1947.
9. David, P. R., and Snyder, L. H. Some interrelations between psychology and genetics, in *Psychology: A Study of a Science. IV: Biologically oriented fields: Their place in psychology and in biological science,* S. Koch (ed.). McGraw-Hill, New York, pp. 1–50, 1962.
10. Denton, D. A., and Sabine, J. R. The selective appetite for Na+ shown by the Na+ deficient sheep. *J. Physiol.* (London), **157**: 97–103, 1961.

11. Dove, W. F. A study of individuality in the nutritive instincts and of the causes and effects of variations in the selection of food. *Amer. Nat.*, **69**: 469–544, 1935.

12. Epstein, A. N., and Stellar, E. The control of salt preference in the adrenalectomized rat. *J. Comp. Physiol. Psychol.*, **48**: 167–72, 1955.

13. Evvard, J. M. Is the appetite of swine a reliable indication of physiological need? *Proc. Iowa Acad. Sci.*, **22**: 375–402, 1915.

14. Fish, H. S., and Richter, C. P. Comparative numbers of fungiform and foliate papillae on tongues of domestic and wild Norway rats. *Proc. Soc. Exp. Biol. Med.*, **63**: 352–55, 1946.

15. Fregly, M. J. Specificity of the sodium chloride appetite of adrenalectomized rats: substitution of lithium chloride for sodium chloride. *Amer. J. Physiol.*, **195**: 645–53, 1958.

16. Goodall, J. My life among wild chimpanzees. *National Geographic*, **124**: 272–308, 1963.

17. Green, H. H. Perverted appetites. *Physiol. Rev.*, **5**: 336–48, 1925.

18. Halstead, W. C., and Gallagher, B. B. Autoregulation of amino acids intake in the albino rat. *J. Comp. Physiol. Psychol.*, **55**: 107–11, 1962.

19. Harriman, A. E. Provitamin A selection by vitamin A depleted rats. *J. Genet. Psychol.*, **86**: 45–50, 955.

20. Harriman, A. E. The effect of a preoperative preference for sugar over salt upon compensatory salt solution by adrenalectomized rats. *J. Nutr.*, **57**: 271–76, 1955.

21. Harris, L. J., Clay, J., Hargreaves, F. J., and Ward, A. Appetite and choice of diet: The ability of the vitamin deficient rat to discriminate between diets containing and lacking the vitamin. *Proc. Roy. Soc. [Biol.]* (London), **113**: 161–90, 1933.

22. Hausmann, M. F. The behavior of albino rats in choosing food and stimulants. *J. Comp. Psychol.*, **13**: 279–309, 1932.

23. Kleiber, M. Dietary deficiencies and energy metabolism. *Nutr. Abstr. Rev.*, **15**: 207–22, 1945–1946.

24. Kuo, Z. Y. Further study on the behavior of the cat towards the rat. *J. Comp. Psychol.*, **25**: 1–8, 1938.

25. Kuo, Z. Y. The genesis of the cat's responses to the rat. *J. Comp. Psychol.*, **11**: 1–35, 1930.

26. Lepkovsky, S. The physiological basis of voluntary food intake. *Advances in Food Research I*, E. M. Mark and G. F. Stewart (eds.). Academic Press, New York, 105–48, 1948.

27. Maller, O., and Kare, M. R. The selection and intake of carbohydrates by wild and domesticated rats. *Proc. Soc. Exp. Biol. Med.*, **119**: 199–203, 1965.

28. McCoy, R. H. Dietary requirements of the rat, in *The rat in laboratory investigation*, E. J. Farris and J. Q. Griffith, Jr. (eds.). 2nd ed. Hafner, New York, Chapter v, 1962.

29. Mosier, H. D., and Richter, C. P. Response of the glomerulosa layer of the adrenal gland of wild and domesticated Norway rats to low and high salt diets. *Endocrinol.*, **62**: 268–77, 1958.

30. Nachman, M. The inheritance of saccharin preference. *J. Comp. Physiol. Psychol.*, **52**: 451–57, 1959.

31. Nachman, M. Taste preferences for sodium salts by adrenalectomized rats. *J. Comp. Physiol. Psychol.*, **55**: 1124–29, 1962.

32. Nevens, W. G. Experiments in self-feeding of dairy cows. *Univ. Ill. Agr. Exp. Sta. Bull.*, **316**: 118–24, 1928.

33. Pilgrim, F. J., and Patton, R. A. Patterns of self-selection of purified dietary components by the rat. *J. Comp. Physiol. Psychol.*, **40**: 343–48, 1947.

34. Richter, C. P. Total self-regulatory functions in animals and human beings. *Harvey Lectures*, **38**: 63–103, 1942–1943.

35. Richter, C. P. The effects of domestication and selection on the behavior of the Norway rat. *J. Nat. Cancer Inst.*, **15**: 727–38, 1954.

36. Richter, C. P. Salt appetite of mammals: its dependence on instinct and metabolism, in *L'Instinct dans le Comportement des Animaux et de l'Homme*, M. Autuori *et al.* (eds.). Masson et Cie, Paris, pp. 577–632, 1956.

37. Richter, C. P., and Eckert, J. F. Mineral metabolism of adrenalectomized rats studied by the appetite method. *Endocrinology*, **22**: 214–24, 1938.

38. Richter, C. P., and Mosier, H. D. Maximum sodium chloride intake and thirst in domesticated and wild Norway rats. *Amer. J. Physiol.*, **176**: 213–23, 1954.

39. Richter, C. P., and Rice, K. K. Comparison of the effects produced by fasting on gross bodily activity of wild and domesticated Norway rats. *Amer. J. Physiol.*, **174**: 305–8, 1954.

40. Rozin, P. Specific hunger for thiamine: recovery from deficiency and thiamine preference. *J. Comp. Physiol. Psychol.*, **59**: 98–101, 1965.

41. Rubin, M. I., and Krick, E. T. Effects of adrenalectomy on salt metabolism in rats. *Proc. Soc. Exp. Biol. Med.*, **31**: 228–29, 1933.

42. Scott, E. M. Self-selection of diet. I: Selection of purified components. *J. Nutr.*, **31**: 397–406, 1946.

43. Scott, E. M., Verney, E. L. Self-selection of diet. VI: The nature of appetites for B vitamins. *J. Nutr.*, **37**: 471–80, 1947.

44. Scott, E. M., Verney, E., and Morissey, P. Self-selection of diet. XI: Appetites for calcium, magnesium and potassium. *J. Nutr.*, **41**: 187–202, 1950.

45. Smith, B. S. W., and Field, A. C. Effect of age on magnesium deficiency in rats. *Brit. J. Nutr.*, **17**: 591–600, 1963.

46. Tribe, D. E., and Gordon, J. G. Choice of diet by rats deficient in members of the

vitamin B complex. *Brit. J. Nutr.*, **7**: 197–201, 1953.

47. Walker, E. P., Warnick, F., Lange, K. I., Uible, H. E., Hamlet, S. E., Davis, M. A., and Wright, P. F. (eds.). *Mammals of the World, I–III.* The Johns Hopkins Press, Baltimore, 1964.

48. Williams, R. J., and Pelton, R. B. Individuality in nutrition: Effects of vitamin A-deficient and other deficient diets on experimental animals. *Proc. Natl. Acad. Sci.*, **55**: 126–34, 1966.

49. Wolfer, J. A., Reid, L. D., Gledhill, M., and Porter, P. B. Feeding and metabolic differences between Tryon bright and dull rats. *J. Comp. Physiol. Psychol.*, **58**: 318–20, 1964.

50. Woods, R. A history of self-selection of diet. I. *Borden Rev. Nutr. Res.*, **10**: 1–9, 1949.

51. Woods, R. Self-selection of diet. II: Experimental investigation. *Borden Rev. Nutr. Res.*, **10**: 1–16, 1949.

52. Young, P. T. Studies of food preference, appetite and dietary habit. VIII: Food seeking drives, palatability and the law of effect. *J. Comp. Physiol. Psychol.*, **40**: 37–72, 1947.

53. Young, P. T. Appetite, palatability and feeding habits: A critical review. *Psychol. Bull.*, **45**: 289–320, 1948.

54. Young, P. T. The role of affective processes in learning and motivation. *Psychol. Rev.*, **66**: 104–25, 1959.

55. Young, P. T. *Motivation and Emotion: A survey of the determinants of human and animal activity.* John Wiley & Sons, New York, 1961.

56. Young, P. T., and Chaplin, J. P. X. Preferences of adrenalectomized rats for salt solutions of different concentrations. *Comp. Psychol. Monogr.*, **19**: 45–74, 1949.

This work was supported in part by a Public Health Service training grant 5 TI MH–8394–02.

16: Some Relationships between Electrophysiology and Behavior in Taste *by Bruce P. Halpern*

Abbreviations

CT	Chorda Tympani nerve
HG	Gymnemic acid
H_2O	Distilled water
i.v.	intravenous
KG	Potassium gymnemate
NFS	Nucleus of the *fasciculus solitarius*
Na-Glu	Sodium Glutamate
n.G.	glossopharyngeal nerve
QHCl	Quinine hydrochloride
QSO_4	Quinine sulphate
VA	vitamin A
VAA	vitamin A acid

T HE NEURAL responses of the gustatory contact chemoreceptors may be examined in relation to behavior from at least two vantage points. Thus, one may inquire whether and how homeostatic requirements and environmental factors may act to modulate gustatory neural responses. Alternatively, behavioral gustatory discriminations and preferences may be viewed with reference to the known differential neural responses. With regard to modulation of responses, four channels of influence can be delineated. These are (1) *neural control* of the gustatory receptors and CNS transfer nuclei; (2) *vascular control* by blood-borne stimuli which reach the gustatory receptors and transfer nuclei through vascular channels; (3) *salivary control*, dependent upon the volume of saliva and its chemical nature; (4) *metabolite and topical control*, which encompasses not only the direct topical effects

of ingesta on the tongue but also the consequences for the gustatory system of the presence or absence of certain metabolites (Fig. 16–1).

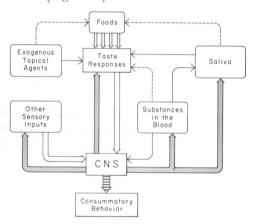

Fig. 16–1. Schematic diagram representing interactions between (a) foods, considered as exteroceptive stimuli; (b) neural responses to the stimuli; (c) mechanisms by which taste responses may be controlled; and (d) consummatory behavior (eating). The clear arrows stand for afferent neural responses; the crosshatched arrows for efferent neural control; the thin solid arrows, known chemical and hormonal interactions; and the thin broken arrows, hypothetical and/or minor interactions.

NEURAL CONTROL OF GUSTATORY RESPONSES

Unequivocal demonstration of centrifugal neural control of a receptor system requires that physiologically meaningful stimuli, when applied to a receptor locus which is separate (through the level of the primary neuron) from the locus under study, modulate the adequately evoked action potential pattern of the receptor system. This modulation must occur through neural pathways to the receptors which are both anatomically observable and neurally functional. These criteria are probably not fully met for the receptor apparatus of any mammal, although several systems present strong cases. What is the situation in gustation?

Data from several laboratories suggest two distinguishable classes of centrifugal neural control of peripheral gustatory responses. A *general enhancement of peripheral gustatory responses* has been reported [24,25,66]. In the rat, Kimura found that summated gustatory responses that were recorded from the chorda tympani nerve (CT) increased in magnitude during direct stimulation of the sympathetic nervous system.[1] In these experiments, the CT recorded from was cut distal to the geniculate ganglion, thus preventing any possible somatic efferent effects. The responses to HCl, NaCl, quinine hydrochloride (QHCl), and sucrose and also the spontaneous activity level were increased. Similar, though smaller, increases in both spontaneous and evoked gustatory activity were elicited by intravenous injection of the sympathomimetic agent, epinephrine. In contrast, injections of the parasympathomimetic agent, eserine (physostigmine), and of the parasympatholytic drug, atropine, caused no change in gustatory responses. This suggests that the general enhancement of gustatory responses is mediated solely through the sympathetic nervous system.[2]

Sympathetic enhancement of gustatory responses was further studied [24] in the frog. The frogs were eviscerated and double-pithed and the cranial nerve roots were cut intracranially, which abolished general circulation [25]. Only the anterior portion of the head and trunk remained intact. In these preparations the first sympathetic ganglion was stimulated electrically, while tap water or "instant coffee" in Ringer's solution was applied to the tongue. The gustatory responses recorded from the glossopharyngeal nerve (n.G.) increased in both unit firing rates and number of units active, following the sympathetic stimulation. The increased gustatory responses were observed for ten seconds or more following sympathetic stimulation.

The anatomical pathways mediating sympathetic general enhancement of gustatory responses have not been fully described, but some parts of the pathways can be recognized. In the frog, the first sympathetic ganglion is joined by two "connectives" to the pneumogastric (jugular) ganglion, from which the n.G. and vagus nerves arise [25]. Electrical stimulation of the first sympathetic ganglion elicited neural activity in the glossopharyngeal nerve, thus demonstrating functionally that sympathetic fibers enter the n.G. In the rat, sympathetic efferents from the cervical sympathetic ganglion may enter the tongue along with the lingual artery branch of the external carotid artery [42], as in man [77].

A potential efferent pathway in the mammalian CT and in taste buds has also been suggested [17]. The argument was as follows: Nerve fibers with diameters up to $6\,\mu$ reach the neural plexus beneath taste buds (subgemmal plexus). Thus, afferent conduction velocities up to 36 m/sec would be expected. Direct measurement gave maximum CT gustatory afferent conduction velocities of 17.8 m/sec. This implied that the nerve fibers with diameters over $3\,\mu$ ($3\,\mu \times$ multiplication factor of $6 = 18$ m/sec) might be efferents to the taste buds. However, the relationship between small diameter A fibers and their conduction velocity may be 3 [21] rather than 6. This would produce a close approximation between the maximal subgemmal fiber diameter of 6 μ and the maximum conduction velocity of CT gustatory afferents. At the level of the taste bud receptor cells, a possible efferent role was suggested for the larger diameter intragemmal fibers, which terminate between receptor cells [17].

Only enhancement of gustatory responses was produced by sympathetic nervous system stimulation in the frog and rat (generalized enhancement of gustatory responses). The increase in response magnitude appeared to be similar for all gustatory stimuli tested, although quantitative data are lacking.

In contrast, *chemical stimulus-dependent reductions and increases in responses* from the n.G. of the frog were observed [36]. The frogs were "decerebrated,"[3] pithed, and the most central end of the n.G. was dissected out. Gastric distention with water produced a 50 per cent increase in the number of nerve impulses per second during tongue stimulation with water and a 25 per cent increase in the gustatory response to NaCl. In contrast, during quinine irrigation of the tongue surface, gastric distention gave a *reduction* of 17 per cent in impulse rate. Gastric chemical stimulation with 0.5 ml of peptone had quite different effects. In this case, responses to water were reduced by one-third and a slight decrease in the response to NaCl was seen, but peptone in the stomach did not alter gustatory responses to quinine. Thus, gustatory responses to water and NaCl were modulated in opposite directions by mechanical versus chemical stimulation of the frog's stomach. Responses to quinine were depressed by gastric mechanical, but not chemical, stimulation. Changes in gustatory responses during gastric distention by balloon and during gastric chemical stimulation with protein hydrolyzate have

also been studied [97]. Summated responses to 0.5 M NaCl were consistently larger during gastric distention (Fig. 16–2), thus confirming Esakov's report [36].

The gastric receptors necessary for differential modulation of gustatory responses were also investigated by Esakov. Distention-produced gustatory modula-

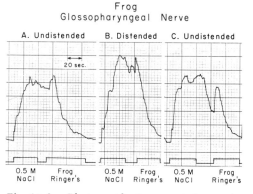

Frog
Glossopharyngeal Nerve

A. Undistended   B. Distended   C. Undistended

20 sec.

0.5 M   Frog   0.5 M   Frog   0.5 M   Frog
NaCl   Ringer's   NaCl   Ringer's   NaCl   Ringer's

Fig. 16–2. Photograph of summated neural responses recorded from the glossopharyngeal nerve of Rana pipiens p. *The general recording procedures in this and subsequent figures were as described by Halpern and Nelson [52] and Halpern [50], except when noted. Urethan anesthesia was used. The nerve was exposed and a short portion carefully freed. A silver-silver chloride hook electrode, insulated except for a small region, was slipped under the nerve, and nerve and bare electrode were covered with a mineral oil pool at 24 ± 1°C. The tongue was placed in a tongue chamber with an open top and stabilized with stainless steel insect pins through its tip. Each stimulus was 10 ml liquid, at 24 ± 1°C, which flowed into the tongue chamber from a pipette and covered the tongue for ca. thirty-two seconds. A rubber balloon, connected to a mercury manometer, was sewn into the stomach through the pylorus. A. Response before gastric distention. B. Response during gastric distention. Between this record and A the intragastric balloon was brought up to 2 mm Hg. The response summated to 0.5 M NaCl is 20 per cent larger than the response just before distention (A) and 22 per cent larger than the next—post-distention—response. C. Response after intragastric pressure was lowered to atmospheric.*

tion was blocked by the application of cocaine to the interior of the stomach. This suggests that the gastric mechano-receptors involved are located in the mucosa or submucosa. These mechano-receptors may correspond to the mech-anoreceptors of the toad gastric mucosa and submucosa [82], which are inner-vated by the vagus nerve.

The pathways within the central ner-vous system that mediate differential gustatory modulation have not been de-termined. Some data are available, how-ever. The hindbrain must remain intact, since extirpation of the medulla oblong-ata eliminates the gastric modulation of gustatory responses [36]. The vagal, gen-eral visceral afferent neurons from the gastric receptors presumably reach the nucleus of the *fasciculus solitarius* (NFS) of the medulla oblongata [59]. The gus-tatory, special visceral afferent neurons of the n.G. also reach NFS. Electrical stimulation of the *central* end of the cut n.G. decreased the gustatory responses to water and NaCl that were recorded from the contralateral n.G. [36].

Efferent connections from the NFS or other nuclei must eventually enter the subgemmal plexus, thus completing the reflex pathway. Indeed, electrical stimu-lation of the *peripheral* end of the cut n.G. also decreased contralaterally re-corded gustatory responses. This sug-gests that inhibitory efferents to the gus-tatory receptors descend through the n.G. The neurons involved might be part of the parasympathetic system. How-ever, the intravenous injection of para-sympathomimetic and parasympatholytic drugs did not affect peripheral gustatory responses in the rat [66]. The efferents may reach the contralateral subgemmal plexi through the intergemmal connec-tions [98].

In summary, two types of direct neu-ral control of gustatory responses have been demonstrated. One type produces only generalized enhancement of gusta-tory responses, and may affect gustatory responses to all chemical stimuli equally. It is dependent on adrenergic sympa-thetic input. The second type of cen-trifugal control system can decrease or increase gustatory responses. The direc-tion of change in response is a function of both the particular gustatory stimulus employed and the manner in which the feedback system is activated. This latter system, which can be activated by gastric stimulation, seems suited for more-or-less specific alterations in gustatory respon-siveness that could contribute to the maintenance of homeostasis [5]. On the other hand, the centrifugal system medi-ating generalized enhancement would produce a general increase in responsive-ness, perhaps leading to greater CNS activation by the strengthened afferent inflow.

Neural control of gustatory responses in the CNS can be briefly considered. Although inhibitory modulation of CNS sensory transfer nuclei is a common observation, there are few examples of inhibition in gustation. One report in-volved the first gustatory transfer nu-cleus, NFS. In the rostral portion of the rat NFS, neural responses were recorded from the composite response area, which receives gustatory input from both the anterior and posterior regions of the tongue [54]. Response magnitudes to posterior tongue stimulation increased when CT was anesthetized, thus block-ing afferent input from the anterior re-gion of the tongue. This was interpreted as a release from a possible inhibitory influence.

Inhibition of ongoing activity is said to be common in the thalamic gustatory transfer nuclei of the cat. Ishiko *et al.* [61] observed that stimulation of the tongue of the cat with HCl and quinine sometimes gives inhibitory responses in the cat thalamus, while responses to NaCl were usually inhibitory in nature. Thus there are indications of inhibitory control of CNS gustatory transfer nuclei, but functional conclusions cannot yet be drawn.

Behavioral studies also support the concept of *centrifugal control of gustatory receptors*. It has been observed that, in man, gustatory sensitivity rapidly decreased after food was introduced into the stomach through a gastric fistula [115]. In these experiments, four fungiform papillae were individually stimulated every two to three minutes with suprathreshold solutions of sucrose or NaCl, and the number of reports of taste was noted.[4] For each time of measurement, the mean number of responsive (i.e., "functional") papillae was calculated. Within five minutes after a test meal was introduced into the stomach, the number of functional papillae fell below the control (empty stomach) level. It is reasonable to assume that at least a modest amount of fat was included in the meal. Very little gastric emptying would occur during the first five minutes, even less absorption through the gastric walls [26]. Therefore, the observed reduction in the number of responsive papillae was probably mediated by interoceptors of the stomach.

An experiment related to the above observations on human taste sensitivity [65] was done using dogs. First, the NaCl rejection threshold was determined. To accomplish this, four to six bowls, each containing 15 ml milk and a different NaCl concentration, were placed before the dog. All liquids drunk during this phase flowed out through an open gastric fistula. Animals that had stable rejection thresholds during this initial test were used for the second phase of the experiment. For the second phase, 300–500 ml of one of several liquids was introduced into the stomach through the fistula, which was then closed. The NaCl-in-milk rejection threshold was now remeasured at various times after introduction of the gastric load. The results

were that when a hypertonic NaCl solution was placed in a dog's stomach, the more concentrated NaCl-in-milk solutions, which had previously been consumed, were refused within three minutes after stomach loading. The stomach would then be emptied and washed with warm water. Normal NaCl acceptance returned rapidly, sometimes within one to three minutes. The change in taste preference behavior was not due to gastric osmotic stimulation, since the introduction of equal volumes of isosmotic sucrose or glucose solutions through the fistula did not change behavioral taste preference for NaCl. The above observation, plus the lack of effect of a gastric water load or gastric inflation by a balloon, eliminated gastric distention receptors as a likely afferent input source for the preference change. Some dogs showed preference change to a gastric load of 300 ml of 0.75 M NaCl but not to 500 ml of 0.6 M NaCl, although total NaCl was approximately equal. Finally, the volume of liquid recovered from the stomach after an experimental series was "only slightly less" than the original load. Thus it would appear that concentration-sensitive gastric or duodenal chemoreceptors supply the afferent neural inflow for the observed preference changes.

The above experiment by Kassil *et al.* did not completely rule out absorption of some NaCl and subsequent detection by vascular chemoreceptors. However, absorption of NaCl from the stomach would be very slow [26]. In addition, a gastric chemoreceptor system that responds to NaCl has been described [105]. Therefore, absorption is not required for detection of NaCl to occur. The importance of both molecular species and ionic concentrations in the control of NaCl intake by interoceptors is further supported by the observation that gastric loads of isotonic NaCl, or variations in the NaCl concentration of food, did not

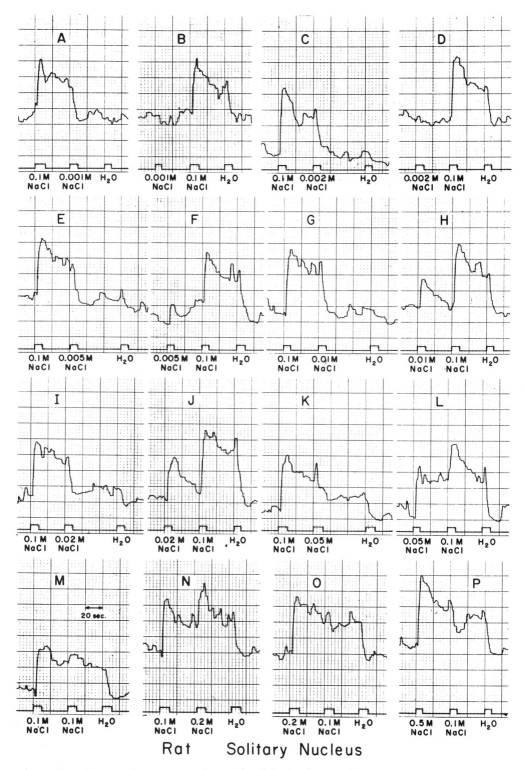

Rat   Solitary Nucleus

Fig. 16–3.   Photograph of summated neural activity in the anterior tongue response zone of the nucleus of the fasciculus solitarius. *The histological procedures were as described by Halpern and Nelson (1965). Responses that matched median magnitudes are shown.   A through L and N through O: For each pair of responses, stimulation with 0.1 M NaCl first preceded and then followed stimulation with NaCl*

modify the ingestion of NaCl in the rat [40].

In summary, neurophysiological, pharmacological, anatomical, and behavioral data that suggest efferent control of gustatory afferent responses have been discussed. Modulation of peripheral input, perhaps by both sympathetic and somatic routes, seems clear, as does rapid modification of gustatory preference or sensitivity following gastric stimulation. The nature of the relationship between the peripheral neural and behavioral events is still unclear. The preference and sensitivity changes may represent events in CNS transfer nuclei, peripheral modulation, or an interaction between the two.

SALIVARY CONTROL

In the preceding section, neural mechanisms were examined which may rapidly alter, for a short period of time at least, the sensitivity of gustatory receptors to some, or all, stimuli. However, many circumstances will not require the prompt, highly labile influence of neural control of gustatory responses. Instead, slower, tonic effects, leading to sustained modification of food intake patterns, will be more useful. Salivary action may play an important role in such cases.

A major component of the external environment of the gustatory receptor cell microvilli is saliva. This constant salivary application might be expected to influence gustatory responsiveness. Salivary flow, per se, is under neural con-

trol. One of the CNS nuclei that is effective in inducing the flow of saliva when stimulated electrically is the rostral NFS [109]. The rostral NFS receives gustatory afferents from the anterior region of the tongue [54].

Therefore, an afferent-efferent link between gustatory neural input and efferent control of salivary flow could exist in the second-order neurons of NFS. This would permit the characteristics of ingested foods to interact with CNS activity in controlling salivary flow. On the other hand, a number of experiments indicate that salivary control of gustatory responses can be quite significant.

The NaCl gustatory threshold for CT neural responses, and, indeed, the nature of the response, is a function of the liquid bathing the tongue just prior to NaCl stimulation (i.e., the adapting stimulus). In rat, dog, and man, an H_2O adapting stimulus results in minimal CT spontaneous activity, high sensitivity to inorganic salts such as NaCl, and little or no increase in the activity of H_2O, although a decrease may occur [3,30,92, 95].[5] In rat and man, as the NaCl concentration of the adapting stimulus is increased, subsequent stimulation with NaCl concentrations less than the adapting concentration, and with H_2O, gives a decrease in neural activity. Stimulation with NaCl concentrations greater than the adapting concentration produces phasic-tonic increases in neural activity [51,81,95]. Similar effects can be seen in NFS (Fig. 16–3). Thus, NaCl solutions which produce large increases in CT and

---

concentrations from 0.001 M through 0.05 M. No H_2O wash was imposed between the two successive stimulations with NaCl, but an H_2O wash preceded (not shown) and ended every sequence. A through J: NaCl adapting stimuli with concentrations between 0.001 M and 0.02 M had little or no effect ($\not> 10$ per cent) on responses to 0.1 M NaCl. K and L: The 0.05 M NaCl adapting stimulus reduced the response to 0.1 M NaCl by 32 per cent. M through O: Adapting stimuli of 0.1 M and 0.2 M NaCl reduced the response to 0.1 M NaCl by $\geqq 80$ per cent. P: The 0.5 M adapting stimulus reduced the response to 0.1 M NaCl by 100 per cent. A marker lesion, placed at the completion of the experiment, was found in a rostral-lateral position in the nucleus of the fasciculus solitarius.

NFS impulse traffic in the presence of a particular salivary NaCl concentration could become relatively ineffective stimuli, or may evoke a decrease in activity, when the NaCl concentration of saliva increases.

If the above neurophysiological modifications in gustatory responses to NaCl are significant, behavioral responses to NaCl should change under parallel conditions. This was confirmed for humans [74] with observations that recognition thresholds for NaCl increased as the NaCl concentration of an adapting rinse increased. When saliva was the adapting rinse, the NaCl recognition threshold was just above salivary NaCl concentration. In addition, it was reported [9] that solutions with NaCl concentrations greater than the adapting stimulus solution were called "salty"; solutions equal in NaCl concentration to the adapting solution had no taste, and solutions having lower NaCl concentrations than the adapting solution were "bitter."

The preceding neural and psychophysical data on NaCl suggest that for rat and man, at least, a decrease in adapting NaCl concentration would decrease the recognition threshold for NaCl. This might be expected to shift the rat NaCl preference function toward lower NaCl concentration. A direct means of decreasing the NaCl content of the gustatory adapting stimulus, while not changing most body functions, is the elimination of saliva. Contrary to the above expectations, rats that had been made desalivate (all salivary ducts except the minor sublingual ligated) four days prior to testing had maximum NaCl intake at a NaCl concentration about twice that of normal rats (normal: $0.1\ M$; desalivate: $0.2\ M$) [108].

No increased preference for low NaCl concentrations was seen at any time in the desalivate rats. However, increased preference for $0.19\ M$ (1 per cent) NaCl appeared on the second day following desalivation, and NaCl preference continued to increase for three days. During the period of increased preference for $0.19\ M$ NaCl, only NaCl was drunk in a two-bottle NaCl-H_2O test situation. Fluid intake reached a maximum—300 per cent of the controls (desalivate rats, H_2O-H_2O choice)—on the fifth day [108]. From the sixth day on, however, preference for $0.19\ M$ NaCl fell steadily, until all preference for NaCl disappeared. Higher NaCl concentrations were still rejected, but no preference for low NaCl concentrations appeared. The observed rapid increase and subsequent gradual decrease in preference for NaCl is preceded by a major alteration in the external environment of the distal processes of the gustatory receptors: Saliva is removed. Evans [37] has demonstrated that the chemical nature of the environment in which blowfly larvae are raised affects the gustatory preference threshold of adult flies. Since mammalian gustatory receptor cells differentiate from surrounding epithelial cells, move through the taste buds, disappear, and are replaced by new cells within a finite period of time [12,13,27], the salivary environment during development might affect the response of these chemoreceptors. There are several parallels between the time course of gustatory receptor cell turn-over and the sequence of changes in preference for NaCl following desalivation (Table 16–1). The time of desalivation may be considered the initiation of a saliva-free environment (asalivary) in which the new gustatory receptor cells will develop. The old, predesalivation cells may have different functional characteristics. Therefore, as the new receptor cell population replaces the old, changes in the pattern of neural response to NaCl might occur. During the first day or two of postdesalivation some new receptor cells would appear in taste

TABLE 16–1: Time Course of Postdesalivation
NaCl Preference and Receptor Cell Turnover

Time (Hours) after Desalivation	Percentage[a] Increase in Intake of 0.19 M (1%) NaCl	Percentage[b] of Predesalivation Taste Buds Remaining
0	0	100
120	415 (max.)	72
250	213	50
332	182	40
833	41	10
1,200	−8	3

[a] Calculated from Vance [108].
[b] Calculated from Beidler and Smallman [15].

buds [15]. The "precells" still comprise
most of the receptor population during
the first few days, but as they age, their
responsiveness to NaCl appears to decrease [90]. The large number of aging
precells, which probably determines the
neural input during this time, may explain the steady increase in NaCl intake
during the first five days of postdesalivation. By the end of the fifth day the
precells would represent less than 75 per
cent of the receptor population (Table
16–1). This may be a critical value, since
it is coincident with the decline of preference for NaCl from the postdesalivation maximum. Both the number of
"pre" receptor cells and the supranormal
NaCl preference continue to decrease
gradually (assuming no sharp cut-off
time for receptor cells). Eventually, intake of NaCl is below predesalivation
amounts, i.e., preference for NaCl is
gone [108] (Table 16–1). At this time,
more than 90 per cent of the "pre" receptor cells have been replaced. The
neural code for NaCl produced by the
"post" receptor cells may be so altered
or attenuated that the necessary input
to maintain normal NaCl preference behavior is lost. The relationship between
receptor cells that differentiate in the
absence of saliva and the disappearance
of two-bottle preference for NaCl is
probably a quantitative reduction in responsiveness to NaCl, since long-term

desalivates (1,032 hours) develop a strong
preference for 0.19 M NaCl after adrenalectomy and 844-hour desalivates reject high concentrations of NaCl [108].
Thus, it is proposed that the absence of
saliva during the normal turnover of
gustatory receptor cells leads to a population of cells which are subnormally
responsive to NaCl and perhaps less
consistent in encoding it.

In contrast to the above proposal, the
effects of an asalivary environment on
preference for NaCl *may be* one sign of
*a broad, non-specific alteration or desen-
sitization of gustatory receptors.* This is
suggested by a sizable increase in the
QHCl rejection threshold of desalivate
rats [108]. Normal rats showed rejection
(25 per cent of total fluid intake) of
QHCl concentrations below $1.3 \cdot 10^{-5}$
M, while the rejection threshold for the
desalivates was above $2.5 \cdot 10^{-4}$ M. The
QHCl rejection threshold for the nor-
mal rats corresponds closely to that reported by other workers, while the
desalivate's threshold is about one log
unit above the usual electrophysiological threshold [68]. Thus, desalivate rats
may prove to have elevated detection
thresholds for all gustatory stimuli. Perhaps the asalivary environment results
in receptor cell damage at a rate that
intermittently exceeds the renewal capacity of the circumgemmal epithelial
cells [15]. If desalivation produces increased damage to, and decreased neural
output from, the gustatory receptor cells,
other conditions that reduce saliva
should have similar effects. One such
condition is water deprivation. In man,
reduced water intake is followed in a
day or less by a greatly diminished flow
of saliva [41,43]. Human gustatory recognition thresholds for H_2SO_4 and NaCl
have been measured during a three-day
water deprivation period [112]. The human threshold for recognition of NaCl
increased significantly during water de-

privation. An observation that is consistent with this human threshold change is the previous rat data, which showed a large increase in NaCl intake by the second desalivate day. Thus, increase of NaCl preference in desalivate rats and the increase of NaCl recognition threshold in dehydrated man may have a similar time course. In contrast, no change in human recognition threshold for H_2SO_4 occurred.

The preceding hypothesis is that desalivate rats manifest reduced sensitivity to NaCl. This reduced sensitivity was related to gustatory receptor cell turnover in the absence of saliva. Among the data supporting the hypothesis was the observation that desalivate rats eventually lost the preference shown by intact rats for 0.19 M NaCl [108]. This preference loss was seen under the conditions of long-term, two-bottle testing in the presence of food. Desalivate rats tend to eat a small amount, then drink, then eat a small amount, etc., rather than to eat a large meal and then drink after it [67,108]. Indeed, desalivate rats may eventually drink only when eating, if food is available ad lib [67]. The constant mixture of food and liquid complicates the interpretation of the observed preference loss in desalivate rats. The stimulus liquid may be masked or adapted by the food, thus possibly increasing preference thresholds in the eating and drinking situations. Therefore, unless more concentrated (but still normally preferred) solutions were tested, a threshold change dependent upon food in the mouth during drinking could be interpreted as a preference loss. Thus, the reported loss of preference for 0.19 M NaCl in long-term desalivate rats may be a function of the method of testing.

The prandial-drinking explanation of postdesalivation loss of preference for 0.19 M NaCl, described above, is weakened by a series of experiments reported by Falk [38]. In these experiments, rats were maintained on a feeding schedule in which bar-pressing produced a 45 mg pellet once every minute on the average (VI 1'). A daily three-hour feeding session was used. Water was available ad lib in the living cage, and water or another liquid was offered ad lib during each feeding session. Prandial-drinking appeared, with an intake of large volumes of water during each feeding session. When increasing NaCl concentrations were substituted for water during feeding sessions, fluid intake first increased, with a maximum at *ca.* 0.05 M NaCl, then decreased at higher NaCl concentrations. Thus a preference for NaCl is not only still present in this prandial-drinking situation, but also the preference maximum is shifted toward lower concentrations, implying that no loss of sensitivity has occurred.

The method of testing preference is apparently crucial in evaluating the effects of salivary loss. Long-term desalivate rats, tested in a one-bottle rather than a two-bottle situation, retain a preference for NaCl [67]. It may be that in the two-bottle situation the motivating properties of the food-diluted NaCl solution are insufficient to support switching from the H_2O to the NaCl bottle when the H_2O bottle is sampled first. In contrast, in the one-bottle situation the only question is how much will be drunk, since motivation to switch bottles is unnecessary. A useful preparation for testing this alternative hypothesis, i.e., food dilution of the liquid drunk, would be rats equipped for intragastric feeding (viz., Epstein paper, this symposium). These animals usually drink voluntarily. If fluid intake in one- and two-bottle situations were examined in intragastrically fed desalivate rats, a direct test of the food dilution explanation for NaCl preferences in desalivate rats would be possible.

The nature of the salivary environment has been proposed *as a factor in some of the taste preference changes that follow adrenalectomy* [81]. In adrenalectomized and sodium-deficient rats, an increase in the volume of NaCl solution drunk, a lowered preference threshold, and an elevated rejection threshold are usually observed [81,99]. This increased salt intake is relatively specific for Na+. Rats made Na+ deficient by intraperitoneal dialysis with 5 per cent glucose show a prompt preference for 0.1 M NaCl and very little intake of 0.1 M KCl, in a brief-exposure, successive-choice test [92]. The selective preference of adrenalectomized rats for sodium salts, and the rejection of most non-sodium salts, has been confirmed in intermediate-length (ten-minute continuous choice) and long-term preference experiments [79,99]. (It should be noted that adrenalectomized rats will initially respond to LiCl as though it were NaCl [80].)

No anatomical changes are seen in the salivary glands of adrenalectomized rats maintained on NaCl solution, although such rats will ingest normally rejected hypertonic NaCl [6,99]. The adrenalectomy can be assumed to reduce the NaCl concentration of saliva. Adrenaline loss itself would be one factor, since subcutaneous infusion of adrenaline produces a 57 per cent increase in the NaCl concentration of submaxillary saliva in normal rats. A more significant factor is the loss of aldosterone. In uncompensated adrenalectomized animals, there is a large urinary NaCl loss and a coincident reduction in salivary NaCl concentration [20]. In addition, since the ducts of the salivary glands have some anatomical similarities to kidney tubules, a common responsiveness to hormonal control might also exist. Indeed, aldosterone appears to directly affect salivary NaCl concentration in intact animals [28,29]. These observations suggest that the NaCl concentration of saliva might play an important role in the changes in NaCl intake that follow adrenalectomy. However, desalivate rats show a large increase in intake of 0.19 M NaCl following adrenalectomy [108]. Thus, saliva, per se, is not necessary for increased intake of NaCl to occur. Since both urinary loss of NaCl and sodium-deficient diets produce a decrease in plasma Na+ concentration, this vascular change is probably the critical factor in initiating increased oral intake of NaCl after Na+ depletion. The internal afferent input might be through a CNS interocepter in contact with the extracellular compartment [28,29]. Neural output from such an interoceptor could lead to efferent modulation of gustatory responses and thus contribute to the observed rapid changes in intake of, and preference for, NaCl.

It should be noted that alteration in plasma Na+ concentration, which was just proposed as the critical signal in the sodium deficiencies of the adrenalectomized and sodium-deprived rat, is not an adequate explanation for the decreased human gustatory detection threshold observed by Henkin *et al.* during adrenal glucocorticoid insufficiency and certain other conditions, or for the effect of diabetes insipidus on preference for NaCl [57,58,107].

VASCULAR CONTROL

An alteration in the plasma concentration of electrolytes was proposed as the common element in some of the preference changes discussed in the preceding section. In the case of generalized threshold change, alteration in steroid level may be one factor (viz., Henkin paper, this symposium), change in sympathomimetic drug level another (viz., neural control). If alterations in the circulating level of plasma metabolites can both reach and change the activity of the gustatory receptors and/or the gustatory transfer nuclei, a direct link between regulation of homeostatic conditions and control of food intake would be available. The extent to which bloodborne stimuli can exert control on the gustatory system through vascular channels will be considered in this section.

Intravenous injection (i.v.) of the artificial sweetener saccharin, the antipellagra vitamin nicotinic acid, and the bile acid desoxycholic acid, produced neural responses in the distal portion of the incised hamster CT [46,47].

No CT neural responses were produced by i.v. presentation of equal concentrations of NaCl. This observation suggests that the positive responses to the former three substances are valid chemical stimulation of the gustatory receptors through a vascular route. On the other hand, i.v. presentation of higher concentrations of many liquids will produce neural responses, not only from CT but also from other nerves. This multimodality response to concentrated liquids may be caused by a general sympathetic enhancement of cutaneous and gustatory responses (viz., neural control) [24]. The receptors mediating this multimodality enhancement, which follows the injection of concentrated liquids into the vascular system, are presumably osmoreceptors, since the general enhancement was elicited by an increase in the concentration of several molecular species. However, under other circumstances, baroceptors are also involved. The inclusion of baroceptors is based on the observation that the injection of a sufficient volume of Ringer's solution into the common carotid artery also produced increased neural activity in the CT of the root [66].

The possibility that disease-correlated taste preference changes, i.e., specific ap-petites, *are due to direct, non-neural modification of peripheral gustatory responses* has been tested electrophysiologically in hypoglycemia and hyponatremia. Gustatory neural responses to sucrose, recorded from the distal end of the hamster CT, were not altered differentially from responses to NaCl by intraperitoneal injection of insulin [94]. Increased behavioral preference for glucose and fructose following insulin injection has been demonstrated several times [62,63]. Therefore, the failure of insulin to induce differential modification of peripheral gustatory neural responses to sugars indicates that control of gustatory receptors through a vascular route is probably not a factor in the taste preference changes of hypoglycemia. Similarly, no changes in the threshold of the cut CT to NaCl stimulation or in suprathreshold CT responses to NaCl were observed in Na^+-deficient rats, although the same deficient diet produced significant changes in preference for NaCl [81]. Effects of hypoglycemia on the responses of CNS gustatory transfer nuclei have also been examined. As was observed for the CT, responses to sucrose that were recorded from the NFS in the barbiturate anesthetized rat were not differentially affected by insulin injection [1].

The absence of changes in gustatory afferent responses to NaCl during hyponatremia, as noted above, is particularly striking. Several studies have shown that an intact peripheral gustatory apparatus is required for increased preference for NaCl to appear during NaCl deficiency [40,99]. In contrast, a modified preference for NaCl, following adrenalectomy, still develops in animals with ligated salivary ducts [108]. In summary, the foregoing data on the effects of i.v. injection of NaCl, desalivation, and destruction of the periphery gustatory nerves indicate not only that the postadrenalectomy increase in preference for NaCl is independent of salivary and vascular influences on the gustatory receptors but also that possibly, internal chemoreceptors are not sufficient by themselves to elicit the intake change [29].

Examination of gustatory afferent responses in the implanted, unanesthetized preparation, or in the chloralosed animal, may reveal changes during NaCl deficiency that are due to neural efferent control. Alternatively, limbic system or hypothalamic nuclei that respond to plasma Na+ and perhaps to carbohydrate-active steroids may serve to integrate the disrupted homeostatic state with the gustatory afferent information, such that adaptive behavior occurs.

METABOLITE AND TOPICAL CONTROL

Although the direct effects of blood-borne stimuli upon the gustatory system are limited, many indirect influences are possible. Any disruption of normal metabolite levels that alters the environment or substrates of the gustatory receptors or transfer nuclei is likely to change gustatory responses, though probably not in a taste-specific fashion. One of the more potent and easily disrupted classes of metabolites is that of the vitamins. Since the gustatory receptors are modified epithelial cells [14], those vitamins that affect the epithelium would be significant in maintaining normal taste function. The well-known role of vitamin A (VA) in supporting normal epithelium, together with the central nature of VA in photoreceptors [32] and in many biochemical sequences [78], suggested that VA might be important in gustatory function.

It was found that *VA-deficient rats* showed decreased rejection of quinine

sulphate, and decreased selection of NaCl solutions [18]. Continued deficiency led to more-or-less complete loss of gustatory preference behavior. Histological examination of the tongues from deficient animals indicated that keratin blockage of the circumvallate papilla trench and of the fungiform papillae taste pores coincided with the development of significant taste preference changes in the deficient animals [19]. When VA was added to the diet, behavioral rejection of quinine and selection of NaCl returned.

Rats raised on a VA-deficient diet to which *vitamin A acid* (VAA) is added, show normal rejection of quinine [33]. Since VAA cannot be stored biologically [78], rats that are raised on VAA and then deprived of it, would provide a test of whether the gustatory deficits induced by VA deficiency are due to long-term or immediate effects. The effect of VAA deprivation on VA-deficient rats was studied [18]. Rats were fed from weaning on a VA-free diet supplemented with VAA. Taste preferences for NaCl and saccharin and the rejection of quinine sulphate (QSO_4) and sucrose octa-acetate were normal. After this initial period on VAA, the now grown rats were deprived of VAA until taste preference deficits appeared, and then VAA was returned to the diet. Significant preference deficits for 0.005 mM QSO_4 appeared within twelve to sixteen days after the removal of VAA from the diet. Preference recovery was seen within one to four days after VAA was returned to the diet. In the second (and final) VAA-free period, after significant taste preference decreases for 10 mM NaCl had occurred, gustatory neural responses were recorded from the chorda tympani nerves of four VAA- and VA-deficient rats and from two rats of the control group. The neural responses to NaCl from the VA-

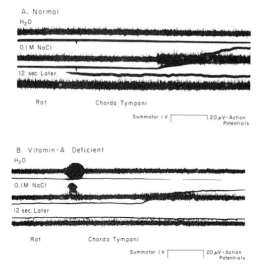

Fig. 16–4. Oscillograph records of neural activity in the distal portion of the incised chorda tympani nerves of rats. The surgical exposure and recording electrodes were as described by Halpern et al. *[51]. The summator calibrations are both one-volt oscilloscope calibrations. The line connecting the summator and action potential calibrations equals one second. The spike-like traces are the direct neural responses, the solid traces are summated neural responses. Each stimulus was 25 ml of liquid, which flowed for ten sec. The time interval between the start of stimulus flow and liquid contact with the tongue was ca. two sec. In both A and B the bottom records show the response 12 sec after the end of the middle records. This was ca. 17.5 sec after the tongue chamber emptied of 0.1 M NaCl, but no H₂O wash had been given. A. Responses from a control rat (raised on a VA–deficient diet to which VA was always added; taste preferences were normal).* Top records: *H₂O flow started at the arrow (first 4.5 sec of flow shown). A decrease in resting activity is seen.* Middle records: *0.1 M NaCl flow started at the arrow. The response had a maximum peak-to-peak apparent action potential amplitude of ca. 70 μV.* Bottom records: *Response continues with summator record, which had risen off scale, reappearing but remaining high.* B. *Responses from a VA–deficient rat (raised from weaning for 384 days on a VA–free diet to which VAA was added. Taste preferences were normal while on this diet). Significant*

deficient group were of a lesser magnitude, had a higher threshold, and adapted faster near threshold than did the responses recorded from non-deficient control animals (Figs. 16–4 and 16–5).

The tongues of those deficient and control rats that underwent electrophysiological examination were also studied histologically. In the deficient rats, keratin proliferation was abundant, with frequent blockage of the pores of fungiform papillae and the grooves of the circumvallate and foliate papillae.

An early sign of VA deficiency is reduction in both positive and negative gustatory preferences. Vitamin A acid can replace VA in maintaining normal taste behavior. The preference reduction and eventual loss appear to be independent of direct neural damage, since preference changes can be rapidly reversed by the administration of VA or its acid. In addition, reduced but unequivocal gustatory neural responses could be recorded from VAA-deficient rats that had shown a significant preference deficit. The relatively rapid development of preference deficit and the even more rapid recovery of normal preference following repletion with VAA (viz., that above) suggests that direct neural damage and general damage to the tongue were not major factors in the observed preference changes. The reduced magnitude of the multiunit CT responses

decrease in preference for 10 mM NaCl occurred thirteen days after the VAA was permanently withdrawn from the diet; neural records were taken eleven days later. Top records: *H₂O flow started at dark circle. A decrease in resting activity occurred.* Middle records: *0.1 M NaCl flow started at the dark circle. The response had a maximum peak-to-peak apparent action potential amplitude of ca. 33 μV (47 per cent of control amplitude).* Bottom records: *Response continues, with summator record below level of middle records and falling steadily.*

(Fig. 16–4) and the reduced magnitude and elevated threshold of the summated CT responses (Fig. 16–5) may indicate

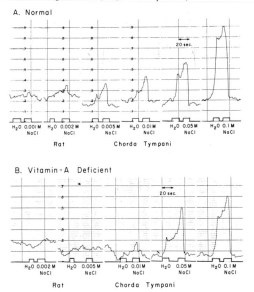

Fig. 16–5. Photographs of summated neural responses recorded from the distal portion of the incised chorda tympani nerves of two rats. The surgical, recording procedures and the characteristics of the animals are the same as those of Fig. 16–4. Records read from right to left. A. Records from a non-deficient control rat. Responses can be seen through a two-log-unit range, from 0.1 M through 0.001 M NaCl. Records that matched the median magnitude are shown. B. Records from a VA–deficient rat. Responses are smaller than those of the control animal at all concentrations and have a higher threshold for increased neural activity.

that fewer neurons were firing at any given stimulus concentration. The reduced magnitude and increased threshold of the neural responses from the VA-deficient rats is consistent with the histological observations, which suggested that the keratin proliferation resulting from VAA removal in the absence of VA reduced the access of potential stimuli to the gustatory receptors.

In summary, the preceding sections of this paper have considered a number of situations in which neural, salivary, hormonal, or metabolic mechanisms act to modify the gustatory system. In most cases the altered gustatory apparatus tended to contribute to a return to normal homeostatic conditions, although some exceptions were noted (e.g., the ageusia of A-hypovitaminosis).

We now turn to a class of *peripheral gustatory response modifications which are not obviously homeostatic* in character. Specifically, we will consider a class of plant and animal extracts which are often voluntarily ingested by humans and which act to modify gustatory responses. These exogenous extracts, which in most cases are not found as a normal body constituent, when topically applied to the tongue, selectively alter electrophysiological and/or behavioral responses to particular gustatory stimuli. The plant extracts include gymnemic acid and "miracle fruit," while the animal extracts referred to are 5'-ribonucleotides.

Topical application of gymnemic acid (HG) and its potassium salt (KG) increase human recognition thresholds for sucrose, saccharin, glycerine, and perhaps QSO_4 [103,110].[6] However, recognition thresholds for H_2SO_4, citric acid, NaCl, NH_4Cl, and KI are unaffected by the topical application of HG to the human tongue [103]. Thus, a clear differential effect occurs. Responses to several sweet-tasting compounds are depressed while inorganic and organic acids and inorganic salts are unaffected. The primary sites of action of the HG and KG could be on the gustatory receptor membrane, within the receptor cells, or on the primary afferent neurons or their synapses with the receptors. Alternatively, the differential suppression of human recognition thresholds by HG and KG might be a central effect caused by a complex change in the afferent code, or possibly brought about by lingual absorption of HG and its subsequent action on the CNS.

The significance of the CNS in HG effects can be easily dismissed. Summated neural responses from the distal portion of the incised human CT were recorded before and after the topical application of HG to the tongue [31]. Responses to sucrose and saccharin were eliminated by prior application of HG. In contrast, human CT responses to NaCl, citric acid, QHCl, and QSO$_4$ were not affected. Thus, peripheral neural responses to a sweet-tasting sugar and to a synthetic sweetener were suppressed while an inorganic salt and an organic acid were unaffected. These neural observations qualitatively duplicate the psychophysical data. Thus, HG acts primarily on the peripheral portion of the gustatory system. Responses to sweet-tasting compounds are suppressed.

The above neural data from the human CT confirm previous observations from the dog and hamster CT. These canine and rodent observations indicated that topically applied HG acts peripherally to block responses to sucrose and saccharin [4,45,94]. In the hamster, responses to NaCl were unaffected by topical HG [45], again in agreement with the data on human beings. The effects of i.v. versus topical HG were also compared in the hamster. Intravenous injection of HG or KG produced a transient depression of CT responses to both NaCl and sucrose [45]. The non-specific effect of i.v. application of HG suggests that regions which might be easily reached by i.v. HG, such as the primary neuron and perhaps the more proximal aspect of the receptor cell, are not involved in the selective action of topical HG. Thus, topical HG probably acts on the distal portion of the receptor cell, presumably affecting the membrane of the microvilli [84].

Behavioral studies of the effects of HG have not been made in dog or hamster. However, the effects of HG on the long-term preference of the rat for sucrose and saccharin were examined [70]. Rats that had been deprived of food and water for twenty-three hours were offered either H$_2$O or an aqueous solution of HG for one hour. During the next hour a choice was offered between 200 mM sucrose (or 0.69 mM Na-saccharin) and H$_2$O. When the animals received H$_2$O prior to the choice hour, significant preferences for both sucrose and saccharin were observed. In contrast, prior drinking of HG (an equal volume ingested) eliminated the preference for saccharin. The preference for sucrose was not decreased.[7]

In summary, electrophysiological and behavioral data from several species indicate that HG selectively depresses responses to compounds that taste sweet to man. The locus of action is peripheral, probably the receptor cell microvilli. Since the structural formula of HG is undetermined, and the empirical formula unsure, it is scarcely possible to speculate on the biochemical basis of the action of HG [75,104]. Additional electrophysiological and behavioral studies on the generalizability of the HG block of sweet-tasting compounds would be valuable. The effect of HG on quinine salts, which is a moot point after the negative observations of Diamant *et al.* [31], needs re-examination. The major requirement, however, is knowledge of the chemical structure of gymnemic acid.

A second plant extract that alters human descriptions of gustatory stimuli is obtained from synsepalum dulcificum [60]. Both the chemical nature of the *Synsepalum dulcificum* (miracle fruit) extract and its effect on taste differ considerably from those of HG. The prior application of miracle fruit to the tongue results in an altered taste of "sour" substances. Organic acids and amino acids, which are normally described as sour, are called sweet when preceded by miracle fruit. Thus, rather than merely suppressing one class of taste responses, as HG does, miracle fruit appears to change the code.

The chemical nature of the miracle fruit active principle is different from that of HG. The active principle is insoluble in water and organic solvents and is inactivated by strong bases or acids and by heat. In contrast, the purified form of HG, KG, is prepared from the leaves of *Gymnema sylvestre* by a hot water extraction, followed by acid precipitation and organic solvent extraction [110]. Unfortunately, miracle fruit extract has received little psychophysical, and no electrophysiological, examination. This most interesting substance deserves considerable attention.

The final class of taste-modifying compounds that will be considered is that of *the 5'-ribonucleotides.* The 5'-ribonucleotides may not decrease human psychophysical gustatory thresholds for common taste stimuli [2]. However, a facilitative relationship does exist between Na-Glu and several 5'-ribonucleotides. Summated neural responses to mixtures of Na-Glu and 5'-ribonucleotides were recorded from the rat CT [101,102]. Responses to aqueous mixtures of Na-Glu plus sodium 5'-guanylate or sodium 5'-inosinate showed enhancement,[8] occurring at temperatures from 15° C to 40° C. Less enhancement was observed with mixtures containing sodium 5'-uridylate or sodium 5'-cytidylate as the 5'-ribonucleotide. More complex mixtures, consisting of 0.017 M NaCl, Na-Glu, and a 5'-ribonucleotide, showed less enhancement than did mixtures made up in H_2O rather than NaCl. Indeed, at 35° C the NaCl, Na-Glu, and 5'-ribonucleotide mixture showed no enhancement. This reduction or elimination of enhance-

ment is probably related to the competitive nature of Na+ and Glu. In summary, not only the behavioral data but also the electrophysiological observations indicate that mixtures of Na-Glu and certain 5'-ribonucleotides give responses that are larger than the sum of the component responses (i.e., enhancement). An understanding of the mechanism of this effect, as well as of the competitive relationship between Na+ and glutamate, might be useful in explaining the transduction process in gustation.

In the first part of this section the effects upon gustation of a deficiency of a widely active metabolite, vitamin A, were reviewed. The ageusia of VA deficiency appears to be an indirect effect brought about by keratin blockage of the taste pores and perhaps by changes in the mucoid substance of the taste pit. The indirect action of VA hypovitaminosis is typical of the action of disease states on gustatory responses. Thus, neural, salivary, or hormonal changes are elicited by the disrupted homeostatic conditions of a disease. The gustatory responses are changed through the action of the disease on hormones, saliva, or efferent neurons rather than by the altered metabolite levels themselves. This additional link interposed between dysfunctions and gustatory contact chemoreceptors may lead to slower or more complex modifications of afferent input, but it probably also permits a variety of interoceptors to interact before the final efferent modulation of taste occurs.

In the second portion of this section the effects of several topically active plant and animal extracts were examined. Two of these extracts, gymnemic acid and miracle fruit extract, modify or eliminate neural and behavioral responses to specific classes of stimuli. The locus of activity is probably the distal segment of the receptor. An understanding of the basic events is important since it may indicate the stimulus and/or receptor membrane attributes that characterize the responses of human beings and perhaps other species to "sweet"- and "sour"-tasting stimuli. Progress in understanding is limited by a lack of knowledge of the molecular construction of HG and miracle fruit extract. The other extracts discussed, the 5′-ribonucleotides, are often considered to enhance gustatory responses.[8] Certain 5′-ribonucleotides do enhance responses to Na-Glu and perhaps to other stimuli. Since the chemical nature of the active agents is both well known and easily modified in this case, the biochemical and neural basis for the action of 5′-ribonucleotides should be actively pursued.

NEURAL CORRELATES OF QUANTITATIVE AND QUALITATIVE JUDGMENTS OF TASTE STIMULI

Behavioral responses to gustatory stimuli can be a function of stimulus intensity, of the chemical characteristics of the stimulus, or of both factors. The sensory basis of the human gustatory judgments are, however, difficult to determine. Limited observations from the human CT have been collected [31], but the experiments are by necessity limited in complexity and duration. Experiments involving non-human observers provide a better opportunity to compare behavioral and neural gustatory responses. However, it is difficult to insure that the differential preference behavior of a non-human observer is based solely upon the stimulus intensity of gustatory stimuli, or upon stimulus quality only.[9]

Correlations between the magnitude of gustatory neural responses to sugars and taste preference measures for the same sugars are available for several species (Table 16–2). In general, for rat, squirrel monkey, and man there is a consistent relationship between the relative magnitudes of neural responses (anterior region of the tongue) and the

TABLE 16–2: Rank Orders of Gustatory Neural Responses and Behavioral Responses to Sugars

Species	Type of Response			Rank Order of Response Magnitudes
Rat	Neural	a. Chorda Tympani[a]		Sucrose > Fructose > Glucose ≥ Lactose ≥ Maltose
		b. Solitary Nucleus	Multiunit[b]	Sucrose > Fructose > Glucose ≐ Maltose
			Single Unit[c]	Sucrose > Glucose > Maltose
	Brief-Exposure Preference[d]			Sucrose > Glucose
Squirrel Monkey[e]	Neural (Chorda Tympani)			Sucrose > Fructose > Lactose > Glucose
	Brief-Exposure Preference			Fructose > Sucrose > Maltose > Glucose ≐ Lactose
Man	Neural (Chorda Tympani)[f]			Sucrose ≥ Fructose > Maltose ≥ Glucose ≐ Lactose
	Sweetness Judgments[g]			Fructose ≥ Sucrose > Maltose > Glucose ≥ Lactose

NOTE: Unless otherwise noted, neural responses were summated, multi-unit activity.
 [a] After Hagstrom and Pfaffmann, [48]; Hardiman [56].
 [b] From Halpern [52].
 [c] From Erickson [35].
 [d] From Guttman [44]; Young [113].
 [e] From Pfaffmann [93].
 [f] From Diamant *et al.* [31].
 [g] After Cameron [22], Pangborn [88], and Diamant *et al.* [31].

magnitudes of those behavioral measures in which very small amounts of liquid are actually ingested. Sucrose and/or fructose occupy the first-rank neural and behavioral positions in all three species. Glucose, maltose, and lactose rank below fructose and sucrose in rat, squirrel monkey, and man, but the specific rank of the three lower-ranked sugars differs both between species (rat versus man) and between measures (squirrel monkey). Thus, a rough ordinal relationship exists for both interspecies and intraspecies responses to these five sugars.

If the actual magnitudes of neural and behavioral responses to sugars and synthetic sweeteners are considered, a nearly linear function is found in man for galactose, sucrose, fructose, and sodium cyclamate [31]. However, glucose gives a neural response that is twice as large as its relative sweetness while the relative sweetness of sodium saccharin is one-third greater than its relative neural response. In the rat, at least, the neural-behavioral relationship is more complicated still. Brief-exposure preference is a linear function of the logarithm of percentage concentration [44] whereas the neural responses are curvilinear functions.

Even the limited relationships between neural and behavioral supra-threshold response magnitude, which were described above, may disappear when the animal being tested is permitted to ingest significant volumes of the sugars used [48]. It is assumed that the ingestion of significant volumes of these sugars (or of anything else) activates a complex of "postingestional" factors. The postingestional factors, which include interoceptors, and metabolic and osmotic effects, can overwhelm the simple relationship between gustatory neural responses and primary taste preference determined by gustatory afferent information [48,64,91,92,93].

CROSS-ADAPTATION AND MIXTURES

Natural feeding does not involve pure chemicals taken in isolation. Rather, complex mixtures are usually ingested. Poly-component solid and liquid food mixtures are at present too complex for analysis in terms of gustatory afferent input. However, the problem of complex natural foods can be approached by examining the effect upon gustatory responses of having one stimulus present on the tongue when a second is applied. If the first, or *adapting* stimulus, is of a different molecular species than the second, or *test* stimulus, the procedure is called cross-adaptation.

An area of particular interest is *cross-adaptation between substances which taste salty to man*. Hahn [49] reported that salty-tasting substances do not cross-adapt psychophysically. This observation appeared to be confirmed by neurophysiological experiments done by Beidler. In these experiments, summated neural responses were recorded from the distal portion of the rat CT [11,13]. The relevant results were that an adapting solution of $0.1\,M$ NaCl did not change the CT response to other monovalent salts used as test stimuli. In addition, responses to a $0.1\,M$ NaCl test solution were not "greatly" affected by a $0.1\,M$ $CaCl_2$ adapting solution. Thus, a rare instance of neural and behavioral agreement was at hand. Subsequently, however, McBurney [71,72] reported that cross-adaptation effects on direct magnitude estimations occurred between KCl and NaCl, NaBr, $CaCl_2$, etc. The magnitude of the cross-adaptation was small when equimolar solutions were used but larger when solutions judged to be of equal intensity were employed. Therefore, instead of the neat compatibility of Hahn's psychophysical observations and Beidler's neurophysiological data, a behavioral interaction was reported that did not appear in the available neural data. This lack of correlation between psychophysical and CT neural responses to cross-adaptation testing suggests that a significant transformation of peripheral neural responses to different salts occurs at CNS transfer nuclei. Available data indicate that one important transformation locus is the NFS. Multiunit responses in the NFS to cross-adaptation of the anterior region of the tongue with NaCl and KCl, LiCl, or CaCl$_2$ provide neurophysiological evidence that these salts do cross-adapt when responses of second-order neurons are measured (Fig. 16–6). In addition, stimuli that produce equal magnitude neural responses cross-adapt more uniformly than do responses to equimolar solutions. Both observations are in agreement with McBurney's psychophysical reports. Thus, neural and behavioral data once again appear to coincide, but the transformation of gustatory neural responses across the first synapse (in the NFS) is an important factor.

The cross-adaptation experiments described above are a maximally simplified approximation of natural eating. A somewhat closer, though still very "unnatural," approach is the use of mixtures as gustatory stimuli.

There are several *psychophysical studies on human responses to two-component gustatory mixtures* available. In general, "depression" of judged magnitude of each component was observed with heterogenous mixtures [10,85,86,87]. This means: (1) that the two components tasted quite differently, e.g., one was called salty, the other sour, by man; (2) that the judged intensity of each of the components of the mixture was smaller than the intensity of the separate component. A few instances of increase in the judged intensity of heterogenous mixtures have also been reported

[88,96]. Homogenous mixtures (whose components have similar tastes to man) of sugars, artificial sweeteners, or glycerine are additive in terms of the judged sweetness of the components, although mixtures of glycine and alanine show a much lower summation of sweetness [23].

Neural responses to stimulation of the anterior region of the tongue with two-component mixtures have been recorded from the distal portion of the rat, dog, and cat CT, and from the rat NFS. Stimulation with homogenous mixtures of inorganic salts produced CT responses with algebraic summation of the response magnitudes to the components of the mixture [11,111].[10] Heterogenous mixtures of sucrose plus citric or acetic acid also produced algebraic summation of the CT response magnitudes to the separate components [4,50], but mixtures of sucrose and NaCl were reported to show no addition [3]. In the latter case, however, the separate components produced near-maximum responses.[10]

Central nervous system responses to mixtures appear to differ from the responses recorded in CT. Responses from the anterior tongue zone of the NFS to mixtures of NaCl and KCl and to mixtures of sucrose and acetic acid did not show algebraic summation [50]. Instead, the magnitudes of the NFS responses to the mixtures were always smaller than the sum of the responses to the components. However, the NFS responses were usually of a greater magnitude than the separate response to either component alone. The concentrations of each component were selected to produce approximately equal magnitude responses separately. In addition, the concentrations used were well below those that would be required to produce maximum response magnitude. Accordingly, the absence of full additivity of the NFS responses is presumably a function of a transfer process between the primary and

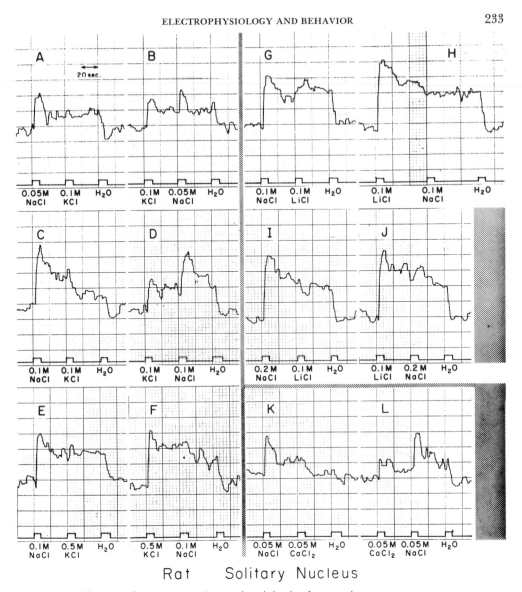

Rat   Solitary Nucleus

Fig. 16–6. Photograph of summated neural activity in the anterior tongue responses zone of the nucleus of the fasciculus solitarius. *The experimental procedures and the histological results were as in Fig. 16–3. A through F (i.e., left half of figure): Cross-adaptation between NaCl and KCl. C and D: Equimolar concentrations do not equally cross-adapt. The response to 0.1 M KCl was reduced by 63 per cent, while the response to 0.1 M NaCl was reduced by only 33 per cent. Note that the magnitude of the response to 0.1 M KCl is only 44 per cent of the response to 0.1 M NaCl. E and F: Responses of similar magnitude (0.5 M KCl response was 119 per cent of response magnitude to 0.1 M NaCl) give similar cross-adaptation. The response to 0.5 M KCl was reduced by 71 per cent, the response to 0.1 M NaCl, by 94 per cent. G through J: Cross-adaptation between NaCl and LiCl. As with KCl, equimolar concentrations do not equally cross-adapt (G and H), but equal response magnitudes (I and J; response to 0.1 M LiCl is 103 per cent of response to 0.2 M NaCl) produce approximately equal cross-adaptation (response to 0.2 M NaCl was reduced by 88 per cent, response to 0.1 M LiCl, by 93 per cent). K and L: Cross-adaptation between NaCl and CaCl₂. Once again, equimolar solutions do not equally cross-adapt. Equal magnitude responses were not tested.*

secondary neurons rather than of the saturation of primary neuron responses.

In summary, the algebraic summation observed for most CT responses to mixtures did not fit the depression of judged intensity found for most human responses to two-component heterogenous mixtures. However, the responses recorded in the NFS from the second-order neuron population are a closer approximation to the psychophysical judgments since algebraic summation is also absent from these neural responses. A depression of response magnitudes below those of the most effective component of each mixture was observed only a few times in the NFS, but the available data do indicate that an interaction between responses to different chemical classes may occur in the NFS. The number of animals in which NFS responses to mixtures were studied was small $(N = 4)$; therefore, the data must be considered preliminary. However, since the cross-adaptation experiments also suggest increased interaction in the NFS (see above), and both sets of observations have clear behavioral correlates, further exploration seems warranted [2,8].

SUMMARY

The responses of the gustatory afferent system to adequate stimulation can be altered through salivary, neuroendocrine, direct neural, and topical pathways, although non-hormonal direct effects through vascular channels are probably of minor importance. Since the salivary and neural influences can be initiated by the ingestion of foods and are controlled by the CNS and chemicals circulating in the blood, a feedback system exists. Deviation from the normal, regulated values of metabolic components acts to control a receptor system that is important in securing the components or their precursors. Thus, homeostatic regulation is maintained.

Behavioral responses often confirmed the available neural data. In several instances, gustatory neural responses from primary neurons are at variance with behavioral observations, but the neural activity of second-order neuron populations is less deviant from the final behavior. Presumably, additional transfer functions at thalamic and cortical sites produces a still closer correlation between neural and behavioral gustatory responses.

Discussion

Henkin: Hodgson showed us some data about the effects of epinephrine on taste sensitive cells of the hydra. After epinephrine was applied to the taste cell, the cell became more sensitive to the application of other drugs. Also, norepinephrine did not have this propensity in the magnitude observed with epinephrine. In the studies you have reported, cervical ganglion stimulation was used to produce your effects. Generally, norepinephrine would be released by this stimulation and influence the responses. Have you specific information about the effect of norepinephrine in the system which you have described, and have you considered any differential effects on alpha or beta receptor types?

Halpern: Unfortunately, the pharmacological aspects have not been followed through fully. Kimura (*Kumamoto Med. J.*, 14: 95, 1961) used epinephrine. At least in published data, he does not report norepinephrine. Chernetski (*J. Neurophysiol.*, 27: 493, 1964) used only epinephrine on isolated skin-nerve preparations; even there, it produced effects.

Chauncey: From your first slide, I had the impression that in both instances the material you were testing was distilled water and the variable was stimulation of the sympathetic ganglion.

Halpern: I would suspect that it probably was not very good because, if you have very good distilled water, you don't get much of a response to water in a frog, but let's say it was water (Nomura and Sakada, *Jap. J. Physiol.,* **15:** 433, 1965).

Chauncey: I expect there will be sodium chloride in the saliva of frogs and this might produce the effect noted.

Halpern: Do you find this in a frog?

Chauncey: I don't know. You will find it in most other vertebrae.

Halpern: Chernetski's preparation was a frog with all its cranial nerves cut intracranially, there was no systemic circulation, and brain and spinal chord were completely transected.

Chauncey: If any blood vessels go into the salivary gland, sympathetic nerves will follow the blood vessels.

Halpern: I'm sure there are blood vessels, but there is no blood flowing in them.

Chauncey: There still could be stimulation.

Halpern: I doubt it. Chernetski pins out the tongue on a cork. Unless the secretion is coming out of the tongue itself, it couldn't reach it, since similar effects are produced by taking an isolated piece of frog skin, with a nerve attached, and applying epinephrine to it. There is a problem of epinephrine/norepinephrine, but in this case they may be somewhat interchangeable. Quantitatively Kimura could not produce as big a response with epinephrine as he could by electrical stimulation, so, as is often the case in mammals, epinephrine may be quantitatively less efficient than norepine-phrine in activating the system. In the replication of Esakov's experiments in our laboratory, the frog's tongue was in a tongue chamber.

Chauncey: I don't know about the frog, but the human has salivary glands on its tongue. This may follow through with your stimulation of the glosso-pharyngeal nerve. This, in a human, innervates the parotid gland.

Halpern: We did not stimulate the glossopharyngeal nerve. We recorded from it.

Chauncey: But you had stretched it. What about the stretching procedure?

Halpern: I agree that we stretched it slightly since it was necessary to tease it underneath to lift it up.

Chauncey: So your manipulation might have provided stimulation.

Epstein: There are two things about rats without saliva that are relevant. Both apply to the way they drink when eating dry food. First, their total water intake is greatly exaggerated. Second, all of the water is drunk in small draughts immediately after a morsel of food is taken into the mouth. We saw this in animals from which we removed the glands (Epstein *et al., Nature,* **201:** 1342, 1964), and Vance (*Psychol. Monogr.,* **79:** 1, 1965) later confirmed it in his animals with tied ducts. In other words, the rat with food in his mouth is always drinking. The fluid he is drinking is always contaminated by food.

Now, the work you mentioned is not mine but my student Kissileff's. He is using animals without saliva by duct ligation. He has confirmed Vance's findings that, in such animals, two-bottle sodium chloride preferences, done with food present, are absent or greatly attenuated. But he thinks this is largely due to the contamination of the fluid with food. If the test is repeated with no food present, the preferences reappear. In addition, in the one-bottle test, where the animal takes all of its fluid from a single source and probably takes larger draughts, the preferences are present even with food available.

Halpern: You said that the desalivate rat only drinks when he is eating. Can you get him to avoid shock to drink?

Epstein: When food is present, all the water is taken at mealtime. We call this prandial drinking. If you take the food away, the salivarectomized rat continues to drink and the drink is not contaminated by food. It is the recovered lateral rat that drinks *only* when it eats and in the prandial style.

Halpern: Is the NaCl intake quantitatively the same in terms of detection thresholds?

Epstein: These are preference-aversion curves across a broad range of concentrations.

Halpern: Is the preference threshold quantitatively the same in the desalivated rats?

Epstein: I'm not sure. I can see how these salivary effects could be of major importance in threshold determinations, but I have yet to understand how they can be of importance in choices of fluids that are suprathreshold.

Halpern: I suspect that in many cases we are working in the threshold range. When we eat a normal meal, just as this rat is doing, we do not wash our mouth thoroughly with distilled water and then drop sodium chloride on our tongue to see if we want to take it as the next

thing in our mouth. We always have a mouth full of contaminants, full of a variety of liquids that are fabulous in man in terms of what the stimulating properties are. It may be similar to the case of the Bartoshuk *et al.* data *(Science,* 143: 967, 1965),* that if you can get just a bit above the adapted threshold, you get one kind of input, and if you get just a bit below it, the human taste description of it is quite different. Functionally we may always be at a threshold, so a small sensitivity difference could conceivably be important.

Epstein: Vance showed that the preferences for dilute salt are present within the first few weeks after saliva is removed. This is when the fluid intake, whether it is water or a solution, is most exaggerated. We see 300-fold increases in daily water intake in our animals without saliva when they are eating dry food. However, intake slowly returns to normal. The animal takes progressively smaller draughts after each morsel of food, taking less water into its mouth. About thirty days after salivarectomy, water intake in many animals is down to near normal levels. According to Vance, this is where sodium chloride preference disappears.

Halpern: I am not suggesting that desalivate rats are unable to detect sodium chloride. Perhaps there is quantitative reduction in their ability to detect sodium chloride in a more sensitive situation, such as in a one-bottle test. In a two-bottle test, the animal may pick the "wrong" bottle. He must be sufficiently motivated to switch to the other bottle. In the one-bottle situation, if he's drinking, he just has to continue drinking a little longer to show a preference.

Epstein: Kissileff worked with both two-bottle and one-bottle tests.

Halpern: Was the preference-function the same?

Epstein: The preferences were the same, the volume intakes different. In both situations preference reappeared.

Halpern: Do his desalivate rats take the same quantity in two-bottle versus one-bottle tests?

Epstein: One of the paradoxes of these desalivated animals is that when they are not eating they drink less than normal animals.

Fregly: The interaction between potassium and sodium, which you cite, is very interesting. Did you say that $0.5\,M$ potassium chloride and $0.1\,M$ sodium chloride gave similar responses?

Halpern: Right. In a rat, potassium chloride is a less effective, anterior tongue region stimulus than sodium chloride; $0.5\,M$ KCl approximates $0.1\,M$ NaCl.

Fregly: In terms of the rat's preference in a choice situation, much less potassium chloride than sodium chloride will be ingested when the two have the same concentration.

Halpern: In using a preference test, one brings in not only the stimulus intensity aspect but also the motivation aspect. My experiment on cross-adaptation was designed to approximate what McBurney asked his subjects to do. A person can be asked to match for intensity and forget about quality. If the stimuli match for intensity of responses, then effective cross-adaptation occurs, both psychophysically and neurophysiologically.

NOTES

[1] Preganglionic nerve of cervical sympathetic plexus.

[2] Intravenous injection of acetylcholine or strychnine increased the magnitude of evoked gustatory responses but did not alter spontaneous activity. Previous observations have shown that the *topical* application of acetylcholine to the tongue does not alter taste-bud slow potentials [106], but does depress n.G. gustatory responses [69]. Therefore, the enhancing effects of intravenous acetylcholine and strychnine are probably due to CNS stimulation and subsequent sympathetic outflow.

[3] The medulla oblongata, and perhaps other non-telencephalic structures, were spared.

[4] This procedure is called the "Method of Functional Mobility [114].

[5] In the frog, H_2O produces very low firing rates, but minimal n.G. activity follows application of $0.1\,M$ NaCl to the tongue [83].

[6] Diamant *et al.* [31] found no effect of HG upon human judgments of QHCl or QSO_4.

[7] Lovell *et al.* [70] suggest that gastric chemoreceptors may have been involved in the maintenance of sucrose preference in rats that had drunk HG. Vascular interoceptors might also be implicated. The sucrose would rapidly pass through the empty stomach and be quickly absorbed in the small intestine. Before passing into the blood, all the sucrose would have been converted to glucose. Thus, an elevation in blood glucose level would occur. Intravenous injection of glucose has been shown to be an effective reinforcer [23]. The reinforcing effect of i.v. glucose would be strengthened by the hypoglycemic action of the previously ingested HG [76]. Thus, maintenance of preference for sucrose after drinking HG may be a function of non-gustatory detection of sucrose by interoceptors.

[8] Gustatory enhancement: The response magnitude to a mixture is larger than the sum of the individual responses to the several components of the mixture when presented separately.

[9] The experimental model that is used to differentiate between color vision (i.e., wavelength discrimination) and intensity discrimination might serve to separate gustatory discriminations based upon stimulus intensity from differential behavior dependent upon chemical species.

[10] If the response to one component of the mixture, presented separately, is at or near the maximum response magnitude of the neural preparation or the maximum response magnitude of the class of stimuli, then the addition of the second component of a homogenous or heterogenous mixture will have little or no effect on neural response magnitude [56, 89].

REFERENCES

1. Aldrich and Pfaffmann. Unpublished observations, cited by Frommer, G. P., in *Physiological and Behavioral Aspects of Taste*, M. R. Kare and B. P. Halpern (eds.).

University of Chicago Press, Chicago, p. 115, 1961.

2. Amerine, M. A., Pangborn, R. M., and Roessler, E. B. *Principles of Sensory Evaluation of Food*. Academic Press, New York, 602 pp., 1965.

3. Andersen, H. T., Funakoshi, M., and Zotterman, Y. Electrophysiological Responses to Sugars and Their Depression by Salts, in *Olfaction and Taste*, Y. Zotterman (ed.). Pergamon, New York, p. 177, 1963.

4. Andersson, B., Landgren, S., Olsson, L., and Zotterman, Y. The sweet taste fibers of the dog. *Acta Physiol. Scand.*, **21**: 105–19, 1950.

5. Aschkenasy-Lelu, P. Le rôle des characteristiques sensorielles et des propriétés nutritive des aliments dans la régulation du comportement alimentaire. *Ann. Nutri. et Aliment.*, **19**: 55–101, 1965.

6. Baker, B. L., Clapp, H. W., Jr., and Light, J. A. Hormonal influences on the cytology and physiology of salivary glands, in *Salivary Glands and Their Secretions*, L. M. Sreebny and J. Meyer, (eds.). Macmillan, New York, p. 63, 1964.

7. Bartoshuk, L. M. Taste of Water in Man. Paper read at the Thirty-seventh Annual Meeting, Eastern Psychological Association, April, 1966 (Program, p. 54).

8. Bartoshuk, L. M. Taste, in *Experimental Psychology*, Woodworth and Schlosberg (eds.). Holt, New York, 1967 (in press).

9. Bartoshuk, L. M., McBurney, D. H., and Pfaffmann, C. Taste of Sodium Chloride Solutions after Adaptation to Sodium Chloride: Implications for the "Water Taste." *Science*, **143**: 967, 1964.

10. Beebe-Center, J. G., Rogers, M. S., Atkinson, W. H., and O'Connell, D. N. Sweetness and saltiness of compound solutions of sucrose and NaCl as a function of concentration of solutes. *J. Exp. Psychol.*, **57**: 231–34, 1959.

11. Beidler, L. M. Properties of chemoreceptors of tongue of rat. *J. Neurophysiol.*, **16**: 595–607, 1953.

12. Beidler, L. M. Biophysical Approaches to Taste, *Amer. Sci.*, **49**: 421–31, 1961.

13. Beidler, L. M. Taste Receptor Stimulation. *Prog. in Biophys. Biophys. Chem.*, **12**: 107–51, 1961.

14. Beidler, L. M. Comparison of gustatory receptors, olfactory receptors, and free nerve endings. *Cold Spring Harbor Symposium on Quantitative Biology*, **30**: 191–200, 1966.

15. Beidler, L. M., and Smallman, R. L. Renewal of cells within taste buds. *J. Cell. Biol.*, **27**: 263–72, 1965.

16. Benjamin, R. M., Halpern, B. P., Moulton, D. G., and Mozell, M. M. The Chemical Senses. *Ann. Rev. Psych.*, **16**: 381–416, 1966.

17. Bernard, R. A., and Halpern, B. P., The role of vitamin A and vitamin A acid in taste. *Proceedings of the Seventh International Congress of Nutrition* (in press).

18. Bernard, R. A., Halpern, B. P., and Kare, M. R. Effect of Vitamin A Deficiency on Taste. *Proc. Soc. Exp. Biol. Med.*, **108**: 784–86, 1961.

19. Bernard, R. A., Halpern, B. P., and Kare, M. R. The reversible effect of vitamin A deficiency on taste. *Fed. Proc.*, **21**: 362, 1962.

20. Bessou, P., and Perl, E. R. A movement receptor of the small intestine. *J. Physiol.*, **182**: 404–26, 1966.

21. Blair-West, J. R., Coghlan, J. P., Denton, J. R., and Wright, R. D. The effect of adrenal cortical steroids on parotid salivary secretion, in *Salivary Glands and Their Secretion*, L. M. Sreebny and J. Meyer (eds.). Macmillan, New York, p. 253, 1964.

22. Cameron, A. T. The Taste Sense and the Relative Sweetness of Sugars and Other Sweet Substances. *Scientific Report Series*, No. 9. Sugar Research Foundation, Inc., New York, 1947.

23. Chambers, R. M., Effects of intravenous glucose injections on learning, general activity, and hunger drive. *J. Comp. Physiol. Psychol.*, **49**: 558–64, 1956.

24. Chernetski, K. E., Cephalic sympathetic fibers in the frog. *J. Comp. Neurol.*, **122**: 173–79, 1964.

25. Chernetski, K. E. Sympathetic enhancement of peripheral sensory input in the frog. *J. Neurophysiol.*, **27**: 493–515, 1964.

26. Davenport, H. W. *Physiology of the Digestive Tract*. Year Book Medical Publishers, Chicago, 221 pp., 1961.

27. DeLorenzo, A. J. Studies on the Ultrastructure and Histophysiology of Cell Membranes, Nerve Fibers and Synaptic Junctions in Chemoreceptors, in *Olfaction and Taste*, Y. Zotterman (ed.). Pergamon, New York, p. 5, 1963.

28. Denton, D. A. Evolutionary Aspects of the Emergence of Aldosterone Secretion and Salt Appetite. *Physiol. Rev.*, **45**: 245–95, 1965.

29. Denton, D. A., Goding, J. R., and Wright, R. D. Control of adrenal secretion of electrolyte-active steroids. *Brit. Med. J.*, **2**: 444–56, 522–30, 1959.

30. Diamant, H., Funakoshi, M., Ström, L., and Zotterman, Y. Electrophysiological Studies on Human Taste Nerves, in *Olfaction and Taste*, Y. Zotterman (ed.). Pergamon, New York, p. 193, 1963.

31. Diamant, H., Oakley, B., Ström, L., Wells, C., and Zotterman, Y. A comparison of neural and psychophysical responses to taste stimuli in man. *Acta Physiol. Scand.*, **64**: 67–74, 1965.

32. Dowling, J. E. The Biologic Activity of Vitamin A Acid. *Am. J. Clin. Nutr.*, **9**: 23–26, 1961.

33. Duncan, C. J. The Taste Bud Membrane and the Role of Vitamin A. *Int. Zeitschrift. fur Vitamin-forschung*, **34**: 410–14, 1964.

34. Epstein, A. N., Specter, D., Samman, A., and Goldblum, C. Exaggerated prandial drinking in the rat without salivary glands. *Nature,* **201**: 1342–43, 1964.

35. Erickson, R. P. Responsiveness of single second order neurons in the rat to tongue stimulation. Ph.D. thesis, Brown University, 1958, in *Dissertation Abst.,* **19**: 1835, 1959.

36. Esakov, A. I. The efferent control of receptors (on the example of the chemoreceptors of the tongue). *Bull. Exp. Biol. Med.* (English translation), **51**: 283–89, 1961.

37. Evans, D. R. Depression of Taste Sensitivity to Specific Sugars by Their Presence during Development. *Science,* **133**: 327–28, 1961.

38. Falk, J. L. Studies on schedule-induced polydipsia, in *Thirst,* M. J. Wayner (ed.). Macmillan, New York, p. 95, 1964.

39. Farbman, A. I. Fine Structure of Taste Buds. *J. Ultrastructure Res.,* **12**: 328–50, 1965.

40. Fregly, M. J., Harper, J. M., Jr., and Radford, E. P., Jr. Regulation of sodium chloride intake by rats. *Amer. J. Physiol.,* **209**: 287–92, 1965.

41. Gnatt, W. H. Salivary Secretion and the Intake of Fluid. *Amer. J. Dis. Child.,* **37**: 1125–27, 1929.

42. Greene, E. C. *Anatomy of the Rat.* American Philosophical Society, Philadelphia, 1935.

43. Gregersen, M. I., and Bullock, L. T. Observations on thirst in man in relation to changes in salivary flow and plasma volume. *Amer. J. Physiol.,* **105**: 39–40, 1933.

44. Guttman, N. Equal-reinforcement values for sucrose and glucose solutions compared with equal-sweetness values. *J. Comp. Physiol. Psychol.,* **47**: 358–61, 1954.

45. Hagstrom, E. C. Nature of Taste Stimulation by Sugar. Ph.D. thesis, Brown University, in *Dissertation Abst.,* **18**: 676, 1958, 1957.

46. Hagstrom, E. C. Gustatory nerve responses to intravenous injection of chemicals. Unpublished data, cited in *Physiological and Behavioral Aspects of Taste,* M. R. Kare and B. P. Halpern (eds.). University of Chicago Press, Chicago, p. 101, 1961.

47. Hagstrom, E. C. Unpublished observations, 1966.

48. Hagstrom, E. C., and Pfaffmann, C. The relative taste effectiveness of different sugars for the rat. *J. Comp. Physiol. Psychol.,* **52**: 259–62, 1959.

49. Hahn, H. *Beiträge zur Reizphysiology.* Scherer, Heidelberg, 1949.

50. Halpern, B. P. Gustatory responses in the medulla oblongata of the rat. Ph.D. thesis, Brown University, in *Dissertation Abst.,* **20**: 2397, 1959.

51. Halpern, B. P. Chemical coding in taste-temporal patterns, in *Olfaction and Taste, I,* Y. Zotterman (ed.). Pergamon, New York, p. 275, 1963.

52. Halpern, B. P. Chemotopic coding for sucrose and quinine hydrochloride in the nucleus of the fasciculus solitarious, in *Olfaction and Taste, II,* T. Hayashi (ed.). Pergamon, New York, 549–62, 1967 (in press).

53. Halpern, B. P., Bernard, R. A., and Kare, M. R. Amino Acids as Gustatory Stimuli in the Rat. *J. Gen. Physiol.,* **45**: 681–701, 1962.

54. Halpern, B. P., and Nelson, L. M. Bulbar gustatory responses to anterior and to posterior tongue stimulation in the rat. *Amer. J. Physiol.,* **209**: 105–10, 1965.

55. Ham, A. W. *Histology.* 5th ed. Lippincott, Philadelphia, 1041 pp., 1965.

56. Hardiman, C. W. Rat and Hamster Chemoreceptor Responses to a Large Number of Compounds and the Formulation of a Generalized Chemosensory Equation. Ph.D. thesis, Florida State University, in *Dissertation Abst.,* **25**: 2587–88, 1964.

57. Henkin, R. I., Gill, J. R., and Bartter, F. C. Studies on taste thresholds in normal man and in patients with adrenal cortical insufficiency: The role of adrenal cortical steroids and of serum sodium concentration. *J. Clin. Invest.,* **42**: 727–35, 1963.

58. Henkin, R. I., and Solomon, D. H. Salt-Taste Threshold in Adrenal Insufficiency in Man. *J. Clin. Endocrinol. Metab.,* **22**: 856–58, 1962.

59. Herrick, C. J. The fasciculus solitarius and its connections in amphibians and fishes. *J. Comp. Neurol.,* **81**: 307–31, 1944.

60. Inglett, G. E., Dowling, B., Albrecht, J. J., and Hoglan, F. A. Taste-modifying properties of miracle fruit (*Synsepalum dulcificum*). *J. Agr. Food Chem.,* **13**: 284–87, 1965.

61. Ishiko, N., Amatsu, M., and Sato, Y. Thalamic representation of taste qualities and temperature change in the cat, in *Olfaction and Taste, II,* T. Hayashi (ed.). Pergamon, New York, 1967 (in press).

62. Jacobs, H. L. Studies on sugar preference. I: The preference for glucose and its modification by injection of insulin. *J. Comp. Physiol. Psychol.,* **51**: 304–10, 1958.

63. Jacobs, H. L. Studies on sugar preference. II: Learning vs. homeostasis as mediators of insulin induced sugar preferences. Unpublished observations, 1959.

64. Jacobs, H. L. The osmotic post-ingestion factor in the regulation of glucose appetite, in *Physiological and Behavioral Aspects of Taste,* M. R. Kare and B. P. Halpern (eds.). University of Chicago Press, Chicago, p. 16, 1961.

65. Kassil, V. G., Ugolev, A. M., and Chernigovskii, V. N. Gastric receptors and regulation of feeding behavior in the dog. *Doklady Akademii Nauk SSSR, Biol. Sci. Sec.* (English translation), **126**: 546–48, 1959.

66. Kimura, K., Factors Affecting the Response of Taste Receptors of Rat. *Kumamoto Med. J.,* **14**: 95–99, 1961.

67. Kissileff, H., and Epstein, A. Unpublished observations, 1966.

68. Koh, S. D., and Teitelbaum, P. Absolute Behavioral Taste Thresholds in the Rat. *J. Comp. Physiol. Psychol.*, 54: 223–29, 1961.

69. Landgren, S., Liljestrand, G., and Zotterman, Y. Chemical transmission in taste fiber endings. *Acta Physiol. Scand.*, 30: 105, 1954.

70. Lovell, M. R. C., Gross, C. G., and Weizkrantz, L. A. A note on the effect of gymnemic acid on taste perception. *Anim. Behav.*, 9: 31–33, 1961.

71. McBurney, D. H. A Psychophysical Study of Gustatory Adaptation. Ph. D. thesis, Brown University, 1964, in *Dissertation Abst.*, 25: 4833, 1965.

72. McBurney, D. H. Gustatory Cross Adaptation Between Salts. Paper read at the Thirty-sixth Annual Meeting of Eastern Psychological Association, April, 1965.

73. McBurney, D. H., and Lucas, J. A. Gustatory cross adaptation between salts. *Psychon. Sci.*, 4: 301–2, 1966.

74. McBurney, D. H., and Pfaffmann, C. Gustatory Adaptation to Saliva and Sodium Chloride. *J. Exp. Psychol.*, 65: 523–29, 1962.

75. Manni, P. E. A chemical investigation of *Gymnema Sylvestre* R. Br. Leaves. Ph.D. thesis, University of Michigan, 1963, in *Dissertation Abst.*, 25: 1592, 1964.

76. Mhaskar, K. S., and Caius, J. F. A study of Indian medicinal plants. II: *Gymnema sylvestre*, Br. *Indian Medical Research Memoirs*, No. 16, pp. 1–49, 1930.

77. Mitchell, G. A. B. *Anatomy of the Autonomic Nervous System*. E. and S. Livingstone, Ltd., Edinburgh, 1953.

78. Moore, T. The Biochemical Mode of Action of Vitamin A. *Bibl. Nutrition et Dieta.*, 3: 1–21, 1962.

79. Nachman, M. Taste preferences for sodium salts by adrenalectomized rats. *J. Comp. Physiol. Psychol.*, 55: 1124–29, 1962.

80. Nachman, M. Taste preferences for lithium chloride by adrenalectomized rats. *Amer. J. Physiol.*, 205: 219–21, 1963.

81. Nachman, M., and Pfaffmann, C. Gustatory nerve discharge in normal and sodium deficient rats. *J. Comp. Physiol. Psychol.*, 56: 1007–11, 1963.

82. Niijima, A. Afferent impulses in the vagal and splanchnic nerves of the toad's stomach and their role in sensory mechanism. *Jap. J. Physiol.*, 12: 25–44, 1962.

83. Nomura, H., and Sakada, S. On the "water response" of the frog's tongue. *Jap. J. Physiol.*, 15: 433–43, 1965.

84. Oakley, B., and Benjamin, R. M. Neural mechanisms of taste. *Physiol. Rev.*, 46: 173–211, 1966.

85. Pangborn, R. M. Taste interrelationships. *Food Res.*, 25: 245–56, 1960.

86. Pangborn, R. M. Taste interrelationships. II: Suprathreshold solutions of sucrose and citric acid. *J. Food Sci.*, 26: 648–55, 1961.

87. Pangborn, R. M. Taste interrelationships. III: Suprathreshold solutions of sucrose and sodium chloride. *J. Food Sci.*, 27: 495–500, 1962.

88. Pangborn, R. M. Relative taste intensities of selected sugars and organic acids. *J. Food Sci.*, 28: 726–33, 1963.

89. Pfaffmann, C. Gustatory afferent impulses. *J. Cellular Comp. Physiol.*, 17: 243–58, 1941.

90. Pfaffmann, C. Preface, in *Physiological and Behavioral Aspects of Taste*, M. R. Kare, and B. P. Halpern (eds.). University of Chicago Press, Chicago, p. vii, 1961.

91. Pfaffmann, C. Sensory processes and their relation to behavior: Taste as a model S-R system, in *Psychology: A Study of a Science*, S. Koch (ed.). McGraw-Hill, New York, p. 380, 1962.

92. Pfaffmann, C. Taste stimulation and preference behavior, in *Olfaction and Taste*, Y. Zotterman (ed.). Pergamon, New York, p. 257, 1963.

93. Pfaffmann, C. De Gustibus. *Amer. Psychol.*, 21–33, 1965.

94. Pfaffmann, C., and Hagstrom, E. C. Factors influencing taste sensitivity to sugar. *Amer. J. Physiol.*, 183 (3) (Abstr.), 1955.

95. Pfaffmann, C., and Powers, J. B. Partial adaptation of taste. *Psychon. Sci.*, 1: 41–42, 1964.

96. Pilgrim, F. J. Interactions of suprathreshold taste stimuli, in *Physiological and Behavioral Aspects of Taste*, M. R. Kare and B. P. Halpern (eds.). University of Chicago Press, Chicago, p. 66, 1961.

97. Postles, D., and Halpern, B. P. Facilitation of gustatory responses in the frog. *Fed. Proc.*, 26(2) (Abstr.), 1967.

98. Rapuzzi, G., and Casella, C. Innervation of the fungiform papillae in the frog tongue. *J. Neurophysiol.*, 28: 154–65, 1965.

99. Richter, C. P. Salt appetite of mammals: Its dependence on instinct and metabolism, in *L'Instinct dans le Comportement des Animaux et de l'Homme*, M. Autuori et al. (eds.). Masson et Cie, Paris, p. 577, 1956.

100. Roels, O. A. Present knowledge of vitamin A. *Nutr. Rev.*, 24: 129–32, 1966.

101. Sato, M., and Akaike, N. 5′-ribonucleotides as gustatory stimuli in rats: Electrophysiological Studies. *Jap. J. Physiol.*, 15: 53–70, 1965.

102. Sato, M., and Yamashita, S. 5′-ribonucleotides as gustatory stimuli in rats: Effects of temperature. *Jap. J. Physiol.*, 15: 570–78, 1965.

103. Shore, L. E. A contribution to our knowledge of taste sensations. *J. Physiol. (London)*, 13: 191–217, 1892.

104. Stecher, P. G., Finkel, M. J., Siegmund, O.

H., and Szafransk, B. M. (eds.). *Merck Index*. 7th ed. Merck and Co., Rahway, N.J., p. 503, 1960.

105. Sudakov, K. V., and Rogacheva, S. K. The afferent and efferent activity of the gastric fibers of the vagus nerve during fasting and after taking food. *Fed. Proc.*, **22**: T306–10, 1963.

106. Tateda, H., and Beidler, L. M. The receptor potential of the taste cell of the rat. *J. Gen. Physiol.*, **47**: 479–86, 1964.

107. Titlebaum, L. F., Falk, J. L., and Mayer, J. Altered acceptance and rejection of NaCl in rats with diabetes insipidus. *Amer. J. Physiol.*, **199**: 22–24, 1960.

108. Vance, W. B. Observations on the role of salivary secretions in the regulation of food and fluid intake in the white rat. *Psych. Monogr.*, **79**: #598, 1965.

109. Wang, S. C. Central nervous representation of salivary secretion, in *Salivary glands and their secretion*, L. M. Sreebny and J. Meyer, (eds.). Macmillan, New York, p. 145, 1964.

110. Warren, R. M., and Pfaffmann, C. Suppression of sweet sensitivity by potassium gymnemate. *J. Appl. Physiol.*, **14**: 40–42, 1959.

111. Yamashita, S., Akaike, N., and Sato, M. Stimulation of taste receptors of rat by certain salts. *Kumamoto Med. J.*, **16**: 184–93, 1963.

112. Yensen, R. Some factors affecting taste sensitivity in man. III: water deprivation. *Quart. J. Exp. Psychol.*, **11**: 239–48, 1959.

113. Young, P. T. Psychologic factors regulating the feeding process. *Am. J. Clin. Nutr.*, **5**: 154–61, 1957.

114. Zaiko, N. S. Regularity in appearance of the functional activity of the human gustatory receptor aparatus. *Bull. Exp. Biol. Med.* (English translation), **41**:21–23, 1956.

115. Zaiko, N. S., and Lokshina, E. S. Reflex reaction of the taste receptors of the tongue to direct stimulation of the gastric receptors. *Bull. Exp. Biol. Med.* (English translation), **53**: 9–11, 1963.

Dr. John Hubbard assisted with the vitamin A neurophysiological experiments. Doctor Hubbard and Mr. Postles were Upstate Medical Center student fellows. The receptor cell turnover times were calculated by Mr. Robert J. O'Connell.

The preparation of this communication, and the original data in it, were supported by NINDB Grant NB–04121 and Hendricks Fund Grant #37.

17: Critic's Comments

by Carl Pfaffmann

HAMILTON HAS raised the question "Is taste necessary?" He appears to conclude that man at least is a creature in which taste is not really necessary nor very essential. I would like to begin by directing my comments to that premise because it was the prevailing view for a long time, based, I suppose, on such historical, anthropological documentation. People have been known to eat things that were deleterious to their well-being, and, in fact, taste has generally been regarded as an unreliable indicator of the wholesomeness of foodstuffs. Richter's role was to call for a re-examination of this concept; he also raised the question of whether, at least in animals, the natural preferences that are displayed by such modified creatures as domestic animals might not, in fact, provide clues as to what is needed for better development and well-being.

The notion that behavior is a component of the homeostatic chain of events was the essential idea that Richter documented in his demonstrations. But to say that behavior is homeostatic is not so much to explain it as to describe an over-all end result. What we are really faced with here is the attempt to find out how homeostasis comes about. The term is a general description of the fact that an organism doesn't get very far out of balance, but fares well in some situations, poorly in others. The point made by Brobeck was quite relevant when he brought up the question of the regulation of oxygen versus that of CO_2; blood gases are primarily under CO_2 control, and other components do not necessarily guarantee high quality regulation. The case of sodium chloride is under debate, for there is evidence that sodium regulation is really not all that sharp. We have run some experiments similar to Fregly's studies; but with the use of different concentrations of NaCl solutions, regulation does not seem to occur. Once a compensation for a deficiency that has been introduced is attained, there is a tremendous overshoot, and the animal ends up with more salt than he needs. And, as a matter of fact, the salt preference-aversion functions show that the animal is taking more salt than he needs, even though he is in the normal non-deprived state of affairs. The general proposition, I think, which I would like to emphasize, is that we are trying to understand the operation of various components with the aid of models which apply primarily to food ingestion. My model includes a motivational component that lies beyond the first step of the consumatory response. The reinforcing effectiveness of the various phases of this system is more complicated, especially if one is interested in learning per se.

I would like to make one or two com-

243

244 THE CHEMICAL SENSES AND NUTRITION

ments with regard to the ability of the theory of learning mechanisms to account for the changes in response to different taste solutions, or, to the sensory qualities of a food, which has been ingested, that lead either to an aversion or an increased preference. Here there is quite clearly a paradox; the time factors in the absorption of the ingested material seem too long to permit the operation of normal learning processes in modifying natural responses to stimuli. I think the studies that were mentioned briefly by J. Garcia and F. R. Ervin (*XVIII International Congress of Psychology, I* [Abstr.], p. 135, 1966) are of interest because they do suggest that we should perhaps re-examine our conceptions of learning from a more naturalistic point of view. His general principle is that stimuli of the oral cavity—taste and odor—may be linked to metabolic postingestional effects more readily than may the exteroceptor stimuli—vision, hearing, or something of this kind. Therefore, it may be that not every stimulus can be attached to every response with equal ease. Another demonstration of this is found in the case of salt preferences displayed by normal animals. One would expect that when an animal takes more of one solution than another, a preference is reflected; one might also assume that the most preferred stimulus is also the most reinforcing. Actually, in the salt preference of an animal that is not deficient, it has been fairly well demonstrated that the most-preferred salt solution is not a good reinforcer for a response like bar pressing. Lewis (*J. Comp. Physiol. Psychol.*, **53**: 464, 1960) and a number of other people, including myself, in unpublished studies, have found that the normal rat, presented with a 0.15 M sodium chloride solution, will not learn to press a bar. Yet, if you take a sugar solution, for which he will show an equal preference,

and use that as a reward, he will rapidly learn the bar pressing response. True, salt preference is a complicated interaction between water- and salt-handling capabilities of the animal, but it is still possible to show that salt preference is not just purely a response of the animal to the volume of sodium chloride and water necessary in terms of its internal regulation. While working at Brown a few years ago, Fisher (*J. Exp. Anal. Behav.*, **8**: 295, 1965) devised a test in which he was able to show that salt is preferred and is a reinforcing stimulus if you do not try to make an animal press a bar. If you give the animal something to do that is easy for it, such as licking, and use that response as an operant, as an instrumental response, the response can be reinforced. Such an animal was presented with two tubes, one of which contained water, the other a salt solution that would be presented if he licked a predetermined number of times at the first tube. In other words, he had to lick at tube number *1* in order to lick at tube number *2*. It was shown that even if he was not thirsty or only mildly thirsty, he would lick at the first tube in order to get the second tube with the salt solution. Licking was being rewarded by the presentation of the saline. Therefore, whether or not salt is a reinforcing stimulus, depends on the actual behavior you measure. The natural link-up between licking and taste stimulation might be an easier connection to establish than a connection between taste stimulation and bar pressing. In interpreting the changes in behavior toward taste stimulation in relation to nutrition, we should not take our conceptions of the way learning operates from the more typically used operant situations.

I would like to refer to Kare's remarks because he raised a very interesting question, which Maller also emphasized, of the difference among species or strains, domesticated versus wild. I will reply specifically to the question of sugar response. I'm perfectly aware of the fact that cats do not taste sugar because I demonstrated that in 1941; but the thing that is more impressive to me is that there are so many similarities and not so many differences among the animals, especially with regard to the use of something like sugar and saccharin or a sugar substitute as a reinforcer. I know well from Kare's work on the birds that they will not go for it, and many other animals will not; but there are a great many that will, for example, the squirrel monkey, the baboon, the mule, a number of animals besides rats, Phormia, and babies. There are a lot of animals that will be positively rewarded and show preference behavior. It might be an interesting exercise to see if some order or reason could be found for these organisms that do respond positively to the sugars, that have the "sweet tooth." I'm perfectly willing to accept the fact that there may not be a simple biologically derived basis for the sweet tooth. I'm still not worried about that; I'm much more interested in how it works. When it works, it is a good model from which to study both the learning process and the relationship of sensory stimuli to control of ingestive behavior and instrumental responses.

I was pleased to see the point made by Halpern. He gave us evidence that was somewhat lacking in our discussion yesterday. It was nice to have it reviewed because many studies showing modulation of sensory receptors do not point to the method we originally expected, the method that Richter had emphasized and that P. T. Young had talked about, namely by changes in the level of electrolytes bathing the sense organs. You can push all that around as Henkin has very well shown, but the mere change of

electrolyte level is not sufficient. I don't think Beidler got much change in the receptors by perfusing the tongue with dramatic changes in salt concentration of the perfusate. I don't know if he published it, but he told me about this. We have done similar experiments by direct intralingual injection into the arterial supply but haven't gotten much effect. So the first proposition that the sense cells are modified by the change in surrounding electrolytes, I think, is clearly disproven. The efferent control story is just beginning to emerge, and that of course is an important place to look in relation to changes in behavior.

To come back to the question of whether salivation and changes through that route are important, I myself am somewhat skeptical at the moment of how these can affect behavior toward suprathresholds, despite the fact that my students Bartoshuk et al. (Science, 143: 967–68, 1964) were instrumental in showing their importance. This would be a nice feedback route by which one could modulate receptors. I once talked in Henkin's lab and tried to make the proposition that Addisonian patients were responding to changes in the saliva, but as it turns out now, I don't think this is a defensible position at all. In spite of the fact that Fregly made good use of some of those experiments, I am still skeptical of this route as a means of modifying salt behavior. McCutcheon made some attempts at showing how adaptation could modify drinking behavior of a rat with a drinkometer setup. It is immediately apparent that the effect of the saliva can only be present in the first one or two licks, and from there on in, the normally behaving rat will drink for quite a period of time while the receptor is being flooded by the stimulus intensity that is in the drinking tube. This swamps the effect of saliva. I would like to think that it is the saliva, but I can't really bring my-self to believe that it is the mechanism that is operating.

On the last point that Hamilton raised about taste as a satiety signal, I'm wondering whether or not oral stimula-tion is part of the satiety system in the way that Adolph showed it to be. A cer-tain amount of sensory stimulation may be necessary; this system is primed for a small amount of sensory stimulation. When it gets this amount of stimulation, essentially it has metered what has come in. This shuts off the behavior. I'm won-dering if in this way the sensory systems might not in fact be part of the satiety system.

Finally, to return to man, who is the most domesticated animal of all, maybe taste is not necessary, but at any rate other creatures are interesting and in-structive to work with. For some of them, taste is demonstrably necessary, especially when they're not looked after by man.

Part Four

18: *The Interrelations of the Chemical Senses* by *David G. Moulton*

To REMAIN ALIVE most organisms must extract chemical information from their environment. They do so by exploiting one or more of a range of chemosensory systems, including the olfactory and vomeronasal organs, taste receptors, and "free" nerve endings in a variety of epithelia. In many vertebrate groups—and occasionally in man—these four systems coexist in the same individual.

This multiplicity of inputs is emphasized in Fig. 18–1—a scheme that stresses the existence of a problem by proposing its solution. But even this is an oversimplification since it ignores the existence of chemoreceptors monitoring the internal environment and of free nerve endings distributed throughout the general body surfaces of lower vertebrates. Furthermore, chemical information may be imparted by receptors not normally considered to be chemoreceptors. For example, Hellekant [21]—in recording from the lingual supply to the cat tongue —found single fibers that would not

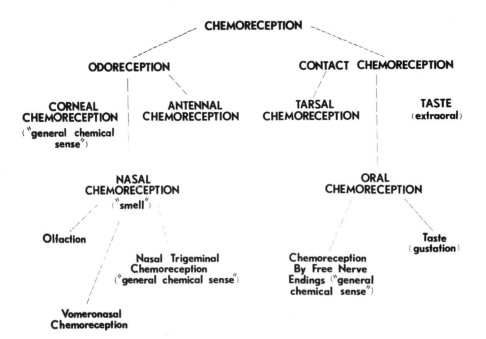

Fig. 18–1. *The range and relations of chemosensory functions.*

respond to NaCl, acetic acid, or quinine; yet they did respond to ethyl alcohol, to cooling, and to mechanical stimuli. Possibly the cooling sensation elicited by menthol vapor is also mediated by receptors primarily responsive to non-chemical stimuli.

This curious proliferation of mechanisms for detecting chemicals raises some intriguing questions: Are we dealing with different categories or qualities of information, or do certain of these systems merely extend the detectable intensity range for certain compounds? Where clear distinctions do exist, are they determined more by differences in receptor mechanisms, in access of stimulus molecules to the receptors, or in the central destinations and connections of the various afferent pathways? What are the relative contributions of these senses to the perception of flavor?

A further set of problems more specifically concerns their interactions. Is there any evidence that interaction among these systems does, in fact, occur? If so, at what level? Does it enhance the capacity of the organism to make chemosensory quality discriminations, or is it of greater significance as a protective or controlling mechanism? For example, how are interactive effects involved in controlling the chain of physiological and behavioral activities initiated by the detection and terminated by the ingestion of food?

Recent years have seen clear advances in our knowledge of the functional properties of the various chemosensory systems in vertebrates. This work—much of it coming from Beidler's laboratory—gives a partial answer to some of the above questions. In particular, it has demonstrated the distinctiveness and high sensitivity of the non-olfactory chemosensory systems in the nose, information that is reflected in the scheme outlined in Fig. 18–1. But, on the other hand, we lack even the most elementary

facts concerning interactive effects; and there have been few, if any, systematic attempts to determine the relevant variables. This is surprising since the area is fundamental to an understanding of flavor perception. Furthermore, sensory interaction has been extensively studied in relation to other modalities—especially by workers in the Soviet Union—and a number of these studies have involved the action of nasal or oral chemoreception on auditory and visual perception (see [29]).

Nevertheless, it is clear from what little evidence we do have that some degree of interaction among the chemical senses does occur. For example, Schutz and Pilgrim [37] examined sensitivity to sour taste when the subject was being stimulated by a pleasant odor and when no test odor was present. The threshold of subjects with normally high thresholds for sour taste was lowered by the odor while those with normally low thresholds experienced the reverse effect. A third group of subjects with moderate levels of threshold showed no significant change in threshold during odor presentation. Unfortunately it is not clear from such psychophysical studies at what level the interaction occurs, which chemical senses are involved, and whether only chemical senses are involved.

However, it is convenient to consider three areas, or sets of factors, which may limit or control the degree of interaction possible. These involve: (1) control of access of molecules to receptor sites; (2) relative sensitivities of the receptor systems; (3) central destinations of the afferent pathways and their connections.

FACTORS CONTROLLING ACCESS OF MOLECULES TO RECEPTOR SITES

Structural Diversity Stimulation of chemoreceptors is to some extent dependent on the configuration of the organs and of neighboring structures. Thus, the aerodynamical properties of the nose partly determine the proportion of those odorous molecules entering the nostrils that finally reach the receptors, whereas nerve endings on the general body surface may receive a different set of stimuli than those located in the oral mucosa. But perhaps the most striking feature of the chemical senses is the curious diversity in the location and juxtapositioning of the organs in different species. This variation is richer than that found in any comparable group of related sensory systems. Even within one modality such as taste, taste buds occur on the body surface of certain fish, on the superior or inferior surface of the tongue, or only at the tongue's base (Fig. 18–2).

sequently the biological significance of the information they impart, varies widely from species to species; and it is important to note that this variation is seen among the common laboratory species. Clearly, we must view generalizations about function or interrelations of the chemical senses with considerable caution.

Structural Control of Access in Specific Organs In addition to direct structural controls of intercommunication between the oral and nasal chemoreceptor systems, there is a further set of devices controlling access of molecules to specific organs. Since these mechanisms are activated according to different temporal rhythms, there is always an elaborate and shifting balance in the

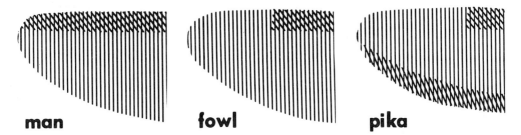

man   **fowl**   **pika**

Fig. 18–2. Schematic sagittal section through the tongues of various species to show approximate areas of taste bud concentration (diagonal lines). Based on descriptions by Lindenmaier and Kare [28] for the fowl, and by Kubota and Hayama [27] for the Japanese pika.

Still more marked is the variation in the interrelations of the oral and nasal chemosensory systems (Fig. 18–3). This is mainly because the vomeronasal organ can open into the nasal or oral cavities, or both. In addition it is vestigal in some groups, notably birds, and in most—but not all—species of fish. It is also vestigal in most human adults, although occasional individuals appear to possess the organ [40,26]. Such contrasts occur even among closely related species, as in certain bats and in primates [30,39]. But the essential point is this: The structural interrelation of these systems, and con-

relative quantities of stimulating molecules reaching the various receptor groups. For example, it has long been known that movements of the tongue seem to enhance sensitivity to taste substances. Electrophysiological confirmation of this has come from the studies of Ishiko and Amatsu [22] on the cat chorda tympani nerve. Movements of the tongue insufficient to excite tactile receptors elicited a marked augmentation of the integrated responses to taste substances, especially to HCl and water. The most probable explanation of this effect is one advanced by Beidler [6]. He

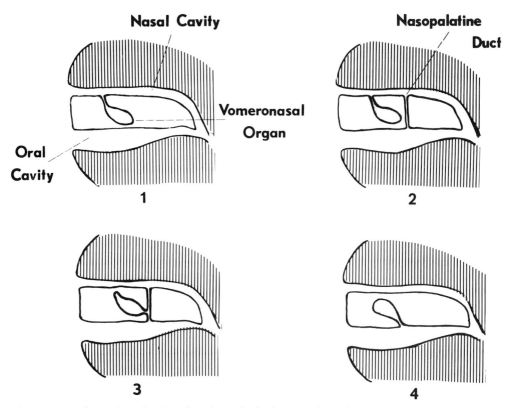

Fig. 18–3.   Schematic sagittal section through the head to show the various existing functional interrelations between oral and nasal chemosensory systems in different vertebrate species: (1) tailess amphibia; (2) lagomorphs and certain rodents; (3) dogs and cats; (4) snakes and lizards.

suggests that the movements redistribute existing concentration gradients near the receptors. The resulting variations in stimulus intensity tend to oppose adaptation to a particular stimulus strength.

It has also been shown that movement of the circumvallate papillae enhances the integrated responses of the glossopharyngeal nerve to taste substances in goats, sheep, and calves [9]. But here there may be an additional factor— movement could permit molecules to reach deeply lying receptors not otherwise accessible [4]. In this general context it is interesting that odor stimulation of the nasal chemoreceptors in the lightly anesthetized rabbit will sometimes elicit movements of the tongue.

Access of molecules to taste receptors may also be under vasomotor control.

At any rate, stimulation of the sympathetic supply to the tongue enhances the response of the frog glossopharyngeal nerve to taste substances, and similar effects have been noted in the rat [11,19, 25]. It is not clear, however, whether this pathway can normally effect an enhancement of sufficient magnitude to be of much physiological significance.

More striking changes involving alterations in the width of the nasal cavity follow stimulation of the cervical sympathetic nerve in the tortoise; and in some species, complete closure of the lumen may be possible [33,42]. Vasomotor changes in the richly vascularized walls of the nasal cavity are presumably responsible for or contribute to this effect. In the case of the vomeronasal organ a similar mechanism causes mucous to be drawn into or expelled from the lumen of the organ [20,30]. In some species of bats a cartilaginous spur protects the nasal entrance to the vomeronasal duct. When the bat is excited it apparently raises its upper lip. Since the levator labii muscles are also attached to the spur, raising the lip forces the spur open, thus exposing the vomeronasal duct [30].

In these examples control of odorant access to nasal chemoreceptor systems is evidently influenced by the physiological status of the animal and in at least one case is associated with a specific pattern of behavior. Clearly, any stimulus acting through one chemosensory system to influence the level of autonomic activity, or the level of "excitability" of the central nervous system, is potentially capable of altering odorant access to other chemosensory systems.

Spatiotemporal Patterning of Response
As odorant molecules cross the olfactory organ they set up distinct spatiotemporal patterns of excitation which may be exploited in odor quality discrimination. The more extensive the sheet—the more widely separated the points of comparison—the finer the resolution of the pattern is likely to be. The geometrical arrangement of the chemosensory systems favors this kind of analysis, and there are marked differences in the latencies of response between the vomeronasal and trigeminal receptors on one hand and the olfactory receptors on the other [41]. If the animal has means of comparing the inputs from these systems, it has means of enhancing its powers of chemosensory discrimination.

RELATIVE SENSITIVITIES OF THE CHEMICAL SENSES

The Chemosensitivity of Free Nerve Endings The environment of many organisms frequently contains potentially noxious chemicals. These compounds may appear as food constituents, defensive secretions, environmental pollutants, or metabolic byproducts. If present in sufficiently high concentrations, certain of them can elicit avoidance or withdrawal movements (often reflexive), including, for example, reversal of cilia beat, retraction of proboscis, or sneezing. In vertebrates, the receptors that primarily elicit such responses are thought to be the free nerve endings in the skin and exposed mucous surfaces—systems comprising the so-called common or general chemical sense. However, it has long been clear that such "free" nerve endings do not constitute a homogeneous population in terms of their chemosensitivity. For example, Parker [32] noted differences in the concentrations necessary to elicit a response in certain species of fish. In *Petromyzon* species the epidermis of the tail was more sensitive than that of the midtrunk when tested with HCl, quinine hydrochloride, NaOH or NaCl. Whether these differences are a function of the depth of the endings within the epidermis or reflect intrinsic properties of the receptors is not clear.

Nevertheless, the chemosensitivities shown by Parker in fish are of a relatively low order—comparable to those found in the non-gustatory regions of the oral mucosa. This raises the possibility that receptors mediating pain and the common chemical sense are identical. Crozier [13] objected to this view, citing his experiments on frogs. He found that cocainization abolished the leg flexion elicited by pinching the frog's foot but not that elicited by immersing the foot in acid; he therefore concluded that the common chemical sense was quite distinct from pain. However, as Pfaffmann [35] has pointed out, chemical stimulation might involve a larger area of the foot than would a pinch, allowing spatial summation to increase the effectiveness of the chemical. Psychophysical experiments by Jones [23] also throw doubt on the distinctiveness of the "common chemical sense" and pain. She compared the sensitivity of the mucous membrane inside the lower lip to chemical, mechanical, and electrical stimuli. No significant differences emerged in sensitivity to mechanically induced pain, or piperidine (the active ingredient in pepper), even with cocainization; she concluded that chemical stimuli act by destruction of the ordinary fibers of pain.

But, while this may be a valid explanation of the irritating effects of piperidine at one site, it is questionable whether it can be generalized to include the effects of this and other compounds on free nerve endings at other sites in the body. In fact, as can be seen in Table 18–1, even psychophysical threshold

TABLE 18–1: Minimum Detectable Concentrations of Ethyl Alcohol and Amyl Acetate for Certain Chemical Senses, Derived by Electrophysiological (e) and Psychophysical (p) Techniques

Receptor System	Compound	
	Ethyl Alcohol	Amyl Acetate
Taste	3 (p)	
Smell	10^{-4} (p)	10^{-7} (p)
Olfactory		5×10^{-7} [e]
Oral Mucosa	5–10 (p)	
Cornea		10^{-5} (p) 10^{-4} [e]
Nasal Trigeminal		3×10^{-6} [e]

NOTE: The data for ethyl alcohol are from Parker and Stabler [34] while those for amyl acetate are as follows: Smell (p): Allison and Katz [3]; olfaction (e): Beidler and Tucker [8] (rabbit); nasal trigeminal (e): Beidler and Tucker [8] (rabbit); corneal (e): Dawson [15] (cat); and corneal (p): Katz and Talbert [24]. All concentrations are molar.

values show that the cornea is stimulated by very low concentrations of certain chemicals and at levels not necessarily associated with painful effects. This sensitivity has been confirmed electrophysiologically by Dawson [15]; (see Table

18–1). In addition, Tucker [41,42] has recorded simultaneously from small bundles of olfactory and trigeminal nerves supplying the nasal mucosa in the gopher tortoise. Responses show that the free nerve endings of this system are even more sensitive to odorants than are those of the cornea. Indeed, for some compounds, such as phenyl ethyl alcohol, the trigeminal response lies below that of the olfactory response. For most, such as amyl acetate, the reverse is true, although no compounds were identified as purely olfactory stimuli (see also [7]).

Such evidence suggests that we are dealing with two quite distinct systems of free nerve endings: a relatively unspecialized system which may be identical with the free nerve endings subserving pain sensations in man and which shows low chemosensitivity; and a more specialized system apparently confined to the nasal mucosa and the cornea, showing relatively high chemosensitivity.

CENTRAL DESTINATIONS OF THE AFFERENT PATHWAYS AND THEIR CONNECTIONS. PRIMARY AND SECONDARY INTERACTIVE EFFECTS

Conceivably, inputs from certain chemical senses may interact at the level of the central nervous system. Single units responsive to stimulation of more than one modality have been described in a variety of central nervous system loci—including the hippocampus, the superior colliculus, and the posterior thalamic nuclei—and it would not be surprising if signals initiated by, say, nasal trigeminal and taste receptors converged on the same cells in the thalamus. However, we have no direct objective evidence of such phenomena, although the sensation of flavor itself would seem to imply integration of information from various oral and nasal receptors. Interactive effects of this kind, occurring within, and restricted to the central nervous system, might be called primary interactions.

But sensory systems do not function in isolation: they are intimately integrated into the economy of the organism; and changes which influence the basic activities of the body will influence the behavior of its parts. Thus, if information from one chemosensory channel alters autonomic activity, it is potentially able to modify the response of another chemosensory system. Where such effects are mediated in part by accessory structures lying outside the central nervous system, it is convenient to call them secondary interactions. While we lack direct proof of such interaction, there is ample evidence to show, on the one hand, that changes in autonomic activity influence the output of the taste and olfactory receptors and, on the other hand, that odors and taste substances can exert powerful effects on autonomic functions, including parotid gland secretion rate, heart rate, and respiration. While there is general agreement about the nature of these effects, much of the evidence concerning the mediating pathways is conflicting.

The most striking example of the influence of odors on the oral environment is the so-called olfactory-parotid reflex. In 1901, Snarski [38] noted that the injection of certain odorants into the nasal cavity of dogs produced an increase in the secretion of the salivary glands. But it was not until the work of Elsberg et al. [16,17] that a more careful examination of the response was made. They found a marked increase in parotid gland secretion rate when such odorants as citral, menthol, and turpentine (which they claimed to be trigeminal irritants) were injected into the nasal cavities of human subjects. On the other hand, other odorants, including coffee and phenyl ethyl alcohol (which they claimed to have little or no effect on the trigeminal nerve) had only slight inconsistent effects.

The ability of certain odors to increase parotid gland secretion rate was confirmed by Chauncey et al. [10], who compared the mean parotid secretion rates induced by acids applied to the tongues of students with and without nose clamps. Secretion rates in response to lactic and isobutyric acid were markedly reduced when nose clamps were worn, but no differences appeared with the four other fatty acids tested. Although Bassi and Manci [5] report increased salivation with trigeminally acting odorants, they also found that certain substances (which they claimed were acting on the olfactory receptors) inhibited salivation.

The point which emerges from these studies is that certain odors—but not all —can increase the rate of parotid gland secretion. It is now clear from the work of Dawes and Jenkins [14] and others that an increase in the rate of parotid gland secretions is accompanied by an increase in the concentration of Na ions. It has further been shown by McBurney and Pfaffmann [31] that taste thresholds for sodium chloride are dependent on the concentration of salivary Na. Thus there exists a potential route by which odors may alter taste sensitivity, although it is doubtful whether it has much biological significance.

A similar control over parotid gland secretion rate is exercised by taste substances [11], and at rates of flow above 1 ml/min the amylase concentration was found to be greater when salt-containing than when other stimuli were used [14].

In addition to their effects on salivary secretion rates, odors can produce striking alterations in heart rate and respiration. However, the intensity of effect seems partly dependent on the species, with the rabbit being more responsive than dog, cat, guinea pig, or man. In addition, the two measures do not always show parallel effects [18].

For example, Allen [1,2], in a series of careful experiments, confirmed earlier observations that odorous and irritating substances introduced into the nasal cavity produced marked depression or inhibition of respiration and circulation in anethestized animals. Rolandus [36], working with rabbits and a controlled flow system, found that only certain odors were effective in lowering heart rate. Both of these workers concluded that the effects were primarily mediated by nasal chemosensory systems. They eliminated the possibility that the vagus and other nerves supplying the lower respiratory area were involved by experiments in which odorants were introduced independently into the trachea (by a cannula) and into the nasal passage. Where they differ, however, is in regard to the particular chemosensory systems implicated. Thus Allen concluded that the respiratory and circulatory reactions that he observed could be elicited by stimulation of either the olfactory or trigeminal paths. Rolandus claimed that only the trigeminal nerve was implicated in decelerating heart rate. But, Rolandus failed to perform one critical experiment: He did not examine the effect of ablating the trigeminal supply to the nasal mucosa. This Allen did. On the other hand, Allen appears to have used only high concentrations of test substances.

The interesting conclusion that emerges from these studies is that certain odors seem to have powerful effects on autonomic function while others have little or no effect. Furthermore, although the nasal trigeminal supply may play a dominant role in mediating these effects, the olfactory system may also be implicated. This is not too surprising when we remember that the main projection areas of the olfactory system are those rhinencephalic centers implicated in the control of autonomic functions and emotional behavior.

SUMMARY AND CONCLUSIONS

The chemical senses show extraordinary diversity in the geometrical disposition of their organs, in their relative degrees of development, and in their structural interrelations in different species. It is clear that their relative biological significance must vary widely from group to group. This fact alone implies that extrapolation of findings concerning their interrelations and functions from laboratory animals to man must be viewed with more than the usual caution. There is also a striking multiplicity of inputs imparting chemical information in any given individual. Yet, in spite of this, each system may serve a distinct role in the economy of the organism. For example, the nasal trigeminal receptors exert a marked influence on certain autonomic activities and initiate protective reflexes such as sneezing.

An understanding of the interactive effects among these senses is basic to an understanding of the mechanisms of flavor perception; yet they have received very little attention. Interactions may be primary (confined to the CNS) or secondary (involving one or more intermediate links outside of the CNS). An example of a secondary interaction is the "olfactory-parotid" reflex by means of which odors can exert a direct control on the oral environment.

Discussion

Halpern: Would you comment on the effect of odors of ingested food subsequently moving from the lungs and probably through an olfactory system route as well.

Moulton: There are two aspects: the possible significance of the effect, and the mediating pathways. First, mass spectrometric analysis of mouth air showed up to 9 ppm methyl mercaptan, 2–51 ppm carbon disulfide, 0–160 ppm sulphur dioxide, 3–34 ppm hydrogen sulfide, and 31–104 ppm ethanol (Rickter and Tonzetich, *Arch. Oral. Biol.,* **9**: 47, 1964). These are partly metabolic breakdown products that presumably pass through the nasal airways during nasal respiration. They may be expected to modulate the responsiveness of the olfactory receptors to the same and to related compounds, possibly by adaptation or even by sensitization (Moulton, *J. Food Sci.,* **30**: 908, 1965). In addition to the retronasal route, food odorants may normally enter the blood stream either by absorption through the lungs or from the gastrointestinal tract. They reach the nasal region where they stimulate the receptors. The question then arises: What is the mechanism of this "hematogenic" olfaction? In spite of a number of studies, it is not clear whether the odorants diffuse into the nasal cavity and stimulate by the normal route or stimulate directly within the epithelium (Moulton and Beidler, *Physiol. Rev.,* 1966 [in press]).

Henkin: We have evaluated arm-to-tongue and arm-to-"nose" circulation time for the perception of various substances after intravenous injection in approximately thirty patients. After intravenous injection of 5 per cent ethanol, patients perceived the odor of alcohol within seven to twelve seconds. They tasted the solution injected intravenously within ten to fourteen seconds. Generally, patients perceived the vapor before they were aware of the taste sensation. A satisfactory technique for measuring arm-to-tongue circulation time has been in clinical use for a long while.

This technique employs the bile salt desoxycholate, a substance that tastes bitter to normal subjects for approximately ten to fourteen seconds after intravenous injection. In left-sided cardiac failure this circulation time is significantly increased. Ether has been injected intravenously to obtain an arm-to-lung circulation time, the end point here being the patient's cough.

Moulton: There is, of course, extensive literature on "hematogenic" olfaction that has established that the phenomenon occurs (Moulton and Beidler, *Physiol. Rev.,* 1966 [in press]); but insofar as olfaction is concerned, there is an important question to ask: What is the pathway? If it is simply olfaction through the normal route, then we are not dealing with anything too surprising.

Halpern: I don't think that Diamant et al. (*Acta Physiol. Scand.,* **64**: 67, 1965) have tested this in their human chorda tympani preparations, but they may have had the opportunity to do it. Hagstrom (in *Physiological and Behavioral Aspects of Taste,* University of Chicago Press, Chicago, 1961) looked at the olfactory pathway in the hamster. Bile salt, saccharin, and nicotinic acid at relatively low concentrations gave responses in the hamster chorda tympani. Other chemicals of the same concentrations would not. So the human data on psychophysical judgments and the hamster's electrophysiological responses are rather coincidental. They seem to fit rather nicely into the suggestion that it is a peripheral phenomenon, and is a valid measure of a heart-to-tongue conduction time.

Chauncey: In some of Shannon's recent work with us, we used various lozenges containing citric acid but having different odors—lemon, cherry, and grape. The nose of the subject was either clamped or unclamped and the order of stimulus presentation was changed. It was observed that when the nose was unclamped there was at least a 20 per cent increase in parotid secretion. Using different acids, some with odors—butyric and such—we noted that some had an effect on gland secretion whereas others had no effect, even though there was a definite odor. We think that some of these variations in parotid gland response may be due to trigeminal stimulation.

Moulton: There have been several studies on this. For example, Elsberg *et al.* (*J. Exp. Psychol.* **27**: 58, 1940; *Arch. Neurol. Psychiat.,* **47**: 707, 1942), using their blast-injection technique, which is of somewhat questionable value, claimed that they could separate odorants into those with, and others with little or no, trigeminal effects. They later found that "trigeminal irritants" were particularly effective in increasing the parotid gland secretion rate, while the remaining compounds had only slight, inconsistent effects. "Anosmic" patients showed responses similar to normal subjects, but in patients with disturbances affecting the trigeminal supply to the nasal mucosa, the "olfactory-parotid" reflex was reduced or absent. They concluded that the trigeminal supply to the nasal mucosa constituted the afferent limb of the reflex arc.

Adolph: Have any of your studies included adaptation of these senses, are these adaptations mostly peripheral, and do they have a relation to food intake?

Moulton: In rabbits with electrodes chronically implanted in the olfactory bulb and primary neurones, there is little evidence of adaptation of the multiunit discharge at either level until relatively high concentrations are reached,

although the effects are different at different sites (Moulton, in *Olfaction and Taste,* Macmillan, New York, 1963). Tucker and Beidler have seen a similar absence of adaptation to prolonged stimulation in the primary neurones of acute preparations. This would suggest that any adaptation to odors may be a central phenomenon occurring at levels above the olfactory bulb. Adaptation might have some significance in increasing the acceptability of foods with otherwise unacceptable odors or tastes. Volatile sulfur compounds, for example, are significant constituents of many foods.

Beidler: Some of the results you mentioned would indicate that the electrophysiological techniques we now use are very limited in answering some of the questions that arose concerning flavors because we don't have much information about hedonic value. For example, in recording the electrophysiological response of the primary olfactory receptors to odors and in simultaneously looking at either the respiratory rate or the heart rate, you showed that you could not predict beforehand which odor would have a greater effect on the respiratory heart rate, not by simply looking at the intensity of the neural activity. This is very similar to what Schneider *et al.* (*Z. vergl. Physiol.,* **48**: 632, 1964) have shown, i.e., the difference between the general and specific receptors. The specific receptor initiates very stereotypic behavior.

Jacobs: An example of electrophysiological measurement of effect is provided by Kawamura (Y. Kawamura and Y. Kasahara, Second International Conference on the Regulation of Food and Water Intake, September, 1965). Application of a 1 per cent NaCl or 10 per cent glucose solution, both highly palatable, increased electrical activity of the lateral hypothalamus, presumably a hunger center. Application of a 5.0 per cent NaCl or 0.04 per cent quinine solution, both highly unpalatable, had its major effect in the area of the ventromedial nucleus, or satiety center. This is a finding at the electrophysiological level, which, if verified, might lead to meaningful behavioral correlations.

Pfaffmann: These findings, if confirmed, are very important. We suppose that somewhere there is an anatomical segregation. It would be nice if it were exactly as Kawamura described it. I would like to see more electrophysiological evidence to confirm the existence of this kind of differential action.

Beidler: Pfaffmann, how well established is Hess's work (*Sci. Amer.,* **213**: 46, 1965) on the relationship between pupil size and hedonic value?

Pfaffmann: Much additional work needs to be done on this question.

Beidler: So psychologists do not have a good objective measure of hedonic value except the psychophysical one.

Morrison: Should we jump directly from the recording of an outside nerve to hedonic value? Don't we have enough to do on the sort of things we've spoken of before—the division of nerve pathways, the parts of the nervous system reached? You might even get a fiber size analysis in the periphery. Why must we go to something like hedonic values?

Beidler: The reason I raised the question is that acceptance of a food is very important in nutrition, and food acceptance is related to hedonic value. Researchers of the chemical senses present nutritionists with information obtained by electrophysiological techniques. These

may be of limited value to the nutritionist.

Morrison: I see; it is because of our interest in applied research.

Pfaffmann: These polarities, acceptance and avoidance or rejection, are two of the most fundamental parameters of any behavioral response. The chemical senses provide us with a fundamental area for investigation. We have a chance, through insights on selective action or switching on and off through different sensory channels, of coming to grips with this in an objective way. This polarity of positive attraction toward a stimulus and aversion or rejection movement away is important.

Hodgson: If I may inject just a note of soothing resignation, it has taken ten years for us to work out the operation of four single chemoreceptor cells in the fly. Only within the last year did we find what really produces rejection in this animal under all conditions; it is the anionic fiber. When you talk about these much more complex systems, it seems likely that we're going to be confused, probably for decades, because the sampling error of the electrophysiological methods is so great.

Lepkovsky: I want to put in a word for applied research. We have talked about the hedonic reaction, but Sherrington says that the sense of pleasure is in the upper nervous system, in the neocortex. We cannot compare a human sense of pleasure with that of an animal.

I also have been listening to talk about deficits. What is the meaning of deficit? With respect to what? Is it of energy of a nutrient? Does it mean that there is depletion, and if so, how much? We talk about a deficit of energy, say of a 200-lb individual with reserves to carry him for a year, but if you deplete him of enough calories to last him for an hour, is that depletion?

There is much talk about taste. But has the animal been forgotten? We've talked about sensory physiology, we've talked about receptors, stimulus, electrophysiology; but that brings the external environment only to the central nervous system. That environment has to be coordinated and integrated with bodily needs. And you've forgotten about the specific character of the integrated organism. The whole central nervous system is built to keep that body going; we have forgotten about this broader approach.

REFERENCES

1. Allen, W. F. Effect of respiration, blood pressure, and carotid pulse of various inhaled and insufflated vapors when stimulating one cranial nerve and various combinations of cranial nerves. I: Branches of the trigeminus affected by these stimulants. *Amer. J. Physiol.,* 87: 319–25, 1928.
2. Allen, W. F. Effect of respiration, blood pressure, and carotid pulse of various inhaled and insufflated vapors when stimulating one cranial nerve and various combinations of cranial nerves. III: Olfactory and trigeminals stimulated. *Amer. J. Physiol.,* 88: 117–29, 1929.
3. Allison, V. C., and Katz, S. H. An investigation of stenches and odors for industrial purposes. *J. Industr. Eng. Chem.,* 11: 336–38, 1919.
4. Appelberg, B. Species differences in taste qualities mediated through the glossopharyngeal nerve. *Acta Physiol. Scand.,* 44: 129–37, 1958.
5. Bassi, M., and Manci, F. Le reazioni vegetative agli stimoli odorosi IV L'influenza degli odori non-alimentari sulla secrezione salivare: Sull'esistenza di un riflesso diretto olfatto-salivare. *Rassegna di Neurologia Vegeratica (Florence),* 3: 57–67, 1940.
6. Beidler, L. M. Properties of chemoreceptors of tongue of rat. *J. Neurophysiol.,* 16: 595–607, 1953.
7. Beidler, L. M. Comparison of gustatory receptors, olfactory receptors, and free nerve endings. *Cold Spring Harbor Symposia on Quantitative Biology,* 30: 191–200, 1965.
8. Beidler, L. M., and Tucker, D. Olfactory and trigeminal nerve responses to odors. *Fed. Proc.* (Abstr.), 15: 43, 1956.
9. Bell, F. R., and Kitchell, R. L. Taste reception in the goat, sheep and calf. *J. Physiol.,* 183: 145–51, 1966.
10. Chauncey, H. H., Feller, R. P., and Shannon, I. L. Effect of acid solutions on human gustatory chemoreceptors as determined by parotid gland secretion rate. *Proc. Soc. Exp. Biol. Med.,* 112: 917–23, 1963.
11. Chauncey, H. H., and Shannon, I. L. Parotid gland secretion rate as a method for measuring response to gustatory stimuli in humans. *Proc. Soc. Exp. Biol. Med.,* 103: 459–63, 1960.
12. Chernetski, K. E. Sympathetic enhancement of peripheral sensory input in the frog. *J. Neurophysiol.,* 27: 493–515, 1964.
13. Crozier, W. J. Regarding the existence of the common chemical sense in vertebrates. *J. Comp. Neurol.,* 26: 1–8, 1916.
14. Dawes, C., and Jenkins, G. N. The effects of different stimuli on the composition of saliva in man. *J. Physiol.,* 170: 86–100, 1964.
15. Dawson, W. W. Chemical stimulation of the peripheral trigeminal nerve. *Nature,* 196: 341–45, 1962.
16. Elsberg, C. A., Spotnitz, H., and Strongin, E. J. The effect of stimulation by odorous substances upon the amount of secretion of parotid glands. *J. Exp. Psychol.,* 27: 58–65, 1940.
17. Elsberg, C. A., Spotnitz, H., and Strongin, E. J. The olfactory parotid reflex. *Arch. Neurol. Psychiat.,* 47: 707–17, 1942.
18. Engen, T., Lipsitt, L. P., and Kaye, H. Olfactory response and adaptation in the human neonate. *J. Comp. Physiol. Psychol.,* 56: 73–77, 1963.
19. Halpern, B. Some Relations between Electrophysiology and Behavior in Taste (this symposium), 1966.
20. Hamlin, H. E. Working mechanism for the liquid and gaseous intake and output of Jacobson's organ. *Amer. J. Physiol.,* 191: 201–5, 1929.
21. Hellekant, G. The effect of ethyl alcohol on non-gustatory receptors of the tongue of the cat. *Acta Physiol. Scand.,* 65: 243–50, 1965.
22. Ishiko, N., and Amatsu, M. Changes in the chorda tympani nerve responses to taste stimuli associated with movement of the tongue in cat. *Jap. J. Physiol.,* 15: 623–37, 1965.
23. Jones, M. H. A study of the common chemical sense. *Amer. J. Psychol.,* 67: 696–99, 1954.
24. Katz, S. H., and Talbert, E. J. Intensities of odors and irritating effects of warning agents for inflammable and poisonous gases. Technical Paper 480. U.S. Department of Commerce, Bureau of Mines, Washington, D.C., 37 pp., 1930.
25. Kimura, K. Factors affecting the response of taste receptors of rat. *Kumamoto Med. J.,* 14: 95–99, 1961.

26. Kolliker, A. von. Uber die Jacobson'sche Organe des Menschen, in *Gratschr. Wurzburg med. Fac. Festschr. fur Rinecker I–XII,* 1877.

27. Kubota, K., and Hayama, S. Comparative anatomical and neurohistological observations on the tongues of pigmy and common marmosets. *Anat. Rec.,* **150**: 473–86, 1964.

28. Lindenmaier, P., and Kare, M. R. The taste end organs of the chicken. *Poultry Sci.,* **38**: 545–50, 1959.

29. London, I. D. Research on sensory interaction in the Soviet Union. *Psychol. Bull.,* **51**: 531–68, 1954.

30. Mann, G. Bulbus olfactorius accessorius in Chiroptera. *J. Comp. Neurol.,* **116**: 135–44, 1961.

31. McBurney, D. H., and Pfaffmann, C. Gustatory adaptation to saliva and sodium chloride. *J. Exp. Psychol.,* **65**: 523–29, 1963.

32. Parker, G. H. The relations of smell, taste and the common chemical sense in vertebrates. *J. Acad. Nat. Sci.,* **15**: 221–33, 1912.

33. Parker, G. H. *Smell, Taste and Allied Senses in the Vertebrates.* Lippincott, Philadelphia, 1922.

34. Parker, G. H., and Stabler, E. M. On certain distinctions between taste and smell. *Amer. J. Physiol.,* **32**: 230–40, 1913.

35. Pfaffmann, C. Taste and smell, in *Handbook of Experimental Psychology,* S. S. Stevens (ed.). John Wiley & Sons, New York, pp. 1143–71, 1951.

36. Rolandus, A. Sur l'influence de substances odorantes sur le coeur du lapin. *Acta Brevia Neerland,* **16**: 15–22, 1948.

37. Schutz, H. G., and Pilgrim, F. J. Psychophysiology in food acceptance research. *J. Amer. Diet. Ass.,* **29**: 1127–28, 1953.

38. Snarski, A. T. Analiz normalnikh usloviy raboti slyunikh zhelyoz u sobaki. (Analysis of the normal conditions for salivary activity in dogs.) Unpublished thesis, St. Petersburg, 1901. Cited by Elsberg, Spontiz, and Sperry, 1942.

39. Stephan, H. von. Der bulbus olfactorius accessorius bei insektivoren und primaten. *Acta. Anat.,* **62**: 215–53, 1965.

40. Story, R. H. The olfactory bulbar formation and related nuclei in the paddlefish (*Polydor spathula*). *J. Comp. Neurol.,* **123**: 285–89, 1964.

41. Tucker, D. Olfactory, vomeronasal and trigeminal receptor responses to odorants, in *Olfaction and Taste,* Y. Zotterman (ed.). Pergamon, New York, pp. 45–69, 1963.

42. Tucker, D. Physical variables in the olfactory stimulation process. *J. Gen. Physiol.,* **46**: 453–89, 1963.

This work was supported in part by Air Force Office of Scientific Research Grant 1056-66.

19: Feeding without Oropharyngeal Sensations

by Alan N. Epstein

A N OBVIOUS WAY to answer one of the major questions raised by this conference is to eliminate taste and smell during feeding, that is, to study feeding in animals that cannot taste or smell the food they are ingesting. Six years ago Teitelbaum and I developed a method that makes this possible [8]. Rats feed themselves food that does not pass through the oropharynx. They eat by manipulating a lever with their paws to inject liquid diet directly into their own stomachs through a chronically implanted gastric tube. In addition to taste and smell, the method eliminates the somesthetic sensations produced by the food in the mouth and pharynx and reduces the proprioceptive feedback from the acts of eating.

What then are the consequences for feeding of the elimination of the oropharyngeal sensations produced by food? To best understand our answers to this question, I suggest that we consider feeding as an amalgam of three separate processes. The first is the choice of food. This involves the detection of the food, its discrimination from the inedible, and its selection when more than one food is available. The second is the motivation to eat. This involves food as an incentive for performance and consideration of the effort the animal will make to reach the food and ingest it. The third is regulation, the quantitative control of ingestion to maintain a relative constancy of food intake.

Our work shows that these three processes are not equally dependent upon oropharyngeal sensations. The quantitative control of food intake continues with remarkable precision in the absence of the sensations. The choice of foods and the motivation to eat are, on the other hand, greatly impaired. This conference is a welcome opportunity to summarize the evidence leading to these ideas.

GENERAL METHOD

The experimental setting is shown in Fig. 19–1. The animals are large adult rats of both sexes of either the Sherman albino or the Long-Evans hooded strain. They are fitted with chronic gastric tubes, passed through the nasopharynx, and fixed to the skull [5,7]. The gastric tubes have been redesigned to simplify the fittings and reduce bottlenecks. As shown in Fig. 19–2, the tube is now a single piece of polyethylene tubing (PE 50) bent to fit the rat's snout and extending into the stomach (5½ in. from snout bend to gastric end). The bend is made by inserting a piece of soft metal wire into the tube, shaping it, and immersing the assembly in hot water.

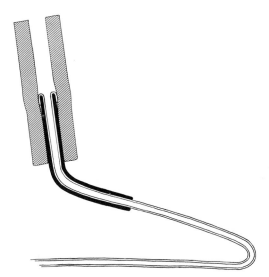

Fig. 19–2. Detail of the redesigned gastric tube. See text for explanation.

Fig. 19–1.   The experimental setting for intragastric self-injection. (Photograph by Harry Kissileff.)

The tube retains the bend without reduction of its lumen when it is cooled and the wire is removed. To facilitate rigid fixation to the skull, the upper end of the tube is passed through a length of stainless steel tubing (seventeen gauge) bent into an open L as shown in solid black in Fig. 19–2. Each arm of the L is a half-inch long. A watertight seal between the polyethylene tube and the steel L-piece is produced as follows: The tube is pushed beyond the upper end of the L-piece and flanged by exposure to a match flame. While still warm the flange is reflected over the end of the L-piece as shown in Fig. 19–2. Lastly, a length of polyvinyl-chloride tubing (⅛ in. wall, ⅛ in. lumen) softened in chloroform is slipped over the flange without rotation and fixed to the stainless steel with epoxy cement (Eastman 910). The polyvinyl-chloride tubing is used here for its great flexibility and resistance to

cracking. It receives at its upper end the metal nose of the watertight swivel joint (just above the rat's head in Fig. 19–1) designed by us [7] to prevent kinking of the delivery tube. The bottom of the joint rotates with the animal while the upper portion connected to the delivery tube does not. It is therefore not necessary to restrain the animal.

The rat injects itself by depressing the bar (at lower right just outside the chamber in Fig. 19–1) available to it through a slot in the wall of the chamber. This starts a peristaltic pump (in the background behind the chamber), which delivers liquid diet through the counterweighted delivery system (over the animal's head) from a refrigerated reservoir. The reservoir is a 250-ml graduated cylinder that can be seen protruding from the top of the ice bucket to the left of the chamber. Water is freely available for ingestion by mouth from the inverted graduated cylinder attached to the wall of the chamber on the left.

The diet is a less expensive version of the Greenstein L-amino acid diet [10] prepared for us by the General Bio-chemicals Corporation as their Soluble Diet No. 116-EC. It contains supple-mented, hydrolyzed casein instead of the more expensive L-amino acids, sucrose instead of glucose, and the fatty acids, vitamins, minerals, and Tween [10]. It yields 2 cal/ml. Despite the modifica-tions, it retains the properties that make it an ideal diet for these experiments. It is nutritionally adequate for the rat. It is a crystal-clear solution (50 per cent solids in water, 580 milliosmols per liter) that resists spoiling and does not clog small tubing.

The animals live in the testing cham-ber (9 in. x 8 in. x 18 in.), side walls of aluminum, front and back walls of plexi-glass), and all experiments, except as described below, are run around the clock without interruption. Electronic gear (not shown) activated by the pulses from the bar operate the pump, count bar presses, record their duration, and operate a Gerbrands cumulative recorder or simple polygraph that gives a perma-nent record of the animal's feeding. The animal's weight, water intake, and total food intake are measured daily.

The animals earn their food in two different ways. In the first procedure, used in our earliest studies, the animal must press the bar a fixed number of times (usually one to six) to receive an intragastric load of fixed volume (usu-ally 2.5–3.0 ml). The animal gets a fixed pay-off for a fixed effort and the pay-off is delivered when the effort is completed. This is the vending-machine method. It has the advantage of allowing a large pay-off for a small effort and easy com-putation of meal volume (multiples of the fixed shot), but it does not give the animal full control of its meal size. We now permit the animal to operate the pump directly from the bar. The injec-tion begins when the bar is depressed, continues at a constant rate (fixed by the experimenter) as long as the bar is held down, and ends when the bar is released. This is the water-fountain method. It is a closer approximation of oral feeding. The animal must sustain his effort to complete the meal, the food is ingested while the feeding effort is being made, and the animal has complete control of the meal size.

In all experiments with both methods, the animal is first trained to press the bar for oral ingestion from a cup or spout near the bar. When it is doing so with normal intake and meal patterns, the delivery tube is transferred from the cup to the gastric tube and thereafter all bar presses result in food injections directly into the animal's stomach. This then becomes the animal's only source of food.

NORMAL CONTROL OF FOOD INTAKE AND MEAL PATTERN

Normal rats continue to eat normal amounts of food, maintain a relative constancy of food intake (and body weight), adjust intake to dilution rapidly and precisely, respond normally to food deprivation, and continue to eat normal meals on a normal diurnal cycle while feeding themselves food that does not pass through the oropharynx. These re-sults are shown in Fig. 19–3 and 19–4 from an animal studied by Mr. Robert Glassman and myself. Fig. 19–3 is a daily record of food intake, number of meals, and average meal size (total intake di-vided by number of meals) for fifty-five days of continuous intragastric feeding. The first fourteen days of this rat's in-tragastric experience are not shown.

Note that on days when the diet is at full strength (*solid black histograms*) in-take varies closely around 30 ml/day and the number of meals is between twelve and fourteen. Sample records of the meal patterns are shown in Fig. 19–4.

Each line across the figure is one complete daily record of feeding as is shown by the clock times at the bottom of the figure. The animal is working on the water-fountain schedule at a rapid rate of delivery (16 ml/min). Bar presses start the pump and advance the recorder pen vertically upward. When the animal is not feeding, the pen draws a horizontal line. Meals then appear as steps in the record. Their volume can be read with the scale at the top of the figure. When the pen reaches its maximum height it resets automatically to the bottom of the record. The reset lines are not data and have been broken to make them less conspicuous.

The meal pattern at the top in Fig. 19–4 (May 6–7) is from *day 49* in Fig. 19–3. On that day the rat ate 37 ml of diet in seventeen meals, fifteen occurring between 6:00 P.M. on May 6 and 9:00 A.M. on May 7. The meals are discrete and vary closely around 2 ml. This is a thoroughly normal performance. Baillie and Morrison, using a similar technique, have also reported normal meal patterns in rats feeding themselves by intragastric self-injection [2].

At the beginning of the next day the diet was diluted to half its density with tap water and the animal made a precise adjustment. Total volume intake rose to 62 ml (the full height of the histogram) and food intake remained well within normal range as shown by the height of the solid portion of the histogram (*day 50* in Fig. 19–3). The animal makes the adjustment by taking con-

spicuously larger meals, beginning with the fifth meal (May 7–8 in Fig. 19–4) and irregularly thereafter. The adjustment to 50 per cent dilution was made with the same precision and in the same way on the six previous dilutions (*days 47, 15, 14, 5, 4,* and *3* in Fig. 19–3). The adjustment to 75 per cent dilution is an exaggeration of the same response. Total volume intakes rise sharply and meals become very large. At these high dilutions more meals are taken (see the large meals taken during the daytime on May 9–10 at 75 per cent dilution). This, again, is quite normal feeding behavior.

The normal character of the response to deprivation is shown in Fig. 19–3 and in Table 19–1. On eight days during

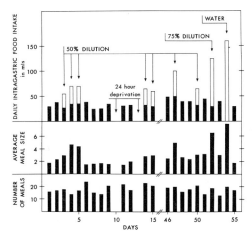

Fig. 19–3. Daily record of a rat feeding itself by intragastric self-injection. Note the relative constancy of intake and meal number on days of full-strength diet (filled bars) and in the face of dilutions (compound bars). Note also the normal response to 24-hour deprivation.

TABLE 19–1: Increased Volume of First Meal Taken by a Rat Feeding Intragastrically after Twenty-four-Hour Food Deprivation[a]

Situation		Meal 1	Meal 2	Meal 3	24-Hour Intake
No Deprivation	Av	1.55	1.09	2.02	31
	R	0.47– 2.33	0.31–3.26	0.47–5.12	20–38
24-Hour Deprivation	Av	8.37	2.33	2.02	38
	R	2.79–13.02	0.31–4.65	0.31–5.85	32–40

[a] All data in milliliters.

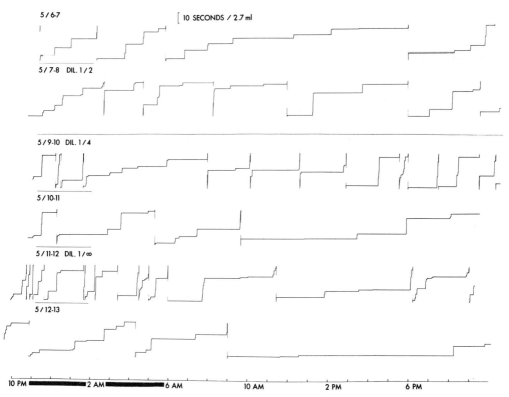

Fig. 19–4. Selected daily meal patterns of the animal whose data are shown in Fig. 19–3. The record of May 6–7 is from day 49 in Fig. 19–3. Note the discrete meals of 1–3 ml volume occurring mostly at night. Response to dilution is signaled by the rapid appearance of abnormally large meals. See, for example, the fifth meal on May 7–8 at 50 per cent dilution.

the middle of the animal's intragastric experience, feeding was studied after the animal had been deprived of food for one day (access to the bar was blocked by a partition). The first such day is *day 11* in Fig. 19–3. Food intake on that day is normal in total volume as it is in rats feeding by mouth after a twenty-four-hour deprivation [1]. However, the first meal taken on the refeeding day is very large. In Table 19–1, the averages of the first, second, and third meals of the refeeding days are compared with the first three meals on days (average of fourteen days) that did not follow deprivation. The first meal taken on the refeeding day is more than five times larger than normal and there is no overlap between the ranges of meal sizes. The difference has disappeared by the

third meal and the twenty-four-hour total intakes are not different. Here again, the feeding of the rat that cannot taste or smell its food is remarkably normal.

The data from this one animal very completely illustrates the evidence with which we drew the conclusion [8] that taste and smell, the feel of food in the mouth, and the proprioceptive feedback from the acts of eating are not essential for the normal operation of the central neural mechanisms controlling food intake. Our animals feeding themselves intragastrically maintain constancy of intake, eat meals on a diurnal cycle, and respond to deprivation all in an essentially normal way. In addition, we showed that such animals were motivated to eat. They maintained normal intakes as the work requirement for a fixed shot was increased from six presses to thirty-six presses in small daily increments. This is shown by another technique and in more extreme form by the data in Fig. 19–5 [14]. This animal had

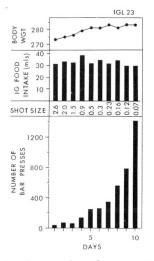

Fig. 19–5. Increased work output (number of presses) in response to decreasing gastric shot size in a rat feeding itself intragastrically. All bar presses were counted including those emitted during delivery of the gastric load. Thus, the volume of food intake is not the simple product of the number of presses times the shot size. (Adapted from Fig. 19–1 in Rogers, Epstein, and Teitelbaum [14].)

been working on the vending-machine schedule for a 2.6 ml load for a week before the experiment shown here was done. On the first day in Fig. 19–5 the animal pressed forty-one times to obtain a ration of 32 ml. As the size of the shot was decreased thirty-five-fold to 0.07 ml, the animal increased its work output thirty-five fold (from 41 to 1,421 presses) to obtain a normal ration of food. Clearly, normal motivation for food can be demonstrated in rats eating without taste and smell.

Our animals make chewing and swallowing movements while feeding themselves intragastrically, perhaps because they are salivating. And they develop what appears to be an avidity for oropharyngeal stimulation. They lick the bar while pressing as if trying to eat it, and they quickly find and lick the small drops of diet that are occasionally left on the walls of the chamber after the daily chores.

CHOICE OF FOODS

Now, we will consider those processes of feeding that are impaired in rats eating without oropharyngeal sensations. The most obvious of these is the detection and discrimination of foods and fluids. The point is made by a study that Katarina Borer and I have recently completed of preference-aversion drinking in the rat, using the technique of intragastric self-injection to bypass taste and smell [4]. Rats prefer sweet and mildly salty solutions and avoid saltier solutions when drinking them by mouth. These phenomena were first described by Richter [13], and a plot of volume intake against increasing concentration yields a peaked function that has been called the preference-aversion curve.

Examples of such curves are shown in Fig. 19–6 taken from Borer's experiment. She used Richter's two-bottle, twenty-four-hour method. That is, a rat has continuous access in its home cage to two sources of fluid offered side by side. One is water, the other a sapid solution. The animal also has free access to food. The concentration of the solution is varied within a broad range, and, to obviate side preferences, each concentration is offered on both sides in the choice arrangement. In Borer's experiment the rat operated a bar (on the water fountain) to obtain the fluid. All animals were studied for oral drinking and the experiment was then repeated with the animal injecting the fluids directly into its own stomach.

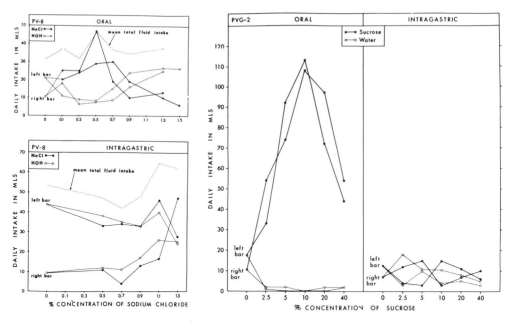

Fig. 19–6. The disappearance of the preferences for sucrose and dilute sodium chloride solutions and of the aversion for hypertonic sodium chloride solutions in rats drinking without taste and smell. (From Borer and Epstein [4].)

Two illustrative animals are shown in Fig. 19–6, one run with salt solutions (*PV-8* on the left) and the other with sucrose (*PV-2* on the right). Intakes from each bar are plotted separately, yielding a family of four curves in each experiment. The oral experiments show Richter's phenomena very clearly. As concentration rises, intake rises to a peak. Thereafter, intake declines, and at the highest concentrations the salt solutions are avoided. The separate plots of intake for the right and left bars emphasize the controlling role of the concentration of the solution in determining behavior. No matter which side the preferred solution is on, the animal ignores its natural side preference (left in both cases; see intakes at 0 per cent concentration) and follows the concentration. At the peak concentrations, total fluid intake greatly exceeds normal water intake, demonstrating in another way the dominant role of concentration in this behavior.

All of these phenomena disappear when the animal cannot taste the fluid it is drinking. In the intragastric experiments, side preferences reappear and the rats treat both bars as if they were delivering water. The only exception is the highest sodium chloride concentration, at which dehydration factors may be operating. Borer has shown that the result is the same for glucose and saccharin. In the absence of taste the preferences disappear.

We do not yet know how far we can generalize these results. Will the choices between fluids reappear when a specific need for the solute is created, for salt by adrenalectomy or for sugar by food deprivation? Will the rat feeding intragastrically be similarly unable to choose purified macronutrients in a cafeteria experiment? This research does show quite clearly that when rats are neither hungry nor thirsty and have no specific nutritional deficits the preferences for salty and sweet solutions and the aversion to concentrated salt solutions are taste functions. These preferences are generated by oropharyngeal sensations and do not occur in their absence.

The result can be generalized to emphasize the crucial role of taste and smell as sensors in feeding. In nature, where feeding and protection from predators, including man, are the cruxes of survival, taste and smell are indispensable. Foods are complex and variable in composition and must be found often after long search; and the edible must be discriminated from the inedible and poisonous. Barnett has shown that wild rats, presumably as the result of unsuccessful poisoning, avoid new foods [3]. They are most offended by new tastes and smells.

TASTE AND SMELL AS MOTIVATORS

Our attention was drawn to the potent role of taste and smell as motivators of the behavior leading to food intake by the observations summarized in Fig. 19–7 made by Mr. Charles Snowdon and myself. These are the records of the first three animals that we studied using the water-fountain technique with rates of delivery that are just less than the rat's rate of ingestion of a liquid diet when eating by mouth (0.6 ml/min). In previous work (such as that shown in Fig. 19–1) we had used very rapid injections (15–18 ml/min). We decided to reduce the rate in order to make the intragastric meal parameters, particularly meal duration, more natural. We set the rate just below normal to prevent wastage in the oral setting.

At 0.6 ml/min delivery, rats eat well when eating by mouth (*open histograms* in Fig. 19–7). They hold the bar down and drink steadily from the spout, taking normal meals and consuming between 30 and 50 ml/day. But when they

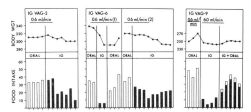

Fig. 19–7.   Failure of bar-pressing for food in three rats abruptly deprived of taste and smell and the reappearance of normal motivation when oral incentives are restored.

are abruptly switched to intragastric injection (the *first vertical line* in each experiment), food intake drops off, typically very sharply (*IG VAG-6* and *IG VAG-9*), and body weight declines. The meals are small and are taken in many short bar presses. I am confident that an animal like *IG VAG-6* would have remained severely anorexic and might in fact have starved to death if we had left it on intragastric feeding. Instead we gave it back the taste and smell of the food, and vigorous bar-pressing and feeding returned. A second experience in the transition from oral to intragastric feeding was more successful, but the animal was still hypophagic.

The experiment with *IG VAG-9* makes the point more emphatically. Here we increased the rate tenfold at transition, but the animal still did not work well at the bar and was hypophagic. On the fifth day of intragastric feeding we added a small oral incentive from the liquid diet. As the animal pressed, diet was injected into its stomach at 6 ml/min (*solid black portion of the histogram*), and diet was available at the oral spout at one-tenth that rate (open portion). The animal began holding the bar again and on the second day ate a normal ration. Taste and smell here are the incentives for which the animal is working. Without them it will not sustain its effort at the bar, despite the fact that the bar is the source of fully adequate nutrition.

When using the vending-machine method in our earliest work we occasionally saw the same failure of motivation at transition but it was never severe and was quickly overcome. The work requirement is less stringent with the earlier technique. The animal need only depress the bar a small number of times to receive a gastric load that approximates a meal. Currently, with the water-fountain method we reduce these motivational difficulties by allowing the animals to make the transition at very high rates (Fig. 19–1) and we then return to the preferred slow rate in small, daily reductions.

THE HYPOTHALAMIC SYNDROMES

The reduction in hunger suffered by rats in both of the hypothalamic syndromes magnifies the role of taste and smell as motivators of feeding. The rat with hyperphagia after ventromedial hypothalamic lesions and the rat with the aphagia and anorexia of lateral hypothalamic damage have a diminished urge to eat [17], and in both, the sensory qualities of the diet dominate postoperative feeding behavior [19]. The lesions that produce the syndromes are shown in Fig. 19–8 where they are compared with a transverse section through a normal hypothalamus.

In the animal with lateral hypothalamic aphagia the case is quite clear. In the immediate postoperative period the animal will eat only the most palatable foods (eggnog, wet chocolate-chip cookies), and even after it has begun to eat standard diet it is exceptionally finicky [18]. This is shown in Fig. 19–9 from an experiment by Mr. Antoine Samman and myself. The daily food intake of four animals with the lateral hypothalamic

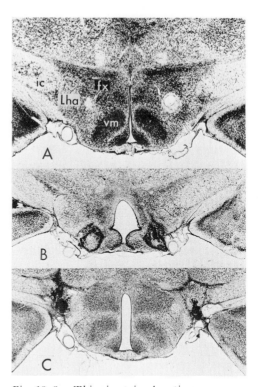

Fig. 19–8. Thionin-stained sections through the hypothalamus of a normal rat (A), a rat with ventromedial hypothalamic lesions (B) producing hyperphagia, and a rat with destruction of the lateral hypothalamic areas (C) producing aphagia and adipsia (vm-ventromedial nucleus; Lha-lateral hypothalamic area; fx-column of the fornix; ic-internal capsule). The hole near the right fornix in the normal section is a surgical artifact. (Section B from Graff and Stellar [9].)

syndrome is shown. They are in different stages of recovery [18]. LAT-61 is in stage four, in which it is eating standard dry food (Purina pellets) and is drinking water. The other three are less advanced. They are eating only foods with high palatability and they are still adipsic (stage three). All four rats became aphagic or severely hypophagic when switched to dry powder or a dilute liquid diet compounded of casein, glucose, and margarine [2]. LAT-60 and LAT-62 were tubed 15 ml of water a day to maintain their hydration during the powder test.

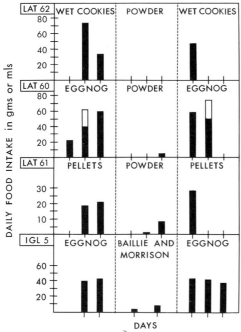

Fig. 19–9. *Aphagia and severe hypophagia produced by sudden restriction to a less palatable diet in four rats in the lateral hypothalamic syndrome. See text for description of diets.*

In *LAT-61* the change in diet was purely textural and in *IGL-5* both diets were liquid and nutritionally adequate. Nevertheless they were not eaten or were only nibbled. In all four animals vigorous feeding returned when the more preferred diet was restored. The palatability of the diet controls feeding throughout the lateral hypothalamic syndrome and the earlier the animal is in its recovery the more complete is the control.

This was shown in another way by Rodgers, Epstein, and Teitelbaum [14]. They deprived the rat, with lateral hypothalamic damage, of the taste and smell of highly palatable foods in the immediate postoperative period and found that the recovery of feeding was delayed. Their results are summarized in Table 19–2. All of their animals were trained to feed intragastrically. They were then given bilateral, lateral hypo-

thalamic lesions through electrodes that had been implanted before the intragastric feeding began, thus minimizing surgical and anesthetic trauma in the immediate postoperative period. Thereafter, the bar for intragastric injection was available at all times. In addition, the animals were offered a cafeteria of highly palatable food for oral ingestion for a few hours each morning to assess their progress in recovery. In Table 19–2

TABLE 19–2: Recovery of Feeding in Rats with Lateral Hypothalamic Lesions—Feeding by Mouth and by Pressing a Bar for Intragastric Food

Rat	Oral Aphagia	No Bar Pressing	IG Aphagia	Adipsia
IGL 14	0	1	1	3
IGL 30 (1)	0	2	2	11
IGL 30 (2)	0	2	2	21
IGL 33 (2)	0	2	5	>14
IGL 23	0	2	5	8
IGL 17	1	3	3	3
IGL 25	1	7	10	16†
IGL 33 (1)	2	3	3	11
IGL 22	2	6	10	16†
IGL 24	3	6	13†	13
IGL 28	5†	5	5	5
IGL 26	15	23†	23	23

SOURCE: From Rodgers, Epstein, and Teitelbaum [14.] IGL 30 and IGL 33 were studied after a second set of lesions. The sequence for each rat is shown by the numbers in parentheses. The crosses indicate that the animal died on the day shown.

the number of postoperative days during which the animal failed to feed itself intragastrically is given in the column *IG Aphagia.* They ranged from one to twenty-three days. In all thirteen cases the animals ate the palatable foods by mouth *(Oral Aphagia)* before pressing the bar to feed themselves food they could not taste or smell. Some of the animals pressed a few scattered times during the night *(No Bar Pressing)* before feeding themselves at the bar, but again this did not occur until after the eggnog and wet cookies were eaten by mouth. Note also that none of the animals drank water before they began eating by mouth. The animal in the lateral hypothalamic syndrome, particularly in its earliest stages, eats for palatability. If the food cannot be tasted or smelled, the recovery of feeding is greatly delayed.

The incentive of high palatability is also necessary for vigorous overeating and for maximum levels of obesity in rats with ventromedial hypothalamic damage. McGinty, Epstein, and Teitelbaum [11] have shown that the phenomenon does not depend entirely upon the taste and smell of the food. Rats with appropriate lesions will overeat while feeding intragastrically but the phenomenon is attenuated. In Fig. 19–10, me-

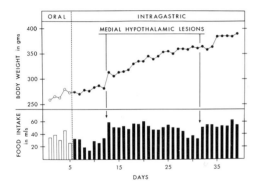

Fig. 19–10. Attenuated hypothalamic hyperphagia produced by ventromedial hypothalamic damage in a rat feeding without taste and smell. Note the sudden increase in daily food intake on the day after lesions. But note also the short duration of the phenomenon and the only moderate increase in body weight.

dial hypothalamic lesions were made through implanted electrodes on the seventh day of intragastric feeding (vending-machine method, 2.5–3.0 ml after six bar presses). There was an immediate hyperphagia and weight gain. Meal patterns during hyperphagia are shown in Fig. 19–11. This is an animal (*IGM-1* [11]) studied by Mr. Glassman and myself working on the water-fountain for

rapid delivery. The top record is the day before lesions. The animal has a sharply limited nocturnal feeding period and its meals are of average volume. The lesions were made shortly after noon. After an episode of frantic bar pressing and hyperactivity (4:00 to 6:00 P.M.) a day of hypophagia ensued. Two days after the lesions were made the hyperphagia appeared. The animal ate in the daytime, breaking out of its rigid nocturnal pattern, and occasionally very large meals were eaten (the first at 5:00 P.M. on the nineteenth day). One month later, while hyperphagic after a second set of lesions, the animal was given a 50 per cent dilution test as shown at the bottom of Fig. 19–11. The animal doubled its already hyperphagic intake by taking many extremely large meals.

But Fig. 19–10 shows that when hyperphagia is produced in an animal eating food that it cannot taste or smell, it is attenuated. Note that after the lesions the food intake had returned to normal levels, and weight had stabilized at only moderate obesity in little more than two weeks. It was necessary to enlarge the lesions *(day 32)* to restore the hyperphagia.

In the five animals studied [11], average daily weight gain during hyperphagia was 4.5 g (range: 2.7–7.6), which is clearly but not maximally above normal. Only two of the animals (Sherman females normally weighing 300–325 g) exceeded 420 g at maximum weight. These were the two studied longest on intragastric feeding. One reached 423 g after seventy-three days, the other 488 g after fifty-eight days (*IGM-1*, whose meal patterns are shown in Fig. 19–11).

Figures 19–12 and 19–13 demonstrate the exaggerated potency of taste and smell as incentives for the work of feeding in the hyperphagic rat. The animal whose data are shown in Fig. 19–12 was one of the most hyperphagic animals

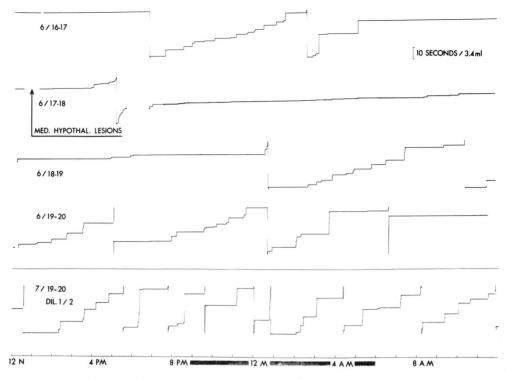

Fig. 19–11.   Selected meal patterns of a hyperphagic rat in the immediate postoperative period. The hyperphagia is expressed by the appearance of daytime eating and by occasional, very large meals (see the meal at 5:00 P.M. on June 19). Note also the response to dilution on June 19–20.

[11]. It was eating over 100 ml of liquid diet a day before intragastric feeding began. Despite the fact that it was working on the motivationally less demanding vending-machine schedule, it suffered a severe anorexia when taste and smell were eliminated, and it had stopped working at the bar entirely by the fifth intragastric day. An oral incentive was added as in *IG VAG-9* (Fig. 19–7) but here it was only a sweet taste (0.1 per cent saccharin, w/v). The animal was enticed to the bar and given a free taste of the saccharin solution. It began working again and within a few days was moderately hyperphagic. When the sweet taste was withdrawn (fourteenth intragastric day) the hyperphagia immediately abated and within two weeks was over. Restoring the incentive (day 45) reinstated the hyperphagia.

We consider this a very powerful case

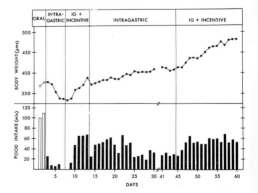

Fig. 19–12.   The potency of the taste and smell of palatable foods in maintaining feeding in the hyperphagic rat (note the severe depression of intake at the oral-intragastric transition) and in sustaining the hyperphagia. Oral incentive is necessary for the restoration of overeating and the hyperphagia quickly abates in its absence. The incentive here is 0.1 per cent saccharin delivered for oral ingestion with, and at one-tenth the volume of, the intragastric load taken by the animal.

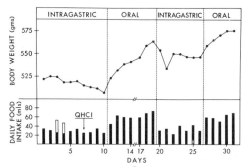

Fig. 19–13. Hyperphagia is turned on by palatable food eaten by mouth (Oral) and turned off (Intragastric) when the food can not be tasted or smelled in an obese hyperphagic rat.

for our argument. Note first that intragastric hyperphagia never reached the oral level. Secondly, removal of taste and smell was catastrophic for feeding. And third, a non-nutritional, sweet-tasting reward for bar pressing is necessary for sustained hyperphagia. Here again palatability rules feeding, and it appears that the more excessive the hyperphagia, the more dominant oropharyngeal sensations are.

This extreme dependence on the palatability of the diet, or finickiness [16], in the hyperphagic rat is most obvious when it has become obese. This is illustrated in Fig. 19–13, which is again data from *IGM-1*. We removed the animal from the intragastric chamber when its weight reached 488 g and allowed it access to Purina pellets for several weeks. When returned to intragastric feeding on the enriched eggnog diet of Williams and Teitelbaum [20] and weighing 520 g, the animal did not overeat and its weight slowly declined. There was no artifact in the experiment preventing intake at hyperphagic levels, as shown by the increase in intake of 50 per cent diluted diet on the third and fourth days of the experiment. In addition, a quinine adulteration test on the seventh day assured us that the food was not being tasted. This was the same concentration of quinine (0.03 per cent quinine HCl)

that had produced a severe anorexia in a prior oral test (see Fig. 19–1 in McGinty, Epstein, and Teitelbaum [11]). When the diet was again offered for ingestion by mouth (the animal pressed the bar to receive an aliquot of diet), the hyperphagia and weight gain reappeared. This sequence was then repeated with the same result. The animal was an impressive hyperphagic when it could taste and smell its food, but its intake reverted immediately to normal and it began losing weight when deprived of palatability.

INTRAGASTRIC SELF-INJECTION IN MAN.

Studies of feeding without taste and smell are being extended to man [15]. As part of an important and comprehensive study of feeding in man, the study of intake by self-injection through nasopharyngeal tubes swallowed by subjects has begun. The subjects, normal young men, agree to a controlled diet regime. They eat lunch and supper on their own and do not eat or drink after midnight. They then take breakfast in the lab. In the oral experiments they drink Metrecal through a straw from a concealed reservoir for twenty minutes while relaxing to music and reading the morning paper. The results with the first intragastric subject are shown in Fig. 19–14. Here the subject is pressing a button to pump the diet into the oral straw at the rates shown. He is a big, hungry boy and takes about a liter of Metrecal when eating his breakfast by mouth. Then he is switched to gastric ingestion. After a period of reduced intake that looks astonishingly like our rat data the volume of his intragastric meal returns to normal. This is a motivational problem of a different sort. The subject said he did not know what to expect during the first few intragastric trials so he pressed very cautiously, fear-

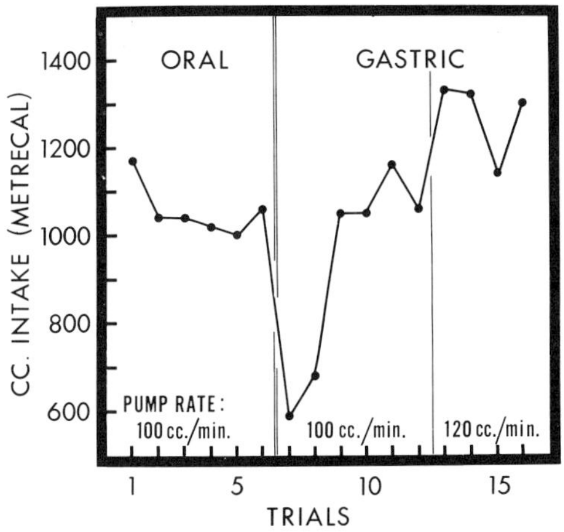

Fig. 19–14. Intragastric feeding in man. See text for explanation. (From Stellar, Jordan, and Wieland [15].)

ing he might blow himself up. What an advantage it is to be able to speak to your subjects! On the thirteenth trial the speed of the pump was accidentally increased and, as can be seen, there were signs of an appropriate adjustment.

SUMMARY

This review can be summarized very quickly. The major processes of feeding behavior are not equally dependent upon taste and smell of food and the other oropharyngeal sensations produced by eating.

The sensations are essential for finding and identifying food and fluid. In their absence, choices between nutrients are impossible or extremely difficult. Survival in the wild, particularly of an omnivorous mammal, is inconceivable without them.

They make an important contribution to the motivation to work for food. They are the ideal and most potent incentives for feeding, and when hunger is diminished or absent, as in the rat with hypothalamic damage, they may be the only motivating stimuli operating.

They therefore have a dual role in feeding. They yield both discriminative and affective stimuli. They both direct and drive behavior. This point of view has been expressed in recent reviews [6,12,21].

Lastly, when a single food is freely available and the motivational demands are slight, the sensations are not necessary for the control of the quantitative parameters of feeding. Rats that cannot taste or smell the food they are eating maintain constancy of intake, eat normal meals on a diurnal cycle, and respond to deprivation. Sensations from the upper gut, the detection of chemical and thermal changes in the internal environment, and experience are sufficient for the central neural control of these phenomena.

Discussion

Hodgson: Would you comment a little further on the mechanism by which the rat cuts off feeding when it has had a normal amount of food. Where would the receptors that mediate this feedback be?

Epstein: I hope Sharma will say something about the receptors available to the animal in the GI tract. It is very likely that the ultimate shut-off takes place somewhere in the brain. It may respond to changes in blood constituents and temperature.

Hodgson: Unless I misunderstood one of your slides, things like the concentration of sugar do not have much effect.

Epstein: Yes, when the fluids do not pass through the mouth the concentration of the solution no longer controls the behavior. But these animals are not taking their food from the bars. Pellets are freely available and are eaten by mouth.

I think it is under these circumstances that the preference-aversion curves are, in fact, taste functions. The animal is feeding freely here and is under no nutrient stress. As Woodbury and Herxheimer (*J. Physiol.*, **151**: 253, 1960) put it: "The rat drinks these solutions because it likes them, from greed rather than need."

Morrison: What happens if you deprive him of anything except what he can get by pressing the button? In the intragastric preference-aversion test, what is the design?

Epstein: I don't know yet. We are doing two experiments to answer that question. First, we present a single glucose solution, 5 per cent or 20 per cent, while the animal is deprived of solid food. It must now eat from the bar. Second, we are looking at sodium chloride solution intake in the adrenalectomized rat. In both situations there is a well-known increase in ingestion when the rats are drinking by mouth. I don't know yet what the truth is when they are drinking intragastrically.

Hamilton: The hyperphagic rat may eat more food because there is a longer delay in its rejection of food on the basis of taste. Did you put your rat on regular oral feeding?

Epstein: I will include some data in the manuscript that answer this very good question (see Fig. 19–12 and 19–13).

Hamilton: These data are still open to the interpretation that taste is involved in the hyperphagia.

Epstein: The experiment of Cohn and Joseph (*Yale J. Biol. Med.*, **34**: 598, 1962) is very relevant here. Obesity is a suppressor of food intake. As the hyperphagic animals become obese, more moti-

vation is required, more incentive from the taste and smell of the food is required for them to go on eating and putting on fat. I think this is what we are taking away from our intragastric hyperphagic animals. They will become moderately obese intragastrically. Some will go up to 350–400 g over a period of a month, but once they reach that level they are not driven to go higher without the motivating input from taste and smell.

Hamilton: Are you saying that in the hypothalamic hyperphagic rat the lesion is related to the initiation of meals?

Epstein: Incentive is required both for initiating meals and for putting out the extra effort necessary to complete a bigger meal.

Stevenson: Why wouldn't your animals press for more food from the "drinking-fountain" system, when they would press so much for water alone in the first experiment? In your "infinite dilution" experiment, when the animal was getting a "shot" of water for each press, it pressed for a tremendous volume of water. With the "vending machine" method, as long as it pressed it got the fluid.

Epstein: This was a very experienced animal. It was expecting food from the bar and was probably working for stomach distension. This is a very interesting aspect of the work that needs more serious attention.

Stevenson: In the experiment where you use the "drinking-fountain" system, or a small shot of water for each press, is there a possibility that the animal has no clues of intake, that it can't even use stomach distension because intake is so gradual that it doesn't excite the animal? Not only has it lost all oral sensations but (with this method) the distension of the stomach is so slow that it is also lost as a cue.

Epstein: Exactly. With 0.6 ml flow per minute and the food going directly into the stomach, the reinforcing stimulus is either too subtle or may be lost. The 0.07 ml experiment (Fig. 19–5) was done on the vending machine. The animal pressed once and got a fixed shot. But if the animal is working at the water fountain, it must hold the bar down for 2.5 minutes to get a meal of 1.5 ml. If it lets go, everything stops. That is a much more demanding situation than the vending machine.

Morrison: But you get a small piece of candy every time you do this.

Epstein: No, no, not if it goes directly into the stomach. That's my point. You don't know it's candy. You're not even sure you've gotten anything. The animal has to know it's being paid off. If you bypass the head receptors by letting the animal put food into its own stomach at a very slow rate, it doesn't know that it's food and it quits.

Morrison: What is the comparison of the rate of this intake with what it would get if it just tapped the bar when 0.6 ml per minute came out of it.

Epstein: The rate is constant. If the bar press is very brief, the volume delivered will be very small. Very small volumes can work (Fig. 19–5). An animal with experience working on the vending machine will press over 1,400 times a night for a ration of food. I would like to know what the nature of the useful experience is.

Kare: We stop eating before nutrients

are absorbed from the intestine. Sodium appetite is satisfied long before intestinally absorbed sodium can reach the involved cells and correct the deficiency related to the sodium appetite.

Some of our recent work suggests that the passage of food through the mouth serves functions beyond that of stimulating the taste and smell receptors. While Epstein limited his animals to intragastric stimulation, we were interested in knowing what information (useful for intake regulation) the animal receives while the nutrients are in the mouth.

We tied off the esophagus and introduced solutions of labeled compounds into the mouth. After a short interval of time, activity was measured in the brain, blood, and liver. The summarized data (Table 19–I) indicate that orally placed

TABLE 19–I: Radioactivity in Tissues after Oral and Duodenal Placement of Labeled Glucose

(^{14}C)

Placement	Dps/G Dry Weight[a]		
	Brain- (N)	Liver- (N)	Blood- (N)
Glucose			
Oral, 9–14 minutes	136 (3)	15 (3)	0 (3)
Oral, 4–5 minutes	32 (3)	11 (2)	0 (2)
Gut, 1 minute	0 (2)	134 (2)	72 (2)
Oleic Acid			
Oral, 14 minutes	0 (2)	0.7 (2)	0 (2)
Control	0 (2)	0 (2)	0 (2)

[a] Normalized to correspond to a 400-g rat body weight and a 5 μc per 0.25 ml application. Adjustments for background have been incorporated. Corrections were made for self-absorption.

glucose provides considerable activity in the brain but little in the liver or blood. However, if the isotopes are introduced into the gut, they are not detectable in the brain but are demonstrable in the liver and blood. The results with sodium chloride (Table 19–II) are even more

TABLE 19–II: Radioactivity[a] in Tissues after Oral, Gastric, and Duodenal Placement of Labeled Sodium Chloride

(^{24}Na)

Placement	Dps/G Wet Weight		
	Brain-(N)	Liver-(N)	Blood-(N)
NaCl			
Oral, 8 minutes	76 (4)	—	—
Gut, 8 minutes	13 (2)	—	—
Oral, 3–4 minutes	88 (9)	4 (5)	15 (5)
Gut, 3–4 minutes	17 (7)	244 (5)	359 (5)
Gastric, 4 minutes	1 (5)	8 (5)	18 (5)
Control	0 (3)	0 (3)	0 (3)

[a] Normalized to correspond to a 400-g rat body weight and a 5 μc per 0.25 ml application. Adjustments for background have been incorporated.

definitive. Apparently there is a rapid movement of salt from the oropharyngeal cavity to the brain. If the salt is placed directly into the gut or into the ligated stomach, little or no activity is detectable in the brain. Details of our method can be found in a preliminary report (Maller *et al., Nature,* 1967 [in press]).

We are currently working with Grossman and Schechter using whole head autoradiography to ascertain the precise pathways of movement and the discrete areas of the brain where the labeled compounds are found.

Collectively these results indicate that nutrients introduced into the ligated oropharyngeal cavity, are, after a brief interval, detectable in the brain. This does suggest that monitoring of nutrients during the oral phase of ingestion is possible.

These findings would be compatible with Adolph's suggestion of a pharyngeal metering device or Fregly's postulation earlier in this symposium of a regulatory mechanism either in the mouth or the pharynx. It could explain the salt-depleted ruminant's ability to correct for its needs with a relatively precise intake of a sodium solution obviously without the benefit of information from absorption in the gut.

Lát: This reminds me of the experiments performed in Tashkent by the Russians, who had two groups of dogs—one with the esophagus closed, the other normal. The dogs were then heat stressed for approximately six hours. The animals with the blocked esophagus had water available but the normal animals did not. The sham drinkers survived while the normal animals died during the stress.

Kare: A certain amount of satiety will occur in the esophageal-fistulated dogs with the water passing through their mouths.

Adolph: There's a temporary satiation from drinking through the sham fistula. I have often wondered about the experiments that we made; as Lát says, maybe we have a key to what happened. Perhaps it is a physiological phenomenon after all.

Epstein: This may be a "radiator" phenomenon. The animal is taking cool water through a hot mouth over a hot tongue and is therefore losing heat to the water.

Jacobs: The statement by Stevenson suggests that what you're doing in the intragastric feeding is removing information about stomach distention, i.e., reward value. Does adding the term "motivation" help here?

Epstein: I don't know how else to describe the fact that introducing a small drop of saccharin that the animal can taste, when he is, in fact, getting all of his nutrient intragastrically, will put him back to work at the bar. Nor do I know how to describe the fact that rats with lateral hypothalamic lesions will not feed themselves food they cannot taste or smell for as long as three weeks, despite the fact that they are, during the same time, eating highly palatable foods by mouth. What is the difference between a bar that will deliver food into your stomach and one that delivers food you can take into your mouth? Why do we see ingestion in the latter and failure of ingestion in the former in the same animal, an animal with brain damage that we know produces anorexia? I believe this is one of the most essential roles of oropharyngeal sensations in feeding. They energize feeding, turn it on, and keep it going. They give the animal immediate positive feedback. There is nothing more reinforcing for the hungry animal than the taste and smell of food.

REFERENCES

1. Adolph, E. F. Urges to eat and drink in rats. *Amer. J. Physiol.,* 151: 110–25, 1947.
2. Baillie, P., and Morrison, S. D. The nature of the suppression of feeding by lateral hypothalamic lesions in rats. *J. Physiol.* (London), 165: 227–45, 1963.
3. Barnett, S. A. Responses of wild rats to offensive tastes and smells. *Brit. J. Anim. Behav.,* 1: 32–37, 1953.
4. Borer, K. T., and Epstein, A. N. Disappearance of salt and sweet preferences in rats drinking without taste and smell. *Physiologist,* 8 (No. 3), 1965.
5. Epstein, A. N. Water intake without the act of drinking. *Science,* 131: 497–98, 1960.
6. Epstein, A. N. Oropharyngeal factors in feeding and drinking, in *Handbook of Physiology* (Section on the Alimentary Canal). American Physiological Society, Washington, D.C. (in press).
7. Epstein, A. N., and Teitelbaum, P. A watertight swivel joint permitting chronic injection into moving animals. *J. Appl. Physiol.,* 17: 171–72, 1962.
8. Epstein, A. N., and Teitelbaum, P. Regulation of food intake in the absence of taste, smell, and other oropharyngeal sensations. *J. Comp. Physiol. Psychol.,* 55: 753–59, 1962.
9. Graff, H., and Stellar, E. Hyperphagia, obesity, and finickiness. *J. Comp. Physiol. Psychol.,* 55: 418–24, 1962.
10. Greenstein, J. P., Otey, M. C., Burnbaum, S. M., and Winitz, M. Quantitative nutritional studies with water-soluble, chemically defined diets. X: Formulation of a nutritionally complete diet. *J. Nat. Cancer Inst.,* 24: 211–19, 1960.
11. McGinty, D., Epstein, A. N., and Teitelbaum, P. The contribution of oropharyngeal sensations to hypothalamic hyperphagia. *Animal Behav.,* 13: 413–18, 1965.
12. Pfaffmann, C. The sensory and motivating properties of the sense of taste, in *Nebraska Symposium on Motivation,* M. R. Jones (ed.). University of Nebraska Press, Lincoln, pp. 71–108, 1961.
13. Richter, C. P. Salt appetite of mammals: Its dependence on instinct and metabolism, in *L'Instinct dans le Comportement des Animaux et de l'Homme.* Masson et Cie, Paris, pp. 577–629, 1956.
14. Rodgers, W. L., Epstein, A. N., and Teitelbaum, P. Lateral hypothalamic aphagia: Motor failure or motivational deficit? *Amer. J. Physiol.,* 208: 334–42, 1965.
15. Stellar, E. Hunger in man: Comparative and physiological studies. Eastern Psychological Association Presidential Address, New York, April, 1966.
16. Teitelbaum, P. Sensory control of hypothalamic hyperphagia. *J. Comp. Physiol. Psychol.,* 48: 156–63, 1955.
17. Teitelbaum, P. Disturbances in feeding and drinking behavior after hypothalamic lesions, in *Nebraska Symposium on Motivation,* M. R. Jones (ed.). University of Nebraska Press, Lincoln, pp. 39–65, 1961.
18. Teitelbaum, P., and Epstein, A. N. The lateral hypothalamic syndrome: Recovery of feeding and drinking after lateral hypothalamic lesions. *Psychol. Rev.,* 69: 74–90, 1962.
19. Teitelbaum, P., and Epstein, A. N. The role of taste and smell in the regulation of food and water intake, in *Olfaction and Taste,* Y. Zotterman (ed.). Pergamon, New York, pp. 347–60, 1963.
20. Williams, D. R., and Teitelbaum, P. Some observations on the starvation resulting from lateral hypothalamic lesions. *J. Comp. Physiol. Psychol.,* 52: 458–65, 1959.
21. Young, P. T. The role of hedonic processes in motivation, in *Nebraska Symposium on Motivation,* M. R. Jones (ed.). University of Nebraska Press, Lincoln, pp. 193–238, 1955.

The writing of this review and the author's research reported here were supported by USPHS Grant NB 03469.

20: Alimentary Receptors and Food Intake Regulation

by Kamal N. Sharma

REGULATION OF food intake is now generally regarded as a "central" phenomenon in which the hypothalamus plays a major and decisive role [1,2,3]. However, recent studies [4,16] point to the increasing recognition of alimentary involvement in modulating central nervous control of food intake. The role of olfactogustatory cues in influencing feeding behavior have been commented upon by many speakers in the symposium. The present discussion will be mainly confined to those "nontaste" factors which operate at the gastrointestinal level in the regulation of food ingestion. The studies are far from complete and there are wide gaps in our experimental knowledge, but the available evidences seem to substantiate the idea that the alimentary receptor mechanisms modulate central control. Results have been obtained in a variety of animals (rats, cats, dogs, monkeys) studied in ad lib, food-deprived, or manually fed states.

Gastric distension is known to be an important satiety signal. It has been reported that the duration of eating is related to the size of intragastric feeding, and inert bulk in the stomach is as effective as food in producing short term inhibition of eating [11,12]. In recent years attempts have been made to investigate the electrical correlates of these

signals. Distension of the stomach has been shown to evoke afferent impulses in cervical vagal fibers [8,14]. There is a conspicious increase in the frequency of firing which continues with little decrement during maintained distension (Fig. 20–1). The receptors are slow in adapt-

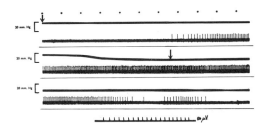

Fig. 20–1. Shows the response of a receptor in the pyloric antrum to distension of the whole stomach. The records are continuous. Inflow of 50 ml of saline began at the arrow at top left hand corner and finished at the arrow in the second row. The fluid remained in the stomach for the rest of the record. Time in one-sec intervals. (From Iggo [8].)

ing and the most sensitive units responded to an intraluminal pressure increase as low as 2 mm. The impulses disappeared with the release of distension. Iggo [6] believes that the distension-sensitive gastric receptors, present in the outer layers of the stomach wall, are "in series" with the smooth muscle and signal the increase of tension caused either by distension or by contraction.

Distension produced by balloon in-flation or by warm saline (0.9 per cent NaCl) gave similar results. However, the rate and the degree of distension were reflected in the response pattern ob-tained. Distending the lumen with the same volume of fluid but introducing the fluid at more rapid rates produced a higher peak frequency of impulses than when the fluid was given at slower rates. It was also found that in keeping with the increase in the degree of dis-tension, the frequency of firing increases in a linear fashion until it reaches a plateau. In the cat the plateau has been obtained by distending the stomach with 150 ml of air (Fig. 20–2).

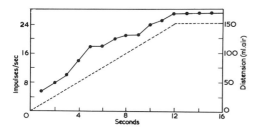

Fig. 20–2. *Increasing frequency of dis-charge obtained in a gastric afferent fiber with increasing distension of the stomach. Rate of distension is indicated by the interrupted line. (From Paintal [14].)*

"Distension" and "tension" receptors have been localized in the esophagus, stomach, duodenum, jejunum, and small intestine [6,15]. Distension effects have also been obtained from the colon, but single nerve fiber activity has not been worked out in any detail. Thus, there is ample electrophysiological evidence to suggest the presence of mechanorecep-tors widely distributed in the gastroin-testinal tract. Based on these and be-havioral studies, it has been suggested that these mechanoreceptors play an im-portant role in the peripheral mechan-ism of hunger and satiety. Experimental evidence is also available to show that these mechanosensitive impulses project

to various areas of the limbic-hypotha-lamic complex which have been shown to participate in feeding behavior.

In a series of studies in cats and mon-keys, paired electrodes were implanted stereotaxically in various regions of the hypothalamus. Approximately one week after the animals recovered from the operative trauma, they were deprived of food for twenty-four hours before the recording of activities began. On the experimental day, the animals were an-esthetized with intraperitoneal nembu-tal, balloons attached to rubber cathe-ters were introduced into their stomachs and connected to stathum pressure transducers. Sudden or gradual, gradu-ated distension could be produced through this balloon-catheter system. Fig-ure 20–3, *A* presents typical records of changes in the electrical activities of the hypothalamic centers as a result of dis-tension of the stomach by increasing the pressure in the intragastric balloons by water or by air. Upon increasing the gastric distension, electrical activity in the region of the satiety center showed a well-demonstrated change, which in most cases consisted of irregular, com-paratively high-voltage waves. Sometimes spikes were also observed in the activity from this region. No such changes were observed in the electrical activity re-corded from the region of the feeding centers (Fig. 20–3, *B*) or from other hy-pothalamic regions (Fig. 20–3, *C*). The increased activity of the satiety centers persisted as long as the raised intragas-tric pressure was maintained and did not show much adaptation. Intestinal distension produced similar results.

In another series of studies, chronic gastric fistulae (in dogs) or intragastric intubations (in rats) were produced in animals possessing chronically implanted electrodes in various hypothalamic re-gions. In such preparations hypotha-lamic activity could be recorded in un-

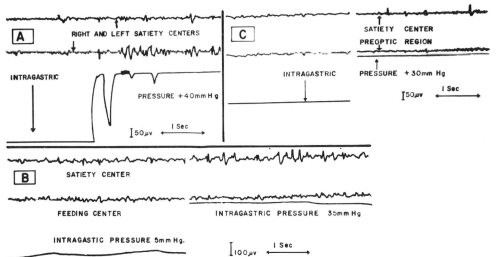

Fig. 20–3. A. *Bipolar recording of the activity of left and right satiety centers of a cat with the intragastric pressure recorded through a water-filled balloon-catheter system. On raising intragastric pressure to + 40 mm Hg, irregular high-voltage waves appear in the satiety regions.* B. *Bipolar recording of the activity of right satiety and feeding centers in a monkey. On raising the intragastric pressure, irregular high-voltage waves appear in the satiety region while no such change occurs in the feeding region.* C. *Bipolar recording of the activity of left satiety center and preoptic region in a cat. On raising the intragastric pressure, spikes appear in the satiety region and not in the preoptic region. (From Sharma et al.* [16].)

anesthetized, freely moving states before, during, and after gastric distension. Though the direction of responses was similar to those obtained in the anesthetized series, the magnitude of responses was greater with a lower threshold of stimulation.

Studies using microelectrodes have also been conducted to record unit activity from various hypothalamic regions and to observe the effects of stomach distension on the activities of the hypothalamic neurons. It has been found that a high percentage (56 per cent) of the neuronal population, in and immediately rostral to the ventromedial nuclei of the dog, show a significant increase in neuron firing rate in response to gastric distension. The frequency of discharge of these units is roughly linear to the increase in gastric distension. Cutting the vagii eliminated the response in a majority of the cases. Figure 20–4 shows the maximal frequency of impulses re-

corded in one of the twenty-two units studied in the region of ventromedial nuclei. There is a three- to fourfold increase in firing rate during moderate gastric distension, which persists for a few minutes after release of distension.

Activity changes produced by gastric distension have also been observed from the orbital surface of the frontal lobe, cerebellum, pyriform cortex, and caudate [18]. Studies of the caudate have been done in the anesthetized as well as the unanesthetized situations. Graded gradual distension of the stomach with 20–80 ml of water produced depression of the spontaneous caudate rhythm in the cat with a 30–35 per cent drop in voltage. The rhythm becomes regular and synchronous with a general reduction in the amplitude of oscillation. The response occurred within a second or so of the distension and persisted from ten seconds to about one to three minutes, after which the activity settled down to

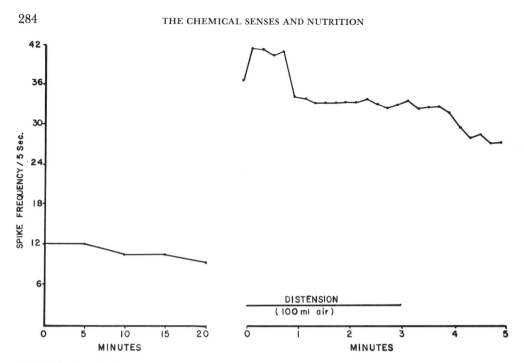

*Fig. 20–4.   Maximal frequency of impulses recorded in a unit localized in the
ventromedial nuclei. The average activity calculated for five seconds is denoted at the
points plotted.*

predistension patterns. However, if the
balloon is left inflated for longer intervals, the activity changes persist. The
positive loci were found in the ventromedio-marginal regions of the rostral
part of the head of the caudate.

In the behavioral series, inflation of
a miniature intragastric balloon passed
through a chronic gastric fistula was
found to inhibit locomotor and food in-
vestigatory activity in rats trained in a

T-maze. The rats moved in the right direction but either did not reach the goal
box, turned back, or reached the goal
box but returned to the starting point
without touching the food. Distension
of the stomach after subdiaphragmatic
vagotomy, however, did not produce any
appreciable change in locomotor activity
or alimentary reactions, and the rats ran
straight to the goal box and ate the
food readily. Table 20–1 shows the be-

TABLE 20–1: Behavior of Rats before and after Subdiaphragmatic Vagotomy

	Prior to Stomach Denervation		After Stomach Denervation	
Number of Rats	Percentage of Erroneous Runs	Food Behavior during Stomach Distension	Percentage of Erroneous Runs	Food Behavior during Stomach Distension
14	15.0	rejected food	15.0	ate readily
15	15.0	" "	18.5	" "
16	14.5	" "	17.0	" "
17	15.0	" "	16.5	ate lazily
18	13.0	" "	18.0	ate readily

SOURCE: Chernigovsky [4].

havior of the rats before and after sub-diaphragmatic vagotomy. The food was rejected after distension in the rats with innervated stomachs but was eaten readily in the denervated situations. It would seem that filling the stomach affects alimentary excitability in the vagally innervated stomach, the reflex acting through hypothalamic and other central nervous structures [4]. We have attempted to see the effect of rhythmic distension of Thiry-Vella loops on the food intake of cats. Figure 20–5 shows

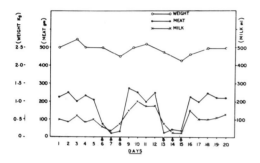

Fig. 20–5. Shows drop in daily meat and milk intake of the cat as a result of Thiry-Vella loop distension produced on the days marked by arrows. (From Sharma et al. [18].)

the daily meat and milk intake of the cat. On the test days *(arrows)* rhythmic distension lasting for a period of four hours was alternated with four-hour rest periods. There was a significant drop in both meat and milk intake on these test days. The average intake immediately returned to normal on the day following the test and sometimes even overshot the daily average. An appreciable drop in food intake was never observed in denervated loops.

Besides mechanosensitive impulses, chemoreceptors [7,17] which are distributed in the gastrointestinal tract and which take part in the regulation of food ingestion also appear to be present. Impulses from the peripherally cut ends of the mesenteric nerves innervating selected segments of the gut were recorded

oscilloscopically in anesthetized cats. The loops were perfused with various solutions at constant temperature and pressure. Dogs with Thiry-Vella loops and electrodes implanted in mesenteric nerves were used for chronic studies. After observing spontaneous activity for ten to thirty minutes, the lumen of the gut was carefully flushed with a 0.9 per cent NaCl solution and activity was observed for an additional ten to fifteen minutes. After saline, 5–10 ml of 5.4 per cent glucose was passed slowly into the lumen of the gut. Glucose perfusion increased frequency of firing of larger *(open bars)* and smaller *(solid bars)* fiber groups from 100 to 400 per cent and from 20 to 100 per cent respectively (Fig. 20–6). The latency of response

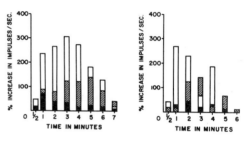

Fig. 20–6. Percentage increase in the activity of mesenteric nerves observed in response to glucose perfusion. Mean values calculated for five seconds at time intervals shown. Black, shaded, and open bars indicate responses from small, medium, and large fiber groups, respectively. (From Sharma and Nasset [17].)

varied from twenty to thirty seconds to four to five minutes, and maximum activity was obtained one to six minutes after the start of the perfusion. Occasionally, increased firing persisted for fifteen minutes or more, but no consistent pattern of increased discharge was observed. A second glucose perfusion at this stage failed to change the activity. If the gut contents were washed out with 0.9 per cent NaCl, glucose would again increase the activity. The latency of response to the second perfusion was usually longer; firing was less intense and lasted for a shorter period of time.

Perfusing the gut lumen with a single amino acid caused an increase in the frequency of firing that was more conspicuous in smaller fiber groups (Fig. 20–7). Generally, the latency of response was shorter than that observed after glucose perfusion and ranged from ten seconds to three minutes. Table 20–2 shows the activity in different fiber groups be-

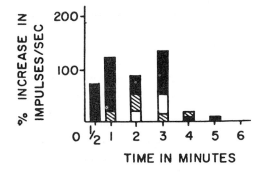

Fig. 20–7. Percentage increase in small (black), medium (shaded), and large (open bars) fiber groups of mesenteric nerves after glycine perfusion. (From Sharma and Nasset [17].)

fore and after perfusion with glucose and amino acids. Although there was some overlap in response pattern, glucose and amino acids seemed to affect different fiber groups. Even though relatively specific features of the response could be predicted, it was difficult to establish a specific pattern for the particular substance used.

Perfusion of Thiry-Vella loops in chronically prepared dogs produced responses similar in many respects to those obtained in acute experiments with cats. The preferential effects of various nutrient substances on different fiber groups were, however, less clear than those obtained in cats, and the latency of response (one to eight minutes) and the duration of firing (six to fifteen minutes) were often longer.

Sirotin [20] made electrophysiological observations of chemoreception in the human stomach and small intestine removed during surgery. He perfused blood vessels or applied various chemical substances (glucose, peptone, calcium chloride, caffeine, and alcohol) to the mucosa and found an increase in activity in the peripherally cut ends of the affer-

TABLE 20–2: Maximal Frequency of Impulses per Second in Mesenteric Nerves

Cat Number	Spontaneous Activity			After Glucose			After Amigen			After Amino Acids			
	S	M	L	S	M	L	S	M	L	S	M	L	
5	47	32	6	76	71	32	72	109	35	112	58	8	Glycine
6	24	17	0	26	14	0	24	18	0				
7	51	72	3	69	120	11	96	90	5				
	54	36	0	69	102	4	84	102	3				
9	57	24	6	66	54	21				111	36	9	Glycine
10	16	11	0				29	23	0	32	13	0	Glycine
	14	7	0	19	24	0							
12	24	11	0	32	25	2				47	19	0	Histidine
13	0	8	0	0	17	0							
14	22	12	0	23	12	0							
15	37	19	0							a	22	0	Glutamine
16	28	35	7	53	53	24				a	48	7	Glutamine
17	9	16	1	14	38	5	29	23	3	12	18	2	Glutamine

SOURCE: Sharma and Nasset [17].
NOTE: S = small, M = medium, and L = large fiber group.
a Indeterminate.

ent nerves from these organs. The best responses were obtained after the application of glucose (twenty of twenty-two experiments).

The central effects of gastrointestinal perfusion with nutrient substances have been more variable than gastrointestinal distension effects. The quantitative effects are less marked, show longer latency and duration of response; and the responses are not obtained in the anesthetized situation. Figure 20–8 shows a

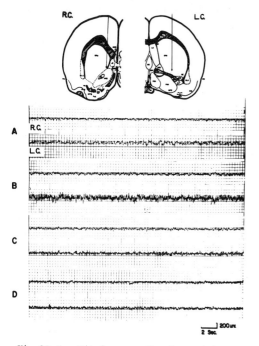

A. R.C.
L.C.
B
C
D

Fig. 20–8. *Bipolar recording from right* (RC) *and left* (LC) *caudate of a rat.* A. *four hours food deprived.* B. *four mintues after intragastric glucose load.* C. *One and a half hours after intragastric glucose load.* D. *twenty minutes after subcutaneous insulin injection. (From Sharma* et al. [18].)

record from a freely moving rat in which bipolar electrodes were implanted at two sites—one in the rostromedial area designated as *RC* (right caudate) and the other in the caudolateral part *(LC)* just anterior to anterior commissure. The animal also possessed an intragastric

tube through which various solutions could be directly passed into the stomach. *A* represents the basal activity in the four-hour food-deprived animal and *B* represents the activity changes after four minutes of intragastric glucose load. There is a conspicuous increase in the frequency amplitude of the left caudate electrode. *C* represents the activity after one and a half hours, by which time the activity in the left caudate head appears to be returning to the basal pattern. *D* shows the activity changes after twenty minutes of subcutaneous insulin, and one finds that there is some depression in the activity of the left caudate head as compared to the basal activity. Thus the same recording site shows an increase in activity after intragastric glucose load and some depression after insulin treatment. On the other hand, the activity from the rostromedial electrode, shown here as the right caudate, responds in the opposite direction. It shows some decrease in frequency after intragastric glucose, an increase in activity after insulin.

The problem of osmometric mechanisms existing in the gastrointestinal tract has been investigated by many workers [5,19], but the picture is far from clear. In delayed loading experiments (Fig. 20–9), Jacobs [9] found that hypertonic intragastric glucose served to hydrate rather than dehydrate the animal. Intra-

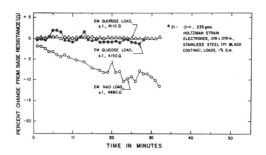

Fig. 20–9. *Effects of intragastric loads of sucrose, glucose, and NaCl on AC brain resistance in the rat. (From Jacobs [10].)*

gastric loads of NaCl significantly increased the intake of water while the glucose load significantly decreased liquid intake. It was also observed that intragastric NaCl induced a marked fall in AC brain resistance [10], a response obtained by injecting known dehydrators. These results may be interpreted to show that osmotic effects of intragastric NaCl, causing shifts of water from the extracellular compartments, may in some way signal the CNS and thereby influence the central mechanisms concerned with food and water regulation. Chernigovsky [4] concludes that, at least in dogs, salt preference seems to be dependent on peripheral neural information, the critical receptor system being located in the stomach. Accumulating information indicates that in spite of the variable water content of diets, the contents of the intestinal lumen are closely regulated and may influence food intake [13].

Oral manifestations of consumatory behavior like chewing, licking, salivation, and swallowing produce potential changes in the lateral hypothalamus, ventromedio-marginal regions of the head of the caudate, and the orbital surface of the frontal lobe. The responses are particularly impressive from the lateral hypothalamus. Coincident with the spontaneous licking, swallowing, or chewing of bananas in monkeys, well-marked potentials are recorded from the lateral hypothalamus. Stimulation of these areas in turn produces oral movements, thus suggesting a reciprocal relationship.

In summary, diverse receptor mechanisms which serve as peripheral sources of information for food intake regulation seem to be distributed in the gastrointestinal tract. Structures in the central nervous system are influenced in a variety of ways by these mechanisms. The over-all independence of peripheral

mechanisms and their interaction with central processing structures may be the action of both positive and negative feedback systems.

Discussion

Stevenson: Did you get a decrease in electrical activity in the caudate from distension of the stomach and an increase in activity from perfusion with foodstuffs?

Sharma: The sites were different. Distension decreased the activity of the ventromedio-marginal regions of the head of the caudate. Depression of the same zone was also produced by intragastric glucose load. In more caudolateral areas, just anterior to anterior commissure, an intragastric glucose load enhanced the electrical activity.

Grossman: Would you comment on the specificity of the VMH response as far as the nature of the stimulus is concerned? We have been collecting some E.E.G. and some single-unit data from the hypothalamus and particularly from the VMH. The ease with which one can change both the single-unit activity and the E.E.G. activity of the ventromedial area is striking. Pinching a rat's tail, for example, does wonders to the single-unit activity in the VMH. Have you any experience with this kind of observation?

Sharma: The non-specific responses of hypothalamic neurons have been observed by us as well as other workers, but the overlap in responsiveness (Cross and Green, *J. Physiol.* (London), **148**: 554, 1959; Cross and Silver, *Exp. Neurol.*, 7: 375, 1963) to varying the stimulus modality is present more markedly in lateral and posterior hypothalamic neurons. We have been struck by the high degree of convergence of various stimuli on the hypothalamic neurons and therefore one should define carefully his parameters of stimulation. At the same time, one finds a fairly large percentage of neurons in VMH which are sensitive specifically to chemoreceptive stimulation (Anand *et al., Amer. J. Physiol.,* **207**: 1146, 1964) or mechanosensitive impulses. In a total of about forty units studied in the VMH, I have come across three units that responded both to gastric distension and i.v. glucose loads. However, the increase in activity after glucose was never so impressive as that obtained with gastric distension. In a series of papers, Sutin and his associates (*Electroenceph. Clin. Neurophysiol.,* **15**: 786, 1963) have shown the effects of various substances and mesencephalic influences on the VMH neurons.

Epstein: Are there gastric chemoreceptors?

Sharma: There is the beautiful work of Iggo, which demonstrates the presence of pH receptors in the stomach. Vagal afferent endings, characteristically sensitive to pH, are present in the gastric mucosa. The mucosal receptors can be very clearly distinguished from similar afferent fibers present in the outer walls of the stomach. Mucosal receptors are not excited by moderate gastric distension, gastric contraction, or digital compression of the gastric wall but are stimulated by mucosal application of alkali or acid. Activity in the acid-sensitive unit could be abolished by alkali. Similarly, activity in the alkali-sensitive unit evoked by 0.1 *M* NaOH disappeared on addition of 0.1 *M* HCl. Gastric afferents sensitive to intragastric glucose or intragastric NaCl (Sudakov and Rogacheva, *Fed. Proc.,* **22**: 197, 1963) have been demonstrated, but single fiber preparations have not been reported. The technical difficulties in recording from single gastric afferents in vivo preparations is perhaps partly responsible for interpretations leading to negative results obtained from cervical vagal afferent recording. Our preliminary results suggest that a majority of the chemoreceptive impulses from the gut travel via mesenteric and splanchnic nerves, which may account for the absence of such impulses in cervical vagal afferents.

Morrison: What evidence do you have for the existence of these fibers?

Sharma: The evidence available is predominently electrophysiological. There is also behavioral data to support the notion of afferent impulses evoked by gastric perfusion with various substances. The chemoreceptors are particularly sensitive to anaesthesia.

Halpern: In reference to Sharma's observation on the question of behavioral versus neurological data, Sudakov and Rogacheva (*Fed. Proc.,* **22**: T306–10, 1963) studied gastric chemoreceptor responses with sodium chloride. Behavioral data from Kassil, Ugolev, and Chernigovsky (*Dokl-Biol. Sci. Sect.* (English translation), **126**: 546, 1959) show a dog's sodium chloride rejection threshold with gastric sodium chloride loads. Adequate controls indicate that it is not a simple osmotic effect. It depends upon the appropriate concentration of sodium chloride.

Hodgson: Am I correct in thinking that no one has found any specialized receptor endings in these internal chemoreceptors?

Sharma: In the gut, as far as I know, specialized receptor endings responding to chemosensitive impulses, have not been shown. A variety of chemosensitive impulses do travel in C fibers and the responses are also obtained in larger fiber groups, e.g., after glucose perfusion. However, evidence showing specialized morphological features of the afferent endings is lacking.

Epstein: The temporal variable is crucial here. McCleary (*J. Comp. Physiol. Psychol.*, **46**: 411, 1953) showed some time ago that hypertonic loads placed in the rat's stomach, fifteen minutes before access to fluid, would shift the rat's preferences to hypotonic glucose solutions. Stellar *et al. J. Comp. Physiol. Psychol.*, **47**: 220, 1954) showed the same shift in preference for sodium chloride solutions. These effects occurred in five or ten minutes. In Chernigovsky's experiments, what were the delays between stomach loading and behavioral testing?

Sharma: Chernigovsky (*Brain and Behavior, II,* American Institute of Biological Sciences, Washington, D.C., 319, 1963) has used preference measures in a free-choice situation and studied the effects of intragastric loads of hypertonic saline and sugars on the intake of NaCl-milk mixtures before and after subdiaphragmatic vagotomy. Various concentrations of salt in milk (1.0 per cent, 2.5 per cent, 3.5 per cent, 5.0 per cent) were available to the dog. The animal accepted the various solutions and did not show any significant preference for a particular concentration of salt-milk mixture. Introduction of 200 ml of water into the stomach did not shift the preference for any particular concentration. On the other hand, administration of 200 ml of 3 per cent and 5 per cent NaCl solution into the stomach made the dog reject three out of four salt-milk mixtures (2.5 per cent, 3.5 per cent, and 5.0 per cent). The animal began to reject the salt-milk solutions three to ten minutes after the administration of NaCl solution to the stomach, while the evidence

of thirst appeared within twenty-five to thirty minutes. The pattern of choice for the different mixtures returned within five minutes of the washing out of the stomach load. After vagotomy, intragastric loading with 5 per cent NaCl did not produce rejection of the more concentrated salt-milk mixtures. It was also found that hypertonic glucose (27 per cent) solution, did not affect the selection of salt solutions, but did produce an inhibition in the general food excitability.

Epstein: Our rats, on intragastric preference, do not show any sign of discriminating salt from water in the stomach from 0.1 per cent to 3.0 per cent salt.

Halpern: If you salt-load these rats and wait long enough for osmotic effects, does preference change?

Epstein: Yes. Intragastric hypertonic loads shift preference of both salt and hypotonic glucose solutions.

Halpern: Is there a simultaneous choice of several different concentrations?

Epstein: No, the single-stimulus technique was used.

REFERENCES

1. Anand, B. K. Nervous regulation of food intake. *Physiol. Rev.,* **41**: 677–708, 1961.
2. Anand, B. K. Influence of the internal environment on the nervous regulation of alimentary behavior, in *Brain and Behavior, II.* American Institute of Biological Sciences, Washington, D.C., 43–116, 1963.
3. Anand, B. K., and Brobeck, J. R. Hypothalamic control of food intake in rats and cats. *Yale J. Biol. Med.,* **24**: 123–40, 1951.
4. Chernigovsky, V. N. The significance of interoceptive signals in the food behavior of animals, in *Brain and Behavior, II.* American Institute of Biological Sciences, Washington, D.C., 319–48, 1963.
5. Hunt, J. N. Some properties of alimentary osmoreceptor mechanism. *J. Physiol.,* **132**: 267–88, 1956.

6. Iggo, A. Tension receptors in the stomach and the urinary bladder. *J. Physiol.,* **128**: 593–607, 1955.

7. Iggo, A. Gastric mucosal chemoreceptors with vagal afferent fibers in the cat. *Quart. J. Exp. Physiol.,* **42**: 398–409, 1957.

8. Iggo, A. Gastrointestinal tension receptors with unmyelinated afferent fibers in the vagus of the cat. *Quart. J. Exp. Physiol.,* **42**: 130–43, 1957.

9. Jacobs, H. L., in *The Physiological and Behavioral Aspects of Taste.* University of Chicago Press, Chicago, pp. 16–28, 1955.

10. Jacobs, H. L. Effect of intragastric hypertonic glucose loads on AC brain resistance in rats. *Proc. Soc. Exp. Biol. Med.,* **114**: 657–59, 1963.

11. Janowitz, H. D., and Grossman, M. I. Some factors affecting food intake of normal dogs and dogs with esophagostomy and gastric fistula. *Amer. J. Physiol.,* **159**: 143–48, 1949.

12. Janowitz, H. D., and Grossman, M. I. Effect of prefeeding, alcohol and bitters on food intake of dogs. *Amer. J. Physiol.,* **164**: 182–86, 1951.

13. Lepkovsky, S., Lyman, R. L., Fleming, D., Magumo, M., and Dimick, M. M. Gastrointestinal regulation of water and its effect on food intake and rate of digestion. *Amer. J. Physiol.,* **188**: 327–31, 1957.

14. Paintal, A. S. A study of gastric stretch receptors: Their role in the peripheral mechanism of satiation of hunger and thirst. *J. Physiol.,* **126**: 255–70, 1954.

15. Paintal, A. S. Responses from mucosal mechanoreceptors in the small intestine of the cat. *J. Physiol.,* **139**: 353–68, 1957.

16. Sharma, K. N., Anand, B. K., Singh, B., and Dua, S. Role of stomach in regulation of activities of hypothalamic feeding centers. *Amer. J. Physiol.,* **201**: 593–98, 1961.

17. Sharma, K. N., and Nasset, E. S. Electrical activity in mesenteric nerves after perfusion of gut lumen. *Amer. J. Physiol.,* **202**: 725–30, 1962.

18. Sharma, K. N., Sharma, S., and Jacobs, H. L. Alimentary signalisation and limbic-forebrain activity. *Physiology and Behavior* (in press).

19. Sircus, W. Studies on the mechanism in the duodenum inhibiting gastric secretion. *Quart. J. Exp. Physiol.,* **43**: 114–33, 1958.

20. Sirotin, B. Z. Electrophysiological study of reception from certain internal organs in man. Report I: Impulses from receptors of the resected stomach and small intestine. *Bull. Exp. Biol. Med. U.S.S.R.* (English translation), **50**: 873–77, 1961.

Work of the author quoted in the chapter has been supported in part by the following sources: Foundations Fund for Research in Psychiatry (62–252), PL–480 Funds (524315), and National Institutes of Health (M 5754).

21: The Central Regulation of Food and Water Intake

by Sebastian P. Grossman

MOST OF THE PAPERS that have been presented at this symposium have demonstrated that the selection and ingestion of nutrients and fluids is importantly influenced by sensory signals arising from taste and other chemoreceptors. Some largely unknown central mechanism integrates these sensory signals and controls the qualitative aspects of nutrient and fluid intake in accordance with the organism's innate or acquired preferences.

Dr. Epstein's gastric feeding experiments have demonstrated, however, that an adequate regulation of the organism's energy balance is possible when these signals are totally absent. This suggests that the quantitative control of food intake is exercised by central mechanisms that respond to sensory afferents arising in the internal environment as the result of deviations in various homeostatic mechanisms and that this control is independent of taste afferents.

It has long been assumed that the regulation of the organism's energy and fluid balance is exercised by anatomically discrete hypothalamic "centers" which initiate or terminate feeding behavior in accordance with this sensory input. On the basis of recent work from our own as well as other laboratories, I would like to suggest that the central mechanisms that control food and water intake in accordance with the organism's needs may be more complex and more diffusely represented in many parts of the central nervous system than this simple "center" hypothesis implies. It might be useful to introduce this notion by briefly considering the nature of the experimental evidence which appears to support the center concept.

THE HYPOTHALAMIC SATIETY CENTER

The center hypothesis assumes that food and water intake are controlled by anatomically defined excitatory and inhibitory centers in the hypothalamus which interact to determine the momentary level of hunger or thirst. The postulation of a discrete inhibitory center is based on clinical and experimental evidence which suggests that the ventromedial nuclei of the hypothalamus appear to exert a restraining influence on feeding behavior.

Tumor growth or vascular infarct in the hypothalamus has long been known to be associated clinically with bulimia and obesity [9,12]. Experimental studies of this phenomenon have shown that damage restricted to the ventromedial nuclei of the hypothalamus produces overeating and obesity in rats, cats, and monkeys [31], and that electrical stimulation of this region decreases or stops food intake [3]. The notion of an inhibitory or satiety center is further supported by those electrophysiological studies which demonstrate that the EEG and single-unit activity of the VMH appear to correlate, at least to some extent, with arteriovenous glucose differences, which according to Mayer [38] may be an index of central glucose utilization [2,52]. Finally, there is some evidence from histochemical experiments that goldthioglucose may be selectively deposited in the ventral hypothalamus of mice and produce local lesions which result in hyperphagia and obesity [36].

Stimulation or lesions in the ventromedial hypothalamus undoubtedly influence food intake but the specificity of this influence has been questioned. Lesions in the ventromedial nuclei not only induce hyperphagia but also modify the organism's sexual responsiveness and reaction to aversive stimulation [30,59], suggesting that the ventromedial nuclei may be concerned with affective reactions to the environment rather than specifically the reaction to food. A closer look at the feeding behavior of animals with ventromedial lesions indicates that some or all of the observed changes may in fact be related to an exaggerated response to taste and other sensory aspects of the diet. These animals are hyperphagic when given a palatable diet but do not overeat when the food is stale or diluted with roughage. They may even be hypophagic or aphagic when unpleasant tasting substances such as quinine are added to the diet in small quantities which do not deter normal animals [53]. They also overreact to non-reinforcement and work less for food rewards than normal animals when the reinforcements are given aperiodically [40,54]. Electrical stimulation of the ventromedial nuclei has been reported to inter-fere with drinking as well as feeding behavior in deprived animals and to be aversive—rats learn a lever-pressing response to terminate or avoid such stimulation [35].

The results of a recently completed group of experiments from our own laboratory [19] support the conclusion that the effects of ventromedial damage may be much more general than has commonly been assumed. We replicated earlier observations that lesions in the ventromedial hypothalamus increased food intake but decreased food-rewarded operant behavior and that the magnitude of this inhibitory effect increased as the ratio of lever presses to rewards was increased. We also found, however, that these effects were not specific to food-reinforced behavior. Although the lesions produced variable effects on water consumption (some animals were hypodipsic, others showed no effect or drank significantly more than before the operation), all rats worked significantly less for water rewards and responded to changes in the reinforcement contingencies in much the same way as in the food-reward situation. We reasoned that these effects might reflect a general change in the animals' affective response to their environment and that the apparent lowering of the affective response threshold might facilitate rather than inhibit behavior in test situations where emotionality or arousal are relevant drive states. In agreement with this prediction, we found that animals with ventromedial lesions learned and performed an escape-avoidance response reliably better than did the normal animals.

THE HYPOTHALAMIC FEEDING CENTER

The existence of specific excitatory mechanisms in the lateral hypothalamus which contribute to the control of feeding and drinking behavior was first suggested by Brügger's [7] observation that electrical stimulation lateral to the ventromedial nuclei elicited feeding in sated cats. Anand and Brobeck [1] subsequently demonstrated that small bilateral lesions in the lateral hypothalamus produced complete and apparently permanent aphagia. Teitelbaum and Stellar [56] reported that these lesions always produce adipsia as well as aphagia in the rat and that all animals eventually recover a nearly normal control over feeding and drinking behavior if maintained by tube feeding and watering. Teitelbaum and Epstein [55] have described an orderly recovery process that is sufficiently different for the regulation of food than it is for water intake to suggest that the adipsia is independent of the aphagia and vice versa. A "recovered" lateral lesion animal regulates its fluid balance exclusively through prandial drinking and cannot maintain effective control over drinking behavior on a food-deprivation schedule. Its control of food intake appears adequate as long as palatable foods are available. The animal continues to overreact to taste and other sensory aspects of the diet and starves rather than eat an unpleasant tasting diet which is acceptable to normal rats. The recovery process appears to be partially mediated by tissue adjacent to the lesion since an enlargement of the lesion of a recovered animal causes a return of the aphagia-adipsia syndrome [55]. However, cortical influences seem to be essential to the regulatory processes in the recovered animals since a brief cortical depression (induced by topical KCl applications) results in complete and prolonged adipsia and aphagia in these animals [54].

These findings demonstrate that the lateral hypothalamus contains neural mechanisms which contribute important and possibly essential regulatory influences to the organism's energy and fluid balance. They do not, however, represent compelling proof for the common assumption that this mechanism controls food and water intake autonomously. This assumption is based largely on the observation that lesions or stimulation in other portions of the central nervous system rarely upset this regulation as drastically or permanently as an interference or stimulation of the hypothalamic functions. Aside from the obvious fact that this may reflect little more than geographic artifact (a more complex neural circuit may be diffusely represented in other portions of the brain but become concentrated in the diencephalon because of the passage of large sensory and motor pathways), we now have experimental evidence which indicates that extrahypothalamic influences may be much more important than had been assumed in the past. Much of this evidence has been accumulated in recent chemical stimulation studies and it may be worthwhile to describe briefly the basic technique and some relevant results.

CHEMICAL STIMULATION OF THE FEEDING AND DRINKING MECHANISMS

The specific contribution of the hypothalamic mechanisms to the regulation of the organism's fluid and energy balance is difficult to study because food and water intake appear to be controlled by two neural systems which seem to coexist anatomically at the level of the lateral hypothalamus, at least as far as common electrical stimulation and lesioning techniques are concerned. This complication led me several years ago to explore the possibility of selective stimulation or inhibition of these systems by locally applied neurohumoral substances. I would like to summarize the results of these early studies for you because it has been the extension of this approach to other portions of the central nervous system that has provided the most compelling evidence for the importance of various extrahypothalamic mechanisms.

The chemical stimulation technique relies on the fact that neurons, like other cells, conduct their business by means of chemical reactions and are therefore extremely sensitive to changes in the chemical composition of their environment. Particularly the exchange of information between cells, i.e., synaptic transmission, occurs via discrete chemical reactions which can be simulated or inhibited by the local application of the appropriate neurohumoral substance. The expectation of specificity rests on the assumption that the various neuro-

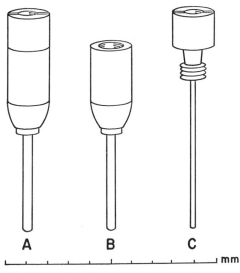

Fig. 21–1.   Double-cannula system allowing repeated applications of chemical substances in crystalline form to central structures: (A) the complete implant; (B) the outer cannula; (C) the inner cannula.

humors that have been demonstrated in the central nervous system may act as transmitters in functionally different neural systems.

In order to modify the concentration

of these transmitter substances in specific parts of the brain, we developed a double cannula that can be stereotaxically implanted much like a standard electrode (see Fig. 21–1 and 21–2). Following recuperation from surgery, chem-

Fig. 21–2.   Cannula permanently affixed to albino rat skull.

icals in crystalline form or solution can be applied repeatedly to the same restricted portion of the brain (see Fig. 21–3) in unrestrained animals, thus permitting an easy analysis of behavioral changes which might result from the application of the chemical substances. The electrophysiological reaction of the tissue immediately affected by the drug can be recorded through the metal cannula.

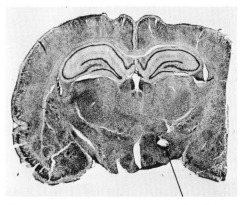

Fig. 21–3.   End of needle tract in the right perifornical region of the rat brain. Stimulation at this point, as well as at loci slightly more medial and ventral, elicited feeding or drinking.

EVIDENCE FOR NEUROPHARMACOLOGICALLY DISTINCT NEURAL SYSTEMS

When we first applied this technique to a study of the hypothalamic feeding and drinking centers [19,20,21], we found that the feeding mechanism appeared to be selectively sensitive to adrenergic stimulation and blockade whereas the drinking mechanism responded selectively to cholinergic and cholinolytic substances.

When norepinephrine or epinephrine were injected into the lateral hypothalamus (Fig. 21-4), sated rats responded

longer stimulating effect on cholinergic neurons) into the same points in the hypothalamus specifically evoked drinking in sated rats.

The overt effects of the chemical stimulation persisted for thirty to fifty minutes. The animals consumed as much as 50 to 75 per cent of their normal *daily* intake during the one-hour test period immediately following the injections. Total daily food and water intake were nearly doubled on the day of the stimulation, and a considerable weight gain was observed on the day following adrenergic stimulation (Fig. 21-5).

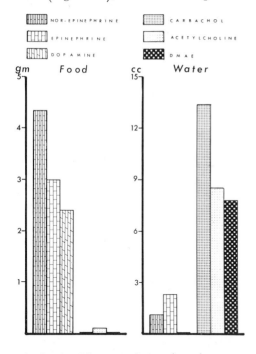

Fig. 21-4. *Effects of adrenergic and cholinergic stimulation of the hypothalamus on food and water intake of sated animals during a one-hour poststimulation period.*

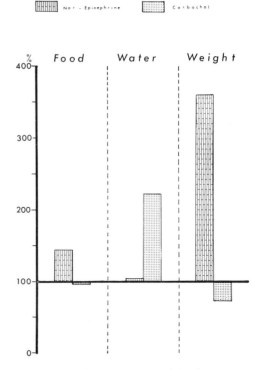

Fig. 21-5. *Effects of adrenergic and cholinergic stimulation of the hypothalamus on food and water intake and body weight during a twenty-four-hour poststimulation period. The results are expressed as a percentage of a base line which represents the average of pre- and poststimulation control tests.*

within minutes by ingesting large quantities of laboratory food that had been totally ignored before the application of the neurohumor. Injections of acetylcholine or carbachol (a parasympathomimetic that is not rapidly destroyed by cholinesterase and therefore produces a

To secure some evidence of the effects of central chemical stimulation on normal regulatory processes, norepinephrine and carbachol were administered to twenty-four-hour food- or water-deprived animals (Fig. 21–6). Hungry rats ate lit-

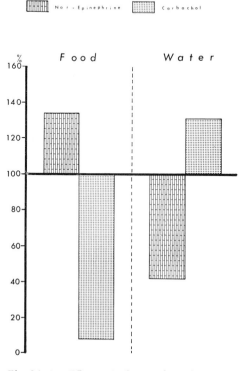

Fig. 21–6. Effects of adrenergic and cholinergic stimulation of the hypothalamus on food and water intake in deprived animals. The results are expressed as a percentage of a base line which represents the average of pre- and poststimulation control tests.

tle or no food following the injection of carbachol although water was not available to avoid direct response competition. Thirsty rats responded to the same injections by drinking significantly more water than normal control animals (which were sham stimulated). Adrenergic stimulation of thirsty animals inhibited water intake and the same injections reliably increased the food intake of hungry rats. These observations suggest a direct, central interaction of the two systems, which may account for the fre-

quently observed interaction of the effects of food and water deprivation.

The effects of central chemical stimulation appeared to have motivational properties similar, if not identical, to those of normal hunger and thirst. Rats were trained to press one of two adjacent levers to obtain food rewards and to work on the other for water reinforcements. When sated animals were placed in this apparatus following adrenergic stimulation of the hypothalamus, they worked only on the food-rewarded lever. Following cholinergic stimulation of the same site, the same animals operated only the water-rewarded lever.

Subsequent experiments demonstrated that the effects of central adrenergic or cholinergic stimulation could be blocked selectively by the systemic administration of the appropriate (i.e., sympathetic or parasympathetic) blocking agents (Fig. 21–7). Normal hunger was also inhibited by the systemic or central administration of sympathetic blocking agents. The water intake of deprived animals was selectively reduced by parasympathetic substances such as atropine.

A number of control experiments demonstrated that the stimulation effects could not be due to local changes in the acid base composition of the tissues, vasomotor responses to the neurohumors, or simple osmotic effects.

Recent observations by Miller and associates [39] showed that adrenergic stimulation of the lateral hypothalamus produces a rise in blood sugar (as well as a small fall in body temperature) suggesting that a general mechanism for the correction of nutritional deficits may be activated.

Our intitial experiments on the response of the hypothalamic feeding and drinking centers to chemical stimulation supported the "center" concept in showing that food and water intake could be elicited only from a restricted portion

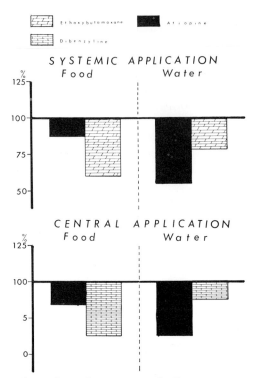

Ethoxybutamoxane   Atropine

Dibenzyline

SYSTEMIC APPLICATION
Food   Water

CENTRAL APPLICATION
Food   Water

Fig. 21–7. Effects of systemically or centrally administered adrenergic (ethoxybutamoxane or dibenzyline) and cholinergic (atropine) blocking agents on food and water intake of deprived animals. The results are expressed as a percentage of a base line which represents the average of pre- and poststimulation control tests.

of the lateral and dorsolateral hypothalamus. The overlap of the two systems seemed to be complete since all positive placements permitted successful adrenergic and cholinergic stimulation. More recently, we have found active points in the anterior, posterior, and ventral hypothalamus, suggesting that the feeding and drinking "centers" are not nearly as discrete, even within the hypothalamus, as earlier lesion studies led us to believe. We have also found a number of hypothalamic sites which respond to cholinergic stimulation but which fail to react selectively to adrenergic substances, indicating that the feeding and drinking mechanisms are not entirely coexistent anatomically.

EXTRAHYPOTHALAMIC INFLUENCES

The relatively broad distribution of the feeding and drinking mechanisms in the hypothalamus suggested that nutritive processes might be regulated by more diffuse and widely distributed mechanisms than are suggested by the concept of discrete hypothalamic centers. A review of the recent research literature as well as some of our own work confirm this suspicion.

We first turned our attention to the amygdaloid complex because a number of investigators reported changes in food intake following temporal lobe damage. Brown and Schäfer [6] reported almost eighty years ago that lesions of the temporal lobe produced persistent hyperphagia in monkeys, and similar observations have been reported in other species [13]. Lesions restricted to the amygdaloid complex have been reported to result in hyperphagia in monkeys [14] and rats [45,46]. Green and associates [18] further reported that selective destruction of the basal and lateral nuclei of the amygdala produced overeating in cats whereas damage to the anterior nuclei resulted in aphagia. Similar inhibitory effects of anterior lesions have been reported by Koikegami and others [33, 34].

We have investigated the role of specific aspects of the amygdaloid complex in the control of food and water intake in some detail. In the first experiment [26], we found that small bilateral lesions in the posteroventral amygdala of rats produced a marked but temporary rise in both food and water intake. Subsequent experiments demonstrated that apparently permanent hyperphagia and hyperdipsia could be produced by slightly larger lesions in the posterior amygdala. Ablation of the anterior amygdala increased food intake but reduced water consumption. Electrical

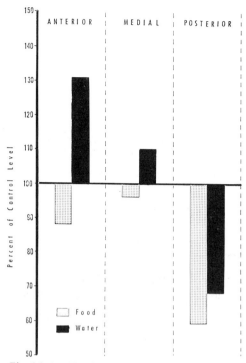

Fig. 21–8. Food and water intake of deprived animals during one hour of "chronic" electrical stimulation of the ventral amygdala. Data are expressed as a percentage of the average intake during control tests without the electrical stimulation.

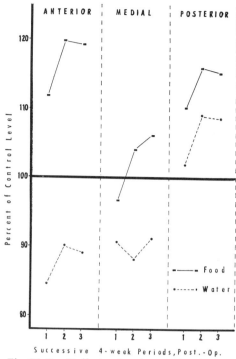

Fig. 21–9. Daily food and water intake following lesions in the ventral amygdala. Data are expressed as a percentage of the average intake during a six-week control period preceding the lesions.

stimulation of the anterior nuclei inhibited food intake in deprived animals but increased their water intake (Fig. 21–8). Stimulation of the posterior nuclei inhibited both feeding and drinking. Stimulation or lesions in the medial aspects of the amygdala did not have consistent effects on either food or water intake (Fig. 21–9).

Since our lesions were minute and the stimulating currents low, it seemed that the amygdaloid mechanisms that contribute to the control of food and water intake were not sufficiently distinct anatomically to permit independent experimental excitation or inhibition by electrical stimulation or electrocoagulation. We therefore decided to investigate the possibility that these mechanisms might

show a selective sensitivity to adrenergic and cholinergic stimulation similar to that previously found in the hypothalamus.

For these experiments [22], we implanted cannulas bilaterally in the posteroventral amygdala of rats previously trained to lever press for their entire daily ration of food and water. Somewhat to our surprise, we found that chemical stimulation elicited neither feeding nor drinking in sated animals but markedly affected the food and water intake of deprived rats (Fig. 21–10). Bilateral injections of norepinephrine into the amygdaloid complex reliably increased their performance of food-rewarded responses but decreased their performance on the water-rewarded lever. Injections of the adrenergic block-

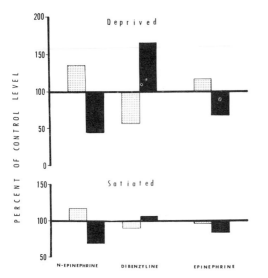

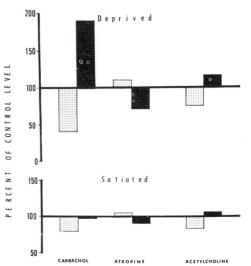

Fig. 21–10.   Average bar-pressing performance for food (grey) and water
(black) after adrenergic stimulation or
blockade. (The data are expressed as a
percentage of the average pre- and poststimulation control level.)

Fig. 21–11.   Average bar-pressing performance for food (grey) and water
(black) after cholinergic stimulation or
blockade. (The data are expressed as a
percentage of the average pre- and poststimulation control level.)

ing agent dibenzyline into the same area decreased the number of food-rewarded responses and increased the number of lever presses for water (Fig. 21–10). Cholinergic stimulation of the same region doubled the animals' water consumption and reduced the number of lever presses for food. Injections of the cholinergic blocking agent atropine reversed this pattern of effects (Fig. 21–11).

A series of control experiments demonstrated the specificity of these effects. Drugs selected to mimic the pH, vasomotor, and osmotic effects of the cholinergic and adrenergic substances failed to affect food or water intake reliably. A number of centrally active substances similarly did not duplicate the selective effects of acetylcholine and norepinephrine. However, injections of GABA (Gamma-amino-butyric acid) increased the water intake of deprived rats in much the same way as carbachol. This may reflect merely a non-specific stimulation effect, but an alternative inter-

pretation may be possible. GABA and carbachol are not chemically related, and there is no evidence for a selective effect of GABA on cholinergic pathways. However, some observations suggest that this drug may act specifically as a transmitter in various inhibitory systems in the brain. It is possible that GABA stimulated a neural pathway that inhibits satiety mechanisms and thus produced a net increase in water intake similar to that seen after cholinergic stimulation of a presumably excitatory mechanism.

Subsequent experiments from our own [23,24] as well as other laboratories [11, 39] have shown that adrenergic or cholinergic stimulation of many sites throughout the limbic system and related subcortical relay stations (hippocampus, cingulate gyrus, septal area, preoptic area, some portions of the thalamus and subthalamus, much of the hypothalamus, and even some midbrain points) elicit or modify food or water intake.

These observations suggest that the regulation of the organism's energy and fluid balance may be mediated by roughly parallel neural circuits that include most of the limbic system as well as subcortical relay stations in the hypothalamus, septal area, and amygdaloid complex.

Such an interpretation is supported by Robinson's [49] observations of the effects of electrical stimulation. He used "roving" electrodes to explore large portions of the brain of several monkeys and found that food and water intake as well as functionally related activities, such as ejection of inedible substances from the mouth and vomiting, could be elicited from a large number of "limbic" and subcortical points. Although the probability of feeding responses was largest when the stimulation was applied to the lateral hypothalamus, fully 85 per cent of the observed feeding responses were elicited by stimulation outside the classical feeding center.

Many lesion studies have reported hyperphagia following hippocampal [8,47], frontal [15,32,58], or thalamic [50,51] lesions, supporting the notion of a broader, diffusely represented system. Even more damaging to the hypothalamic "center" notion are recent reports of complete and permanent aphagia following damage to the ventral portion of the globus pallidus or interruption of the pallidofugal fiber system [41–44], or following relatively small lesions in the midbrain tegmentum [17,48].

It seems clear, at this time, that the regulation of the organism's energy and fluid balance is exercised by a complex network of neural pathways which interrelate with a number of distinct anatomical structures. Much remains to be learned about the specific nature of the contribution of each of the components of this system. Presently available information suggests, however, that different

parts of this system are not equifunctional or equieffective. Each component of the system seems to contribute specific regulatory influences which may normally interact to determine hunger and thirst.

The amygdaloid complex, for instance, appears to supply excitatory as well as inhibitory influences which are effective only when other areas, possibly hypothalamic portions of the system, are active. The hypothalamus, midbrain tegmentum, and globus pallidus, on the other hand, appear to be part of a system which when interrupted at any of these points, ceases to supply excitatory influences that are essential for the initiation of feeding or drinking behavior.

Perhaps the nicest example of a complex, indirect influence on the central regulation of food intake has been suggested by recent observations on the effects of electrical and chemical stimulation of some hippocampal functions. Work currently in progress in our laboratory indicates that small lesions and stimulation of some points in the ventral hippocampus interfere with metabolic processes to the extent that foodstuffs are inadequately or incompletely metabolized. Restricted damage to some portions of this hippocampal mechanism increases food consumption significantly but fails to result in a corresponding weight gain. An analysis of the composition of the feces of these animals indicates that the primary effect of the lesions may be a metabolic disturbance which causes a relatively large portion of the ingested foodstuffs to pass through the gastrointestinal tract without being assimilated. The animal consequently must eat more to maintain a constant caloric balance. Preliminary observations (Mountford, personal communication) indicate that this mechanism may be part of the adrenergic "feeding circuit" which appears to permeate most, if not all, of the limbic system. Injections of adrenergic substances into this portion of the hippocampus elicit food intake.

The experimental evidence can best be summarized by the conclusion that:

1. Lesions in several extrahypothalamic structures (globus pallidus, midbrain tegmentum) produce inhibitory effects on feeding and drinking behavior that appear to be as severe and permanent as those seen after damage to the hypothalamic feeding and drinking center.

2. Chemical as well as electrical stimulation of a large number of extrahypothalamic structures elicits (preoptic area, septum, cingulate gyrus, dorsal hippocampus) or modifies (ventral hippocampus, amygdaloid complex) food or water consumption. The effects of chemical stimulation of extrahypothalamic structures are often more pronounced than those seen after hypothalamic stimulation.

3. Lesions in a number of extrahypothalamic structures (amygdala, hippocampus, frontal cortex, thalamus) result in hyperphagia that appears to be as pronounced and permanent as that seen after damage to the hypothalamic "satiety center." Whether overeating in some or all of these instances may be related to a change in affective response to taste and other sensory aspects of the diet remains to be shown.

CONCLUSIONS

Although all of the components of the feeding circuit appear to be selectively sensitive to adrenergic stimulation and all of the components of the drinking circuit respond selectively to cholinergic substances, the available evidence indicates that the individual components of each system may contribute uniquely to the regulation of food and water intake. A review of the connections which interrelate with the individual components suggests an interesting possibility that may open profitable approaches to the study of central regulatory mechanism in general. I would like to propose a model of the feeding and drinking mechanism that attempts analysis of the complex system in terms of a direct analogy to classical sensory, association, and motor mechanisms which have been shown to regulate other functions in the central nervous system.

This hypothesis suggests, in essence, that the hypothalamus, far from integrating and interpreting all of the complex regulatory influences that appear to act on the nutritive processes, may, in effect, serve primarily as the sensory end organ of a much more complex system, which involves much, if not all, of the old cortex and related subcortical relay stations. This interpretation undoubtedly involves gross oversimplifications of complex interactions but permits a relatively simple synthesis of the research literature.

It is not difficult to find experimental support for a basic "sensory" function of the hypothalamus with respect to food and water intake as well as other basic need states. It has been known for some time, for instance, that neural mechanisms in the hypothalamus regulate sexual behavior by responding directly to the local level of circulating sex hormones [10]. Verney [57] has shown that the hypothalamus also contains osmoreceptors which respond to the osmolarity of the hypothalamic blood supply and initiate the release of antidiuretic hormones to conserve body fluids in time of need. Andersson [4,5] has shown that similar osmoreceptors in the hypothalamus also control thirst and water intake. Mayer [37,38] has suggested that the nutritional needs of the organism may be metered by "glucoreceptors" in the ventral hypothalamus. The evidence for such a glucostatic mechanism is not as compelling as that relating thirst and sexual behavior to specific chemical changes in the immediate environment of the hypothalamus, but it seems clear that some local chemoreceptor system must be the starting point for the regulation of food intake as well.

The specific contribution of the many cortical mechanisms is not yet established. All we know is that the system becomes increasingly diffuse as the sensory input into the hypothalamus is relayed to progressively "higher" centers. If the analogy to classical sensory systems is applied to these higher portions of the feeding and drinking systems, the possibility suggests itself that some of the higher subcortical structures may serve largely as relay stations for the sensory input into allocortical projection and association areas, which function in much the same fashion as the classical sensory projection and association areas of the neocortex.

We know least about the motor outflow of the suggested system. On the basis of Morgane's work it seems plausible to speculate that the globus pallidus and its efferents may constitute at least one important aspect of the effector system involved in the regulation of food and water intake. The work reported by Reynolds [48] and Gold [17] indicates that efferents that carry information from the feeding and drinking systems may course through the midbrain tegmentum. A similar route is suggested by Gilbert's [16] work on the subcommissural organ.

The reticular formation of the brainstem and thalamus may directly or indirectly respond to the same chemical signals that act on the hypothalamic receptor system. This produces a modulating effect on the organism's over-all level of reactivity to sensory input as well as a more selective lowering of re-

activity with respect to specific classes of stimuli such as nutrients or water. Although the empirical basis for this suggestion is, as yet, incomplete, it appears that the reticular formation may, in some fashion, integrate sensory input from internal as well as external sources and adjust the organism's over-all threshold of reactivity in accordance with homeostatic as well as externally elicited needs. We have recently gathered some information on the role of the thalamic and midbrain reticular formation in the control of behavior in appetitive as well as aversive situations. A brief summary of some of the observations will illustrate the suggested interaction:

The first group of experiments [29] demonstrated that cholinergic stimulation of the thalamic midline and reticular nuclei significantly interfered with the acquisition and performance of food- or water-rewarded instrumental responses such as lever pressing or running through a simple T-maze. We subsequently learned that the acquisition of simple escape and avoidance responses showed similar deficits, suggesting a general lowering of reactivity to sensory inputs from external as well as internal receptors. Subsequent experiments [28] demonstrated that a functional blockade in at least some portions of this apparently inhibitory system produced opposite effects (a significant improvement of performance in appetitive as well as escape-avoidance situations). When this line of inquiry was extended to the midbrain reticular formation [25,27], we found that cholinergic stimulation increased the organism's responsiveness to the environment and learned that this lowered threshold could facilitate or interfere with behavior in appetitive as well as escape-avoidance situations, depending on the nature of the task.

Many questions remain to be investigated before we can hope to understand the complex interactions between signals from extero- and interoceptors that seem to influence the regulation of the organism's energy and fluid balance. It seems certain, however, that our progress will be speeded if we disregard the traditional hypothalamic center hypothesis, which concentrates attention on one portion of the system and suggests a complicity of organization which almost surely cannot account for necessary regulatory processes. Chemical excitation or inhibition of selected neural pathways may help unravel the intricacies of the feeding and drinking systems, particularly if it turns out that the apparent pharmacological specificity of the two mechanisms characterizes all portions of the two systems.

Discussion

Hamilton: It's been reported that the hypothalamus of the toad and rat are photosensitive.

Grossman: Yes, there are a number of recent studies on that subject. These experiments demonstrate sensory functions for some hypothalamic cells but the suggested primary sensory role of certain hypothalamic tissues was intended to be specific to chemical signals that are relevant, in one way or another, to the regulation of the organism's energy and fluid balance. We know that the hypothalamus does act in a sensory capacity with respect to many such signals. I suggested, more specifically, that this may be the primary function of hypothalamic mechanisms which have been assumed to perform additional collative and integrative processes.

Henkin: One of the problems that your study raises is the question of specificity in a number of cerebral areas, including the hypothalamus, that are sensitive to

the application of various steroid hormones as indicated by the work of Sawyer and others. To single out the hypothalamus as specific, in terms of its sensory capabilities, may cause us to overlook other important sensory areas of the brain.

Grossman: It is undoubtedly true that many parts of the central nervous system are chemosensitive. However, osmoreceptors, which presumably are essential metering devices for the control of the organism's fluid balance, are found only in the hypothalamus. Goldthioglucose is preferentially deposited in the ventromedial hypothalamus, suggesting a similarly specific distribution of "glucoreceptors." While it is true that steroids and hormones affect various parts of the brain, a clear correlation between sexual arousal and the local level of sex hormones has been demonstrated only for the hypothalamus. I am not suggesting that all central chemoreceptor functions are carried out by the hypothalamus, but rather that chemoreceptor functions specifically related to neural mechanisms that regulate the organism's energy and fluid balance may be located here.

Jacobs: Your generalization that the VM lesion produces much more than an upset in food intake is important. Brobeck suggested that there were emotional changes as well as food-related deficits, but most of us have focused on the latter.

It has been generally agreed that the hyperphagic rat is "finicky" and that this is especially strong in the static phase of hyperphagia, preventing the animal from responding to caloric signals. Thus, these rats decrease their intake of cellulose, presumably overreacting to taste and unable to respond to calories.

All of the experiments making this point have used the single stimulus technique, presenting a single cup of diluted diet in any one test. Simply changing the procedure to allow a choice changes the picture considerably. The figures that follow show the results of a series of experiments with two-choice tests.

Figure 21–I shows the intake of a

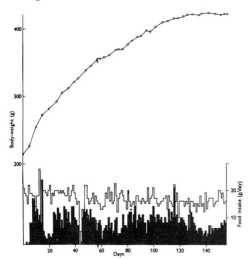

Fig. 21–I.   Body weight and food intake of a sham-operated rat offered a choice between two diets. Black areas, *intake of stock diet;* white areas, *intake of stock diet diluted with 23 per cent cellulose.* Arrow *shows time of operation. (Modified from Khairy, M., Morgan, T. B., and Yudkin, J., Brit. J. Nutr., 17: 557–69, 1963.)*

control animal when it is presented with a choice of stock diet *(black bars)* or 23 per cent cellulose-diluted stock *(white).* This animal takes about equal amounts of both diets, showing no change after the fifty-eighth day of testing *(arrow)* when a sham operation has been performed.

Figure 21–II shows the intake of a VM lesioned rat that has been operated on on the fifty-second day of testing. Prior to surgery this animal also showed no preference. Immediately afterward, he demonstrated a sharp preference for the calorically dense stock diet; this preference sharply reversed itself as the animal reached the static phase and shifted to the diluted diet for the last twenty-two

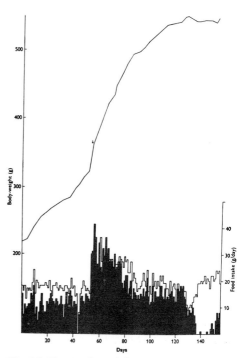

Fig. 21–II.   Body weight and food intake of a rat with ventromedial lesions offered a choice between two diets. Black areas, *intake of stock diet;* white areas, *intake of stock diet diluted with 23 per cent cellulose.* Arrow *shows time of operation. (Modified from Khairy, M., Morgan, T. B., and Yudkin, J., Brit. J. Nutr., 17: 557–69, 1963.)*

days of testing. The authors interpret these results as an indication that as the brain-damaged rat reaches a maximum of weight gain (the "static" phase), it responds to caloric signals, choosing the diluted diet to minimize caloric intake. If these results are verified, they will completely contradict all of the current thinking about static hyperphagia and finickiness.

Maller: "Finickiness" in rats can be produced also by destruction of hypothalamic areas that do not produce hyperphagia or obesity (Graff and Stellar, *J. Comp. Physiol. Psychol.,* 55: 418, 1962).

In relation to De Ruiter's remarks about "finickiness" in mice whose brains have been damaged by goldthioglucose

I add a word of caution about assuming that this type of finickiness is analogous to that of rats. Goldthioglucose also induces lesions in mice outside the VMN region of the hypothalamus and includes damage to the formix, hippocampus, peoptic area, etc. (Perry and Liebelt, *Anat. Rec.*, **133**: 222, 1959).

Hamilton: When we determined quinine-preference thresholds on hypothalamic hyperphagic rats in the static phase using a two-bottle test, no difference was observed.

Grossman: They do object to it more. They certainly do when you put it in food.

Hamilton: Yes, they do respond in a one-bottle test (Corbit, *J. Comp. Physiol. Psychol.*, **60**: 123, 1965) but not in the two-bottle test.

Jacobs: P. T. Young has insisted that we should reserve the use of the word "preference" for direct choice. If choice or single stimulus gives the same results, he is willing to use the term "preference." In general, he prefers to apply the word to a two-choice test.

Pfaffmann: I would like to reinforce that point because I think the differences in certain behavioral tests can be attributed to the fact that choice is present in some tests while in others there is intake of only one solution.

Jacobs: Do you have any idea what differences there are other than operational ones?

Pfaffmann: Yes, but it is speculative. I do not have a precise analysis.

Halpern: I wonder if Hamilton could go further in terms of what I seem to re-

member as a lack of finickiness in ventromedial hypothalamic monkeys.

Hamilton: We just have not seen it.

Grossman: You must have particularly good monkey food.

Stevenson: Has anyone had success yet with electrical or chemical stimulation of feeding or drinking in the cat? I think it is important to bring out some of the species differences.

Grossman: Some data are now available on the response of the cat to electrical and chemical stimulation of the hypothalamus. Electrical stimulation of the lateral hypothalamus, particularly its anterior components, elicits feeding in this species, but it is never a pure feeding response as one sees it in the rat. The primary response to the lateral hypothalamic stimulation is an attack reaction, which, if carried to completion, terminates in feeding behavior. Food intake in this case appears to be a component of attack rather than of an attempt at regulating caloric intake.

Stevenson: Has anybody ever obtained drinking?

Grossman: Many have tried, particularly with chemical (cholinergic) stimulation, which is so effective in the rat. Unfortunately, the feeding and drinking mechanisms appear to be intimately related to neural pathways that contribute to the regulation of emotional behavior, more specifically, to the attack-defense-flight dimension of the emotional response continuum. This is already suggested by the peculiar effects of electrical stimulation, and it becomes clear when one observes the reaction to chemical stimulation. Cholinergic stimulation of the lateral hypothalamus elicits violent rage and attack behavior, which, of course, obscures any concurrent effects on thirst that may be evoked. Adrenergic stimulation seems to affect components of the arousal system primarily. Depending on the exact site of injection, epinephrine and norepinephrine may induce sleep, even stupor, as occasionally seen in the rat, or they may produce states of extreme agitation. These effects are so overwhelming that one could not hope to see food intake due to possibly concurrent changes in hunger.

Stevenson: I thought Hernandez-peon observed cats going to sleep by applying cholinergic substances in the lateral hypothalamus.

Grossman: Yes, he does report that.

Fregly: What happens when an animal is administered a dose of epinephrine and given an aqueous solution of something with caloric value, such as sucrose?

Grossman: I haven't done the very fine experiment you suggest. However, Neal Miller has used Metrecal in most of his experiments because he finds that the feeding effect is much more prominent if he uses wet and especially palatable foods. The Metrecal feeding response appears to be quite distinct from water intake. Sated animals will drink Metrecal following adrenergic stimulation and will consume water following cholinergic stimulation.

Stevenson: To this point, if you stimulate the lateral hypothalamus of the rat electrically, you may obtain an animal that drinks water; in other animals such stimulation produces a feeding animal; in others, you get no response in terms of eating or drinking. Some animals that will not drink water spontaneously in response to lateral hypothalamic stimulation will drink milk spontaneously. If milk and water are presented separately, but concurrently, to such an animal, it will probably drink some water as well as milk, but eventually it will drink water alone in response to stimulation. This shows how complex some of these experimental situations are.

Grossman: In fact, I think the experiment has been tried with beef bouillon, and it works too.

Stevenson: In such a case we don't know whether the animal is drinking food or eating water.

Morrison: Could I ask a simple technical question? About how far away from the tips of the cannulae is the effect of the adrenalin?

Grossman: A mapping of positive and negative implant placements suggests an effective spread of about 0.5 to 1.0 mm. Autoradiographic observations reported by Wagner and De Groot, as well as work in our own laboratory, indicate similar values. The exact extent of spread undoubtedly depends somewhat on the tissue immediately adjacent to the cannula and on the dosage of the chemical injected.

Fregly: Did you administer epinephrine or norepinephrine in solution or as crystals?

Grossman: In the initial studies, chemicals in crystalline form were tamped into the tip of the inner cannula, which was cut to be just a little shorter than the permanently implanted outer cannula. In this way the chemical must go into solution and diffuse through the thin layer of necrotic tissue that surrounds all foreign matter in the brain. The exact concentration that reaches reactive tissue is unknown, but this is, of course, true of any injection of chemicals in solution.

Neal Miller has replicated these studies with solutions and has demonstrated very nice dose-response relationships for both the adrenergic and the cholinergic effects. Both techniques have advantages and disadvantages. The injection of chemicals in crystalline form minimizes spread and thus permits the most exact localization of the effects. Dose-response relationships, on the other hand, are much more easily obtained by injections of substances in solution.

We have in recent years used a combination of techniques. The initial studies make use of drugs in crystalline form to give us some assurance that any effect we may observe is, in fact, elicited from tissue near the implant. Once the anatomical boundaries have been established, we go to liquid injections to establish dose-effect relationships and control for various side effects.

Let me remind you, in this connection, that relatively large dosages are needed to elicit prolonged and overt changes in behavior. If you consider the effects of the total dosage on a single nerve cell, a physiological effect appears to be impossible. However, a relatively large number of cells must be affected by the drug to produce a noticeable change in feeding or drinking behavior, and the drug must act for at least five to ten minutes for this change to become recordable in the laboratory. The total dosage should therefore be fractionated along a spatial as well as a temporal gradient.

Fregly: Another problem is the solubility of crystalline materials in body fluids.

Grossman: Yes, this is a problem. All of the neurohumoral and blocking agents

that we have used readily go into solution in water as well as in the saline solution found at the tip of the cannula implant. On the other hand, some of the control substances, as well as some of the local anesthetics, have turned out to be only poorly soluble, and occasionally we have had to resort to injections of as concentrated a solution as could be obtained under the circumstances.

Morrison: What about the vasomotor effect?

Grossman: We have injected a variety of substances, both in crystalline form and in solution, that are thought to produce vasomotor effects at least as potent as those seen after the topical application of adrenergic or cholinergic substances. None of these experiments has in any way duplicated the feeding and drinking effects, and at this time I am quite confident that we can rule out a significant contribution of vasomotor effects.

Morrison: Of course, your blocking agent experiments help.

Grossman: The blocking agent experiments provide the best demonstration of specificity, but we always try to obtain additional evidence to rule out possible contributory effects of local changes in the acid-base composition of the affected tissue, osmotic changes, and vasodilatation and constriction.

Morrison: The results are really specific for these two things?

Grossman: Yes.

Harper: How much has been done with the infusion of nutrients into the hypothalamic region?

Grossman: The only thing that you can

call a nutrient that has been injected
into the hypothalamus is sugar, because
of the glucoreceptor notion. And as far
as I know, no one has been able to see
any change in the feeding behavior as
a result of that. I certainly have not.

Epstein: I think you are quoting my
experiment (*Amer. J. Physiol.,* **199**: 969,
1960). I was unable to depress feeding
in the hungry rats—by injecting isotonic
glucose into the ventromedial hypothalamus—through bilaterally symmetrical
cannulae. This was in the same animal
in which I could induce feeding by an-
esthetizing the ventromedial hypothalamus with procaine.

Grossman: All the experiments of which
I am aware have been similarly negative. Aside from our own data I recall
reports by Wagner and De Groot (*Amer.
J. Physiol.,* **204**: 483, 1963) and by Fisher
and Coury (*Science,* **138**: 691, 1962).

Hamilton: If Mayer is correct, i.e., if the
cells of the ventromedial hypothalamus
require insulin for the entry of glucose,
then glucose injections alone are not
enough.

Grossman: We have injected insulin into
both medial and lateral hypothalamic
placements without observing any
change in food or water intake. We have
not combined glucose and insulin, as
one should perhaps do, in order to put
this matter to a final test.

Hamilton: I believe Mayer has some evidence that certain hypothalamic cells
require insulin, but I have not seen it
published.

Barnes: All of the cells require insulin,
don't they, for the entrance of glucose?

Epstein: Not the cerebral cortex.

REFERENCES

1. Anand, B. K., and Brobeck, J. R. Localization of a feeding center in the hypothalamus
   of the rat. *Proc. Soc. Exp. Biol. Med.,* **77**:
   323–24, 1951.
2. Anand, B. K., Chhina, G. S., Sharma, K. N.,
   Dua, S., and Singh, B. Activity of single
   neurons in the hypothalamic feeding centers: Effect of glucose. *Amer. J. Physiol.,*
   207: 1146–54, 1964.
3. Anand, B. K., and Dua, S. Feeding responses
   induced by electrical stimulation of the
   hypothalamus in the cat. *Ind. J. Med. Res.,*
   43: 113–22, 1955.
4. Andersson, B. The effect of injections of
   hypertonic NaCl-solutions into different parts
   of the hypothalamus of goats. *Acta Physiol.
   Scand.,* **28**: 188–201, 1953.
5. Andersson, B. Polydipsia, antidiuresis and
   milk ejection caused by hypothalamic stimulation, in *The Neurohypophysis,* H. Heller
   (ed.). Academic Press, New York, 1957.
6. Brown, S., and Schäfer, E. A. An investigation into the functions of the occipital and
   temporal lobes of the monkey's brain. *Phil.
   Trans. Roy. Soc.* [*Biol.*] (London), **179**: 303–
   27, 1888.
7. Brügger, M. Fresstrieb als hypothalmisches
   Symptom. *Helv. Physiol. Pharmacol. Acta,*
   1: 183–98, 1943.
8. Ehrlich, A. Effects of tegmental lesions on
   motivated behavior in rats. *J. Comp. Physiol.
   Psychol.,* **56**: 390–96, 1963.
9. Erdheim, J. Ueber Hypophysenganggesch-
   wulste und Hirncholesteatome. *S.-B. Akad.
   Wiss. Wien.,* **113**: 537–726, 1904.
10. Fisher, A. E. Maternal and sexual behavior
    induced by intracranial chemical stimula-
    tion. *Science,* **124**: 228, 1956.
11. Fisher, A. E., and Coury, J. N. Cholinergic
    tracing of a central neural circuit underlying
    the thirst drive. *Science,* **138**: 691–93, 1962.
12. Fröhlich, A. Dr. Alfred Fröhlich stellt einen
    Fall von Tumor der Hypophyse ohne Akro-
    megalie vor. *Wien klin. Rdsch.,* **15**: 883,
    1902.
13. Fuller, J. L., Rosvolt, H. E., and Pribram,
    K. H. The effects on affective and cognitive
    behavior in the dog of lesions of the
    pyriform amygdala-hippocampal complex.
    J. Comp. Physiol. Psychol., **50**: 89–96, 1957.
14. Fulton, J. F. *Frontal Lobotomy and Affective
    Behavior.* W. W. Norton, New York, pp. 78–
    82, 1951.
15. Fulton, J. F., Jacobsen, C. F., and Kennard,
    M. A. A note concerning the relation of the
    frontal lobes to posture and forced grasping
    in monkeys. *Brain,* **55**: 524–36, 1932.
16. Gilbert, G. J. The subcommissural organ:
    A regulator of thirst. *Amer. J. Physiol.,* **191**:
    243–47, 1957.
17. Gold, R. Aphagia and adipsia following uni-
    lateral and bilateral asymmetrical lesions in

rats. Unpublished Ph.D. thesis, University of Chicago, 1966.

18. Green, J., Clemente, C. D., and De Groot, J. Rhinencephalic lesions and behavior in cats. *J. Comp. Neurol.*, 108: 505–46, 1957.

19. Grossman, S. P. Eating or drinking elicited by direct adrenergic or cholinergic stimulation of hypothalamus. *Science*, 132: 301–2, 1960.

20. Grossman, S. P. Direct adrenergic and cholinergic stimulation of hypothalamic mechanisms. *Amer. J. Physiol.*, 202: 872–82, 1962.

21. Grossman, S. P. Effects of adrenergic and cholinergic blocking agents on hypothalamic mechanisms. *Amer. J. Physiol.*, 202: 1230–36, 1962.

22. Grossman, S. P. Behavioral effects of chemical stimulation of the ventral amygdala. *J. Comp. Physiol. Psychol.*, 57: 29–36, 1964.

23. Grossman, S. P. Effects of chemical stimulation of the septal area on motivation. *J. Comp. Physiol. Psychol.*, 58: 194–200, 1964.

24. Grossman, S. P. Some neurochemical properties of the central regulation of thirst, in *Thirst in the Regulation of Body Water*, M. Wayner (ed.). Pergamon, New York, 1964.

25. Grossman, S. P. The VMH: A center for affective reactions, satiety, or both? *Intern. J. Physiol. Behav.*, 1: 1–10, 1966.

26. Grossman, S. P., and Grossman, L. Food and water intake following lesions or electrical stimulation of the amygdala. *Amer. J. Physiol.*, 205: 761–65, 1963.

27. Grossman, S. P., and Grossman, L. Effects of chemical stimulation of the midbrain reticular formation on appetitive behavior. *J. Comp. Physiol. Psychol.*, 61: 333–38, 1966.

28. Grossman, S. P., and Peters, R. H. Acquisition of appetitive and avoidance habits following atropine-induced blocking of the thalamic reticular formation. *J. Comp. Physiol. Psychol.*, 61: 325–32, 1966.

29. Grossman, S. P., Peters, R. H., Freedman, P. E., and Willer, H. Behavioral effects of cholinergic stimulation of the thalamic reticular formation. *J. Comp. Physiol. Psychol.*, 59: 57–65, 1965.

30. Hess, W. R. *Das Zwischenhirn: Syndrome, Lokalisationen, Functionen.* Schwabe, Basel, 1949.

31. Hetherington, A. W., and Ranson, S. W. Hypothalamic lesions and adiposity in the rat. *Anat. Rec.*, 78: 149, 1940.

32. Kirschbaum, W. R. Excessive hunger as a symptom of cerebral origin. *J. Nerv. Ment. Dis.*, 113: 95, 1951.

33. Koikegami, H., Fuse, S., Hiroki, S., Kazami, T., and Kageyama, Y. On the inhibitory effect upon the growth of infant animals or on the obesity in adult cat induced by bilateral destruction of the amygdaloid nuclear region. *Folia Psychiat. Neurol. Jap.*, 12: 207–23, 1958.

34. Koikegami, H., Fuse, S., Yokoyama, T.,

Watanabe, T., and Watanabe, H. Contributions of the comparative anatomy of the amygdaloid nuclei of mammals with some experiments of their destruction or stimulation. *Folia Psychiat. Neurol. Jap.*, 8: 336–68, 1955.

35. Krasne, F. B. General disruption resulting from electrical stimulus of ventromedial hypothalamus. *Science*, 138: 822–23, 1962.

36. Marshall, N. B., and Mayer, J. Energy balance in goldthioglucose obesity. *Amer. J. Physiol.*, 178: 271–74, 1954.

37. Mayer, J. Genetic, traumatic and environmental factors in the etiology of obesity. *Physiol. Rev.*, 33: 472–508, 1953.

38. Mayer, J. Regulation of energy intake and the body weight. The glucostatic theory and the lipostatic hypothesis. *Ann. N.Y. Acad. Sci.*, 63: 15–43, 1955.

39. Miller, N. E. Chemical coding of behavior in the brain. *Science*, 148: 328–38, 1965.

40. Miller, N. E., Bailey, C. J., and Stevenson, J. A. F. "Decreased hunger" but increased food intake resulting from hypothalamic lesions. *Science*, 112: 256–59, 1950.

41. Morgane, P. J. Electrophysiological studies of feeding and satiety centers in the rat. *Amer. J. Physiol.*, 201: 838–44, 1961.

42. Morgane, P. J. Evidence of a "hunger motivational" system in the lateral hypothalamus of the rat. *Nature*, 191:672–74, 1961.

43. Morgane, P. J. Medial forebrain bundle and "feeding centers" of the hypothalamus. *J. Comp. Neurol.*, 117: 1–26, 1961.

44. Morgane, P. J. Limbic-hypothalamic-midbrain interaction in thirst and thirst motivated behavior, in *Thirst in the Regulation of Body Water*, M. Wayner (ed.). Pergamon, New York, 1964.

45. Morgane, P. J., and Kosman, A. J. A rhinencephalic feeding center in the cat. *Amer. J. Physiol.*, 197: 158–62, 1959.

46. Morgane, P. J., and Kosman, A. J. A rhinencephalic feeding center in the cat. *Fed. Proc.*, 18: 108, 1959.

47. Peretz, E. The effect of hippocampal ablation on the strength of food-obtained responses. *Amer. Psychol.*, 18: 464, 1963.

48. Reynolds, D. V. A preliminary study of changes in food consumption following lesions in the septum and tegmentum in the albino rat. Unpublished Ph.D. thesis, Stanford University, 1962.

49. Robinson, B. Forebrain alimentary responses: Some organizational principles, in *Thirst in the Regulation of Body Water*, M. Wayner (ed.). Pergamon, New York, 1964.

50. Ruch, T. C., Blum, M., and Brobeck, J. R. Taste disturbances from thalamic lesions in monkeys. *Amer. J. Physiol.*, 133: 433, 1941.

51. Ruch, T. C., Patton, H. D., and Brobeck, J. R. Hyperphagia and adiposity in relation to disturbances of taste. *Fed. Proc.*, 1: 76, 1942.

52. Sharma, K. N., Anand, B. K., Dua, S., and Singh, B. Role of stomach in regulation of activities of hypothalamic feeding centers. *Amer. J. Physiol.*, **201**: 593–98, 1961.

53. Teitelbaum, P. Sensory control of hypothalamic hyperphagia. *J. Comp. Physiol. Psychol.*, **48**: 158–63, 1955.

54. Teitelbaum, P., and Cytawa, J. Spreading depression and recovery from lateral hypothalamic damage. *Science*, **147**: 61–63, 1965.

55. Teitelbaum, P., and Epstein, A. N. The lateral hypothalamic syndrome: Recovery of feeding and drinking after lateral hypothalamic lesions. *Psychol. Rev.*, **69**: 74–90, 1962.

56. Teitelbaum, P., and Stellar, E. Recovery from the failure to eat, produced by hypothalamic lesions. *Science*, **120**: 894–95, 1954.

57. Verney, E. B. The antidiuretic hormone and the factors which determine its release. *Proc. Roy. Soc. [Biol.]* (London), **135**: 25–106, 1947.

58. Watts, J. W., and Fulton, J. F. Intussusception—the relation of the cerebral cortex to intestinal motility in the monkey. *New Eng. J. Med.*, **210**: 883–96, 1934.

59. Wheatley, M. D. The hypothalamus and affective behavior in cats. *Arch. Neurol. Psychiat.*, **52**: 296–316, 1944.

The research reported in this communication as well as the presentation of the manuscript were supported by U.S.P.H.S. grants MY–5331 and MH–10130.

22: Neural Coding of Taste Quality

by Robert P. Erickson

M Y MAIN INTERESTS are in the coding processes used by the nervous system to represent sensory information. As a result of this, I have become interested in the problem of gustatory "primaries" and the related possibility of stimulus dimensions underlying gustation. If stimulus dimensions are found, primaries should appear as groupings of either stimuli or neurons along these dimensions, or in the form of separate dimensions. The task of the research to be reported here is to provide evidence for such dimensions and primaries from the responses of individual taste neurons to chemical stimulation of the tongue.

The conclusions to be reached in this paper are relatively simple. However, the methods used to reach these conclusions are rather complicated. Because of the complexity in the methods used it may be difficult for the reader to consider critically the conclusions reached. Therefore, it would be useful to first demonstrate these methods in another sensory system where the conclusions may be more easily evaluated. For this purpose we will turn to color vision. It will be shown that, using the kind of data we obtain in taste or olfaction, these methods can develop the wavelength dimension known to underlie color vision, and that they can disclose

the existence of three "primary" receptor (cone) types.

In Fig. 22–1 are given some of Marks's

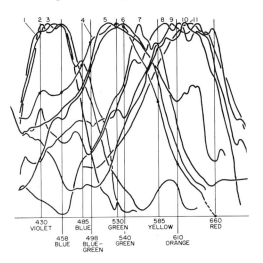

Fig. 22–1. *Difference absorption spectra of eleven individual goldfish cones* [2]. *Maximum absorption adjusted to be equivalent for each cone. Data from these cones are numbered 1–11. These numbers also appear in Table 22–1 and Figs. 22–8 and 22–9. The points in Figs. 22–2– 22–5 refer to data from these eleven cones. The filled-in circles on the curve obtained for the green cone represent the responses of this receptor to nine stimuli. The responses of these eleven receptors to these nine stimuli are the data used for demonstration of the methods used in the present paper. Curves of this type for any sensory modality are herein called Neural Response Functions (NRFs).*

313

data [2] on the difference absorption spectra of individual goldfish cones. These curves show that the sensitivity of each cone falls off on both sides of an area of maximum sensitivity. The eleven cones shown are selected from a larger population given by Marks. These cones distributed themselves quite nicely into three "primary" groups. Cone 7 is a rare "twin" cone and is presumably a combination of a green cone and an orange cone.

If Marks had done his experiment, as we are doing ours in the chemical senses, without knowledge of appropriate stimulus dimensions, he would not have been able to vary his stimuli systematically. Then he probably would have chosen several different stimuli to use as do we in the chemical senses; the selection of nine stimuli that will be used here in an hypothetical experiment is indicated on the abscissa in Fig. 22–1. Then Marks's data would not take the form shown by the curves in Fig. 22–1 but would be of the form shown in Table 22–1. His data in Table 22–1 are now in the *form* resulting from single-neuron taste experiments. We will now manipulate the data in this form, using two different methods, to see if we can

derive the stimulus dimension for color vision and disclose the existence of three receptor types.

COLOR VISION—INTERSTIMULUS DISTANCE METHOD

With the first method, the relative distance of each stimulus from every other stimulus is estimated from the neural data, and then these stimuli are placed in relation to each other on dimensions according to these distances. This method has been presented in detail elsewhere [1] and thus will only be discussed briefly here. The method assumes that the sensitivity of a neuron along its stimulus dimensions is of a simple form as shown in Marks's data (Fig. 22–1). Such relatively simple and broad tuning of neurons is found in all senses where the relevant dimensions are known [1]. They will herein be called "Neural Response Functions" (NRFs).

How could the fact that two stimuli are relatively close to each other on the stimulus dimension be derived from the data in Table 22–1? Let us use the two greens, *530 mμ* and *540 mμ*, as examples. If we plot these responses in a scattergram, Fig. 22–2, the data takes on a

TABLE 22–1: Responses (Difference Absorption Spectra) to Nine "Colors" by Eleven Receptors
(scale arbitrary: maximum 154)

	Stimuli								
Receptor	Violet 430	Blue 458	Blue 485	Blue-Green 498	Green 530	Green 540	Yellow 585	Orange 610	Red 660
1	147	153	89	57	12	4	0	0	0
2	153	154	110	75	32	24	23	17	0
3	145	152	125	100	14	0	0	0	0
4	99	101	122	140	154	153	93	44	0
5	46	85	103	127	152	148	116	75	26
6	73	78	85	121	151	154	109	57	0
7	14	2	46	52	97	106	137	92	45
8	44	65	77	73	84	102	151	154	120
9	87	59	58	52	86	79	139	153	146
10	60	27	23	24	56	72	136	144	111
11	0	0	40	39	55	62	120	147	132

NOTE: Receptors 1–3 are "violet" receptors, 4–6 are "green," and 8–11 are "orange." Number 7 is a "twin" green-orange cone.

form characteristic of two stimuli close together. That is, the fact that these two greens are close together is betrayed in the particular arrangement of these points on the scattergram. It may be noticed in Fig. 22–2 that receptors *4, 5,* and *6* give large responses to both green stimuli. These are the "green" receptors in Fig. 22–1. Receptors *8, 9, 10,* and *11* give intermediate responses to both stimuli ("orange" receptors), and receptors *1, 2,* and *3* give small responses to both stimuli ("violet" receptors). The actual distance of these stimuli from each other is given by the scattergram profile from Fig. 22–6 that most accurately conforms to these points [1]. The fact that there are three receptor types results in the grouping of these points into three areas on the scattergram.

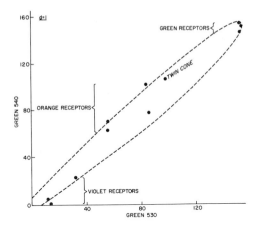

Fig. 22–2. *Responses of the eleven visual receptors shown in Fig. 22–1 to two of the stimuli indicated on the abscissa of Fig. 22–1, green (530 mμ) and green (540 mμ). Each receptor gives approximately the same response to both of these stimuli. This indicates that these two stimuli are close together on the stimulus dimension. The scattergram profile chosen from Fig. 22–6 that most nearly fits these data indicates their degree of proximity, one unit (arbitrary); d = 1. See text and reference [1] for a more complete discussion. That there are three receptor types is indicated by the grouping of the points into three families. A summary of these d values appears in Table 22–2.*

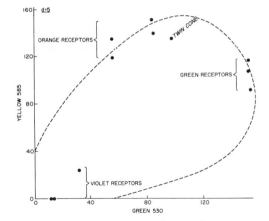

Fig. 22–3. *As Fig. 22–2. Distance between green (530 mμ) and yellow (585 mμ) is five units since the best fitting curve from Fig. 22–6 is d = 5.*

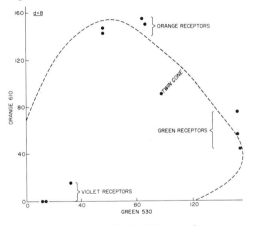

Fig. 22–4. *As Fig. 22–2. Distance between greeen (530 mμ) and orange (610 mμ) is eight units.*

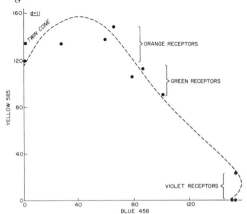

Fig. 22–5. *As Fig. 22–2. Distance between blue (458 mμ) and yellow (585 mμ) is eleven units.*

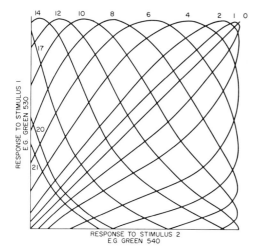

Fig. 22–6. *Hypothetical scattergram pro-*
files that would be generated by color
stimuli various distances apart on the
wavelength dimension. Profiles and inter-
stimulus distances in Figs. 22–2—22–5 and
Table 22–2 are taken from this figure.
Derived from Table 22–1. For a more
detailed discussion see text and
reference [1].

How could the fact that two stimuli are farther apart be derived from Table 22–1? The data for yellow *(585 mμ)* and green *(530 mμ)* are plotted as a scattergram in Fig. 22–3. The form of this scattergram is that characteristic of two stimuli five times as far apart as the two greens since the curve for stimuli this far apart in Fig. 22–6 most nearly fits the data [1]. Again, the existence of three receptor types is betrayed in the grouping of the points. In Figs. 22–4 and 22–5

are seen the data which represent the stimuli that are evidently eight and eleven times as far apart as the two greens. The distances between all the stimuli estimated in this manner are given in Table 22–2.

The result of arranging these stimuli together in such a way that the distances between each pair of stimuli are preserved as nearly as possible is shown in the lower part of Fig. 22–7. The straight wavelength dimension drawn to the same scale is shown directly above it. Above this is given a dimension divided into the arbitrary distances shown in Table 22–2. It may be seen here that the use of this method, based on the inter-stimulus distances, places the stimuli in proper order in a line, but the line is curved so that it resembles the color circle rather than simply a straight wavelength dimension. The NRFs must now be conceived as inverted cones standing on the plane of these stimuli. The meaning of the curve of the wavelength dimension is not clear but suggests that for the nervous system red and blue are more alike than the straight wavelength dimension indicates.

Although not directly relevant to the purposes of the present paper, an average or generalized cone NRF is shown in the upper part of Fig. 22–7 on the scale of dimension distances, along with one each of Marks's broader and nar-

TABLE 22–2: Dimension Distances between Visual Stimuli

	Violet	Blue	Blue	Blue-Green	Green	Green	Yellow	Orange
Blue	2							
Blue	5	2½						
Blue-Green	6	3	1½					
Green	9	7	4	3				
Green	9	8	5	4	1			
Yellow	11	11	8	8	5	4		
Orange	12	12	10	8	8	6	2	
Red	18	17	14	8	10	10	6	3

NOTE: Dimension distances between visual stimuli are from scattergram profiles as shown in Figs. 22–2 to 22–5.

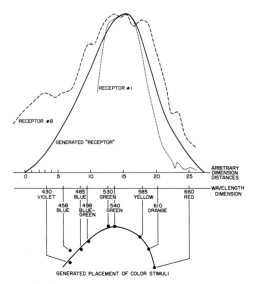

H. Schiffman; the details of this procedure are to be published elsewhere. The program was devised to place the stimuli and the neurons in a number of dimensions such that simple NRFs would account for the data. That is, they were arranged such that each neuron would show its largest response to the stimulus nearest the center of its NRF and would show progressively smaller responses to stimuli that were progressively farther away. The results of this analysis are shown in Fig. 22–8. The similarities be-

Fig. 22–7. Center: Wavelength dimension with stimuli from Fig. 22–1 is indicated. Bottom: Arrangement of these nine stimuli to be most nearly in accord with the interstimulus distances given in Table 22–2 (same scale as the dimension given in the center). Notice that the distances between the adjacent stimuli are roughly correct but that the wavelength dimension is now curved so that the stimuli near the ends of the dimension are closer to the stimuli at the opposite end of the dimension than is given in the straight wavelength dimension. Top: One of the narrower and one of the broader NRF's from Fig. 22–1, in addition to a generalized NRF derived from Table 22–1 via Fig. 22–6 [1], along a dimension of the arbitrary interstimulus distances drawn to the same scale as the dimensions in the center and lower parts of this figure.

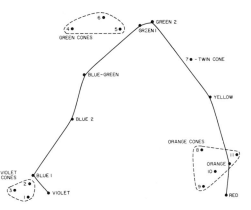

Fig. 22–8.   Arrangement of stimuli by simple NRF method. Similarity to the arrangement of stimuli by the interstimulus distances method, shown in the lower part of Fig. 22–7, should be noted. Placement of the centers and NRF's for the eleven cones is also shown. Each NRF should now be visualized as a conical surface standing on the plane of the figure with its apex at the numbered point. The computer program providing this arrangement of stimuli and receptors is written so that the stimuli closest to the centers of each NRF produce the largest response in that receptor and stimuli further away give progressively smaller responses. That this is correct is shown in Fig. 22–9.

rower difference absorption spectra curves. This NRF was generated from the data in Table 22–1 and was used to derive the family of curves in Fig. 22–6 [1].

COLOR VISION—SIMPLE NRF METHOD

For the second method, the data in Table 22–1 were subjected to computer analysis using a program developed by

tween the placement of the stimuli shown here and that shown in the lower part of Fig. 22–7 should be noted. It may also be seen that the neurons are placed in the three groups that may be labeled as violet, green, and orange receptors.

The success of this method for describing the neural data may be easily evaluated by determining if the responsiveness of these receptors does drop off as a function of distance from their points of maximum sensitivity, as is required for simple NRFs. That this is in fact true is shown in Fig. 22–9, where the

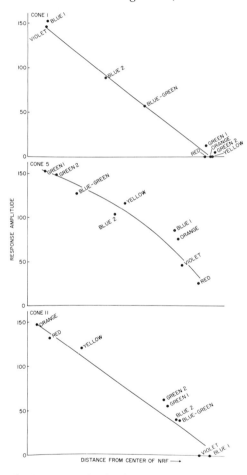

Fig. 22–9. An indication that the arrangement of receptors and stimuli in Fig. 22–8 does account for the visual data (Table 22–1) in terms of simple NRFs. Abscissae are distances of the various stimuli from the centers of NRFs in Fig. 22–8. Ordinates represent the response of each receptor to the various stimuli. Curves are fitted by inspection.

sensitivities of a "violet," a "green," and an "orange" receptor to the various stim-

uli are plotted. The NRFs so described do take simple forms with maximum sensitivity in the center and progressively decreasing sensitivity toward the periphery.

Thus, both methods used give similar results in placing the stimuli in proper order, with a similar curve in both. If it had not been known before, the relation of this particular order to wavelength might now be noticed. Both methods show that there are three color receptor types with one deviant "twin" cone. The computer method also shows where these receptor NRFs are located in the stimulus space.

GUSTATION—INTERSTIMULUS DISTANCES METHOD

We will now use the same methods as were used in the analysis of the color vision data for the analysis of gustatory data. These data, which appear in Table 22–3a, consist of the number of impulses occurring in the first second of evoked activity in single chorda tympani neurons in female, pentobarbital anesthetized Sprague-Dawley rats. The analysis of these data will proceed as for the color vision data, except that we will not have the benefit of a figure analogous to Fig. 22–1 for reference. It is such a figure that we are attempting to derive.

It was necessary that the color stimuli be of equal intensity so that simple NRFs *could* result should such a concept prove to be consistent with the data. The stimuli in Table 22–3a are obviously not of equal stimulating efficiency since some produced many more impulses in general than did others. For example, the sucrose, quinine hydrochloride, and HCl stimuli used produced relatively few impulses while NaOH, $CaCl_2$, and NaCl produced much activity. Thus, the data in Table 22–3a were transformed, as seen in Table

TABLE 22-3a: Raw Data: Impulses in First Second of Evoked Activity—Taste (Rat Chorda Tympani)

							Stimuli						
Neuron	NaCl	Na_2SO_4	$NaNO_3$	NaOH	KCl	NH_4Cl	$MgCl_2$	$CaCl_2$	LiCl	Li_2SO_4	HCl	QHCl	Suc
1	26	20	28	34	4	4	5	5	25	24	11	5	0
2	4	5	2	19	13	23	10	23	16	9	28	8	1
3	24	17	20	20	19	13	11	14	13	9	6	4	2
4	44	36	42	50	3	8	16	18	28	17	6	1	6
5	22	21	27	20	8	7	19	18	17	21	11	7	8
6	22	20	19	32	5	16	24	24	23	22	3	3	3
7	0	0	1	11	3	3	2	2	1	1	6	0	0
8	21	1	15	23	63	65	45	66	20	2	20	25	2
9	23	15	20	29	22	28	28	35	23	17	9	17	7
10	25	12	12	23	21	32	23	24	15	16	47	21	2
11	22	10	18	20	17	23	29	21	19	11	18	17	6
12	33	26	20	35	4	5	10	7	26	27	12	3	7
13	31	29	33	33	13	6	13	16	25	37	10	14	2
14	13	9	10	15	4	6	11	6	6	10	4	1	4
15	8	7	4	11	5	5	7	12	5	7	3	3	1
16	8	3	3	3	16	1	2	56	4	3	1	3	8

TABLE 22–3b: Data from Table 22–3a, Corrected for Strength of Stimuli

Stimuli

Neuron	NaCl	Na$_2$SO$_4$	NaNO$_3$	NaOH	KCl	NH$_4$Cl	MgCl$_2$	CaCl$_2$	LiCl	Li$_2$SO$_4$	HCl	QHCl	Suc
1	37	41	45	42	8	7	8	7	43	50	26	16	0
2	6	10	3	23	25	39	17	31	28	19	67	25	8
3	34	35	32	25	36	22	19	19	22	19	14	12	17
4	62	73	68	62	6	14	27	24	48	35	14	3	50
5	31	43	44	25	15	11	32	24	29	44	26	22	67
6	31	41	31	40	10	27	41	32	40	46	7	9	25
7	0	0	2	14	6	5	3	2	2	2	14	0	0
8	30	2	24	29	121	105	76	88	34	4	48	78	17
9	32	31	32	36	42	48	47	47	40	35	21	53	58
10	35	25	31	29	40	54	39	32	26	33	106	66	17
11	31	20	29	25	33	39	49	28	33	23	43	53	50
12	47	53	32	43	8	8	17	9	45	56	28	9	58
13	44	59	53	41	25	10	22	21	43	77	24	44	17
14	18	18	16	19	8	10	19	8	10	21	9	3	33
15	11	14	6	14	10	8	11	16	9	15	7	9	8
16	11	6	5	4	31	2	3	75	7	6	2	9	67

NOTE: To be used as Table 22–1. Figures 22–10 (in part), 22–11 to 22–13, and Table 22–4 derived from this table (see text and reference [1]).

22–3*b*, so that each stimulus now is seen producing about the same amount of activity across all neurons. Again, the graphic, interstimulus distance method will not be given in detail here. A typical scattergram is to be noted in Fig. 22–10 showing no evidence of a clustering

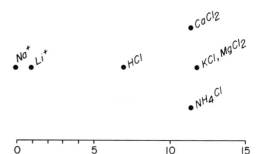

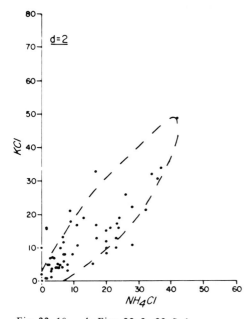

Fig. 22–10. *As Figs. 22–2—22–5, for gustation. Responses of fifty-seven neurons to KCl and NH₄Cl. Axes, number of impulses occurring in the first second of evoked activity. Each point represents responses of one taste neuron. Notice the absence of grouping of these points into families as was seen in Figs. 22–2—22–5, which would indicate the presence of receptor types for taste. This, and other data of this form [1], suggest the absence of neuron types for gustation.*

Fig. 22–11. *As Fig. 22–7 (lower), for gustation. KCl two units above plane, MgCl₂ two units below plane of figure. Na⁺ — Li⁺ indicates sodium-lithium family containing also Na₂SO₄, NaNO₃, Li₂SO₄ and NaOH. This, and arrangement of stimuli in Fig. 22–12, suggests the absence of stimulus primaries, except possibly for sucrose. These stimuli are better described by dimensions. These also point out the relatively greater importance of the cation than the anion in determining the stimulating characteristics of these substances for taste quality.*

of points that would characterize the existence of several receptor types as detected in color vision. Table 22–4 presents a summary of the interstimulus distances obtained by this method.

The location of several of these stimuli as given by the interstimulus distances is shown in Fig. 22–11. The general location of all sodium and lithium salts and NaOH is given by the Na⁺ and

Li⁺ symbols; this method is not sensitive enough to give the exact locations of these stimuli (relative to each other) in this small section of the dimensions.

The only grouping of *stimuli* evident in this figure is that of the sodium and lithium compounds. Thus the cation seems to be more important in determining the location of the stimuli than the anion since the compounds containing chlorine appear scattered in these dimensions. It should be noted that the plane containing these stimuli accommodates HCl and NaOH as well as the salts, giving no indication of stimulus primaries as far as these stimuli are concerned. The locations of sucrose and quinine are left indeterminate at this point, partly because of the insensitivity of the method, but largely because the rat chorda tympani responds poorly to these stimuli. A clearer picture of the location of these stimuli will emerge with the more sensitive method that follows.

TABLE 22–4: Scattergram Summary of the Interstimulus Distances Method

Na₂SO₄	NaNO₃	LiCl	Li₂SO₄	NaOH	KCl	NH₄Cl	MgCl₂	CaCl₂	HCl	QHCl	Sucrose	
2	2	1	2	3	12	12	8	12	8	18	21	NaCl
	2	2	2	3	12	15	8	15	12	12	21	Na₂SO₄
		3	2	3	12	8	8	8	12	12	?	NaNO₃
			3	3	12	12	8	12	5	15	18	LiCl
				2	12	8	8	8	8	12	?	Li₂SO₄
					8	8	8	8	8	12	?	NaOH
						2	5	2	5	15	18	KCl
							3	5	5	15	18	NH₄Cl
								3	5	15	15	MgCl₂
									5	15	15	CaCl₂
										15	15	HCl
											?	QHCl

NOTE: Dimension distances between gustatory stimuli from scattergram profiles. See text and reference [1] for derivation. Distances for ambiguous profiles omitted.

GUSTATION—SIMPLE NRF METHOD

The results of the computer analysis of these data are shown in Fig. 22–12. The similarity of the placement of the stimuli here and in Fig. 22–11 should be noted. More exact locations of the sodium and lithium salts and NaOH (relative to each other) are also given. It may also be seen that quinine hydrochloride (QHCl) is successfully placed in these dimensions by this method whereas sucrose is not.

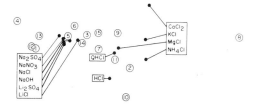

Fig. 22–12.   As to Fig. 22–8, for gustation. Similarity of arrangement of stimuli in Fig. 22–11 should be noted. Centers of neuron NRF's indicated by numbers. Absence of neuron types as well as stimulus types (except for Na⁺ − Li⁺ group) is evident. Sucrose not successfully plotted in this figure.

Again, we see no evidence of stimulus types since all the salts, as well as an

acid, a base, and a bitter substance, are placed in these dimensions. When a different set of data was used to compute the location of these stimuli, a very similar result was obtained, indicating that these results would not be obtainable given only the data in Table 22–3. Both times there was no grouping of receptor types as was seen for color vision.

To be of any use, the placements of stimuli and neurons shown in Figs. 22–11 and 22–12 should bear a close relationship to both the neural data and the psychophysical data. The similarity of the tastes of the sodium and lithium salts is well known, and Henning has pointed out the saltiness of the taste of NaOH. The difference between the taste of NaOH and the other salts may be caused by a trigeminal component of the input for the NaOH. The bitter and sour components of many of these salts are also well known. We, and others, are at present studying further the comparative tastes of these stimuli. With new behavioral methods, R. Morrison [3] has provided evidence from rats that is in considerable accord with these data.

If these data make sense as far as the neural data are concerned, then, as one moves from the center of an NRF, the responses to the various stimuli should drop off as a function of the distance of the stimuli from the center of the NRF. This was seen to be true for the computer analysis of the color vision data in Fig. 22–9. In Fig. 22–13 we see plots of

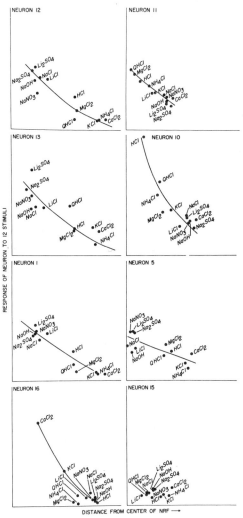

Fig. 22–13. As Fig. 22–9, for gustation. Of the sixteen neurons, only four of the most poorly responding were not adequately described by simple NRF's; neuron 15 presented as an example. Abscissae distances, giving distance from center of NRF to each stimulus, are from Fig. 22–12. Amplitude of response from Table 22–3b.

the responses of a number of neurons to the various stimuli as a function of the

stimuli's distance from the center of the NRF. The fit seems to be good for ten of the stimuli, fair for three, and bad for four (3, 7, 14, 15). It should be noted that the four that did not fit well with the present scheme included the three most poorly responding neurons. Such relatively quiet neurons may not be as involved in the coding of taste quality as the others. However, they are sensitive to changes in stimulus intensity.

CONCLUSIONS

In conclusion, it may be said for the taste neural data that the NRFs and dimensions for taste are approximately similar when measured by both inter-stimulus distances and simple NRF methods. No evidence for separate stimulus primaries is seen by either method. The only possible exception to this conclusion is sucrose. The rat, however, gives poor responses to sucrose and quinine, so we are pursuing these investigations with animals that give better responses to a broader range of taste stimuli. Also, both methods suggest many primary neuron types rather than a few. These methods suggest the existence of stimulus dimensions underlying taste and the possibility of disclosing them in some detail. They should apply to olfaction as well as to the other senses.

Discussion

Pangborn: Is this analysis like using the distance chart on a road map?

Erickson: Yes, with the added attraction that we can find the city with the distances. Of course, we have to use straight-line distances. If we know that Atlanta is 585 miles from Chicago and 745 from New York City, then we may conclude that it is in Georgia or in Canada. If you also know it is 425 miles from New Orleans, then you know that

Georgia is the right answer. This is exactly how we are arranging stimuli with the interstimulus distance method described in this paper.

Pangborn: Does it take into consideration the difference in altitude between two points as well as the map distances?

Erickson: Yes, it does take this into consideration. In both analyses you are asking if there is another (a third) dimension. The computer analysis of the first dimension accounts for 76 per cent of the data and that of the second dimension for 16 per cent; the 8 per cent left over might be accounted for by a third dimension. However, the reliability of our measures is not great enough to consider the 8 per cent as anything other than a result of inaccuracies of measurement. A third dimension does not help much in accounting for the data.

Pangborn: Are you saying that the first dimension is an ionic effect?

Erickson: No. I can't put any labels on these dimensions now. In this presentation I put the color stimuli in order. I could give this arrangement of color stimuli to a physicist and ask for a description of the dimensions. He might realize that wave length is a concept that would largely account for this arrangement. Similarly, with arrangements of enough taste stimuli, perhaps some chemist will give me labels for the taste dimensions. I do not have enough data for that yet.

Henkin: Did you do a factorial analysis on the responses?

Erickson: Yes, two factors account for 90 per cent of the data and three for 95 per cent. The meaning of this in the present context is not clear to me. The concept of related dimensions, such as the two describing a plane in this report, carries meaning that is not contained in the concept of factors.

Henkin: Could you not structure your tests to obtain information in a number of areas? If you can obtain data from subjects concerning their response to a number of taste stimuli, it would be possible to analyze the responses factorially and to obtain information about what the subjects respond to in the stimuli. These may or may not correspond to our concepts of salty, bitter, sweet, or sour, but they may help you to understand what is similar in your schema.

Erickson: This is not really a factor analysis. We are getting interstimulus distances, and thus dimensions, by psychophysical as well as physiological methods. For our dimensions to make sense they must relate to both psychophysical and neural events.

Beidler: The danger, of course, is that in another species this is going to change dramatically. For example, in the bat, the responses to sodium and lithium are quite different. So it may be difficult to go from this rat data to your human data. Furthermore, you must remember that electrophysiologically we only measure intensity. Potassium is very bitter and sodium is very salty, but if you change the concentration, the quality changes.

Erickson: I hope the problems you suggest with the bat will be the most difficult. I expect worse. As long as the various aspects of this research hang together—as physiological data from the rat with human psychophysics—I am content. I will try to modify my procedures as discrepancies arise.

As far as intensity goes, a weak salt might easily set up an across-fiber pattern characteristic of a sweet substance; then it would move in its location on the dimensions toward sweet stimuli. We are investigating this.

Beidler: In other words, concentrated chemicals are what you use. The location of the stimuli depends somewhat on concentration.

Erickson: Yes, and this is known in other sensory modalities as well (e.g., Bezold-Brücke effect in color vision).

Kare: Your idea, then, is challenged by what Harper brought up earlier. At one point you were inferring that there was a much simpler system for evaluating nutrient content that goes into the body, rather than a very complicated, very extensive informational system. When an animal decides whether or not to take something, is it not a complex situation?

Harper: I was limiting my suggestions strictly to a state of deficiency, where the presence or absence of an essential nutrient can be related to some general physiological reaction resulting in a sense of well-being or lack of well-being. I'm not sure that this could be applied to the normal animal in a healthy state.

Henkin: The data we have collected from normal volunteers may be of use in interpreting some of the data you have presented. As you may recall from my presentation, detection thresholds for the taste of all the salts presented to the normals—sodium chloride, sodium bicarbonate, and potassium chloride— were essentially the same. The median detection thresholds for sucrose were essentially the same as those found for the various salts, although sucrose is chemically quite different from the salts. The detection thresholds determined for hydrochloric acid were much lower than those for the salts and sucrose whereas those for urea were much higher. Thus, as you evaluate detection thresholds for various chemical substances in man, there are quantitative similarities in response to quite different chemical substances. The information contained in these responses about the taste mechanism is not clear, and perhaps studies such as yours will offer us a clue. I wonder if it would be possible to relate psychophysical responses to electrophysiological responses, and thus to identify the relationship between similar taste responses and dissimilar chemical substances.

Hodgson: In pooling data it would seem important to stick to either electrophysiological data or psychophysical data in any one pool. The results that pass through a human brain have, in a sense, already been "computerized" before work is begun on them. In other words, it is hard to imagine that a human subject would avoid imposing some sort of pattern on these sensations before or during the reporting of them. Both types of data would be interesting to analyze, of course, but they must be kept separate.

Epstein: Concerning Von Békésy's reports (*J. Appl. Physiol.,* **21:** 1, 1966) as an outsider to taste electrophysiology, is he claiming modality specificity in the human?

Erickson: Yes; two of his experiments point to this conclusion. In the first he electrically stimulated single taste papillae in the human being. The person was then asked what he tasted. In the second he used chemical stimulation of single papillae. In both instances he reported the papillae were specific only to salty, sour, sweet, or bitter sensations. These results are difficult to understand in the face of earlier, similar studies (Oehrwall, *Scand. Arch. Physiol.,* 2: 1, 1891; Kiesow, *Phil. Studien,* 14: 591, 1898) that brought contrary results, or with the well-known "non-specificity" of taste neurons in mind.

I do not know what is done when one directly stimulates electrically a large part of a sensory system as Von Békésy did with the taste papillae. I do not think that this gives us much information about the way biological systems work except in very special cases when the stimulus is limited to one neural element or to a very homogeneous group of neural elements. This is probably not true with a taste papilla.

Insofar as chemical stimulation is concerned, we undertook this type of study after reading Von Békésy's first paper (*J. Appl. Physiol.,* 19: 1105, 1964) on electrical stimulation. Our method involved the use of a flow chamber designed for stimulation of single taste papillae in the human being. Our results were similar to those reported earlier by Oehrwall and Kiesow; that is, some papillae seemed to be specific and others seemed sensitive to more than one, sometimes to all four of the sweet, sour, salty, and bitter stimuli used.

One difference between our procedures and Von Békésy's was that we used stronger stimuli. But if he means specific papillae in the sense that I think he means it, that is, if the neural activity produced by each represents one definite taste quality, then they should be specific to all stimulus intensities. In our study they were clearly non-specific (Harper *et al., Physiol. Behav.,* 1 [No. 4], 1966). I doubt that the papillae are the proper units for analysis.

Pfaffmann: There is clearly a discrepancy here among the electrophysiological data that show a broad range of not very precise specificities. Von Békésy's observations are a classical reaffirmation of the four sensory-specific taste papillae, taste sensations. There is one main point on this specificity problem, namely, that we are looking at the receptor end and the filtering in from the receptor to the activation. Von Békésy is looking at the stimuli applied and the sensations produced. He has used four stimuli primarily, but he has also used electrical stimulation, saying that these are the only sensations produced. I don't know the real resolution to this. Everyone else knows that discrepancies exist between what electrophysiology has shown and what the psychophysical specificity of sensation has shown. What you really need is to see whether the electrophysiology of humans is as broad and nonspecific as that of most animals, including the primates; if that is the case, then there may be a sharpening or funneling from the afferent input to the neurological basis of sensation. But these two sets of data do not fall together easily.

Erickson: If you want to represent many stimuli in any particular modality, any funneling must be limited in its extent. Funneling to the point of having strictly sweet, sour, salty, and bitter neurons would leave the organism with its taste-dependent behavior on a par with that of an insect. I have discussed this problem elsewhere (Erickson *et al., J. Gen. Physiol.,* 49: 247, 1965).

Beidler: With respect to this problem, a single taste fiber is not highly specific. But Von Békésy is stimulating three to five taste buds, which contain perhaps a total of one hundred taste receptors. All this integrated information could produce a specific quality. On the other hand, Von Békésy's concentrations are very, very low. They are much lower than what some people use when they place a whole glass of gustatory substance over the tongue. This is at variance with the work done in the 1890's.

REFERENCES

1. Erickson, R. P., Doetsch, G. S., and Marshall, D. A. The gustatory neural response function. *J. Gen. Physiol.,* **49**: 247–63, 1965.
2. Marks, W. B. Difference spectra of the visual pigments in single goldfish cones. Unpublished Ph.D. dissertation, The Johns Hopkins University, 1963.
3. Morrison, G. R. Behavioral response patterns to salt stimuli. *Canad. J. Psychol.,* 1967 (in press).

Illustrations by Stephanie Peach Doetsch. Supported by PHS Grant NB–04793 and NSF Grant GB–2087.

23: Critic's Comments

by James A. F. Stevenson

THIS AFTERNOON we have been discussing various sensory and monitoring systems and their roles in the control of food and water intake by the central nervous system. Moulton began by showing us an organized scheme of the functions of the olfactory and taste receptors. As the afternoon went on, we realized that there may be many other chemical receptors in the body that contribute to the control of food and water intake. In particular, evidence was presented or discussed for the presence of various types of receptors in the stomach and small intestine. In this regard, one may also mention the report of the Russian investigators Inchina and Finkinshtein (*Fed. Proc.,* **24**: T189, 1965) who perfused the pancreas of the dog through a branch of the pancreaticoduodenal artery with solutions of various osmotic concentrations and measured the effect on urine flow. They came to the conclusion that there are osmoreceptors in the pancreas. In studies of this type, there is the question of the specificity of the experimental stimulus. It has been suggested, for instance, that hyperosmotic solutions used for perfusion might produce the effect observed through stimulation of free nerve endings for pain rather than of osmoreceptors.

Although we have talked a good deal about chemical taste, there has been little discussion about the "texture" of materials. Nevertheless, this appears to be an important aspect of the oral sensation of food. The hypothalamic-hyperphagic rat is as finicky about "texture" as about chemical taste (e.g., quinine). For example, these animals will not show their hyperphagia when fed a dry, powdery meal, although, when this is mixed with water, they eat it avidly and become very obese. "Texture," of which we are all aware subjectively, is a factor that must be kept in mind.

If there is any question of the importance of taste and smell to animal and man, I think that Epstein has demonstrated that oral sensation is important both for the discrimination of intake and as a feedback mechanism in the control of intake. On the other hand, he also showed the importance of experience in the use of other gastrointestinal signals; the animal that had experience with a particular feeding situation apparently used gastric distension as a signal much more efficiently than an animal that had not had such previous experience. To the latter animal, therefore, oral sensation was all the more important. The importance of a positive feedback from oral sensations has also recently been demonstrated by Mogenson and our group at the University of Western Ontario. Some rats with stimulating

329

electrodes in the lateral hypothalamus will press spontaneously for electrical stimulation and, if water is available, will drink in response to this stimulation or to stimulation applied by the investigator. The stimulation appears to influence both what has been called the reward system and the drinking system. These animals will self-stimulate even if water is not available, but they will stimulate at much greater rates if they can drink water in response to the stimulation. In other words, the animal appears to be getting a positive feedback from the oral sensations involved in the ingestion of water. This effect is immediate so it cannot be caused by the absorption of water.

Sharma presented evidence, not only of the pathways and central representation of gastric distension, a well-recognized signal in the control of intake, but also of chemoreceptors for various foodstuffs in the intestine. Russek, who is visiting our department this year, is presently examining the possibility that there are receptor cells in the liver that monitor some aspect of the availability of energy to the cell.

I think it was worthwhile that Grossman took some time to emphasize the view, which some have held for many years, that the central control systems for feeding and drinking are complex and have widespread ramifications in the central nervous system. The use of the term "center," such as the feeding center, the drinking center, the satiety center, tends to make the situation look too simple and to inhibit further investigation of what is a very complex system. Even in the ventromedial hypothalamus, which is often spoken of as the satiety center, there is confirmed evidence of facilitatory or reinforcing systems as well as of the well-recognized inhibitory or satiety systems. If apparently the same lesion is made, as accurately as possible by present techniques, in a series of animals, all may show certain deficits but will vary in other deficits. For instance, as has been pointed out, some hypothalamic-hyperphagic rats can control their food intake in response to a change in environmental temperature while others cannot. There are obviously many subsystems in the hypothalamus that influence food and/or water intake. A microscopic variation in the position of a lesion can cause a variation in the subsystems destroyed and thus in the characteristics of the syndrome observed. The ventromedial region of the hypothalamus contains a predominence of satiety or inhibitory systems for food intake, but the presence of facilitatory systems here must not be overlooked. It is also worthwhile to remember that even a subsystem for some facet of control is probably represented by many fibers or cells and thus that there can be quantitative as well as qualitative differences in the effect of lesions or stimulations; frequently a specific deficit or effect will not be apparent under neutral conditions but will appear under stress or exaggerated demand.

Grossman has referred to his work, and that of others such as Fisher and Coury (in *Thirst*, M. J. Wayner [ed.]. Pergamon Press, New York, pp. 515–31, 1964), on the effect of chemical stimulation in the brain on feeding and drinking behavior. This technique has provided evidence of the distribution of an "adrenergic" feeding system and a "cholinergic" drinking system in the brain. This has led to the suggestion that there is a chemical coding of these two systems. The implications of the term "coding" are not quite clear here. Does it mean simply that there is a consistency from one synapse to the next in certain systems—as one sees in the peripheral parasympathetic system? With the complex interrelations of the feeding and drinking systems that have been demonstrated, there must be many association pathways between them. Does the synaptic transmitter change from one synapse to the next in these pathways as it does in the peripheral sympathetic system?

We have been impressed with the high rate of drinking we obtain from electrical stimulation of the lateral hypothalamus compared to that which Fisher has reported for cholinergic stimulation here. One possible explanation is that the electrical stimulation activates neurons of the drinking system that are not cholinergic. Electrical stimulation in the lateral hypothalamus, as Mogenson and I have observed, may cause water intake up to 30–40 ml/hour. The rats that were mentioned earlier, which self-stimulate in the lateral hypothalamus and show stimulus-bound drinking in response to this or to applied stimulation, will, if left in the cage where they can self-stimulate and drink, develop an apparently permanent state of self-imposed polydipsia. Although they have had water freely available, they start pressing and drinking as soon as they are put in the experimental situation. After about twenty minutes of this behavior, a diuresis appears—just when one would expect it from suppression of antidiuretic hor-

mone release. They just go on with this behavior all day. They tend to approach a new steady state of water exchange as a result of this stimulation of the central nervous system, which is perhaps not unlike the psychogenic diabetes insipidus seen in man.

Although it is apparent that there are important projections of the drinking and feeding systems throughout the central nervous system, particularly the visceral brain, the medial and lateral midhypothalamus and surroundings appear to contain a fundamental focus of these systems. The most profound effects of experimental interference, particularly of ablation, are seen in this region. There is no doubt, however, that very important ramifications of these intake control systems occur in other parts of the visceral brain. These would appear to be particularly important to motivation, decisions as to the priority of response, learning, and to the discrimination of both external and internal cues that affect these behaviors. Some of the feedback systems of signals, receptors, central integrating mechanisms and responses for food intake are schematically described in Fig. 23–1.

Present evidence, some of which you

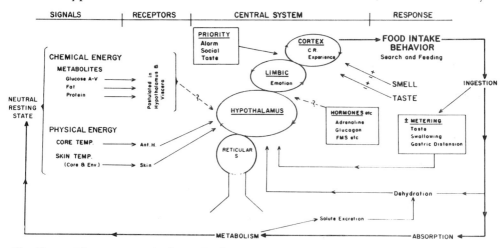

Fig. 23–1. *Diagram of probable feedback systems and modulating systems for the control of food intake.*

have just heard, suggests that there are central and/or peripheral receptors that respond to changes in the level of food metabolites available to them. The effect of environmental temperature on food intake is well known, and the recent observations of Andersson and his group have revealed the influence of changes in hypothalamic temperature on food and water intake. These indirect chemical and physical indexes of the energy available to the body appear to be the fundamental signals to activate food intake. As these indexes return to normal with intake, stimulation of the receptors decreases and the central system is no longer activated. Many factors in both the external and internal environment act through other receptors and central systems to facilitate or inhibit the degree to which this activation of the basic food intake system commands the behavior of the animal. Some of these factors are shown in Fig. 23–1. Smell and taste are, of course, vitally important to the discovery and discrimination of food.

The next figure (Fig. 23–2) shows a similar scheme for the feedback systems controlling water intake. The effective osmotic pressure of the internal environment, which governs the water content (i.e., the volume) of the cell, is probably the most important hour-to-hour signal. Special osmoreceptors have been postulated to occur in the hypothalamus, in the brain stem, and in the gastrointestinal tract. Plasma volume, which reflects extracellular fluid volume, is also probably monitored by stretch receptors in the vascular system. The receptors for temperature are probably the same as those which affect the control of food intake. These fundamental systems are also involved in the control of antidiuretic hormone release so that there is a reciprocal central control of the intake and renal output of water. As for food intake, there are many modulators that facilitate or inhibit the implementation of water intake behavior. In particular, a "dry mouth," as Epstein has shown, not only enhances water intake but can serve as the only signal to activate this intake. Taste not only provides for discrimination but may also serve as a positive feedback thereby enhancing intake. Gastric distension is an early inhibitory signal for both food and

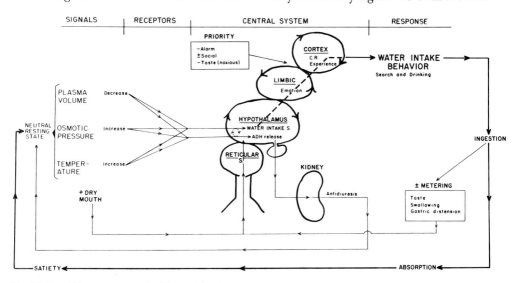

Fig. 23–2. Diagram of probable feedback systems and modulating systems for the control of water intake.

water intake. Evidence suggests that it can serve as a learned cue for the metering of food intake and water intake. We have also discussed today some of the evidence for chemoreceptors, in addition to smell and taste, in several regions of the gastrointestinal tract.

This has been an attempt to remind you briefly of the over-all control systems for food and water intake and to suggest how the senses of smell and taste may function in these control systems. Smell and taste are essential to the discovery and discrimination of food and water in the natural environment. They provide a positive or negative feedback for actual ingestion which is probably integrated with other signals in the determination of hunger and satiety.

Part Five

24: The Etiology of Different Forms of Taste Behavior

by I. Snapper

THE METHODS used for the investigation of taste have gained considerably in perspective from the introduction of taste-testing substances containing the group H—N—C═S. The two most popular test substances of this group are phenylthiourea (PTC) and propylthiouracil (PROP).

These new testing methods have made it possible to analyze different qualities of taste in a more detailed fashion. In addition, taste testing of patients submitted to modern otologic and neurosurgical procedures has corrected certain erroneous notions about the conduction of taste in *humans*.

PARAGEUSIA AND AGEUSIA AFTER SECTION OF THE CHORDA TYMPANI NERVE IN HUMANS

Based upon experimental data and clinical observations, most textbooks of neurology and physiology offer the following analysis of the conduction of taste in humans:

1. The greater part of the fibers that convey the taste sensation, allegedly from the anterior two thirds of the tongue only, are contained within the chorda tympani nerve. The fibers of the chorda tympani when leaving the brain run with the nervus intermedius of Wris-

berg, i.e., the sensory root of the facial nerve. During its passage through the petrous bone, the facial nerve and its sensory root are lodged within a bony channel, the tunnel of Fallop. About 3–4 mm before reaching the sylomastoid foramen, the gustatory fibers leave the intermedius nerve and run upward as the chorda tympani.

For the following discussion of the transmission of taste sensations from the tongue to the chord, it is important to note that the chorda enters and transverses the middle ear in a fold of the mucous membrane of the cavum tympani. This fold issues from the inner aspect of the drum. After the nerve has left the tympanic cavity it emerges from the base of the skull near the spine of the sphenoid.

2. Before the chorda reaches the tongue it joins the lingual nerve (a branch of the mandibular nerve, i.e., the third division of the trigeminal nerve). The experts are divided as to whether or not the lingual nerve plays a role in the conduction of taste sensations from the anterior two-thirds of the tongue.

Taste sensations registered on the posterior third of the tongue are allegedly conducted via the glossopharyngeus nerve. All taste sensations are assembled within the solitarius tract of the chord. These neurons have an intermediate ter-

mination in the solitarius nucleus located in the medulla. From here, fresh
neurons conduct the taste sensation via
the thalamus to the cortex of the temporal lobes. Each side of the tongue is
bilaterally represented in the sensory
cortex. Hence, the rarity of unilateral
loss of taste caused by a brain lesion.

These neuroanatomical details offer
the explanation of loss of taste in:

a. Paralysis of the facial nerve. If the
lesion affects the nerve during its passage through the Fallopian tunnel in the
petrous bone.

b. Patients who have received an alcohol injection in the gasserian ganglion. This loss of taste sets in immediately after the injection but is only
temporary. It is therefore hardly possible
that degeneration of the lingual nerve
by the alcohol injection could be the
cause of this transitory ageusia. Such a
connection is also improbable because
resection of the sensory root of the trigeminal nerve does not cause any change
of taste, although all other sensations
carried by the lingual nerve are abolished. The temporary ageusia following
the injection of the gasserian ganglion
is apparently the result of the edema in
the neighborhood of the injected area.
This edema after injection is known to
damage various distant neurons.

c. Patients suffering from bulbar paralysis, a disease of the medulla which
may affect the nucleus solitarius.

d. Diseases of the thalamus which the
taste fibers pass on their way to the
cortex.

e. Temporal seizures during which
taste hallucinations have been frequently
observed.

f. After skull traumas.

In all of these conditions, the lesion to
the nervous system can only be studied
at autopsy. In contrast, a modern otologic operation, which damages the
chorda tympani nerve in one special location, can be compared with a carefully

devised experiment to study alterations
of taste caused by different traumas to
this taste nerve.

g. Otosclerosis, which produces deafness in older people, is caused by scle-
rotic changes of the bone in the neighborhood of one of the auricular bones,
i.e., the stapes and the basal plate of the
stapes. Rosen [11] has invented a special
surgical technique to correct the hearing
defect caused by otosclerosis. He removes
the stapes and/or cuts the tendon of the
stapedius muscle which inserts at the
stapes. In order to reach the posterior
recess of the cavum tympani, where the
stapes is located, the modern otologists
first temporarily remove the tympanic
membrane, i.e., the eardrum. When the
cavum tympani is entered, the chorda
tympani is immediately encountered.
Often the nerve has to be stretched in
order to make space for the necessary
surgical manipulations, but more frequently the nerve must be cut. In addition, part of the fibers of the chorda
tympani nerve may be found within the
layers of the eardrum itself. Thus, the
stapes operation is considered to be a
well-controlled experimentum in vivo.
In hundreds of patients whose taste was
normal preoperatively, the chorda tympani is severed or damaged, by stretching, always at the same level.

It is not surprising that taste testing of
these patients has led to a considerable
improvement of our former concepts of
taste sensations in humans. Bull [2] has
reported the results of taste testing in
126 patients where, in the course of
stapes surgery, the chorda tympani had
been sectioned, in 32 patients where
both chorda tympani nerves had been
divided, and in 100 patients where the
chorda tympani has only been subjected
to a moderate degree of stretching
(Table 24–1).

After sectioning of one chorda tympani, 101 of the 126 patients (80 per
cent) noticed either an alteration in taste

TABLE 24–1: Taste Responses of Patients after Surgical Intervention in the Chorda Tympani

Taste Response	Section of One Chorda	Section of Both Chordae	Stretching of One Chorda
Total Number	126	32	100
Parageusia			
None	25	5	49
Transitory	61	2	44
Persistent	40	25	7
Taste Testing of Ipsilateral Side of Tongue			
Normal	none	none	62
Absent	all	all	29
Impaired	none	none	9

or dryness of the mouth. In 61 patients, the alteration of taste vanished after some time; in 40, the parageusia persisted. All of the 101 patients noted a metallic taste on the tongue which lasted for periods varying between one week and twenty-one years. Thirty-seven patients complained about dryness of the mouth.

In nearly half of these patients the abnormal taste was limited to one-half of the tongue and in the remaining cases the metallic taste was either spread over the entire tongue or limited to the tip; in 7 of the patients food was tasteless until it had reached the back of the tongue. These patients could taste food just before swallowing. In addition, 66 (52 per cent) of the patients complained that tea and/or coffee tasted bad, bread doughy, butter and/or chocolate greasy, biscuits gritty, and wine and liqueurs "different." Whereas in only 101 of the 126 patients parageusia existed, in all the patients the taste sensations (salt, sweet, bitter, and sour) had completely disappeared at the side of the tongue that had been innervated by the cut chorda tympani.

Electrical testing of taste sensation was also performed and it confirmed the presence of complete ageusia after sectioning of the chorda tympani. In 5 of the 32 patients where both chordae tympani had been severed no parageusia

developed; two had abnormal taste sensations which disappeared after some time; in 25 patients parageusia persisted with the perception of a metallic taste prevailing. Testing proved that taste sensations had completely disappeared in all patients. Seven patients (22 per cent) tasted food only a moment before it was swallowed. Actually this sensation came at such a late stage of the swallowing act that sometimes they realized too late that they disliked the food they were eating.

In 100 patients where the chorda tympani had only been stretched the sequelae were much more serious. On testing, the taste sensation was normal in 62 persons, absent in 29, and impaired in 9. No subjective signs of paraguesia were found in 49, transitory symptoms appeared in 44, and parageusia persisted in 7 patients. Twenty-two of the 62 patients, where the tests showed normal persistence of taste, had temporary symptoms of parageusia. Just as is the case after section of the chorda tympani, metallic taste was by far the most frequent manifestation of parageusia after stretching of the nerve.

It must be added that this group of patients has not been tested either with PTC or with PROP. Since some of the patients who show a negative reaction to quinine may still taste one of these thiouracil derivatives, these patients should be re-examined with the modern methods available. This holds especially true since Bull [2] has encountered considerable difficulties in testing taste on the dorsum of the tongue.

On the other hand, Bull's [2] results must be correct, because after resection of the chorda the fungiform papillae of the tongue are atrophic and the surface of the tongue becomes smooth and pale on the denervated side. Unfortunately, the condition of the papillae circumvallatae is not mentioned.

NON-PARTICIPATION OF LINGUAL AND GLOSSOPHARYNGEUS NERVES IN THE CONDUCTION OF TASTE SENSATION IN HUMANS

Examination of patients whose chorda tympani had been severed proves that this nerve carries not only the taste perception of the anterior two-thirds of the tongue but that of the entire tongue as well; after section of the chorda the taste perception of the lateral aspect of the *posterior third* of the tongue had also disappeared. This is proved not only by taste testing but also by the observation that certain patients, after the chorda has been cut, do not taste the food until just before the swallowing act. Whereas it may come as a shock to most that the conduction of taste sensations from the posterior third of the tongue by the glossopharyngeus cannot be demonstrated, the non-participation of the lingual nerve had been suspected by several neurologists. Both lingual and glossopharyngeus nerves may, however, carry fibers that conduct touch and pain sensations of the tongue.

After the chorda tympani has been severed, no regeneration of nerve fibers or reinnervation occurs in the intact chorda tympani of the contralateral side. The ageusia is permanent. These results

confirm again the well-known fact that conclusions obtained by experiments upon one family of the animal kingdom do not necessarily pertain to another family. In the rat—the prototype of the laboratory animals used for studies of animal taste—stimulation by quinine reveals that the taste fibers of the anterior and posterior parts of the tongue are located in different areas of the medulla. In addition, Halpern and Nelson [7] concluded that in the rat gustatory input via the glossopharyngeus is more important than that via the chorda tympani—sectioning of both nerves causes more loss of taste than sectioning of the chorda alone. In the chicken the glossopharyngeus nerve conducts nearly the entire taste sensation from tongue to chord.

THE INFLUENCE OF FREEZING THE VENTROLATERAL NUCLEUS OF THE THALAMUS ON TASTE PERCEPTION

Another modern operation interrupts the taste sensation at a much higher level, i.e., in the thalamus where the neurons carrying taste sensations pass on their way to the temporal cortex. Many neurosurgeons following the example of Cooper [3] now try to improve the condition of patients with Parkinson's disease by freezing a specific part of the thalamus, especially the posterior ventrolateral nucleus. Although the resulting lesion is usually somewhat anterior to that part of the thalamus involved in the sensory relay system, encroachment upon this area cannot always be avoided. It would appear that in these patients, too, an analysis of the deviations of taste might be of value. In view of the difference in the level of interruption of taste conduction, it could hardly be expected that the changes in taste sensation brought about by this operation would be similar to those caused by the severing of the chorda tympani. As far as I know, careful testing of taste sensation of the tongue with modern methods after cryothalamectomy has not yet been performed. However, some of these patients, though not specifically developing a metallic taste, complain about other modalities of parageusia.

OTHER INSTANCES OF DYSGEUSIA IN DISEASE

At this point it should be pointed out that a metallic taste, though not caused by a mechanical trauma to the chorda tympani, is a rather frequently observed symptom in the practice of medicine. In cases of lead poisoning in which patients received iodides or antimony preparations, metallic taste has often been encountered.

Iodides appear in the saliva and could cause the abnormal taste. The amount of lead present in the saliva is too small to cause a change of taste. On the other hand, lead often causes neuritis; by a stretch of the imagination slight damage to the chorda tympani could cause the abnormal taste. However, patients often complain of a metallic taste although no obvious cause can be determined.

Bitter taste is a frequent complaint in many diseases. In hepatic ailments the bitterness of the taste could be connected with the increase of the bile acid content of the blood. The ammonia taste in uremia is usually ascribed to excessive NH_3 formation from the increased urea content of the gastric juice by the urease of the stomach.

TASTE AND DIETARY HABITS IN DISEASES AND IN DIFFERENT ETHNIC GROUPS

Testing with PTC and PROP has revealed that duodenal ulcer patients are better tasters than gastric ulcer patients or healthy volunteers [10]. In patients with glaucoma, especially those with hypocorticism, changes in taste sensation have been described [1]. Henkin et al. [8] found that hypersensitivity to taste existed in patients with Addison's disease, adrenogenital syndrome, and cystic fibrosis. The hypersensitivity in hypocorticism persisted notwithstanding the fact that sodium and potassium metabolism had returned to normal under the influence of desoxycorticosterone. Only after the glucocorticoids had been given in the form of predniselone did the hypersensitivity for taste completely disappear. Since then, using the PTC and PROP tests, an increased incidence of non-tasters has been found among patients with nodular goiters and cretins, whereas among patients with toxic diffuse goiters, very few non-tasters have been present [5]. These findings are especially intriguing because derivatives of thiouracil cause the formation of goiters and block the synthesis of thyroxine within the thyroid gland. However, only some of the latter investigators have confirmed the differences in the tasting of PTC among patients with thyroid diseases [9].

Special interest has been evoked by the research of Fukuoka [6], who, using PTC, found only 7 per cent non-tasters among the Japanese whereas 30 per cent of the Caucasians tested were non-tasters. This finding points to the possibility that differences in taste perception of population groups may explain why the choice of nutrients in different countries varies so greatly. Although other authors have also found a smaller percentage of non-tasters among Orientals, Negroes in Africa, and American Indians, the findings of Fukuoka have not been confirmed completely. In other PTC taste tests, 17.1 per cent and 21.0 per cent of the non-tasters were found among Japanese test persons [9]. These figures are not *too* far removed from the percentage of non-tasters discovered among Caucasians.

The fact that the Orientals may be better tasters than the Caucasians may be only partly responsible for the differences in the diets of different ethnic groups. The Chinese who, when poor, is satisfied with his meager hypocaloric, mainly vegetarian diet, becomes a gourmet as soon as financial circumstances permit. He then indulges in eggs, pork, veal, chicken, and other animal food which he could not buy when he was poor. As a result, gout and coronary sclerosis, a rarity among poor Chinese in China, are frequent afflictions among the Chinese patients admitted to the New York hospitals located near the Chinese districts.

All this notwithstanding, experiments trying to connect the sense of taste with preferences for specific foods should certainly be continued. It should be emphasized, however, that the choice of nutrients by population groups also depends on factors that are not connected with inborn racial characteristics of taste.

OTHER FACTORS INFLUENCING THE CHOICE OF NUTRIENTS BY DIFFERENT POPULATION GROUPS

A "unique" taste sensation is prevalent in the United States since a great number of adult citizens drink milk; adult milk drinkers are rare specimens in other Western countries. This exceptional custom is based upon the official recommendation of our nutrition authorities that the daily average intake of calcium should never fall below 800 mg. A few years ago an effort to increase the calcium requirement to 1,000 mg/day was defeated. Since all other nutrients do not contain enough calcium to raise the daily calcium consumption to such a

level, anyone who wishes to ingest 800 mg of calcium/day is automatically obliged to drink several glasses of milk each day. This 800 mg calcium requirement has been thoroughly impressed upon the public by the lay press, radio, and television propaganda, and also by physicians. Thus, every American citizen is afraid that unless he drinks several glasses of milk each day, his nails will either stop growing or, worse still, fall off, his teeth will crumble, his bones soften, and other still more horrible diseases will shorten his lifespan. There is little doubt that the recommendation of a daily intake of 800 mg of calcium is erroneous. "The proof of the pudding is in the eating"; the intake of calcium in other Western countries averages around 450 mg daily and the health statistics of these nations are impressive.

The addiction of the American people to milk drinking is in sharp contrast to the aversion to dairy products that prevails in China and many other Oriental countries. Before efforts are made to ascribe the abhorrence of the Orientals to different taste perceptions, the following points should be weighed.

After untold centuries of agriculture without even the most elementary methods of soil conservation, extensive areas of the Orient cannot be used for production of food any more. Therefore, it has become mandatory to obtain a maximum of calories from every available acre. The planting of carbohydrate products results in a much larger production of calories than can be obtained by using the same soil for animal husbandry. Since the Chinese cannot obtain milk or dairy products, in their Oriental wisdom they teach their children that milk is loathsome, that butter is only cow oil, and that educated people should not think of consuming the malodorous product that goes under the name of cheese. In China the truth of an Italian proverb "poverty is the mother of health" is proved. Since the Chinese do not eat dairy products, which are full of saturated fats, they do not suffer from our ubiquitous medical scourges, i.e., arteriosclerosis, thrombophlebitis, or cholesterol gallstones.

Even the young Chinese who have had the privilege of a Western education can only with difficulty be persuaded to drink milk. Nevertheless, he fully realizes that food rich in fats and cholesterol, such as milk, if added to the Chinese diet, would help to build up resistance to the ubiquitous exposure to tuberculosis that exists in China. Milk must be mixed with cocoa to make it palatable to the house staff members of Chinese hospitals, and, even then, strict supervision is necessary to make certain that these young men drink milk twice daily. Without such supervision, many of them "forget" to take their milk. In the same hospital where at least the house staff members took some milk daily, the nursing staff tenaciously refused to drink any milk, notwithstanding education, persuasion, coaxing, etc.

Opposite conditions are of course present in the milk- and cheese-producing Western countries. In the European countries where the ominous daily requirement of 800 mg calcium is not accepted, adults do not drink milk. The European child after his tenth birthday resents being treated as a child. He wishes to act as quickly as possible as adults do and, therefore, he steadfastly refuses to drink milk. In Europe a fat boy is considered ridiculous. He becomes automatically isolated because his being overweight would make it impossible for him to participate in the national sport, e.g., soccer. The attitude of children to the problem of obesity is evidently different in the United States. The American child sees that his father drinks milk with great pleasure and hears the praise

of the health-bringing milk products. Therefore, to American children milk is a necessity, and ice cream, banana splits, and other allied products are not forbidden—hence, the large number of plump and obese children.

Since no member of the animal kingdom drinks milk after weaning, the milk drinking of the adult American population must be considered abnormal. This dangerous habit is based upon erroneous official recommendations backed up by clever propaganda.

In this connection it must be mentioned that the damage from the abuse of milk fat becomes evident in early adulthood. Fifty per cent of the American soldiers killed in Korea—average age, twenty-two—during autopsy were found to have sclerosis of at least one coronary artery. In 10 per cent of the American casualties one coronary artery was completely closed [4]. Among the Korean soldiers no arteriosclerosis was found; their diet had consisted of about 3,000 calories with 4–10 per cent fat, 73–87 per cent carbohydrates. All of them were either underweight or normal. When, for experimental reasons, a group of Koreans was put on the diet of the American soldiers, 17 per cent became overwieght [12] within two to four weeks.

There are other examples of the unfortunate results of well-meant advice given by competent agricultural economists. Since rice requires excellent soil, efforts were made to find another food that would grow on relatively poor soil and produce even more calories than rice. For this purpose the population was advised to plant cassave, also known as tapioca or manioc and made from a tuber which can be grown in soil unsuitable for rice. Unfortunately, the cassave tuber contains hydrocyanic acid which has to be removed by washing the flour. This washing carries away most of the protein content in which the cassave root is low from the beginning. This protein-poor staple caused the most severe epidemics of edema caused by hypoproteinemia and beriberi [14].

In other countries the author has observed many examples of customs adhered to in the parental home that are the decisive factors in molding dietary choices for the child who has reached adulthood. Many children whose parents adhered to religious rules forbidding the eating of non-ruminating mammals, of aquatic animals without scales, and a few other choice dishes, became agnostics when they grew up. They completely refused to recognize these dietary laws. Nevertheless, a large number of these neoagnostics avoid pork chops and ham. They do not enjoy the hedonistic sensation of the cold, amorphous, elastic oyster slithering through the oral cavity and gliding smoothly toward the orifice of the gullet. Evidently the image of uncleanliness taught in the parental home still clings to the formerly forbidden animal products. The Dutch language has many true and wise proverbs, and none is better than "What the peasant does not know, the peasant does not eat."

Another example of the dependence in the choice of foods on customs is the craving of the Orientals for *white* polished rice. This craving is one of the main causes of beriberi endemics. Wholly polished rice is nutritionally far inferior to "dirty" rice, that is, partly polished rice. Ample amounts of vitamin B_1, minerals, and even fat (1–2 per cent) are present in the outer layer of the rice but are lost during the milling and polishing. Hence, the frequency of beriberi in such areas as southern China and the Philippines, where not only the urban populace but also the peasant population eat white polished rice primarily. In large rural areas of India and Indonesia the population eats only hand-pounded rice—beriberi does not occur. When the native women pound the rice with their primitive utensils, only the hard outer husk is removed. The outer layer of the rice proper, the silver fleece, however, remains intact, and the hand-pounded rice, the brownish looking "gabah," contains enough vitamin B_1 to protect the population against beriberi.

It is well-nigh impossible to induce all Oriental rice-eating people to eat the hand-pounded rice that gives such good protection against beriberi. In China, for instance, there is a pronounced preference for white polished rice, and the man who eats brown, so-called dirty rice loses considerable face. Poor farmers have no choice but to eat their own brown hand-pounded rice and remain healthy. People who are in a higher income bracket can buy white polished rice and develop avitaminosis! The same thing was observed in Indonesia at the time when large estates employed hundreds of thousands of Chinese laborers. The estates provided these laborers with only partially milled silver fleece rice, and the incidence of beriberi among them fell to a negligible minimum. Only the Chinese overseers of the estates occasionally suffered from beriberi. It goes without saying that these overseers earned larger salaries than the laborers and could afford to buy their own white polished rice in the village instead of accepting the despised, "dirty" silver fleece rice which the estates put at their disposal. The beriberi of the overseers demonstrated again how a selection of special nutrients—in this case, white rice—may lead to disease [13].

INSTINCT AND DIET

The experiments with adrenalectomized rats, who after a short time showed a preference for health-bringing sodium chloride solution over damaging lithium chloride, have of course impressed the clinicians.

These results fitted well with the osteophagia of cows in certain parts of South Africa. In the areas where the soil is poor in phosphates, the cows, in order to restore the decreased calcium phosphate content of their skeletons to normal, will search for old bones which may lie hidden in the subsoil. At night, crossing the "Veldt" of South Africa, the traveler may hear the crunching of bone by a large animal. The foreigner, afraid that he has lost his bearings and has strayed into a lion's den, is well satisfied to discover that the large animals are bone-eating cows. Incidentally, because these bones may have been buried in the soil for many years, the cows often develop botulism. Comparable instincts drive the chickens living in a calcium-deficient part of the Amazon River basin to eat the shells of the eggs they produced themselves.

Instincts for healthy nutrients are found in the jungle population. In the eastern part of the Indonesian Archipelago, i.e., in the Moluccas and in New Guinea, sago flour is the staple food of the population. Sago flour, prepared from the marrow of the sago palm, must be washed before it is dried. After this purification process, sago (like cassava flour) contains practically nothing but carbohydrates, with mere traces of protein and vitamins. The native population supplements their cassave and sago diets with animals caught in the forest, ranging from lizards, spiders, caterpillars, worms, and larvae to small game. These animals, high in vitamin B and protein content, form the necessary addition to the sago-flour diet.

In New Guinea the Papuans put maggots into the marrow of a living sago palm and close with mud the opening through which the maggots are introduced. Every morning the Papuan auscultates the inoculated area. Only when the noise of the growing maggots is loud enough is the tree opened again. The large maggots are eaten as a delicacy. As long as these tribes remain in the virginal forests and follow their centuries-old dietary habits, their health is relatively satisfactory. As soon as civilization teaches these natives to despise the animals of the forest, deficiency diseases appear. However, jungle inhabitants often have eating habits that conserve their health and these should not be changed.

In the population of the Western world these instincts are apparently obtunded. When children scrape chalk from walls and eat it, we are inclined to ascribe this urge to a calcium deficiency. However, children also scratch walls covered with lead-containing paint, a frequent cause of lead poisoning in childhood. Some children have an urge to suck on hairy objects. The swallowed material accumulates in the stomach, resulting in the formation of large hair balls and bezoars, which ultimately require surgical intervention. In other words, we often measure with two different standards; if the abnormal craving has an incidentally favorable influence on a food deficiency, we admire the child for its correct intuition. If the craving damages the health, we condone it and try to cure the ensuing disease.

When Minot discovered that pernicious anemia could be cured by the ingestion of liver, only one or two of the patients described kept themselves alive by eating large amounts of liver. These cases, however, were exceptions. Only a few children are known who consumed abnormally large quantities of salt and later proved to suffer from Addison's disease. During the World War II in the occupied Netherlands, it was found that the consumption of large amounts of a patent medicine that soothed the pains of patients with stomach ulcers caused edema and hypertension. After the war, analysis of these tablets revealed that the active part of this medication consisted of licorice. It was then found that licorice contains considerable amounts of desoxycorticosterone, a derivative of the hormones of the adrenal cortex. Actually, it was then proved that patients with adrenocortical insufficiency could be treated successfully with licorice. However, no patient with Addison's disease has ever treated himself with licorice.

SUMMARY

The taste sensation reaches the central nervous system via the chorda tympani nerve without any participation of the lingual nerve, i.e., the trigeminus or the glossopharyngeus nerve. After sectioning of the chorda tympani the taste sensation disappears at the ipsilateral side of the tongue, but dysgeusia, mainly in the form of a metallic taste, develops, usually temporarily, in 80 per cent of the cases. Destruction of the ventrolateral nucleus of the thalamus leads to a different dysgeusia. Different diseases and medications may lead to various dysgeusias. The differences in the diets of the peoples of the world probably depend only rarely on inborn differences of the taste sense. In countries where advertisement techniques are highly developed, erroneous nutritional concepts may lead to a completely unbalanced national diet. In other countries where certain foods are not available to the population, an aversion for these foods may be cultivated.

Customs adhered to in parental homes often decide the food choices that children, after reaching adulthood, will make. In other countries prestige or status is the main reason why certain wholesome foods are refused and less valuable nutrients are chosen.

Aborigines complete their qualitatively insufficient food intake by consuming insects, reptiles, and small game living in the jungle forests. Their health status is immediately endangered if they are persuaded to abandon their original way of living. Unfortunately, in the Western population the instinctive choice of correct diets is practically nonexistent.

REFERENCES

1. Becker, B., and Morton, W. R. Phenylthiourea taste testing and glaucoma. *Arch. Opthalm.*, **72**: 323–27, 1964.
2. Bull, T. R. Taste and the chorda tympani. *J. Laryng. and Otol.*, **79**: 479–93, 1965.
3. Cooper, I. S. Surgical Treatment of Parkinsonism. *Ann. Rev. Med.*, **16**: 309–19, 1965.
4. Enos, W. F., Beyer, J. C., and Holmes, R. H. Pathogenesis of coronary disease in American soldiers killed in Korea. *JAMA*, **158**: 912–14, 1955.
5. Fischer, R., and Griffin, F. Taste-blindness and variations in taste threshold in relation to thyroid metabolism. *J. Neuropsychiat.*, **3**: 98–104, 1961.
6. Fukuoka, G. Frequency of taste-blindness among Japanese and related races. *Eugenical News*, **21**: 52–57, 1936.
7. Halpern, B. P., and Nelson, L. M. Bulbar gustatory responses to anterior and posterior tongue stimulation in the rat. *Amer. J. Physiol.*, **209**: 105–10, 1965.
8. Henkin, R. I., Gill, J. R., and Bartter, F. C. Studies on taste thresholds in normal men and in patients with adrenocortical insufficiency. *J. Clin. Invest.*, **42**: 729–38, 1963.
9. Hollingworth, D. R. Phenylthiourea taste testing in Hiroshima subjects with thyroid disease. *J. Clin. Endocr.*, **23**: 961–63, 1963.
10. Kaplan, A. R., Fischer, R., Glanville, E., Power, W., Kamionkowski, M., and Flesher, B. Differential taste sensitivities in duodenal and gastric ulcer patients. *Gastroenterology*, **47**: 604–9, 1964.
11. Rosen, S. Simple method for restoring hearing in otosclerosis; mobilization of stapes. *Acta Otolaryng.*, **44**: 78–88, 1954.
12. Sandstead, H. R., and Koehn, C. J. Nutrition of Korean Army: Field Studies, May-June, 1953. *Amer. J. Clin. Nutr.*, **13**: 25–34, 1963.
13. Snapper, I. Food Preferences in Man: Special Cravings and Aversions. *Ann. N.Y. Acad. Sci.*, **63**: 92–106, 1955.
14. Snapper, I. *Chinese Lessons to Western Medicine.* 2nd ed. Grune & Stratton, New York and London, 1965.

25: *Final Remarks*

L. M. BEIDLER

I T HAS BEEN demonstrated many times during this conference that food acceptance plays a dominant role in the relation between the chemical senses and nutrition. Although the acceptance of food depends upon many factors, including social ones, flavor is probably the most important. But what is food flavor? It is the sensual evaluation of the food. In order to study the physiological basis of flavor we simplify the problem and try to determine the relevance of the various sense organs, usually considering the contribution of each, one at a time. The importance of taste and smell in flavor evaluation is obvious, but several participants in this conference emphasized the contribution of the tactile, temperature, auditory, pain, and visual senses. Pangborn fooled the majority of the participants by coloring citrus-flavored lollipops cherry red. Few of us correctly determined the flavor after eating one of the lollipops.

In order to obtain objective measurements of the relation of food intake to nutrition, many of us turn away from the study of humans and rely upon animal experimentation. This allows us to use a number of powerful physiological and psychological techniques that cannot be easily applied to human subjects.

But how do we communicate with laboratory animals concerning the relation of flavor to their intake of specific foods necessary for good nutrition? We try to avoid this problem by varying one food flavor parameter (for example, sweetness) at a time and observing some change in the behavior of the animal that might give us a clue as to the controlling or regulating mechanisms. Herein lies a major difficulty. How do we know on what basis an animal may make a discrimination? Surely he doesn't know that we designed a taste or odor experiment? Henkin described to us an experiment he originally designed to determine whether humans can smell sucrose or sodium chloride solutions. He was amazed to find that his human subjects could correctly discriminate these solutions on the basis of odor. Later he found that the subjects did not use the sucrose or sodium chloride contained in the solutions in order to discriminate but used instead the odor of small amounts of contaminants. Kare also mentioned that birds might detect odors not by stimulation of their olfactory receptors but by stimulation of their corneas. We found in our laboratory that we could easily determine taste thresholds of young children. However, if we highly motivated these children by immediate monetary rewards, the taste thresholds often dropped considerably. It was only after much experimentation that we discovered many clues other than taste that children use to discriminate between solutions that supposedly differ only in concentration of a particular taste component! All of these examples indicate the difficulty for the experimenter who wants to control one flavor parameter at a time.

How complex is the receptor basis for odor detection or quality evaluation in experimental animals? Most vertebrates studied have three different sensory systems by which they can respond to odors; namely, the olfactory organ, Jacobson's or the vomeronasal organ, and the free nerve ending of the trigeminal nerve. Tucker showed in our laboratory that it is difficult to predict which of these systems respond to low concentrations of a particular odor. For example, phenyl ethyl alcohol, a rather fragrant odor to man, stimulates the trigeminal endings at a lower concentration than that necessary to stimulate the olfactory receptors. Unfortunately, there is little evidence available concerning the relative importance of these three odor-detecting systems in eliciting a given behavioral response. Henkin showed us that similar problems exist for the human detection of taste substances. In addition, the ability of an animal to detect a given odor greatly depends upon the state of the animal, particularly the level of sympathetic nerve activity. Thus, we conclude that many variables are involved in chemical detection and discrimination and that we may expect that some of these may vary with the nutritional need of an animal. It should also be emphasized that threshold values of odors and tastes need not be directly related to the intensity of response to suprathreshold concentrations. The chemical senses, which are not the only determinants of food intake that may be related to the animal's nutritional state, are very complex indeed.

SAMUEL LEPKOVSKY

If we are going to make progress in our understanding of nutritional processes, we must bridge the gap that exists between current work on the nervous system and work on the biochemistry of the body. In order to do this, the psychologists, neurophysiologists, and biochemists must work together. We have made a good start at this conference. We will have to communicate with each other and that seems to be difficult, but the difficulty is not unique to this conference. Scientists dealing with biochemistry and behavior also found that communication was difficult since individuals held different views (Eiduson et al., Biochemistry and Behavior, Van Nostrand, New York, 1964) on semantics and methods. One individual "believed that a sequential causal relationship existed and that any behavioral process must be preceded by biochemical reactions." All agreed "that the brain (or almost any organ for that matter) was [such] a complex mechanism that it was indeed difficult even to consider causal relationships." There was agreement "that interdisciplinary thinking and approaches to problems involving biochemistry and behavior could indeed be fruitful ... [and] not only may biochemistry provide some of the bases for behavior and thus greater understanding and explanation of phenomenon on a psychological level, but conversely perhaps, behavioral data, once meaningfully schematized, may provide clues and ideas for biochemical research."

We also have dealt with biochemistry and behavior at this conference. It is accepted that in living systems nothing "just happens"; everything that happens is made to happen, and for everything that happens there must be a mechanism. The mechanism or mechanisms are probably biochemical in nature. Eating is alimentary behavior and has a "biochemical core" that deals with "the translation of bodily needs into behavior" (Kubie, *Psychosom. Med.,* **10**: 15, 1948).

For example, *palatability* does not have the same meaning for everyone. Many psychologists use the term operationally, but many of them use it anthropomorphically. Nutritionsts link taste or palatability with the nutritional value of food—the higher the nutritional value of the diet, the more palatable the food. Nutritionists are not dealing with taste as a sensation experienced by human beings when they consider acceptability of food by animals. A good example of this is the use of wet food. It has been asserted that wet food is more palatable than dry food. Those who make this claim must show that foods treated with water do not undergo chemical changes that have increased their nutritional value. Animals may eat more wet food, not because of improved palatability, but because of increased nutritional value. This will be illustrated by the following experiment. Some chickens were fed dry mash and others a wet mash. The chickens ate more of the wet mash. The wet mash was then carefully dried so that it reverted to a dry mash. The chickens continued to eat approximately the same amount of this dry mash as they did when this mash was wet. The experiment was interpreted to mean that chickens ate more wet mash, not because the food was wet, but because the nutritional value of the diet had increased.

Saccharine has no nutritional value; yet solutions of saccharine are preferred by rats to water. The inference is that saccharine is preferred because it tastes sweet. Sucaryl is also sweet, but the rat

shows an aversion for it (Murray *et al., J. Comp. Physiol. Psychol.,* **46**: 134, 1953). Moreover, many other animals do not prefer saccharine. The meaning of the preference for saccharine by rats remains to be elucidated; it cannot be explained anthropomorphically by its sweet taste as experienced by human beings.

With such conferences as this one, we shall learn not only to communicate with each other but, more important, eventually to work with each other. Such interdisciplinary collaboration will produce results that will help to close the gap now existing between the results of workers on the nervous system and those of the workers on bodily biochemistry. Thus our understanding of the nutritional processes will be enhanced.

PAUL B. PEARSON

It is a great pleasure to extend the Foundation's congratulations to you on the occasion of this very important symposium. John Masefield has said: "The days that make us happy make us wise." By that criterion I should be very wise. The opportunity to be here with such distinguished and erudite ladies and gentlemen has been a most stimulating and rewarding experience.

While this conference has been concerned primarily with an understanding of the chemical senses, it has yielded great potential application to the broad field of nutrition. Over the ages man has been concerned with taste and odor, yet even in this modern age of science these senses are probably less well understood than any of the other senses. The mechanisms of the senses of vision and hearing are well understood, and there are means of correcting their deficiencies.

In his treatise on the physiology of taste published in 1825, Brillat de Savarin wrote in discussing the mechanism of taste: "It is not easy to determine exactly wherein the faculty of taste consists. It is more complicated than it appears. Certainly the tongue plays a great part in the mechanism of taste." While our knowledge of the mechanism of taste is much greater than it was 140 years ago, the statement made by De Savarin is quite applicable to the situation today. He then went on to say: "The sensation of taste is a chemical operation, made in the humid way, as we called it formerly; that is to say, that it is necessary for the sapid molecules to be dissolved by some fluid to be finally absorbed by the nervous ganglia, papillae, or suckers which cover the interior of the organ of taste."

The taste mechanism is likely the same in all parts of the world and in all races of men even though there are individual genetic differences in man's taste response to various substances. There is little doubt that different people have quite different tastes and that certain food preferences follow definite psychological, national, and cultural practices. Some of these differences may be based on different individual taste thresholds.

To a large degree, man's taste reaction to food is a product of his environmental background. His taste sensations have developed against a background of chemical complexity. Food is, as a rule, complex in chemical composition and only rarely approaches chemical purity such as does salt or sugar.

It has long been known in man that molecular configuration affects the taste or degree of sweetness. Some amino acids are tasteless in both the D- and L-forms. In others, and particularly in the aromatic amino acids, the D-forms are sweet whereas the L-forms, which are the naturally occurring form, are bitter. L-trytophane is half as bitter as caffeine while the D-form is about thirty-five times as sweet as sucrose. On the other hand, D-glutamic acid is tasteless whereas the L-form exhibits the well-known glutamate flavor.

It is common knowledge that we can learn to like foods which at first did not have an acceptable taste and odor. To some Eastern peoples, rice is the natural staff of life and bread is not a very acceptable food. The rice-eating Bengali in 1944 would starve rather than use wheat flour. Riots broke out in Kerala in January, 1966, when people felt the central government was trying to force them to eat wheat. It took at least 200 years after the white potato was introduced into Europe before it was widely used. In general, food habits are resistant to change. This tendency is greater in less-educated and less-traveled people. Taste is one of the major factors in changing food habits and the acceptability of food. In most cases, taste and odor play a much more important role in acceptability than does the actual nutritive value of the food.

The molecular approach toward understanding the chemical senses is still in its early stages of development. Still, much progress has been made since the preceding conference on taste, held here on the Cornell campus in 1960. I would expect that great strides will be made during the coming years toward understanding the chemical senses. The diversity of the disciplines represented at this conference and the high scientific talent of the participants give reason for optimism. An understanding of the chemical senses promises to have application of major importance in world food problems. Many countries where a large proportion of the people suffer from malnutrition have high-quality food materials that are not going into human food channels. If these high-protein materials, such as fish and the protein residues from oil seeds, can be made acceptable and can be incorporated into the diet of the population, it would go a long way toward improving the nutrition of the people in the developing countries.

This conference has been a very exciting and satisfying experience for me. It has brought together leaders in psychology, microbiology, nutrition, genetics, physiology, medicine, neurophysiology, zoology, and others having a common interest in the sense of taste. The various disciplines and tools being brought to bear in the search for an understanding of the sense of taste makes me optimistic about the progress that will be made in the next few years. I think it is one of the most productive activities that the Foundation has had an opportunity to undertake. We in the Foundation are pleased to have had the opportunity to sponsor this conference on the chemical senses and the nutritive processes.

Bibliography

on the Sense of Taste
(1566-1966)

Prepared by
Rose Marie Pangborn and Ida M. Trabue
Department of Food Science and Technology
University of California

PREFACE

This compilation of over 3,000 references consists of published material on the sense of taste, including anatomical, physiological, chemical, genetic, and behavioral aspects for all species. Excluded from this collection are articles on olfaction, odor, aroma, flavor, and general food intake per se.

With the exception of references preceded by an asterisk, all citations were verified from the original publication. All foreign language titles were freely translated into English. To conserve space, journals are listed by a four-letter code, CODEN.* A complete listing of the CODEN and corresponding journals are listed alphabetically in the appendix of this bibliography. A partial subject index also appears in the appendix.

Appreciation is extended to the reference library staff of the University of California, Davis, for assistance in locating obscure journals. We also thank the secretarial staff of the Department of Food Science and Technology for the extensive typing and collating, and Mrs. Rosalind Chrisp and Mrs. Linda Bertolero for technical assistance.

Interested readers are cordially invited to correct and/or supplement this listing.

Rose Marie Pangborn
Ida M. Trabue

Davis, California
July, 1966

*CODEN for Periodical Titles. ASTM Special Technical Publications Nos. 329 and 329-S1, American Society for Testing and Materials, Philadelphia, Pa., 1963. Supplement, 1964.

ABASOV, I. T. 1961 Izmeneniia vkhusovoi chuistvitel' nosti u bol'n'ikh rakom. (Changes in gustatory sensitivity in patients with cancer.) SOME, 25: 47–52.

ABBOTT, P. S. 1948 A study of the taste sensitivity of the Bufo marinus. Unpublished Master's thesis, University of Hawaii, 66 pp.

———. 1953 The effect of temperature on taste in the white rat. Unpublished Ph.D. thesis, Brown University, 130 pp.

ABESHOUSE, B. S., and LERMAN, S. 1947 Parageusia as a symptom of genitourinary disease. UCRE, 51: 621–26.

ABLES, M. F., and BENJAMIN, R. M. 1960 Thalamic relay nucleus for taste in albino rat. JONE, 23: 376–82.

ABRAHAM, G. R. 1944 Über die Beteiligung der Vorderbeine au der Chemorezeption bei einigen Wasserwanzen. (On participation of the anterior legs of some water bugs in chemoreception.) ZVPH, 30: 321–42.

ABRAHAMS, H., KRAKAUER, D., and DALLENBACH, K. M. 1937 Gustatory adaptation to salt. AJPC, 49: 462–69.

ABULADZE, K. C. 1952 K fiziologii votovogo ximieskogo vkysovogo analizatora. (Toward the physiology of the oral chemical taste analyzer.) in Soveshchanie po Progleman Vysshei Nervnoi Deiatel' Nosti 15th, I. P. Pavlova (ed.). Leningrad, 294 pp. (see pp. 130–134).

ACKERMANN. 1885 Ueber die Geschmacks-Veränderung oder—Beeinträchtigung durch Gebissplatten. (Influence of dentures on taste changes.) DMZK, 5: 259–69.

ADACHI, A. 1962 (Study on the taste mechanisms of Na-glutamate and Na-inosinate.) JPSJ, 24: 607–13. (In Japanese; English summary.)

———. 1964 (Neurophysiological study of taste effectiveness of seasoning.) JPSJ, 26: 347–55. (In Japanese; English summary.)

ADACHI, A., FUNAKOSHI, M., KASAHARA, Y., and KAWAMURA, Y. 1964 (Electrophysiological analysis of taste of soda water.) JPSJ, 26: 306–12. (In Japanese; English summary.)

*ADAMS, J. R., and HOLBERT, P. E. 1963 The fine structure of insect contact chemoreceptors. PCZO, 3: 93–95.

ADAMTZIK, K. H. 1936 Über die Geschmackswirkung von anorganischen Doppelsalzen. I. (On taste effects of inorganic salts.) Inaugural Dissertation, B. Sporn, Jena, 36 pp.

ADLER, A. 1934 Zur Topik des Verlaufes der Geschmackssinnsfasern und anderer afferenter Bahnen im Thalamus. (The course of the taste fibers and other afferent pathways in the thalamus.) ZGNP, 149: 208–20.

———. 1935 Zur Topik der corticalen Geschmackssphäre. (Cortical localization of the sphere of taste.) ZGNP, 152: 25–33.

———. 1940 The phenomenon of taste and smell. BNEM, 2: 237–38.

ADRIAN, E. D. 1947 The Physical Background of Perception. Clarendon Press, Oxford, 95 pp. (see p. 60).

ADUCCO, V., and MOSSO, U. 1886 Ricerche sopra la fisiologia del gusto. (Research on the physiology of taste.) GMDT, 34: 39–42.

AEBY. 1877 Sinnesorgane. I: Allgemeines. Geruch und Geschmack. (Sense organs. I: General. Smell and taste.) JFPN, 6: 317–24.

AGEEVA-MAĬKOVA, O. G. 1946 Neirokhirurgicheskie dannye o khode vkuso pro vodiashikh volokon. (Neuro-surgical data on the path of taste-conducting nerve.) VONE, 10: 61–63.

AHOKAS, A. J., PAYNE, J. G., and GOETZL, F. R. 1950 The influence of amphetamine sulfate upon the acuity of the sense of taste for sucrose and upon the sensation complex of appetite and satiety. PFMB, 8: 107–12.

AITKEN, R. S., and BRAIN, R. T. 1933 Facial palsy and infection with Zoster virus. LANC, 1: 19–22.

AJTAI, A. K. von. 1872 Ein Beitrag zur Kenntniss der Geschmacksorgane. (A contribution to the knowledge of taste organs.) AMAE, 8: 455–60.

AKESSON, H. O. 1959 Taste deficiency for phenylthio-urea in southern Sweden. AGMG, 8: 431–33.

———. 1959–60 Taste sensitivity to phenyl-thiourea in tuberculosis and diabetes mellitus. ANHG, 23: 262–65.

ALAJOUANINE, T., THUREL, R., MIGNOT, H., and BRISSAUD, H. 1939 Poliomyelite chronique cervico-bulbaire avec agueusie. (Chronic cervicobulbar poliomyelitis with ageusia.) RENE, 71: 182–88.

ALBERT, A. 1936 Geschmacksstörungen bei vollständiger Aufmeisselung der Mittelohrräume. (Disturbances of taste in complete exposure of the middle ear cavities.) Inaugural Dissertation, Koch, Marburg-Lahn, 14 pp.

ALBERTI, C. 1935 Variazioni di sapore nella dulcina. (Variation in the taste of dulcin.) ACNC, 5: 271–79.

———. 1939 Su alcune trasformazioni di dulcina. (Some transformations of dulcin.) ACNC, 3: 21–26.

———. 1939 Su alcune trasformazioni della dulcina. Nota V sulla dulcina. (Some transformations of dulcin. V.) GCIT, 69: 150–62.

ALCOCK, B. 1836 Determination of the question, which are the nerves of taste. DJMC, 10: 256–79.

ALEXANDER, J. 1949 Odor detection. CENE, 27 (2) : 2227.

ALEKSANDROVA, A. E. 1955 Mekhanizm deistviia gorechi na pishchevye refleksy. (Mechanism of action of bitters on digestive reflexes.) FZLZ, 41: 630–34.

ALLARA, E. 1937 I dispositivi vaso-sensoriali della lingua. (Vaso-sensory disposition of the tongue.) AIAE, 37: 125–46.

———. 1939 Ricerche sull'organo del gusto dell'uomo. 1: La struttura delle papille gustative nelle varie età della vita. (Research on the organ of taste in man. 1: The structure of the taste papilla at various ages.) AIAE, **42:** 506–64.

———. 1940 Il contenuto minerale delle formazioni gustative della lingua umana nelle varie età della vita. (The mineral content of the gustatory formation of the human tongue at different ages.) BSIB, **15:** 1187–88.

———. 1941 Ricerche sull'organo del gusto dell'uomo. 2: Le sostanze minerali delle formazioni gustative nelle varie età della vita. (Research of the organ of taste in man. 2: The mineral substance of the formation of taste at the different ages of life.) AIAE, **46:** 96–126.

———. 1950 Modificazioni nell'organo del gusto di *Mus rattus albinus* in seguito a castrazione. (Changes in the organ of taste of *Mus rattus albinus* following castration.) MZOI, **58** (Supplement): 46–48.

———. 1952 Sull'influenza determinata dalla castrazione e dalla somministrazione di propionato di testosterone sulle formazioni gustative di *Mus rattus albinus*. (Influence of castration and administration of testosterone propionate on taste formation of the white rat.) BSIB, **28:** 68–59.

———. 1952 Sull'influenza esercitata dagli ormoni sessuali sulla struttura delle formazioni gustative di *Mus rattus albinus*. (Effect of sex hormones on the structure of the taste buds in the *Mus rattus albinus*.) RBIL, **44:** 209–99. (English summary.)

ALLEN, F. 1957 The sensations of taste and the logarithmic law of response. ZEPS, **160:** 276–81.

ALLEN, F., and SCHWARTZ, M. 1940 The effect of stimulation of the senses of vision, hearing, taste, and smell upon the sensibility of the organs of vision. JGPL, **24:** 105–21.

ALLEN, F., and WEINBERG, M. 1925 The gustatory sensory reflex. OJEH, **15:** 385–420.

ALLEN, I. M. 1944 Spontaneous olfactory and gustatory phenomena with and without organic lesions of the brain. NZMJ, **43:** 165–68.

ALLEN, W. F. 1922–23 Origin and destination of the secondary visceral fibers in the guinea pig. JCNE, **35:** 275–311.

———. 1923. Origin and distribution of the tractus solitarius in the guinea pig. JCNE, **35:** 171–204.

ALLIEZ, J., and NOSEDA, M. 1945 Considérations statisques et cliniques sur les hallucinations olfactives et gustatives. (Statistical and clinical considerations on olfactory and gustatory hallucinations.) AMPY, **103:** 134–41.

ALLISON, A. C. 1951 A note on taste-blindness in Kenya Africans and Arabs. MANA, **205:** 119–20.

ALLISON, A. C., and BLUMBERG, B. S. 1959 Ability to taste phenylthiocarbamide among Alaskan Eskimos and other populations. HUBI, **31:** 352–59.

ALLISON, A. C., and NEVANLINNA, H. R. 1952–53 Taste deficiency in Lappish and Finnish populations. ANEU, **17:** 113–14.

ALLISON, J. B. 1931–32 Stimulation by hydrochloric acid and by the normal aliphatic acids in the sunfish *Eupomotis*. JGPL, **15:** 621–28.

ALLISON, J. B., and COLE, W. H. 1934 Stimulation of fundulus by hydrochloric and fatty acids in fresh water, and by fatty acids, mineral acids, and the sodium salts of mineral acids in sea water. JGPL, **17:** 803–16.

ALVIAL, B., and HENCKEL, C. 1944 La agusia relativa a la fenil-tio-urea. (Ageusia relative to phenylthiourea.) BOBC, **18:** 73–76.

AMAN, C. W. 1955 The relation of taste and odor to flavor. TOCJ, **21:** 1–4.

AMBILINO, R. 1898 Sui rapporti del ganglio genicolato con la corda del timpano e col facciale. (Report on the geniculate ganglion with the chorda tympani and facial nerve.) PISN, **19:** 123–40.

AMICI, A., and RASCHELLA, D. 1958 Sulla opportunità di ricerche sistematiche relative ad un trascurato aspetto dei rapporti tra i sensi chimici. (An opportunity for a systematic research on a neglected aspect of the interrelation of the chemical senses.) RBIL, **50:** 237–45.

ANDERSEN, H. T., FUNAKOSHI, M., and ZOTTERMAN, Y. 1962 Electrophysiological investigation of the gustatory effect of various biological sugars. APSC, **56:** 362–75.

———. 1963 Electrophysiological responses to sugars and their depression by salt, in *Olfaction and Taste*, Y. Zotterman (ed.). Macmillan, New York, 396 pp. (see pp. 177–92).

ANDERSON, A. L. 1932 The sensitivity of the legs of common butterflies to sugar. JEZO, **63:** 235–59.

ANDERSON, C. D. 1955 The effect of subliminal salt solutions on taste thresholds. JCPP, **48:** 164–66.

ANDERSON, W. D., and SMITH, O. A., JR. 1963 Taste and volume preferences for alcohol in *Macaca Nemestrina*. JCPP, **56:** 144–49.

ANDERSSON, B., and JEWELL, P. A. 1957 Stimulation and ablation of the taste pathway within the thalamus of the goat. JPHY, **137:** 22–23P. (Abstract.)

———. 1957 Studies of the thalamic relay for taste in the goat. JPHY, **139:** 191–97.

ANDERSSON, B., JEWELL, P. A., and LARSSON, S. 1958 An appraisal of the effects of diencephalic stimulation of conscious animals in terms of normal behavior, in Ciba Foundation Symposium, *Neurological Basis of Behavior*, G. E. W. Wolstenholme and C. M. O'Connor (eds.). J. & A. Churchill Ltd., London, 400 pp. (see pp. 76–89).

ANDERSSON, B., LANGREN, S., OLSSON, L., and ZOTTERMAN, Y. 1950 The sweet taste fibres of the dog. APSC, **21:** 105–19.

ANDERSSON, B., and ZOTTERMAN, Y. 1950 The water taste in the frog. APSC, **20:** 95–100.

*ANDREEV, N. A. 1954 (Toward a physiology of the taste analyzer of cattle.) Unpublished Dissertation, Lenin Library, Moscow.

ANDREW, B. L. 1949 Chemoreceptors on the tongue of the toad. JPHY, 108: 7P. (Abstract.)

ANDREW, B. L., and OLIVER, J. 1951 The epiglottal taste buds of the rat. JPHY, 114: 48–49P. (Abstract.)

ANONYMOUS. 1826 Ist der Geschmacksinn ein besonderer Sinn? (Is the sense of taste a special sense?) NGNH, 14: 65–73.

———. 1926 The gustatory sensory reflex. NATU, 118: 246–47.

*———. 1938 Taste and terminology. FLAV, 1: 2.

———. 1940 The taste of carbonated water. FLAV, 3: 11.

———. 1942 Some factors affecting taste and flavour of beverages. FLAV, 5: 11–12.

———. 1943 Relative taste potency. Competitive and compensatory flavour action of salt, sour and sweet constituents in foods. FLAV, 6: 12–14, 16, 19–21.

———. 1944 We have with us, the taste blind. FMTE, 4: 11–12.

———. 1950 Salivary taste hormones. JAMA, 142: 113.

———. 1952 The mechanism of taste. BMJO, 1: 860–61.

———.1955 Chemicals on tongue test people's tastes. FOEG, 27: 196.

———. 1956 The anatomy of taste and related olfactory areas. WHNE, 193: 9. (Diagram only.)

———. 1960 Eighty years of synthetic sweetening agents. CPCN, 23: 111–14.

———. 1964 Glaucoma and phenylthiourea taste sensitivity. NURE, 22: 298–300.

———. 1964 Miracle fruit still a mystery. CENE, 7: 196.

———. 1965 Malic acid now offers economy. FOPR, 26: 101, 103–4.

———. 1965 Of duplexity, VORP, and Asofoetida. FOTE, 19: 31–32.

ANOSOV, N. N. 1939 Vkusovoĭ razdrazhitel' kak algogeniĭ faktor. (Gustatory stimulus as algogenic factor.) SOPE, 15: 79–81.

ANREP, B. VON. 1879 Über die physiologische Wirkung des Kokains. (On the physiological effect of cocain.) PAGP, 21: 38–77.

APPELBERG, B. 1958 Species differences in the taste qualities mediated through the glossopharyngeal nerve. APSC, 44: 129–37.

APPELBERG, B., KITCHELL, R. L., and LANDGREN, S. 1959 Reticular influence upon thalamic and cortical potentials evoked by stimulation of the cat's tongue. APSC, 45: 48–71.

APPELBERG, B., and LANDGREN, S. 1958 The localization of the thalamic relay in the specific sensory path from the tongue of the cat. APSC, 42: 342–57.

AQUINO, J. T. 1928 Sobre as "Papillae vallatae" da lingua do tatùs, preguicas e tamaduàs.

(The vallate papilla of the tongue of armadillos, three-toed sloths and anteaters.) Inaugural Dissertation, São Paulo, 53 pp.

ARDASHNIKOV, S. N., LICHTENSTEIN, E. W., MARTYNOVA, R. P., SOBOLEVA, G. V., and POSTNIKOVA, E. N. 1936 The diagnosis of zygosity in twins; three instances of differences in taste acuity in identical twins. JOHE, 27: 465–68.

ARDIN-DELTEIL, M., and LEVI-VALENSI. 1925 Tubercule de la protuberance. Syndrome de Raymond et Cestan avec spasme facial, paralysie du trijumeau et troubles du goût. (Protruding nodule. Raymond and Costan syndrome with facial spasm, trigeminal paralysis and taste disorders.) RENE, 32: 464–73.

AREY, L. B. 1941 Can hypoglossal nerve fibers induce the formation of taste buds? ANRE, 81 (Supplement) : 118. (Abstract.)

———. 1942 The regeneration of lingual papillae and taste buds after cautery. QBNU, 16: 100–4.

AREY, L. B., and CROZIER, W. J. 1919 The sensory responses of chiton. JEZO, 29: 157–260.

AREY, L. B., and MONZINGO, F. L. 1942 Can hypoglossal nerve fibers induce the formation of taste buds? QBNU, 16: 170–78.

AREY, L. B., TREMAINE, M. J., and MONZINGO, F. L. 1935–36 The numerical and topographical relations of taste buds to human circumvallate papillae throughout the life span. ANRE, 65: 9–26.

ARFMANN, B. L., and CHAPANIS, N. P. 1962 The relative sensitivities of taste and smell in smokers and non-smokers. JGPS, 66: 315–20.

ARIAS VALLEJO, E. 1950 Hormonas gustativas contenidas en la saliva. (Taste hormones in the saliva.) REEA, 9: 380–81.

ARIËNS KAPPERS, C. U. 1908 Weitere Mitteilungen über Neurobiotaxis. II: Die phylogenetische Entwickelung des horizontalen Schenkels des Facialiswurzelknies. (Further reports on neurobiotaxis. II: The phylogenetic development of the horizontal branch of the facial root joint.) FNBI, 2: 255–61.

———. 1908 Weitere Mitteilungen über Neurobiotaxis. VIII: Ueber den motorischen Glossopharyngeus und Facialis bei niederen Vertebraten. (Further reports on neurobiotaxis. VIII: The motor glossopharyngeal and facial nerves in lower vertebrates.) FNBI, 2: 383–94.

———. 1909 Weitere Mitteilungen über Neurobiotaxis. III: Über den Einfluss der Neurone der Geschmackskerne auf den motorischen Facialis und Glossopharyngeuskern und ihr Verhalten zur Radix descendens nervi quinti. (Further reports on neurobiotaxis. III: The neurone effect of the taste nucleus on the motor facial and glossopharyngeal nucleus and their behavior in the radix descendens fifth nerve.) FNBI, 3: 259–74.

———. 1941 Der Geschmack, perifer und central; zugleich eine Skizze der phylogenetischen

Veränderungen in den sensiblen 7, 9 und 10 Wurzeln. (Taste, peripheral and central; simultaneously a sketch of phylogenetic changes in the sensitive 7, 9, and 10 roots.) PSNE, 18: 82–138.

ARNÉUS, T. 1934 Geschmacksschwellenbestimmungen mit Nipakombin und Natriumbenzoat, um die Eignung dieser Stoffe als Rohkonservierungsmittel vergleichend festzustellen. (Determination of threshold of taste for nipakombin and sodium benzoate, in order to establish comparative fitness of these substances as agents for preservation of raw foods.) UPSF, 39: 257–60.

———. 1934 Smaktröskelbestämningar utförda med nipakombin A samt natriumbenzoat för att utröna dessa ämnens inbördes lämplighet sasom råkonserveringsmedel. (Determinations of taste thresholds for nipakombin and sodium benzoate, in order to establish comparative fitness of these substances as agents for preservation of raw foods.) NOMT, 7: 276–77.

ARNOLD, A. 1918 Ueber den Wert der Konzentrationsschwelle für die Beurteilung der Süssigkeit eines Stoffes. (The value of the concentration threshold for the estimation of a sweet substance.) Inaugural Dissertation, Marburg, 26 pp.

ARNOLD, J. 1900 Die Demonstration der Nervenendausbreitung in den Papillae fungiformes der lebenden Froschzunge. (The demonstration of the expansion of nerve endings in the fungiform papillae in the living frog tongue.) ANAN, 17: 517–19.

ARNSTEIN, C. 1893 Die Endapparate der Geschmacksnerven. (The end-apparatus of the taste nerves.) BIZN, 13: 444–45.

———. 1893 Die Nervenendigungen in den Schmeckbechern der Säuger. (The nerve endings in the taste buds of mammals.) AMAE, 41: 195–218.

ARNSTEIN, K. A. 1893 Kontsevye apparaty vkusovogo nerva. (A new ending of gustatory nerve.) NVKU, 1: 79–98.

ARONOV, M. P. 1962 Metodi izucheniia vkusa i oboniaaniia u ryb (Methods for the study of taste and olfaction in fish); in Rukovodstvo po Methodike Issledovanii Fiziologii Ryb (Manual of Methodology in Physiological Research on Fish), E. N. Pavlovskii (ed.). USSR Akad. Nauk, Moscow, 375 pp. (see pp. 283–301).

ARTOM, G. 1923 Die Tumoren des Schläfenlappens. (The tumors of the temporal lobe.) APNV, 69: 47–242.

ARVOLA, A., and FORSANDER, O. A. 1963 Hamsters in experiments of free choice between alcohol and water. QJSA, 24: 591–97.

ARVY, L. 1961 Enzymes et appareil gustatif lingual chez le lapin domestique. (Enzymes in the lingual gustatory apparatus of the domestic rabbit.) ABAB, 1: 145–51.

ASANO, M., and KANEMATSU, T. 1926 (Substances

of pungent taste and their chemical constitution.) JJPA, 531: 375–80. (In Japanese.)

ASH, P. 1951 The sensory capacities of infrahuman mammals: Vision, audition, gustation. PSBU, 48: 289–326.

AUDRIETH, L. F., and SVEDA, M. 1944 Preparation and properties of some N-substituted sulfamic acids. JOCE, 9: 89–101.

AUERBACH, F. 1922 Die Süsskraft der künstlichen Süsstoffe. (Sweetening power of artificial sweetening substances.) NATW, 10: 710–14.

AUTENRIETH, J. H. F. 1802 Geschmack (Taste), in Handbuch der Empirischen Menschlichen Gesellschaft. 3 vols. J. F. Heerbrandt, Tübingen, 396 pp. (see pp. 89–114).

AYERS, H. 1881–82 Der Mund. Zunge (The mouth. Tongue), in Beiträge zur Anatomie und Physiologie der Dropnoër. JEZN, 18: 479–527.

AZEVÊDO, E., KRIEGER, H., MI, M. P., and MORTON, N. E. 1965 PTC taste sensitivity and endemic goiter in Brazil. AJHG, 17: 87–90.

BACHARACH, A. L. 1951 The man of taste. CHIN, 48: 1040–47.

BACHARACH, E. 1926 Untersuchungen über den sauren Geschmack. (Research on the sour taste.) ZEBL, 84: 335–46.

BACKMAN, E. L. 1917 Några trötthetsfenomen inom lukt - och smaksinnenas område. (Some fatigue phenomena in the fields of smell and taste.) HYGI, 79: 886–96.

BAEGE, F. P. 1929 Geruch und Geschmack. (Smell and taste.) NAUC, 18: 1–4.

BAGLIONI, S. 1913 Die niederen Sinne. IV: Die chemischen Sinne (Geruchssinn und Geschmackssinn). (The lower senses. IV: The chemical senses [Smell and Taste]), in Handbuch der Vergleichenden Physiologie, H. Winterstein (ed.). G. Fischer, Jena, 1000 pp. (see pp. 538–54).

BAGSHAW, M. H., and PRIBRAM, K. H. 1953 Cortical organization in gustation (Macaca mulatta). JONE, 16: 499–508.

BÄHR, F. 1919 Ein weiterer Beitrag zur Störung der Geruchsempfindung verbunden mit Störung des Geschmackes. (Further study of disturbance of smell associated with disorder of taste sense.) MOUI, 26: 17–19.

*BAILEY, E. H. S. 1884 Relative sweetness of sugars. Report, Kansas Board of Agriculture.

BAILEY, E. H. S. 1887 Some experiments on the relation between the taste and the acidity of certain acids. TSAS, 11: 10.

———. 1894 On the delicacy of the sense of taste among Indians. KAUQ, 2: 95–98.

BAILEY, E. H. S., and FRANKLIN, E. C. 1885–86 The relative bitterness of different bitter substances. TSAS, 10: 23–24.

BAILEY, E. H. S., and NICHOLS, E. L. 1887 On the delicacy of the sense of taste. PAAS, p. 138.

————. 1888 Acuité du sens du goût chez l'homme et chez la femme. (Acuity of sense of taste in men and women.) RPOG, 4: 245.

————. 1888 On the sense of taste. SCIE, 11: 145–46.

————. 1888 The delicacy of the sense of taste. NATU, 37: 557–58.

BAIN, A. 1864 Senses and the Intellect. 2nd ed. Arthur King & Co., Aberdeen, 640 pp. (see pp. 152–63).

BAKER, G. A., MRAK, V., and AMERINE, M. A. 1958 Errors of the second kind in an acid threshold test. FORE, 23: 150–54.

BALAVOINE, P. 1943 La gustation des denrées alimentaires et des boissons. (The tastes of food products and beverages.) TCAH, 34: 368–73. (German summary.)

————. 1945 Sensibilité du goût aux sel cupriques. (Sensitivity of taste to some copper salts.) ASPN, 27: 33–35.

————. 1948 L'olfaction et la gustation au service de la pharmacie. Cas des huiles grasses (olea pinguia) et de la glycérine. (Smell and taste in the service of pharmacy. Fatty acids and glycerol.) PAHE, 23: 82–84.

————. 1948 Sensibilité du goût envers quelques sels toxiques. (Sensitivity of taste to some toxic salts.) MGLH, 39: 27–30.

BALDWIN, B. A., BELL, F. R., and KITCHELL, R. L. 1959 Gustatory nerve impulses in ruminant ungulates. JPHY, 146: 14–15P.

BAÑUELOS GARCIA, M. 1916 Dos casos de trastornos del sentido del gusto. (Two cases of disturbances of the sense of taste.) PEES, 5: 273–83.

BARADI, A. F., and BOURNE, G. H. 1951 Gustatory enzymes. BJNU, 5: 7.

————. 1951 Localization of gustatory and olfactory enzymes in the rabbit, and the problems of taste and smell. NATU, 168: 977–79.

————. 1951 Theory of tastes and odors. SCIE, 113: 660–61.

————. 1953 Gustatory and olfactory epithelia. IRCY, 2: 289–330.

————. 1957 Gustatory and olfactory epithelia. PEOR, 48: 434–41, 485–98.

————. 1959 Histochemical localization of cholinesterase in gustatory and olfactory epithelia. JHCY, 7: 2–7.

————. 1959 New observations of the alkaline glycerophosphatase reaction in the papilla foliata. JBBC, 5: 173–74.

BARADI, A. F., and BRANDES, D. 1963 Electron microscopic localization of alkaline phosphatase in papilla foliata. JHCY, 11: 815–17.

BARADI, A. F., and JOLLIE, W. P. 1962 Electron microscopic observations on cell surface modifications in gustatory epithelium. ACAT, 50: 305–11.

BARÁTII, E., and VÁNDORFY, J. 1926 Experimentelle Untersuchungen über die physikalisch-chemischen Grundlagen der Geschmacksempfindung nach Säurelösungen. (Experimental studies on the physico-chemical foundations of taste sensations with acid solutions.) BIZE, 176: 473–77.

BARAVELLI, P. 1961 Le alterazioni della sensibilità gustativa nella gravidanza. (Alteration of gustatory sensitivity during pregnancy.) RIGI, 45: 171–88. (English and German summaries.)

*BARBER, S. B. 1951 Contact chemoreception in Limulus. ANRE, 3: 561–62. (Abstract.)

————. 1956 Chemoreception and proprioception in Limulus. JEZO, 131: 51–73.

————. 1961 Chemoreception and thermoreception, in The Physiology of Crustacea, II, T. H. Waterman (ed.). Academic Press, New York, 681 pp. (see pp. 109–31).

*BARBER, S. B., and HAYES, W. F. 1963 Properties of Limulus chemoreceptors. PCZO, 3: 76–78.

BARBER, T. X., CHAUNCEY, H. H., and WINER, R. A. 1964 Effect of hypnotic and nonhypnotic suggestions on parotid gland response to gustatory stimuli. PSME, 26: 374–80.

*BARBERA, S. 1950 (Thiamine and gustatory function.) AIOR, 58: 198–200.

BARD, P. 1956 The chemical senses, smell and taste, in Medical Physiology. 10th ed. C. V. Mosby, St. Louis, 1421 pp. (see pp. 1273–76).

BARDACH, J. E., and CASE, J. 1962 The sensory function of modified fins of some marine fishes. AMZO, 2: 504. (Abstract.)

BARDACH, J. E., and CASE, J. 1965 Sensory capabilities of the modified fins of squirrel hake (Urophycis chuss) and Searobins (Prinotus carolinus and P. evolans). COPA, 2: 194–206.

BARDACH, J. E., FUGIYA, M., and HOLL, A. 1965 Detergents: Effects on the chemical senses of the fish Ictalurus natalis (le Sueur). SCIE, 148: 1605–7.

BARE, J. K. 1949 The specific hunger for sodium chloride in normal and adrenalectomized white rats. JCPP, 42: 242–53.

BARNARD, J. W. 1936 A phylogenetic study of the visceral afferent areas associated with the facial, glossopharyngeal, and vagus nerves, and their fiber connections. The efferent facial nucleus. JCNE, 65: 503–602.

BARNES, C. J. 1959 The amino acids present in the protein material isolated from two areas of the surface of the tongue. DIAS, 20: 1146.

BARNES, C. J., and FERGUSON, L. N. 1960 Amino-acid composition of proteins from surface tissue of the tongue. NATU, 186: 617–19.

BARNES, L. 1933 Parageusia associated with chronic suppurative otitis media; case. AORH, 42: 909–10.

BARNES, T. C. 1939 Experiments on Ligia in Bermuda VI: Reactions to common cations. BIBU, 76: 121–26.

BARNETT, S. A. 1963 Smell and taste. DMCN, 5: 516–17.

BARNETT, S. A., and SPENCER, M. M. 1953 Eperi-
ments on the food preferences of wild rats
(*Rattus norvegicus, Berkenhout*). JOHY, 51:
16–34.

———. 1953 Responses of wild rats to offensive
smells and tastes. BJAB, 1: 32–37.

BARNICOT, N. A. 1949–50 Taste deficiency for
phenylthiourea in African Negroes and
Chinese. ANEU, 15: 248–54.

BARNICOT, N. A., HARRIS, H., and KALMUS, H.
1951 Taste thresholds of further eighteen
compounds and their correlation with P.T.C.
thresholds. ANEU, 16: 119–28.

BARRAL, F., and RANC, A. 1918 La chimie des
édulcorants. (The chemistry of sweetening
agents.) RESC, 56: 712–23.

———. 1918 Sapidité et stéréoisomérie. Contribution á l'étude physico-chimique des édulcorants. (Taste and stereoisomerism. Contribution to the physico-chemical study of
sweeteners.) ICPH, 5: 279–81.

———. 1920 La chimie de la sapidité. (The
chemistry of sapidity.) JPSY, 17: 16–30.

BARRON, D. H. 1936 A note on the course of
proprioceptor fibres from the tongue. ANRE,
66: 11–15.

BARTALENA, G. 1962 La geusimetria ematogena
in soggetti normali. (Hematogenous geusime-
try in normal subjects.) BMOG, 80: 414–44.

BARTLEY, S. H. 1958 Taste and smell perceptions, in *Principles of Perception*. Harper &
Brothers, New York, 482 pp. (see pp. 337–54).

BARTOLI, G. 1937 Richerche morfologiche in
vivo sui recettori del senso chimico. (Morphologic study in vivo of oropharyngeal receptors
of chemical sense.) AIAE, 38: 185–208.

———. 1939 Osservazione sulle gemme gustative
sopravviventi dei Mammiferi. (Observations
on supravital taste buds of mammals.) MZOI,
50: 109–15.

BARTON-BROWNE, L., and HODGSON, E. S. 1962
Electrophysiological studies of arthropod
chemoreception. IV: Latency, independence,
and specificity of labellar chemoreceptors of
the blowfly, *Lucilia*. JCCP, 59: 187–202.

BARTOSHUK, L. M., McBURNEY, D. H., and PFAFF-
MANN, C. 1964 Taste of sodium chloride solutions after adaptation to sodium chloride: Implications for the "Water Taste." SCIE, 143:
967–68.

BARTOSHUK, L. M., and PFAFFMANN, C. 1965 Effects of pretreatment on water taste response
in cat and rat. FEPR, 24: 207. (Abstract.)

BARVELARE, B., and RICHTER, C. P. 1938 Increased
sodium chloride appetite in pregnant rats.
AJPH, 121: 185–88.

BARYSCHEVA, E. 1926 Über die Synthese der
Geschmacksempfindungen. (Synthesis of sensations of taste.) PAGP, 215: 103–5.

BARYSHEVA, E. P. 1936 Opredelenie poroga osch-
chyshchenii vkysa i chelovcka. (Determination
of taste threshold in man.) ASBU, 40: 139–41.
(English summary.)

BATE-SMITH, E. C. 1954 Astringency in foods.
FOPP, 23: 124–27, 135.

———. 1961 The chemistry of taste and flavour.
NWSC, 11: 329–31.

BATH, W. 1905 Über das Vorkommen von Geschmacksorganen in der Mundhöhle von Crocodilus niloticus Laur. (On the occurrence of taste
organs in the mouth of *crocodilus noloticus*
Laur.) ZOAN, 29: 352–53.

———. 1906 Die Geschmacksorgane der Vögel.
(The taste organs of birds.) Inaugural Dissertation, Friedrich-Wilhelms-Universität, Berlin,
45 pp.

———. 1906 Die Geschmacksorgane der Vögel
und Krokodile. (Taste organs of birds and
crocodiles.) AVBI, 1: 1–48.

BAT-MIRIAM, M., ADAM, A., and HANANEL, Z.
1962 A survey of some genetical characters in
Ethiopian tribes. VI: Taste thresholds for
phenylthiourea. AJPN, 20: 190–93.

BATTEN, D. E., and SHOEMAKER, H. A. 1961 The
effects of deprivation and incentive palatability on a conditioned operant response.
JCPP, 54: 577–79.

BAUDREXEL, A. 1915 Mechanismus unserer Ger-
uchs- und Geschmacksempfindungen. (Mechanism of our sensations of smell and taste.)
DESS, 19: 96–97, 105–7, 112–14, 120–21.

BAUER, L. 1938–39 Geschmacksphysiologische
Untersuchungen an Wasserkäfern. (Physiology
of taste in water beetles.) ZVPH, 26: 107–20.

BAUME-HALENSEE, W. L. 1908 Die Geschmacksorgane der Vögel und Krokodile. (The taste
organs of birds and crocodiles.) ZENF, 4: 248–
51.

BAUMGARTNER, E. A. 1917 The development of
the serous glands (von Ebner's) of the vallate
papillae in man. AJAN, 22: 365–76.

BAY, E. 1947 Geruch- und Geschmackstörungen
nach Kopftraumen. (Smell and taste disturbances after head injuries.) NERV, 18: 350–60.

———. 1961 Geruchs- und Geschmackstörungen.
(Smell and taste disorders.) MEWE, 42: 2143–
47.

BAYER, H. G. A. 1937 Nachuntersuchungen bei
Laryngektomierten. I: Über katarrhalische In-
fecte, Spontangeruchsstörungen und Geschmacksvermögen bei Laryngektomierten. (Examination following laryngectomy. I: On ca-
tarrhal infections, spontaneous disturbances of
smell and taste capacity by laryngectomy.)
HNAO, 28: 329–36.

———. 1937 Nachuntersuchungen bei Laryngektomierten. II: Über das Geruchs- und-Gesch-
macksvermögen bei Patienten mit Larynxkar-
zinomen, bei Tracheotomierten und bei
Laryngektomierten. (Examination following
laryngectomy. II: On odor and taste capacity
in patients with larynxcarcinomas with tra-
chelectomy and laryngectomy.) HNAO, 28:
336–39.

BAYLISS, L. E. 1960 Taste, in *Principles of Gen-*

eral Physiology, II. Longmans, London, 848 pp. (see pp. 423–25).

BAYTON, J. A., and THOMAS, C. M. 1954 Comparative and single stimulus methods in determining taste preferences. JAPS, **38**: 443–45.

BAZIRE. 1867 Case of facial paralysis, with impairment of taste and acoustic hyperaesthesia on the same side as the paralysis. BMJO, **11**: 249.

BEACH, S. A. 1953 The frequency of taste-blindness in Welch populations. HDTY, **7**: 401–7.

BEALE, L. S. 1865 New observations upon the minute anatomy of the papillae of the frog's tongue. PTRS, **155**: 443–57.

———. 1869 New observations upon the minute anatomy of the papillae of the frog's tongue. QJMS, **9**: 1–18.

BEATTIE, G. B. 1940 The problem of sweetness. FLAV, **3** (2): 7–10.

BEATTY, R. M., and CRAGG, L. H. 1935 The sourness of acids. JACS, **57**: 2347–51.

BECHTEREW, V. M. 1913 Conditions anatomo-physiologiques des impressions externes. Voies conductrices des impressions tactiles, gustatives, olfactives, visuelles et auditives. Specificité des courants nerveux (Anatomical-physiological conditions of external expressions. Methods conducted through tactile, gustatory, olfactory, visual and auditory impressions. Specificity of nervous pathways), in *La Psychologie Objective.* Translated from Russian by N. Kostvleff. F. Alcan, Paris, 478 pp. (see pp. 55–66).

BECHTEREW, W. von. 1900 Über die Lokalisation der Geschmackszentra in der Gehirnrinde. (On the localization of taste centers in the cerebral cortex.) AAPA, 145–55.

BECK, G. 1943 Über räumliche Verhältnisse bei Kohlenhydraten, Aminosäuren und Kohlenwasserstoffen. (On steric configuration of carbohydrates, amino acids and hydrocarbons.) WICZ, **46**: 18–22.

BECKER, B., and MORTON, W. R. 1964 Phenylthiourea taste testing and glaucoma. AROP, **72**: 323–27.

———. 1964 Taste sensitivity to phenylthiourea in glaucoma. SCIE, **144**: 1347–48.

BECKER, C. T., and HERZOG, R. O. 1907 Zur Kenntniss des Geschmackes. (On the knowledge of taste.) ZPCH, **52**: 496–505.

BECKER, J. 1907–8 Ueber Zungenpapillen. Ein Beitrag zur phylogenetischen Entwickelung der Geschmacksorgane. (Lingual papillae. A contribution to the phylogenetic development of taste organs.) JEZN, **36**: 537–618.

———. 1908 Über Zungenpapillen. Ein Beitrag zur phylogenetischen Entwicklung der Geschmacksorgane. (Lingual papillae. A contribution to the phylogenetic development of taste organs.) Inaugural Dissertation, G. Fischer, Bern, 82 pp.

BECKER, W. H. 1909 Hypergeusia senilis. (Senile hypergeusia.) MPNE, **26**: 531–34.

BECLARD, J. 1870 Sens du goût (Sense of taste), in *Traité Elementaire de Physiologie Humaine.* 6th ed. P. Asselin, Paris, 1248 pp. (see pp. 926–36).

BEDNAR, M., and LANGFELDER, O. 1929 Über das "intravenose (hämatogene) Riechen." (On intravenous [hematogene] olfaction.) MOLA, **63**: 1292.

———. 1930 Über das "intravenose (hämatogene) Riechen." (On intravenous [hematogene] olfaction.) MOLA, **64**: 1133–39.

BEEBE-CENTER, J. G. 1949 Standards for the use of the gust scale. JOPS, **28**: 411–19.

BEEBE-CENTER, J. G., and BEEBE-CENTER, R. 1946 Measurement of affective power in terms of ratios of partial ε^2s. AJPC, **59**: 290–95.

BEEBE-CENTER, J. G., BLACK, P., HOFFMAN, A. C., and WADE, M. 1948 Relative per diem consumption as a measure of preference in the rat. JCPP, **41**: 239–51.

BEEBE-CENTER, J. G., ROGERS, M. S., and ATKINSON, W. H. 1955 Intensive equivalences for sucrose and NaCl solutions. JOPS, **39**: 371–72.

BEEBE-CENTER, J. G., ROGERS, M. S., ATKINSON, W. H., and O'CONNELL, D. N. 1959 Sweetness and saltiness of compound solutions of sucrose and NaCl as a function of concentration of solutes. JEPS, **57**: 231–34.

BEEBE-CENTER, J. G., ROGERS, M. S., and O'CONNELL, D. N. 1955 Transmission of information about sucrose and saline solutions through the sense of taste JOPS, **39**: 157–60.

BEEBE-CENTER, J. G., and WADDELL, D. 1948 A general psychological scale of taste. JOPS, **26**: 517–24.

BEERS, N. T., JR. 1899 A test case for taste. NYMJ, **70**: 365–66.

BEERSTECHER, E., JR., SUTTON, H. E., KIRBY-BERRY, H., BROWN, W. D., REED, J., RICH, G. B., BERRY, L. J., and WILLIAMS, R. J. 1950 Biochemical individuality. V: Explorations with respect to the metabolic patterns of compulsive drinkers. ARBI, **29**: 27–40.

BEHRMAN, H. R., and MALLER, O. 1965 Appetite for sugar and fat in the thiamine deficient rat. PSCI, **3**: 523–24.

BEIDLER, L. M. 1952 Our taste receptors. SCMO, **75**: 343–49.

———. 1953 Properties of chemoreceptors of tongue of rat. JONE, **16**: 595–607.

———. 1954 A theory of taste stimulation. JGPL, **38**: 133–39.

———. 1954 The physiological basis of taste. ACAF, p. 18A. (Abstract.)

*———. 1955 The physiological basis of taste. ONR Symposium Report ACR–1, Symposium on Physiological Psychology.

———. 1957 Facts and theory on the mechanism of taste and odor perception, in *Chemistry of Natural Food Flavors, A Symposium.* Q.M.F.C.I., 200 pp. (see pp. 7–29).

———. 1957 Physiological basis of taste psychophysics. FEPR, **16**: 9.

————. 1958 Acid stimulation of taste receptors. PYSO, 1: 4.

————. 1960 Physiology of olfaction and gustation. AORH, 69: 398–409.

————. 1960 Physiology of taste. PYSO, 3 (1): 5–12.

————. 1961 The chemical senses. ARPS, 12: 363–89.

————. 1961 Biophysical approaches to taste. AMSC, 49: 421–31.

————. 1961 Mechanisms of gustatory and olfactory receptor stimulation, in *Sensory Communication*, W. A. Rosenblith (ed.). John Wiley & Sons, New York, 844 pp. (see pp. 143–57).

————. 1962 Taste receptor stimulation, in *Progress in Biophysics and Biophysical Chemistry, XII*, J. A. V. Butler, H. E. Huxley, and R. E. Zirkle (eds.). Pergamon Press, New York, 350 pp. (see pp. 109–51).

————. 1963 Dynamics of taste cells, in *Olfaction and Taste*, Y. Zotterman (ed.). Macmillan, New York, 396 pp. (see pp. 133–45).

————. 1965 Chemical excitation of taste and odor receptors. ACAF, pp. 3–4A. (Abstract.)

————. 1965 Comparison of gustatory receptors, olfactory receptors, and free nerve endings, in *Sensory Receptors*. Cold Spring Harbor Symposia on Quantitative Biology, XXX, 600 pp. (see pp. 191–200).

————. 1966 A physiological basis of taste sensation. JFDS, 31: 275–81.

BEIDLER, L. M., FISHMAN, I. Y., and HARDIMAN, C. W. 1955 Species differences in taste responses. AJPH, 181: 235–39.

BEIDLER, L. M., NEJAD, M. S., SMALLMAN, R. L., and TATEDA, H. 1960 Rat taste cell proliferation. FEPR, 19: 302. (Abstract.)

BEIDLER, L. M., and SMALLMAN, R. L. 1965 Renewal of cells within taste buds. JCLB, 27: 263–72.

BEIGUELMAN, B. 1962 Taste sensitivity to PTC among Japanese immigrants in Brazil. RBBI, 22: 93–97.

————. 1964 Taste sensitivity to phenylthiourea among patients affected with both tuberculosis and leprosy. AGMG, 13: 190–92.

————. 1964 Taste sensitivity to phenylthiourea and leprosy. AGMG, 13: 193–96.

————. 1964 Taste sensitivity to phenylthiourea and menstruation. AGMG, 13: 197–99.

BEIGUELMAN, B., and MARQUES, M. B. 1964 Taste sensitivity to phenylthiourea and drugs with anti-leprotic effect. AGMG, 13: 200–2.

BEILHARZ, S., and KAY, R. N. B. 1961 Factors affecting the sodium appetite of sheep. JPHY, 155: 60–61P.

————. 1963 The effects of ruminal and plasma sodium concentrations on the sodium appetite of sheep. JPHY, 165: 468–83.

BÉKÉNY, G. 1951 Gustatoros hemihyperhidrosis sympathectomiára gyógyult esete. (Case of gustatory hemihyperidrosis treated by sympathectomy.) MBAR, 4: 45–48. (French and Russian summaries.)

BÉKÉSY, G. von. 1963 Interaction of paired sensory stimuli and conduction in peripheral nerves. JAPY, 18: 1276–84.

————. 1964 Duplexity theory of taste. SCIE, 145: 834–35.

————. 1964 Olfactory analogue to directional hearing. JAPY, 19: 369–73.

————. 1964 Rhythmical variations accompanying gustatory stimulation observed by means of localization phenomena. JGPL, 47: 809–25.

————. 1964 Sweetness produced electrically on the tongue and its relation to taste theories. JAPY, 19: 1105–13.

————. 1965 Temperature coefficients of the electrical thresholds of taste sensations. JGPL, 49: 27–35.

————. 1965 The effect of adaptation on the taste threshold observed with a semiautomatic gustometer. JGPL, 48: 481–88.

————. 1966 Taste theories and the chemical stimulation of single papillae. JAPY, 21: 1–9.

BELL, C. 1803 Of the sense of tasting, in *The Anatomy of the Human Body*. A. Strahan, London, 495 pp. (see pp. 469–71).

BELL, F. R. 1959 Preference thresholds for taste discrimination in goats. JASI, 52: 125–28.

————. 1959 The sense of taste in domesticated animals. VETR, 71: 1071–79.

————. 1963 Alkaline taste in goats assessed by the preference test technique. JCPP, 56: 174–78.

————. 1963 The variation in taste thresholds of ruminants associated with sodium depletion, in *Olfaction and Taste*, Y. Zotterman (ed.). Macmillan, New York, 396 pp. (see pp. 299–307).

BELL, F. R., and WILLIAMS, H. L. 1959 Threshold values for taste in monozygotic twin calves. NATU, 183: 345–46.

————. 1960 The effect of sodium depletion of the taste threshold of calves. JPHY, 151: 42–43P.

BELL, G. H., DAVIDSON, J. N., and SCARBOROUGH, H. 1959 Sense of taste (gustation), in *Textbook of Physiology and Biochemistry*. 4th ed. E. & S. Livingstone Ltd., Edinburgh, 1065 pp. (see pp. 656–60).

BELLETRUD, M., and MERCIER, E. 1907 Abolition des illusions du goût par l'emploi local de l'acide gymnémique. (Abolition of taste illusions by local application of gymnemic acid.) BUME, 21: 713.

————. 1907 Abolition des illusions du goût par l'emploi local de l'acide gymnémique. (Abolition of taste illusions by local application of gymnemic acid.) ENCE, 2: 251–52.

BELLINI, L. 1665 *Gustus organum novissime deprehensum; praemissis ad faciliorem intelligentiam quibusdam de saporibus.* (Taste organs newly observed; with certain premises about the senses given for easier understanding.) Bologna, 247 pp.

———. 1711 *Exercitationes anatomicae duae de structura et usu renum ut et de gustus organo novissime deprehenso; praemissis ad faciliorem intelligentiam quibusdam de saporibus.* (Anatomical exercises on the structures and on the taste organs newly observed; with certain premises about the senses given for easier understanding.) J. A. Langerack, Leiden, 166 pp.

BELLIZZI, V. 1915 Azione di alcune sostanze chimiche sul gusto. (Action of some chemical substances on taste.) RVSM, 62: 38–44.

BELLOMO, A. 1941 Ricerche cliniche sui rapporti tra sensazioni gustative fondamentali, secrezione gastrica, glicemia e senso d'appetito. (Clinical research on the relation between fundamental taste sensations, gastric secretion, glycemia and appetite.) MIME, 1: 410–17.

BELLOWS, R. T., and WAGENEN, W. P. van. 1939 The effect of resection of the olfactory, gustatory, and trigeminal nerves on water drinking in dogs without and with diabetes insipidus. AJPH, 126: 13–19.

BENDER, M. B., and FELDMAN, D. S. 1952 Extinction of taste sensation on double simultaneous stimulation. NEUR, 2: 195–202.

BENEDEK, L. 1919 Kriegsneurologische Beobachtungen. Traumatische Hemiplegie mit halbseitiger Geschmacksstörung. (War neurological observations. Traumatic hemiplegia with unilateral taste disturbances.) DZNE, 63: 326–42.

BENJAMIN, R. M. 1953 Cerebral mechanisms in gustatory discrimination. Unpublished Ph.D. thesis, Brown University, 140 pp.

———. 1955 The effect of fluid deprivation on taste deficits following cortical lesions. JCPP, 48: 502–5.

———. 1955 Cortical taste mechanisms studied by two different test procedures. JCPP, 48: 119–22.

———. 1958 Absence of deficits in taste discrimination following cortical lesions as a function of the amount of preoperative practice. PYSO, 1: 4–5. (Abstract.)

———. 1959 Absence of deficits in taste discrimination following cortical lesions as a function of the amount of preoperative practice. JCPP, 52: 255–58.

———. 1960 Effect of removal of olfactory bulbs on taste discrimination in normal and brain operated rats. PYSO, 3: 19. (Abstract.)

———. 1963 Some thalamic and cortical mechanisms of taste, in *Olfaction and Taste*, Y. Zotterman (ed.). Macmillan, New York, 396 pp. (see pp. 309–29) .

BENJAMIN, R. M., and AKERT, K. 1959 Cortical and thalamic areas involved in taste discrimination in the albino rat. JCNE, 111: 231–60.

BENJAMIN, R. M., and EMMERS, R. 1960 Locali-

zation of separate cortical areas for taste and tactile tongue afferents in squirrel monkey *(Saimiri sciureus).* FEPR, 19: 291. (Abstract.)

BENJAMIN, R. M., HALPERN, B. P., MOULTON, D. G., and MOZELL, M. M. 1965 The chemical senses. ARPS, 16: 381–416.

BENJAMIN, R. M., and PFAFFMANN, C. 1952 Cerebral mechanisms in taste discrimination. AMPS, 7: 251.

———. 1955 Cortical localization of taste in albino rat. JONE, 18: 56–64.

BERENDES, J., and THEISSING, G. 1953 Geschmackstörungen nach Tonsillektomie. (Ageusia after tonsillectomy.) ZHGE, 4: 15–18.

BERG, C. P. 1942 The metabolism of the D-amino acids. FEPR, 1: 281–87.

———. 1953 Physiology of the D-amino acids. PHRE, 33: 145–89.

BERG, H. W., FILIPELLO, F. HINREINER, E., and WEBB, A. D. 1955 Evaluation of thresholds and minimum difference concentrations for various constituents of wines. I: Water solutions of pure substances. FOTE, 9: 23–26.

———. 1955 Evaluation of thresholds and minimum difference concentrations for various constituents of wines. II: Sweetness: The effect of ethyl alcohol, organic acids and tannin. FOTE, 9: 138–40.

BERGMANN, C., and LEUCKART, R. 1852 *Vergleichende Anatomie und Physiologie.* (Comparative Anatomy and Physiology.) J. B. Müller, Stuttgart, 690 pp. (see pp. 70–71) .

BERGMANN, M., CAMACHO, F., and DREYER, F. 1922 Über einige neue Abkömmlinge des p-Phenetidylharnstoffs (Dulcin). (New derivatives of p-Phenetylurea [dulcin].) DPGB, 32: 249–58.

BERILLON. 1912 La memoire gustative (Taste memory.) RPPA (3rd Series) , 27: 366–67.

BERLATZKY, A., and GUEVARA, T. 1927 El umbral del gusto ácido y la concentración de hidrogeniones. (Sourness threshold and the hydrogen ion concentration.) RABL, 3: 721–34.

———. 1928 Seuil de la sensation gustative de l'acidité et concentration en ions hydrogène. (Threshold of gustatory sensation of acidity and hydrogen-ion concentration.) CRSS, 98: 176–77.

BERNARD, C. 1843 Sur la corde du tympan. (On the chorda tympani.) AMPY, 1: 408–39.

———. 1843 Untersuchungen über die Corda tympani. (Investigations on the chorda tympani.) NGNH, 28: 215–16.

———. 1844 De l'altération du goût dans la paralysie du nerf facial. (Taste alterations in paralysis of the facial nerve.) AGME, 6: 480–96.

———. 1853 On the alteration of the taste in paralysis of the facial nerve. VMSJ, pp. 3–12.

———. 1858 Action de la corde du tympan. Sur le goût. (Action of the chorda tympani. On taste), in *Leçons sur la Physiologie et la*

Pathologie du Système Nerveux, I. J.-B. Baillière et Fils, Paris, 560 pp. (see pp. 172–75).

*BERNARD, R. A. 1962 An electrophysiological study of taste reception in the calf. Unpublished Ph.D. thesis, Cornell University, 74 pp.

———. 1964 An electrophysiological study of taste reception in peripheral nerves of the calf. AJPH, 206: 827–35.

BERNARD, R. A., HALPERN, B. P., and KARE, M. R. 1961 Effect of vitamin A deficiency on taste. PSEB, 108: 784–86.

———. 1962 The reversible effect of vitamin A deficiency on taste. FEPR, 21: 362. (Abstract.)

BERNHARD, C. G. 1959 Somatic functions of the nervous system. ARPH, 21: 325–52.

BERNHARDT, M. 1876 Ueber die Function de Nv. trigeminus als Geschmacksnerv. (The function of the trigeminus nerve as the taste nerve.) APNV, 6: 561–64.

BERNSTEIN, J. 1876 The sense of taste, in *The Five Senses of Man.* D. Appleton and Co., New York, 304 pp. (see pp. 295–301).

*BERNSTORFF, H. von, and ENGLISCH, P. 1932 Der *Geschmack: Eine sexual psychologische und physiologische Darstellung der Rolle und Bedeutung des Geschmackssinns für das Triebleben des Menschen.* (Taste: A sexual psychological and physiological representation of the role and meaning of the sense of taste in the sex drive in humans.) Verlag für Kulturforschung, Vienna, 255 pp.

BERTHOLD, B. 1887 Eine Pflanze welche die Geschmacksqualitäten des Süssen und Bitteren vernichtet. (A plant which destroys the taste qualities of sweet and bitter.) WIMB, 24: 753–54.

———. 1888 Eine Pflanze, welche die Geschmacksqualitäten des Süssen und Bitteren vernichtet. (A plant which destroys the taste qualities of sweet and bitter.) CEMW, 26: 460–61.

BESNARD, W., and PETIT, G. 1929 Sur une structure particulière des papilles linguales et son interprétation fonctionelle. (On a particular structure of lingual papillae and its functional interpretation.) CORE, 100: 475–77.

BEST, C. H., and TAYLOR, N. B. The chemical senses taste, gustation, in *The Physiological Basis of Medical Practice.* 6th ed. Williams & Wilkins, Baltimore, 1357 pp. (see pp. 1213–24).

———. 1958 Taste, in *The Living Body.* 4th ed. Henry Holt & Co., New York, 756 pp. (see pp. 638–40).

BEYER, H. 1904 Nasales schmecken. (Nasal taste.) ZPSI, 25: 260–67.

BEYME, F. 1964 Hyperesthesia of taste and touch treated by reciprocal inhibition. BERT, 2: 7–14.

BEYTHIEN, A. 1949 Die Geschmackstoffe der menschlichen Nahrung. (Taste substances in human nutrition.) TEFO, 50: 1–150.

*BHATTACHARYA, D. K. 1964 Tasting of P.T.C.

among the Anglo-Indians of India. AGMG, 13: 159–66.

*BIDDER, F. 1838 Neue Beobachtungen über die Bewegungen des weichen Gaumens und über den Geruchssinn. (New observations on the movements of the soft palate and on the sense of smell.) Inaugural Dissertation, Dorpat, 27 pp.

———. 1846 Schmecken (Taste), in *Handwörterbuch der Physiologie, III,* R. Wagner (ed.). F. Bieweg und Sohn, Braunschweig, 872 pp. (see pp. 1–12).

*BIDONE. 1901 Alcune ricerche sul senso del gusto nella gravidanza. (Research on the sense of taste during pregnancy.) 12 vols. Lucina, Bologna.

BIESTER, A., WOOD, M. W., and WAHLIN, C. S. 1925 Carbohydrate studies. I: The relative sweetness of pure sugars. AJPC, 73: 387–96.

BIFFI, S. 1846 Sui nervi della lingua; ricerche anatomico fisiologiche. (On the nerves of the tongue; anatomical and physiological research.) AUMM, 119: 369–439.

BIGELOW, H. R. 1881 Anatomy and physiology of the chorda tympani nerve. BRAI, 3: 43–47.

BILANCIONI, G. 1927 Disosmie, disgeusie e disturbi affini dal punto di vista clinico. (Dysosmia, dysgeusia and related disorders from the clinical viewpoint.) RIME, 43: 1155–57.

BILLIMORIA, F. R., SHETTY, H. B., and RINDANI, T. H. 1963 Impaired glucose tolerance: The basis for dislike for sweets. IJMR, 17: 329–33.

BILLROTH, T. 1858 Ueber die Epithelialzellen der Froschzunge, sowie über den Bau der Cylinder- und Flimmerepithelien und ihr Verhältniss zum Bindegewebe. (On epithelial cells in the tongue of the frog, also the structure of cylinder and flicker epithelium and its relation to connective tissue.) AAPM, pp. 159–77.

*BIMAR, A. 1875 Étude physiologique sur le sens du goût. (Physiological study on the sense of taste.) Inaugural Dissertation, Montpellier.

BIRIUKOV, D. A. 1938 Vliianie vykliucheniia vkusovykh oshchushchenil (kokainom i gimnemoi) na reflektornoe sliunootdelenie cheloveka. (Effect of the exclusion of taste perception [cocaine and gymnemic] on a person's reflex salivary emission.) FZLZ, 25: 119–26. (German summary.)

BISSAR, A. 1939 Über den laugigen Geschmack. (The puckery taste.) Inaugural Dissertation, Linke, Berlin, 23 pp.

BLAKESLEE, A. F. 1932 Genetics of sensory thresholds. Taste for phenyl thio carbamide. PNAS, 18: 120–30.

———. 1933 Some differences between people in taste and smell reactions. EUNE, 18: 63.

———. 1935 A dinner demonstration of threshold differences in taste and smell. SCIE, 81: 504–7.

———. 1939 Poll of 3121 persons show wide variation in tastes. SNLE, 35: 51–52.

BLAKESLEE, A. F., and FOX, A. L. 1932 Our different taste worlds. JOHE, 23: 97–110.

BLAKESLEE, A. F., and SALMON, M. R. 1931 Odor and taste blindness. EUNE, 16: 105–9.

BLAKESLEE, A. F., and SALMON, T. N. 1935 Genetics of sensory thresholds: Individual taste reactions for different substances. PNAS, 21: 84–90.

BLANKSMA, J. J. 1946 Preparation of 1-alkoxy-2-amino-4-nitrobenzenes in aqueous solution. RTCP, 65: 203–6.

BLANKSMA, J. J., and BAKELS, H. A. 1939 Connection between taste and constitution of carboxylic acid hydrazides and their derivatives. RTCP, 58: 497–513.

BLANKSMA, J. J., and DE GRAAF, H. 1938 The relationship between taste and constitution of some dihydrazides of alkylmalonic acids and their derivatives. RTCP, 57: 3–12.

BLANKSMA, J. J., and HOEGEN, D. 1946 The sweet taste of 4-nitro-2-aminotoluene, 4-nitro-2-aminobenzoic acid, and 2-nitro-4-aminobenzoic acid. RTCP, 65: 333–37.

BLANKSMA, J. J., VAN DER BROEK, W. J., and HOEGEN, D. 1946 On the sweet taste of the 1-halogeno-2-amino-4-nitrobenzenes. RTCP, 65: 329–32.

BLANKSMA, J. J., and VAN DER WEYDEN, P. W. M. 1940 Relationship between taste and structure in some derivatives of meta-nitraniline. RTCP. 59: 629–32.

BLANKSMA, J. J., and WITTE, C. H. D. 1941 Derivatives of 1-chloro-2-nitro-4-cyanobenzene. RTCP, 60: 811–26.

BLAU, L. 1879 Ein Beitrag sur Lehre von der Funktion der Chorda tympani. (A contribution to the pattern of the function of the chorda tympani.) BKWO, 16: 671–74.

BLEYER, J. M. 1896–97 An essay on the organs of taste. LARY, 1: 329–47; 2: 13–25.

BLOMQUIST, A. J., and ANTEM, A. 1965 Localization of the terminals of the tongue afferents in the nucleus of the solitary tract. JCNE, 124: 127–30.

BLOMQUIST, A. J., BENJAMIN, R. M., and EMMERS, R. 1962 Thalamic localization of afferents from the tongue in squirrel monkey (*Saimiri sciureus*). JCNE, 118: 77–87.

BLOOM, M. 1962 The tongue, in *A Textbook of Histology*. 8th ed. W. B. Saunders, Philadelphia, 720 pp. (see pp. 395–99).

BLUM, D. 1913 Ueber den Verlauf der sekretorischen Fasern zur Tränendrüse und der Geschmacksfasern. (On the course of secretory fibers as taste ducts and taste fibers.) DMWO, 39: 1588–89.

BLUM, M., WALKER, A. E., and RUCH, T. C. 1943 Localization of taste in the thalamus of *Macaca mulatta*. YJBM, 16: 175–91.

BLUMENBACH, J. F. 1805 Von der Zunge (The tongue), in *Handbuch der vergleichenden Anatomie*. H. Dieterich, Göttingen, 549 pp. (see pp. 329–45).

BLYENBURCH, C. 1682 De sapore. (Taste.) Inaugural Dissertation, A. Elzevier, Leiden, 10 pp.

BOCCI, B. 1891 L'Organo del Gusto. (The organ of taste.) F. Vallardi, Milano, 67 pp.

BOEDECKER, F., and ROSENBUSCH, R. 1920 Über die Süsskraft von Derivaten des p-Oxyphenylharnstoffs. (Sweetening power of p-hydoxyphenylurea derivatives.) DPGB, 30: 251–58.

BOEHMER, J. W. 1936 Aliphatic isocyanates and their conversion into α-aryl-β-alkylureas. RTCP, 55: 379–91.

BOELCKE, R. A. 1931 The relation of the hydrogen ion concentration to the absolute threshold of the sensation of sourness. Unpublished Master's thesis, Catholic University, 26 pp.

BOGAERT, L. VAN. 1935 Deux cas de névrite, dont l'un avec dysgueusie, dus a l'α-dinitrophenol. (Two cases of neuritis with dysgeusia, caused by α-dinitrophenol.) BMMH, 51: 1393–96.

BOHM, E., and STRANG, R. R. Glossopharyngeal neuralgia. BRAI, 85: 371–88.

BÖHME, M. 1936 Ueber die Geschmackswirkung von anorganischen Kalcium-und Magnesiumsalzen. (The effect upon taste of inorganic salts of calcium and magnesium.) Inaugural Dissertation, B. Sporn, Zeulenroda, Jena, 23 pp.

BOLLERUP, J. 1962 Smagsmaessig surhed. (Gustatory acidity.) BRYG, 19 (11): 261–72. (English summary.)

BOLTZ, E. 1939 Über die Beeinflussung des Geschmacksfeldes auf der Zunge durch Anaesthetica. IV. (On the effect of anaesthetics on the area of taste on the tongue.) Inaugural Dissertation, B. Sporn, Zeulenroda, Jena, 29 pp.

BONNET, P. 1924 Sur la nature des aliments que les Araignées peuvent absorber et sur le sens du goût chez ces animaux. (On the nature of the food that spiders can ingest and on the sense of taste of these animals.) CRSS, 91: 1194–96.

BONVALLET, M., DELL, P., and HUGELIN, A. 1952 Projections olfactives, gustatives, viscérales, vagales, visuelles et auditives au niveau des formations grises du cerveau antérieur du chat. (Olfactory, gustatory, visceral, vagal, visual, and auditory projections at the level of the gray formation of the anterior brain of the cat.) JOPH, 44: 222–24.

BOONACKER, A. A. 1917 Een abnormale platts voor een smaakpapil. (Abnormal location of a taste bud.) NTGE, 2: 612.

BORDIER, H. 1899 Recherches sur les phénomènes gustatifs et salivaires produits par le courant galvanique. (Research on gustatory and salivary phenomena produced by galvanic current.) AEMP, 7: 252–61.

BORING, E. G. 1942 Smell and taste, in *Sensation and Perception in the History of Experimental Psychology*. D. Appleton-Century Co., New York, 644 pp. (see pp. 437–62).

BORING, E. G., LANGFELD, H. S., and WELD, H. P. 1939 Smell, taste, and somesthesis, in *Intro-*

duction to Psychology. John Wiley & Sons, New York, 652 pp. (see pp. 600–8) .

BORISOV, P. 1903 O znachenii gorbkich sredstv dlia pushchevareniia. (Significance of bitter medical compounds on digestion.) RUVR, 2: 1121–23.

——. 1903 Sootnosheniye mezhdu vkusom i potrebnostyami organisma. (Correlation between taste and the needs of the organism.) RUVR, 2: 953–54.

——. 1903 Über die Bedeutung der Bitterstoffe für die Verdauung. (Significance of bitter substances for digestion.) AEPP, 51: 363–71.

——. 1903 Znachenie razdrazheniia vkusovych nervov dlia pushchevareniia. (On the significance of the taste-nerves and their irritation on digestion.) RUVR, 2: 869–72.

BÖRNSTEIN, W. 1922 Über den Geschmackssinn. (On the sense of taste.) KLWO, 2: 98.

——. 1928 Beitrag zur Frage der Differentialdiagnose corticaler und subcorticaler Herde (Kau-, Schmeck-, Hör-Trias) . (Differential diagnosis of disorders of chewing, tasting and hearing by localization of their origin in cortical and subcortical centers.) KLWO, 7: 2343.

——. 1928 Beobachtungen an einem Gehirn-verletzten: Geschmacksaura als lokaldiagnostisches Symptom. (Observation on an injured brain: Taste aura as a local diagnostic symptom.) MPNE, 67: 216–22.

——. 1940 Cortical representation of taste in man and monkey. I: Functional and anatomical relations of taste, olfaction, and somatic sensibility. YJBM, 12: 719–36.

——. 1940 Cortical representation of taste in man and monkey. II: The localization of the cortical taste area in man and a method of measuring impairment of taste in man. YJBM, 13: 133–56.

——. 1940 The cortical taste area in monkeys and a semi-quantitative method of testing taste in monkeys. AJPH, 129: 314.

BORSANYI, S. J., QUINONES, J., and BLANCHARD, C. L. 1964 Psychogalvanic skin response gustometry. BSMU, 49: 22–24.

BOSMAN, H. 1939 Über die Geschmackswirkung einiger anorganischer Phosphat-Verbindungen. (On the effect of taste of some inorganic phosphate compounds.) Inaugural Dissertation, Hellas, Jena, 14 pp.

BOTEY, R. 1905 Disquisiciones sobre higiene olfatoria y gustativa. (Discussion on olfactory and gustatory hygiene.) RCMB, 31: 131–41, 176–84.

BOTEZAT, E. 1893 Über das Verhalten der Nerven im Epithel der Saugethierzunge. (The behavior of the nerves in the epithelium of mammalian tongue.) ZWZA, 71: 211–26.

——. 1904 Geschmacksorgane und andere nervöse. Endapparate im Schnabel der Vögel. (Taste organs and other nervous end apparatus in the bill of birds.) BIZN, 24: 722–36.

——. 1906 Die Nervenendapparate in den Mundteilen der Vögel und die einheitliche Endigungsweise der peripheren Nerven bei den Wirbeltieren. (The nerve end apparatus in the mouth of birds and the central terminal of peripheral nerves in vertebrates.) ZWZA, 84: 205–360.

——. 1910 Morphologie, Physiologie und phylogenetische Beteutung der Geschmacksorgane der Vögel. (Morphology, physiology, and phylogenetic meaning of taste organs in birds.) ANAN, 36: 428–61.

BOTSZTEJN, C. 1942 Beitrag zur Frage der Geschmacksveränderungen im Verlaufe de Röntgenbestrahlung der Mundhöhlengegend; Geschmacksprüfungen mit Phenyl-thio-carbamid. (Contribution to the problem of taste change during X-ray irradiation of the mouth cavity; taste tests with phenyl-thio-carbamide.) RACL, 11: 164–72.

——. 1942 Zur Kenntnis der Geschmacksblindheit gegenüber Phenylthiocarbamid (P.T.C.) in der Zürcher Bevölkerung und deren Erbgang. (Regarding the knowledge of taste blindness for phenylthiocarbamide [P.T.C.] in the population of Zurich and its hereditary process.) AJKS, 17: 109–23.

BOTTLE, R. T. 1964 Synthetic sweetening agents. A survey of materials, including cyclamates. FOMA, 39: 42–47.

BOURGEOIS, R. 1949 *Semiologie du goût.* (Semeiology of taste.) Traité de Médecine, Masson, Paris, 1254 pp. (see pp. 136–40) .

BOURLIERE, F., CENDRON, H., and RAPAPORT, A. 1959 Action de l'acide acetylsalicylique sur la sensibilité au goût amer chez l'homme. (Action of acetylsalicylic acid on the sensitivity of the taste of bitterness in man.) RFEC, 4: 380–82. (English summary.)

BOURNE, G. H. 1948 Alkaline phosphatase in taste buds and nasal mucosa. NATU, 161: 445–46.

BOWLES, J. W., JR., and PRONKO, N. H. 1948 Identification of cola beverages II: A further study. JAPS, 32: 559–64.

——. 1949 Reversibility of stimulus function under hypnosis. JOPS, 27: 41–47.

BOYD, J. D. 1941 The sensory component of the hypoglossal nerve in the rabbit. JOAN, 75: 330–45.

BOYD, W. C. 1950 Taste reactions to antithyroid substances. SCIE, 112: 153.

——. 1951 "Taste blindness" to phenylthiocarbamide and related compounds. PSBU, 48: 71–74.

BOYD, W. C., and BOYD, L. G. 1936 New racial blood group studies in Europe and Egypt. SCIE, 84: 328–29.

——. 1937–38 New data on blood groups and other inherited factors in Europe and Egypt. AJPN, 23: 49–70.

——. 1937–38 Sexual and racial variations in ability to taste phenyl-thio-carbamide with some data on the inheritance. ANEU, 8: 46–51.

———. 1941 Blood groups and inbreeding in Syria. AMJA, **28**: 319–30.

———. 1941 Blood groups and types in Baghdad and vicinity. HUBI, **13**: 398–404.

———. 1949 The blood groups and types of the Ramah Navaho. AJPN, **7**: 569–74.

BOYD, W. C., and MATSUBARA, S. 1962 Different tastes of enantiomorphic hexoses. SCIE, **137**: 669.

BRADLEY, W. H. 1963 Central localization of gustatory perception: An experimental study. JCNE, **121**: 417–23.

BRAND, N. 1963 Taste sensitivity and endemic goitre in Israel. ANHG, **26**: 321–24.

———. 1964 Taste response and poliomyelitis. ANHG, **27**: 233–39.

BRANDTZAEG, M. B. 1958 Taste sensitivity of P.T.C. in 60 Norwegian families with 176 children: Confirmation of the hypothesis of single gene inheritance. AGSM, **8**: 115–28.

BRAUDE, R. 1948 Some observations on the behaviour of pigs in an experimental piggery. BUAB, **6**: 17–25.

BRAUN, J. VON, and RAWICZ, M. 1916 Synthesen in der fettaromatischen Reihe. XII: Derivate des m-phenylendiamins und m-nitranilins in ihrer Geschmack und hämolytischen Wirkung. (Syntheses in the aliphatic-aromatic series. XII: Derivatives of m-phenylenediamine and m-nitroaniline with regard to their taste and hemolytic action.) BDCG, **49**: 799–809.

BRAVO, J. 1592 De saporum et odorum differentiis, causis et affectionibus (On different tastes and odors, cause and effect), in *De simplicum medicamentorum delectu, et praeparation^ libri duo*. I. & A. Renaut Bros., Salamantica, 240 pp.

BRDIČKA, R. 1964 Chuťové vnímáni fenylthiomočoviny (PTC). (Taste perception for phenylthiourea [PTC].) SBLE, **66**: 116–20.

BREDER, C. M., JR., and RASQUIN, P. 1943 Chemical sensory reactions in the Mexican blind characins. ZOOL, **28**: 169–200.

BREMER, F. 1923 Centre cortical du goût chez le lapin. (Cortical center for taste in the rabbit.) CRSS, **89**: 423–33.

———. 1923 Physiologie nerveuse de la mastication chez le chat et le lapin. Réflexes de mastication. Résponses masticatrices corticales et centre cortical du goût. (Neutral physiology of mastication in the cat and rabbit. Masticatory reflexes. Cortical masticatory responses and the cortical center of taste.) AIPH, **21**: 308–52.

BRICKNER, R. M. 1930 A new tract in Herrick's gustatory system in certain teleosts. JCNE, **50**: 153–57.

BRIGL, P., and SCHEYER, W. 1926 Kohlenhydrate V. Über den bitteren Geschmack von Zuckerderivaten. (Carbohydrates. V. The bitter taste of sugar derivatives.) ZPCH, **160**: 214–33.

BRILLAT-SAVARIN, J. A. 1838 *Physiologie du Goût*. (Physiology of Taste.) Charpentier, Paris, 493 pp.

———. 1879 *Gastronomy as a Fine Art*. Scribner and Welford, New York, 280 pp. Translated from *Physiologie du Goût* (1838) by R. E. Anderson.

———. 1915 *A Handbook of Gastronomy*. Houghton Mifflin Co., Boston, 394 pp. Translated from *Physiologie du Goût* (1838).

———. 1926 *The Physiology of Taste*. Liveright, Inc., New York, 361 pp. Translated from *Physiologie du Goût* (1838).

BRINDLEY, L. D. 1965 Taste discrimination in Bobwhite and Japanese quail. ANBE, **13**: 507–12.

BRODAL, A., SZABO, T., and TORVIK, A. 1956 Corticofugal fibers to sensory trigeminal nuclei and nucleus of the solitary tract. JONE, **106**: 527–55.

BROEG, C. B. 1965 Sweeteners, natural and synthetic. FOEG, **37**: 66–68.

BRONTE-STEWART, B. 1956 Smoking and the cardiovascular system. BMJO, **2** (1) : 659.

BROWN, S., and SCHÄFER, E. A. 1889 An investigation into the functions of the occipital and temporal lobes of the monkey's brain. PTRB, **179**: 303–27.

BROWN, W. 1914 The judgment of very weak sensory stimuli with special reference to the absolute threshold of sensation for common salt. UCPS, **1**: 199–268.

BROWNE, L. B. 1963 Some possible modes of action of humidity and water receptors in insects. PCZO, **3**: 86–88.

BROWNE, L. B., and EVANS, D. R. 1960 Locomotor activity of the blowfly as a function of feeding and starvation. JIPH, **4**: 27–37.

BROWNE, L. B., and HODGSON, E. S. 1962 Electrophysiological studies of arthropod chemoreception. IV: Latency, independence, and specificity of labellar chemoreceptors of the blowfly, *Lucilia*. JCCP, **59**: 187–202.

BRÜCHER, C. 1884 Abhandlung über Vertheilung und Anordnung der Geschmackspapillen auf der Zunge der Hufthiere. (Article on distribution and arrangement of taste papillae on the tongue of ungulates.) DZTP, **10**: 93–111.

BRÜCKE, E. 1876 Geschmackssinn (Taste sense), in *Vorlesungen über Physiologie*. (Lectures on Physiology.) 2nd ed. W. Braumüller, Vienna, 337 pp. (see pp. 243–47).

BRÜCKE, H., HELLAUER, H. F., and UMRATH, K. 1948 Sur la nature cholinergique des bourgeons gustatifs de la papille foliée du lapin. (On the cholinergic nature of the taste buds of the foliate papillae of the rabbit.) AIPH, **55**: 362–65.

BRÜHL, N. P. 1903 Das Geschmacksorgan und die Geschmacksempfindungen, nebst neuen Untersuchungen über die Erregung verschiedener Geschmäcke durch den elektrischen Strom. (The taste organ and taste sensations, in addition to new investigations on the stimulation of different tastes through electrical current.) NAOF, **49**: 291–303.

BRUN, R. 1937 Troubles de l'odorat et du goût comme signe d'une lésion focale du lobe temporal. (Disorders of smell and taste as sign of focal lesion of temporal lobe.) JBEN, **37**: 262–69.

BRUNACCI, B. 1910 Sulla funzione secretoria della parotide nell'uomo. I: Influenza della qualità dello stimolo sulle proprietà fisico-chimiche della saliva parotidea. (Secretory function of the human parotid. I: Influence of the quality of the stimulus on the physico-chemical properties of the parotid saliva.) ARFI, **8**: 421–57.

———. 1914–15 Sulla funzione secretoria della parotide nell'uomo. III: Influenza della qualità dello stimolo su le proprietà chimico-fisiologiche della saliva parotidea umana. (Secretory function of the human parotid. III: Influence of the quality of the stimuli on the physicochemical property of human parotid saliva.) ARFI, **13**: 437–57.

———. 1916–17 Su la funzione secretoria della parotide nell'uomo. IV: Influenza dell'attenzione rivolta a stimoli olfattivi. (Secretory function of the human parotid. IV: Influence of attention to olfactory stimuli.) ARFI, **15**: 169–78.

———. 1916–17 Su la funzione secretoria della parotide nell'uomo. V: Influenza dell'attenzione rivolta a stimoli acustici. (Secretory function of the human parotid. V: Influence of attention to acoustical stimuli.) ARFI, **15**: 179–87.

———. 1916–17 Su la funzione secretoria della parotide nell'uomo. VI: Influenza dell'attenzione rivolta a stimoli luminosi. (Secretory function of the human parotid. VI: Influence of attention to light stimuli.) ARFI, **15**: 189–97.

BRUNI, A. C. 1933 Osservazioni sulle modificazioni morfologiche determinate de soluzioni di sostanze sapide nel protoplasma sopravviventa. (Morphologic changes produced in surviving protoplasma by solutions of sapid substances.) ATPA, **5**: 164–68.

———. 1933 Sulle modificazioni determinate de sostanze sapide nelle aree sensoriali del palato sopravvivente della rana. (Changes produced by sapid substances in the sensory areas of the surviving palate of the frogs.) BSIB, **8**: 1332–34.

BRUNNER, E. 1904 Reaktionsgeschwindigkeit in heterogenen Systemen. (Reaction velocity in heterogenous systems.) ZPCL, **47**: 56–71.

BRUNO, G. 1957 Dati camparativi sull'innervazione della lingua: Il comportamento delle terminazioni nervose di sensibilità generica. (Comparative data on the innervation of the tongue: The behavior of nerve endings of general sensibility.) MZOI, **66** (Supplement) : 264–65.

———. 1957 Dati comparativi sull'innervazione della lingua: Il comportamento delle terminazioni nervose nella sensibilità specifica. (Compartive data on the innervation of the tongue: The behavior of the nerve endings of specific sensibility.) MZOI, **66** (Supplement) : 266–68.

BRUNS, L. 1889 Multiple Hirnnervenläsion nach Basisfractur. Ein Beitrag zur Frage des Verlaufs der Geschmacksnerven. (Multiple brainnerve lesions after a basic fracture. A contribution to the question on the course of the taste nerves.) APNV, **20**: 495–503.

———. 1890 Erwiderung an Herrn Dr. Ziehl in Lübeck, die Innervation des Geschmacks betreffend. (Answer to Dr. Ziehl in Lübeck, regarding the innervation of taste.) APKM. **119**: 185–91.

BRUVOLD, W. H., and GAFFEY, W. R. 1965 Subjective intensity of mineral taste in water. JEPS, **69**: 369–74.

BRUVOLD, W. H., and PANGBORN, R. M. 1966 The rated acceptability of mineral taste in water. JAPS, **50**: 22–32.

BUCCOLA, G. 1883 Il tempo di Reazione ai vari stimoli di senso (Reaction time to various sense stimuli) , in *La Legge de Tempo nei Fenomeni del Pensiero Saggio di Psicologia Sperimentale*. F. Dumolard, Milano, 432 pp. (see pp. 95–111) .

BUCHALOFF, N. A. 1887 K voprosu o prichianakh razlichiia oshchushchenii. (Causes of the diversity of the senses.) APSE, **10**: 1–41.

———. 1888 K voprosu o kachestvakh vkusoyvykh oshchushchenii. (On sensation of taste.) APSE, **11**: 34–48.

*BÜCHI, E. C. 1955 Blood, secretion and taste among the Pallar, a South Indian Community. ANTH. **1**.

———. 1957 Blut, Ausscheiderstatus und Geschmack bei den Ulladan, einem Dschungelvolk in Südindien. (Blood, separation status and taste in Ulladan, a jungle people in South India.) VSNG, **137**: 101–3.

———. 1959 Blut, Geschmack and Farbensinn bei den Kurumba (Nilgiri, Südindien) . (Blood, taste and color sense in the Curumba [Nilgiri, South India].) AJKS, **34**: 310–16.

———. 1959–60 Blut, Geschmack und Farbensinn bei den Kurumba (Nilgiri, Südindian) . (Blood, taste and color sense in the Curumba [Nilgiri, South India].) BUSG, **36**: 4–8.

*———. 1960 Die Geschmacksempfindlichkeit gegenüber Phenylthiocarbamid (PTC) bei Mala-Arayan in Kerala (Südindien) . (Taste perception for phenylthiocarbamide [PTC] in Mala-Arayan in Kerala [South India].) VSNG, 135–37.

———. 1961 Zur genetischen Konstitution der Toda (Nilgiri, Südindien). Ausscheiderstatus, Geschmack, Farbensinn und Mittelphalangealhaar. (The genetic composition of the Toda [Nilgiri, South India]. Separation status, taste, color sense, and middle phalangeal hair.) ASAP, **26**: 12–28.

BUDDENBROCK,W. von. 1952 Der Geschmackssinn (Taste sense) , in *Vergleichende Physiologie*.

I: Sinnesphysiologie. Birkhauser & Co., Basel, 504 pp. (see pp. 427–36) .

———. 1953 *Die Welt der Sinne; eine gemeinverständliche Einführung in die Sinnesphysiologie.* (The world of the senses; a popular introduction to sensory physiology.) Springer, Berlin, 147 pp. (see pp. 106–9) .

———. 1958 *The Senses.* Translated from *Die Welt der Sinne* by Frank Gaynor, University of Michigan Press, Ann Arbor, 167 pp. (see pp. 107–23) .

BUDDENBROCK-HETTERSDORF, W. VON. 1929 Smell and taste, Senses of, in *Encyclopedia Britannica.* 14th ed. XX, 820–23.

BUDGE. 1859 Ueber geschmacksempfindende Stellen. (On areas that are sensitive to taste.) DEKL, **11**: 197.

BUJAS, Z. 1933 O sukcesivnom kontrastu kod okusa. (Successive contrast to the sense of taste.) Report, Psihologijskog Instituta, Univerziteta u Zagrebu, 27 pp.

———. 1934 Le temps d'action des stimuli de la sensibilité gustative. (Stimuli reaction time of the taste sense.) CRSS, **116**: 1307–9.

———. 1934 Quelques remarques sur le contraste el l'inhibition à la suite d'excitations gustatives simultanées. (Remarks on contrast and inhibition as a result of simultaneous gustatory excitation.) CRSS, **116**: 1304–6.

———. 1935 Le rapport entre les quantités liminaires et le temps d'action pour les excitations gustatives. (The relation between liminal quantities and the action time of gustatory stimuli.) CRSS, **119**: 835–37.

———. 1935 Le temps de réaction aux excitations électriques des recepteurs gustatifs. (Reaction time to electrical stimulations of the gustatory receptors.) CRSS, **119**: 716–19.

———. 1935 Le temps de réaction aux excitations gustatives d'intensité différente. (Reaction times for gustatory stimulations of different intensity.) CRSS, **119**: 1360–62.

———. 1935 Prilog tumačenju nekih pojava u području okusa. (Contribution to the explanation of certain gustatory phenomena.) APVZ, 141–44.

———. 1936 L'établissement de la sensation du goût électrique en fonctiõn de la durée d'excitation. (The establishment of the electric sensation of taste as a function of the duration of the stimulus.) CRSS, **122**: 1260–62.

———. 1937 Kontrast-und Hemmungserscheinungen bei disparaten simultanen Geschmacksreizen. (Phenomena of contrast and inhibition for disparate simultaneous taste stimuli.) AIPZ, **2**: 3–12.

———. 1937 La mesure de la sensibilité différentielle dans le domaine gustatif. (Measurement of the differential sensitivity in the gustatory modality.) AIPZ, **2**: 2–18.

———. 1937 O odredivanju intenziteta okusa tvari u različitim koncentracijama. (Determination of gustatory intensity of substances in solutions of different concentrations.) APVZ, **19**: 675–78.

———. 1939 Kontrast- und Hemmungserscheinungen bei disparaten simultanen Geschmacksreizen. (Contrast and inhibition phenomena in the case of disparate, simultaneous taste stimuli.) INPS, **16**: 81–89.

———. 1949 Quelques données sur le goût électrique. (Some data on electric taste.) ANPQ, **50**: 159–68.

———. 1953 L'adaptation gustative et son mécanisme. (Gustatory adaptation and its mechanism.) AIPZ, **17**: 1–10.

BUJAS, Z., and CHWEITZER, A. 1934 Contribution à l'étude du goût dit électrique. (Contribution to the study of so-called electric taste.) ANPQ, **35**: 147–57.

———. 1936 Recherches sur le goût électrique provoqué par les courants a établissement progressif. (Studies on electric taste as elicited by currents set up gradually.) ANPQ, **36**: 137–45.

———. 1937 "Goût électrique" par courants alternatifs chez l'homme. (Electric taste from alternating currents in man.) CRSS, **126**: 1106–9.

———. 1938 Les modifications électroniques d'excitabilité pour le goût électrique. (Electronic modifications of excitability for electric taste.) CRSS, **127**: 1071–72.

BUJAS, Z., MAYER, D., and OSTOJČIČ, A. 1939 Boebachtungen über den Restitution Vorgang beim Geschmacksinn. (Observations concerning the recovery process of the gustatory sense.) AIPZ, **3**: 1–14.

BUJAS, Z., and OSTOJČIČ, A. 1939 L'evolution de la sensation gustative en fonction du temps d'excitation. (The development of taste sensations as a function of excitation time.) AIPZ, **3**: 1–24.

———. 1941 La sensibilité gustative en fonction de la surface excitée. (Gustatory sensitivity as a function of the surface excited.) AIPZ, **13**: 1–19.

BULL, T. R. 1965 Taste and the chorda tympani. JLOT, **79**: 479–493.

BURDACH, K. F. 1826 Geschmack (Taste) , in *Baue und Leben des Gehirns.* (Structure and Life of the Brain.) Dyk, Leipzig, 594 pp. (see pp. 81, 215–18, 232–33, 385, 392–93).

BÜRKL, W. 1954 Über das Vorkommen von Geschmacksknospen im mittleren Drittel des Ösophagus. (On the occurrence of taste buds in the middle third of the esophagus.) ANAN, **100**: 320–21.

BURRIGHT, R. G., and KAPPAUF, W. E. 1963 Preference threshold of the white rat for sucrose. JCPP, **56**: 171–73.

BURTON, M. 1961 Taste, in *Animal Senses.* R. & K. Paul, Ltd., London, 133 pp. (see pp. 79-95) .

*———. 1965 *Animal Senses.* Van Nostrand, Princeton, 141 pp.

BÜSSEM, H. 1894 Über Geschmacksempfindungen

rachitischer und nichtrachitischer Kinder. (Taste sensations in rachitic and healthy children.) Inaugural Dissertation, R. G. Teubner, 22 pp.

———. 1894 Über Geschmacksempfindungen rachitischer und nichtrachitischer Kinder. (Taste sensations in rachitic and healthy children.) JAKI, **39**: 166–83.

BUTLER, C. G. 1940 The choice of drinking water by the honey bee. JEBI, **17**: 253–61.

BYRD, E., and GERTMAN, S. 1959 Taste sensitivity in aging persons. GERI, **14**: 381–84.

BYSTRZANOWSKA, T., and KMITA, S. 1951 Współczesne poglądy na fizjologię węchu i smaku. (Contemporary views on the physiology of smell and taste.) POLE, **6**: 1192–98.

CABANÈS. 1895 Les perversités du goût; antipathies bizarres et dépravations singulières. (Taste perversion; bizarre antipathies and singular depravations.) SANT, **12**: 327–28.

CAMERER, W. 1869 Die Grenzen der Schmeckbarkeit von Chlornatrium in wässriger Lösung. (Taste thresholds for sodium chloride in aqueous solutions.) PAGP, **2**: 322–29.

———. 1870 Ueber die Abhängigkeit des Geschmacksinns von der gereizten Stelle der Mundhöhle. (On the dependency of the sense of taste on the sensitive part of the mouth.) ZEBL, **6**: 440–52.

———. 1885 Die Methode der richtigen und falschen Fälle angewendet auf den Geschmackssinn. (Methods of right and wrong situations used on the sense of taste.) ZEBL, **21**: 570–602.

CAMERON, A. T. 1943 The relative sweetness of sucrose, glucose, and fructose. TRCM, **37**: 11–27.

———. 1944 The relative sweetness of certain sugars, mixtures of sugars, and glycerol. CNRM, **22**: 45–63.

———. 1945 The relative sweetness of various sweet compounds and of their mixtures. CNRM, **23**: 139–66.

———. 1947 The taste sense and the relative sweetness of sugars and other sweet substances. Science Report Series No. 9, Sugar Research Foundation, New York, 72 pp.

CAMPBELL, B. A. 1958 Absolute and relative sucrose preference thresholds for hungry and satiated rats. JCPP, **51**: 795–800.

CAMPUS, G. 1961 La tonsillectomia nei suor reflessi sulla sensibilità gustativa. Richerche geusimetriche. (Tonsillectomy and its influence on gustatory sensitivity. Gustometric research. AIOR, **72**: 554–68. (English summary.)

CANCIULLO, D. 1958 Sensibilità gustativa nei bambini; il tempo di percezione del gusto in popolazione da 5–10 anni. (The sense of taste in children; time of perception of taste

in a group five to ten years of age.) MIOT, **8**: 245–64.

CANNIGGIA, A., and BROGI, G. 1947 Sulle modificazioni vegetative da stimoli sensoriali nell'uomo. I: Variazoni glicemiche da stimoli luminosi, sonori, odorosi e gustativi. II: Variazioni cardiovascolari e respiratorie da stimoli luminosi, sonori, odorsi e gustativi. (Vegetative modifications from sense stimulations in human organism. I: Blood sugar after some light, sound, odor, and taste stimulations. I: Cardiovascular and respiratory variation after light, sound, and taste stimulations.) RSPS, **36**: 592–600, 601–8. (English summary.)

CAPRETTA, P. J. 1964 Saccharin consumption and the reinforcement issue. JCPP, **57**: 448–50.

CARCÒ, P. 1959 Les facteurs périphériques et centraux des disgueusies. (Peripheral and central factors of dysgeusia.) RLOR, **80**: 165–90. (English summary.)

CARCÒ, P., CACIULLO, D., and MOTTA, G. 1958 I fattori periferici e centrali delle disgeusie. (Peripheral and central factors of dysgeusia.) SILO, Bologna, 515 pp.

CARDULLO, H. M., and HOLT, L. E., JR. 1951 Ability of infants to taste P.T.C.; its application in cases of doubtful paternity. PSEB, **76**: 589–92.

CARL, A. 1875 Ein Beitrag zur Frage: Enthält die Chorda tympani "Geschmacksfasern"? (A contribution: Does the chorda tympani have "taste receptors"?) AONK, **10**: 152–78.

CARLSMITH, J. M., and ARONSON, E. 1963 Some hedonic consequences of the confirmation and disconfirmation of expectancies. JASP, **66**: 151–56.

CARMICHAEL, E. A., and WOOLLARD, H. H. 1933 Some observations on the fifth and seventh cranial nerves. BRAI, **56**: 109–25.

*CARPENTER, J. A. 1954 Species differences in taste preferences. Unpublished Ph.D. thesis, Brown University, 183 pp.

———. 1956 Species differences in taste preferences. JCPP, **49**: 139–44.

———. 1958 A comparison of stimulus-presentation procedures in taste-preference experiments. JCPP, **51**: 561–64.

CARPER, J. W., and POLLIARD, F. 1953 A comparison of the intake of glucose and saccharin solutions under conditions of caloric need. AJPC, **66**: 479–82.

CARR, C. J., BECK, F. F., and FRANTZ, J. C., JR. 1936 Sugar alcohols V: Chemical constitution and sweet taste. JACS, **58**: 1394–95.

CARR, W. J. 1952 The effect of adrenalectomy upon the NaCl taste threshold in rat. JCPP, **45**: 377–80.

CARRARI, G. 1934 Sindrome vertiginosa, anosmia, disgeusia da tampone di cerume bilaterale. (Vertiginous syndrome with anosmia and dysgeusia due to bilateral plugs of ear wax.) BMOG, **52**: 234–42.

CARTHAUS, P. 1920 Ein Beitrag zu den Störungen

des Geruchs- und Geschmacksapparates nach Unfällen. (Contribution on smell and taste disorders from accidents.) Inaugural Dissertation, J. F. Carthaus, Bonn, 35 pp.

CARTHY, J. D. 1958 The contact chemical sense, in *An Introduction to the Behavior of Invertebrates*. Allen & Unwin, London, 380 pp. (see pp. 279–300).

*CASE, J. 1964 Properties of the dactyl chemoreceptors of *Cancer antennarius Stimpson* and *C. productus* Randall. BIBU, 127: 428–46.

CASE, J., and GWILLIAM, G. F. 1961 Amino acid sensitivity of the dactyl chemoreceptors of *Carcinides maenas*. BIBU, 121: 449–55.

———. 1963 Amino acid detection by marine invertebrates. PCZO, 3: 75.

CASELLA, C., and NOLLI, S. 1955 Il gusto dell'acqua (water taste) nella rana surrenectomizzata. (Water taste in adrenalectomized frog.) BSIB, 31: 1227.

CASELLA, C., and RAPUZZI, G. 1957 Azione dell'acqua, del CaCl$_2$ e del NaCl sui ricettori linguali nella rana. (Effects of water, CaCl$_2$ and NaCl on the lingual receptors of the frog.) ABSI, 41: 191–203.

———. 1963 Interactions fonctionnelles entre les papilles linguales de la Grenouille. Étude électrophysiologique. (Functional interactions among the lingual papillae of the frog. Electrophysiological study.) JOPH, 55: 219–20.

CASSIRER, R. 1899 Ein Fall von multipler Hirnnervenlähmung. Zugleich als Beitrag zur Lehre von der Geschmacksinnervation. (A case of multiple cerebral nerve paralysis. A contribution to the theory of taste innervation.) AAPA (Supplement), pp. 36–72.

CAUSSÉ, R. 1936 Les signes de la paralysie du glosso-pharyngien. (The signs of glossopharyngeal paralysis.) ANOL, 1: 44–58.

CECHERELLI, G. 1904 Sulle espansioni nervose di senso nella mucosa della lingua dell'uomo. (On the nervous expansion of sensation in the lingual mucosa of man.) ANAN, 25: 56–69.

CHADWICK, L. E., and DETHIER, V. G. 1946 The relationship between chemical structure and the response of blowflies to tarsal stimulation by aliphatic acids. JGPL, 30: 255–62.

———. 1949 Stimulation of tarsal receptors of the blowflies by aliphatic aldehydes and ketones. JGPL, 32: 445–52.

CHAMBERLAIN, A. F. 1903 Primitive taste words. AJPC, 14: 146–53.

CHAPLIN, J. P. 1947 Preferences of adrenalectomized rats for salt solutions of different concentrations. Unpublished Ph.D. thesis, University of Illinois, 89 pp.

CHAPPELL, G. M. 1953 Flavour assessment of sugar solutions. JSFA, 4: 346–50.

CHARONNAT, N. 1939 Quelques observations sur les rapports entre la saveur amère et la constitution chimique. (The connection between bitter taste and chemical constitution.) UNPH, 80: 27.

CHATIN, J. 1880 Le sens du goût (The sense of taste), in *Les Organes des Sens dans la Série Animale*. (The sense organs in the animal series.) J. B. Bailliere et Fils, Paris, 726 pp. (see pp. 139–205).

CHAUCHARD, A. 1927 Recherches quantitatives sur l'excitabilité de l'appareil du goût chez l'homme. (Quantitative research on the stimulation of a taste apparatus in man.) CORE, 184: 1273–75.

CHAUCHARD, A., and CHAUCHARD, B. 1936 La chronaxie de l'appareil du goût. (The chronaxie of the taste apparatus.) CRSS, 121: 533–34.

CHAUNCEY, H. H., FELLER, R. P., and SHANNON, I. L. 1963 Effect of acid solutions on human gustatory chemoreceptors as determined by parotid gland secretion rate. PSEB, 112: 917–23.

CHAUNCEY, H. H., and SHANNON, I. L. 1959 Parotid gland secretion rate as a method for measuring response to gustatory and masticatory stimuli in humans. Publications 59–66, Air University, School of Aviation Medicine, U.S.A.F., Randolph AFB, Texas, pp. 1–7.

———. 1960 Parotid gland secretion rate as method for measuring response to gustatory stimuli in humans. PSEB, 103: 459–63.

CHAUNCEY, H. H., and WEISS, P. A. 1958 Composition of human saliva. Parotid gland secretion: Flow rate, pH, and inorganic composition after oral administration of a carbonic anhydrase inhibitor. AIPT, 113: 377–83.

CHAUNCEY, H. H., WINER, R. A., and BARBER, T. X. 1964 Influence of verbal suggestion on the parotid gland response to gustatory stimuli. PSEB, 116: 898–901.

CHERNETSKI, K. E. 1964 Sympathetic enhancement of peripheral sensory input in the frog. JONE, 27: 493–515.

CHEVREUL, M. E. 1824 Des différentes manières dont les corps agissent sur l'organe du goût. (The different ways by which compounds activate the organ of taste.) JPPG, 4: 127–31.

———. 1824 Des différentes manières dont les corps agissent sur l'organe du goût. (The different ways by which compounds activate the organ of taste.) ACPH, 26: 386–90.

CHIANG, H., and WILSON, W. A. 1963 Some tests of the diluted-water hypothesis of saline consumption in rats. JCPP, 56: 660–65.

CHIARELLI, B. 1959 Dati sulla sensibilità alla P.T.C. (Phenil-thio-carbammide) in primati. (Data on the sensitivity of primates to P.T.C.) ASGI, 5: 275–80. (English summary.)

CHIKAUHI, Y. 1952 (Frequency of taste-blindness among the Japanese.) MEIS, 18: 21–26. (In Japanese.)

CHILDS, W. H. 1944 Salt as a flavor in candy. MACO, 24: 18–19.

CHINAGLIA, L. 1915 De l'influence qu'exerce la température sur la sensibilité gustative. (Influence of temperature on gustatory sensibility.) AIBL, 63: 401–9.

———. 1915 Ricerche intorno all'influenza esercitata dalla temperatura sulla sensibilità gustativa. (Research on the influence exerted by temperature on gustatory sensitivity.) RIPS, 11: 196–226

CHIRONE, E. 1963 Il senso del gusto. (The sense of taste.) PSPR, 70: 470–75.

CHISA, N., MENDELSON, C. G., and DARNLEY, J. D. 1964 Auriculotemporal syndrome. ARDE, 90: 457–59.

CHLENOV, L. G., SHUTOVA, T. A., and LEBEDEVA, N. V. 1957 Klinicheskaya kharakteristika i teoreticheskoe obosnovanie vosstanovleniya funktsii posle rasstroistva mozgovogo krovoobrashcheniya. (The clinical features and theoretical basis of the restoration of function after disturbances of the cerebral circulation of blood.) ZNPP, 57: 161–71. (French summary.)

*CHRISTENSEN, K. R. 1960 Isohedonic contours in the sucrose-sodium chloride area of gustatory stimulation. Unpublished Ph.D. thesis, University of Illinois.

———. 1961 Methodology in preference testing, in Physiological and Behavioral Aspects of Taste, M. R. Kare and B. P. Halpern (eds.). University of Chicago Press, Chicago, 149 pp. (see pp. 79–86).

———. 1962 Isohedonic contours in the sucrose-sodium chloride area of gustatory stimulation. JCPP, 55: 337–41.

CHRISTIAN, J. E., and JENKINS, G. L. 1950 A comparison of a new astringent agent with such agents now commonly used. JAPM, 39: 663–65.

CHUNG, C. S., WITKOP, C. J., and HENRY, J. L. 1964 A genetic study of dental caries with special reference to PTC taste sensitivity. AJHG, 16: 231–45.

CICALA, G. A., and McMICHAEL, J. S. 1964 Quinine aversion thresholds in rats as a function of age and psychophysical procedure. CJPS, 18: 28–35.

CLARK, W. G., and CLAUSEN, D. F. 1943 Dietary "self-selection" and appetites of untreated and treated adrenalectomized rats. AJPH, 139: 70–79.

CLAUS, C. F. W. 1891 Geschmackssinn (Sense of taste), in Lehrbuch der Zoologie 5 Aufl. N. G. Elwert, Marburg, 958 pp. (see pp. 87–88).

CLEMENTI, A. 1935 L'eccitabilità della corteccia cerebrale della sfera gustativa e l'epilessia sensoriale riflessa a tippo gustativo. (Excitability of cerebral cortex in the gustatory sphere and relation to reflex gustatory epilepsy.) FIME, 6: 881–92.

———. 1935 Sfera gustativa della corteccia cerebrale del cane ed epilessia sperimentale riflessa a tipo sensoriale gustativa. (Gustatory sphere of the cerebral cortex of the dog and experimental epileptic reflexes of the gustatory sensory type.) BSIB, 10: 902–5.

———. 1958 L'area gustativa della corteccia cerebrale del cane e i suoi rapporti coi centri dell'area sensitivo-motrice esplorati colla tecnica elettrocorticografica. (The gustatory area of the cerebral cortex of the dog and its relation to centers of the sensorimotor area investigated with elcetrocorticographic techniques.) BSIB, 34: 1550–53.

CLENDENNING, T. 1940 Flavor in confections. Part III: Taste-provoking agents. MACO, 20: 21–22.

CLERICI, J. (J. LeClerc) 1722 De saporibus (On taste), in Physica, Sive de Rebus Corporeis, IV. Rudolph & Gerard, Amsterdam, 360 pp. (see pp. 280–93).

COCHRAN, J. L., and SECTER, I. I. 1956 Restoration by hypnotherapy of a loss of the sense of taste of 4½ years' duration. JNMD, 123: 296–98.

COHEN, J., and OGDON, D. P. 1949 Taste blindness to phenyl-thio-carbamide and related compounds. PSBU, 46: 490–98.

———. 1949 Taste blindness to phenyl-thio-carbamide as a function of saliva. SCIE, 110: 532–33.

———. 1951 Concerning taste blindness to PTC. PSBU, 48: 419–20.

COHEN, M. J., HAGIWARA, S., and ZOTTERMAN, Y. 1955 Impulse pattern of taste. JPHY, 129: 43P. (Title only.)

———. 1955 The response spectrum of taste fibres in the cat: A single fibre analysis. APSC, 33: 316–32.

*———. 1960 Mikaku (Gustation), in Shin Seirigaku. (New Physiology.) C. Toida and K. Uchizono (eds). Igakushoin, Tokyo (see pp. 563–70).

COHEN, M. J., LANDGREN, S., STRÖM, L., and ZOTTERMAN, Y. 1957 Cortical reception of touch and taste in the cat. APSC, 40 (Supplement 135): 1–50.

COHEN, T., and GITMAN, L. 1959 Oral complaints and taste perception in the aged. JOGE, 14: 294–98.

COHN, G. 1904 Ueber angeborene Choanalatresie. (On inherited choanal atresia.) MOLA, 38: 472–89.

———. 1914 Die organischen Geschmacksstoffe. (Organic taste substances.) F. Siemenroth, Berlin, 936 pp.

———. 1915–16 Geschmack und Konstitution bei organischen Verbindungen. (Taste and constitution of organic compounds.) SCCT, 22: 1–100.

COLE, L. W. 1910 Reactions of frogs to chlorides of ammonium, potassium, sodium, and lithium. JCNE, 20: 601–14.

COLE, W. H. 1938 Chemical stimulation in animals. SXQU, 26: 129–35.

COLE, W. H., and ALLISON, J. B. 1930 Chemical stimulation by alcohols in the barnacle, the frog, and planaria. JGPL, 14: 71–86.

———. 1931 Stimulation by hydrochloric acid

in the catfish *Schilbeodes*. JGPL, 15: 119–24.
———. 1933 Stimulation by mineral and fatty acids in the barnacle *Balanus Balanoides*. JGPL, 16: 895–903.

COLLIER, G. 1962 Some properties of saccharin as a reinforcer. JEPS, 64: 184–91.

COLLIER, G., and MYERS, L. 1961 The loci of reinforcement. JEPS, 61: 57–66.

COLMAN, B. H. 1964 Stapedectomy. Observations on 100 cases using an adipose tissue graft and steel-pin prosthesis. AOLA, 57: 97–112.

COOK, M. H. 1915 Are the taste-buds of elasmobranchs endodermal in origin? SCIE, 41: 438.

COOK, M. H., and NEAL, H. V. 1921 Are the taste-buds of elasmobranchs endodermal in origin? JCNE, 33: 45–54.

COOK, R. C. 1933 Inherited variations in the sense of taste. AMRY, 28: 67–69.

COOPER, P. R. 1921 On the cultivation of the senses of smell and taste and their employment in practical medicine. CLJL, 50: 459–61.

COOPER, R. M., BILASH, I., and ZUBEK, J. P. 1959 The effect of age on taste sensitivity. JOGE, 14: 56–58.

COPELAND, M., and WIEMAN, H. L. 1924 The chemical sense and feeding behavior of *Nereis virens*. Sars. BIBU, 47: 231–38.

CORBIT, J. D. 1965 Hyperphagic hyperactivity to adulteration of drinking water with quinine HCl. JCPP, 60: 123–24.

CORDELL, R., and SHORT, D. 1964 Breakthrough: Third synthetic sweetener. FOEG, 36: 63–65.

CORDIER, R. 1964 Sensory cells. Biochemistry, Physiology & Morphology, in *The Cell*, J. Brachet and A. E. Mirsky (eds.). Academic Press, New York, 564 pp. (see pp. 313–86).

CORIAT, I. H. 1918 The presence of taste fibers in the lingual nerve. DECO, 60: 217–20.

CORIN, J. 1887 Action des acides sur le goût. (Action of acids on taste.) BABS, 14: 616–37.
———. 1888 Action des acides sur le goût. (Action of acids on taste.) ABIL, 8: 121–38.

COSMELLI, A. J. 1954 Los órganos de los sentidos en relación con la alimentación. (Relation of the sense organs to nutrition.) DIME, 26: 2344–46.

COVIAN, M. R., and ANTUNES-RODRIGUES, J. 1963 Specific alterations in sodium chloride intake after hypothalamic lesions in the rat. AJPH, 205: 922–26.

COX, G. J., and NATHANS, J. W. 1953 Subthreshold taste of dilute salt solutions with especial reference to sodium fluoride. JAPY, 5: 395–98.

COY, W. A., and MANLY, R. S. 1956 Sweetness and texture thresholds among patients with natural and full artificial dentitions. IADR, 34: 25–26. (Abstract.)

CRAGG, L. H. 1937 The relation between sourness and the pH of the saliva. TRCM, 31: 1–7.
———. 1937 The sour taste: Threshold values

and accuracy, the effects of saltiness and sweetness. TRCM, 31: 131–40.

CRETEUR, C. 1952 Le test à la phenylthiocarbamide (PTC-test). (Phenylthiocarbamide test [PTC test].) RMLI, 7: 415–19.

CRISCI, P. 1930 Intorno alla pretesa proporzionalita fra il pH e il sapore acido delle soluzioni acquose con speciale riguardo al vini. (A supposed relation between pH and acid taste of aqueous solutions, particularly wine.) ACAP, 20: 566–83.

CROCKER, E. C. 1945 The physiology of flavor perception, in *Flavor*. McGraw-Hill, New York, 172 pp. (see pp. 21–31).
———. 1948 Meat flavor and observations on the taste of glutamate and other amino acids, in *Flavor and Acceptability of Monosodium Glutamate*, Proceedings of the Symposium, Quartermaster Food and Container Institute, Chicago, 92 pp. (see pp. 25–31).

CROCKER, E. C., and HENDERSON, L. F. 1932 The glutamic taste. APEO, 27: 156–58.

CROMBIE, A. C., and DARRAH, J. H. 1947 The chemoreceptors of the wireworm (Agriotes species) and the relation of activity to chemical constitution. JEBI, 24: 95–109.

CROSLAND, H. R., GOODMAN, M., and HOCKETT, A. 1926 Anosmia and its effects upon taste perception. JEPS, 9: 398–408.

CROSLAND, H. R., MILLER, R. C., and BRADWAY, W. E. 1928 Oral perceptions in relation to anosmia. JEPS, 11: 161–66.

CROW, S. 1932 The sensitivity of the legs of certain calliphoridae to saccharose. PHZO, 5: 16–35.

CROZIER, W. J. 1915 Ionic antagonism in sensory stimulation. AJPH, 39: 297–302.
———. 1916 The taste of acids. JCNE, 26: 453–62.
———. 1918 On sensory activation by alkalies. AJPH, 45: 315–22.
———. 1918 Sensory activation by acids. I. AJPH, 45: 323–41.
———. 1934 Chemoreception, C. Murchison (ed.). in *A Handbook of General Experimental Psychology*, Clark University Press, Worcester, Mass., 1125 pp. (see pp. 987–1036).

CRUZ-COKE, R., NAGEL, R., and ETCHEVERRY, R. 1964 Effects of locus MN on diastolic blood pressure in a human population. ANHG, 28: 39–48.

CSOKOR, J. 1884 Vergleichend histologische Studien über den Bau des Geschmacksorganes der Haussäugethiere. (Comparative histological studies on the structure of taste organs in domesticated mammals.) OVWV, 62: 117–63.

CUBBAGE, I. H. 1949 The utilization of gustatory cues as sensory control in the learning of a linear maze. Unpublished Master's thesis, University of Delaware, 52 pp.

CUNHA, A. X., and ABREU, M. D. A. 1956 A sensibilidade gustativa da feniltiocarbamida em Portugueses. (Taste sensitivity to phenylthiocarbamide in the Portuguese.) CEAP, **6**: 85–96.

CUSHING, H. 1902 The effect of extirpation of the gasserian ganglion upon the sense of taste. AJPH, **8**: 27.

———. 1903 The taste fibres and their independence of the N. Trigeminus. Deductions from thirteen cases of Gasserian ganglion extirpation. JHHB, **14**: 71–78.

CYBULSKI, N. 1888 Badania poczncia smaku u osoby pozbawionej jezyka. (Inquiry into perception of taste in a man deprived of his tongue.) RWLP, **18**: 207–16.

DA COSTA, J. M. 1889 Gustatory paralysis (peripheral). MENE, **54**: 517.

DAHL, L. K., HEINE, M., and TASSINARI, L. 1962 Role of genetic factors in susceptibility to experimental hypertension due to chronic excess salt ingestion. NATU, **194**: 480–82.

DAHLBERG, A. C., and PENCZEK, E. S. 1941 The relative sweetness of sugars as affected by concentration. NYSC, **258**: 1–12.

D'AJUTOLO, F. 1940 La sensibilità gustativa dei due terzi anteriori della lingua in rapporto ad interventi chirurgici sul nervo trigemino. (Taste sensitivity of anterior two-thirds of tongue in relation to surgical interventions of the trigeminal nerve.) RVOO, **17**: 517–63. (English summary.)

DALLENBACH, J. W., and DALLENBACH, K. M. 1943 The effects of bitter-adaptation on sensitivity to the other taste qualities. AJPC, **56**: 21–31.

DALLENBACH, K. M. 1936 Some gustatory apparatus. AJPC, **48**: 504–7.

DALY, G. D. 1871 Taste, physiologically considered. JPMN, **5**: 520–34.

DANA, C. L. 1886 Case of paralysis of trigeminus followed by alternate hemiplegia: Its relation to the nerve of taste. JNMD, **13**: 65–73.

DANIELS, P. J. 1790 Gustus organi novissime detecti prodromus. (Forerunner of recently discovered taste organs.) Dissertation, Monguntiae, 95 pp.

DAS, S. R. 1955–56 Contribution to heredity of P.T.C. taste character based on study of 845 sib-pairs. AGMG, **20**: 334–43.

———. 1957–58 Inheritance of the P.T.C. taste character in man: an analysis of 126 Rarhi Brahmin families of West Bengal. AGMG, **22**: 200–12.

DAS, S. R., and MUKHERJEE, D. P. 1964 Phenylthiocarbamide taste sensitivity survey among the Pareng Gadaba, the Ollaro Gadaba and the Konda Paroja of Koraput District, Orissa. AGMG, **14**: 168–76.

DAS, S. R., MUKHERJEE, D. P., and BHATTACHARJEE, P. N. 1963 P.T.C. taste threshold distribution in the Bado Gadaba and the Bareng Paroja of Koraput district in Orissa. AGSM, **13**: 369–77.

DASTUR, D. K. 1961 The relationship between terminal lingual innervation and gustation. A clinical and histological study. BRAI, **84**: 499–513.

DAVID, N. J., GABLES, C., and KIRSCH, R. E. 1965 Gustatory lid reaction in congenital Horner's syndrome. AROP, **73**: 796–99.

DAVIDENKOV, S. 1940 Inherited inability to eat sugar. JOHE, **31**: 5–7.

DAVIDS, E. 1822 De signis et sapore varie mutato variis in morbis. (On signs and taste variously changed in various diseases.) Inaugural Dissertation, L. Batavorum, Rotterdam, 66 pp.

DAVIDSON, A. 1875 On the sense of taste and its relation to facial paralysis and anaesthesia. LMMS, **3**: 198–212.

DAVIS, C. 1877 Die becherförmigen Organe des Kehlkopfes. (The goblet-shaped organs of the larynx.) AMAE, **14**: 158–67.

DAWSON, E. H., BROGDON, J. L., and McMANUS, S. 1963 Sensory testing of differences in taste. I: Methods. FOTE, **17**: 45–48, 51.

———. 1963 Sensory testing of differences in taste. II: Selection of panel members. FOTE, **17**: 39–41, 43–44.

DEERR, N. 1922 Relative sweetness of sucrose, levulose, and dextrose. ISUJ, **24**: 481.

DEHN, M. 1894 Vergleichende Prüfung über den Haut- und Geschmackssinn bei Männern und Frauen verschiedener Stände. (Comparative tests on the skin and taste sense in men and women of different status.) Inaugural Dissertation, Dorpat, 88 pp.

DEHNEN, T. 1950 Geschmacksstörungen nach Tonsillektomie. (Taste disorders following tonsillectomy.) ZLRT, **29**: 546–51.

DEJERINE, M. 1891 Chromatic gustation. LANC, **2**: 1253.

DE LAURENZI, V. 1925 Sulla secrezione parotidea nell'uomo provacate da diversi fattori periferici. (The parotid secretion of man excited by various peripheral factors.) AALB, **1**: 599–602.

DELHOUGNE, F. 1930 Über Störungen der Geschmacksempfindung bei Magenkranken. (On taste disturbances in diseases of the stomach.) DAKM, **167**: 97–104.

DE LORENZO, A. J. 1958 Electron microscopic observations on the taste buds of the rabbit. JBBC, **4**: 143–50.

———. 1960 Electron microscopy of the olfactory and gustatory pathways. AORH, **69**: 410–20.

———. 1960 Electron microscopy of the olfactory and gustatory pathways. TALA, **81**: 39–49.

———. 1963 Studies on the ultrastructure and histophysiology of cell membranes, nerve fibers and synaptic junctions in chemoreceptors, in *Olfaction and Taste*, Y. Zotterman (ed.). Macmillan, New York, 396 pp. (see pp. 5–18).

DELORT, M. 1923 Sur la physiologie du goût. (On the physiology of taste.) AESC, **8**: 241–46.

DEMOLL, R. 1917 Geruch- und Geschmacksinn (Odor and taste senses), in *Die Sinnesorgane der Arthropoden ihr Bau und ihre Funktion*. F. Vieweg & Sohn, Braunschweig, 243 pp. (see pp. 26–38).

DEMSHANKO, A. N. 1961 Sostoĭanie vkusovogo analizatora pri nekotorikh zabolevaniĭakh. (The state of the gustatory analyzer in certain diseases of the stomach.) SOME, **25**: 52–55. (English summary.)

DENCKER, S. J., HAUGE, M., and KAIJ, L. 1959 An investigation of the PTC taste character in monochorionic twin pairs. AGSM, **9**: 236–44.

DENCKS, H. 1938 Über die Geschmackswirkung einiger anorganischer Karbonat- und Fluorid-Verbindungen. (On the effect of the taste of some inorganic carbonate and fluoride compounds.) Inaugural Dissertation. Jügelts, Jena, 23 pp.

DENTON, D. A., GODING, J. R., SABINE, R., and WRIGHT, R. D. 1958 Adaptation of ruminant animals to variation of salt intake, Proceedings of the Teheran Symposium, "Salinity Problems in the Arid Zones," *Arid Zone Research, XIV*, 3–8

DENTON, D. A., and SABINE, J. R. 1961 The selective appetite for Na⁺ shown by Na⁺-deficient sheep. JPHY, **157**: 97–116.

———. 1963 The behaviour of Na deficient sheep. BEHA, **20**: 364–76.

DEONIER, C. C. 1938 Effects of some common poisons in sucrose solutions on the chemoreceptors of the housefly, *Musca domestica L.* JEEN, **31**: 742–45.

———. 1938 The gustatory nature of the chemotarsal stimulations in the housefly, *Musca domestica L.* JEZO, **75**: 489–500.

———. 1939 Responses of the blowflies, *Cochliomyia americana* C. & P. and *Phormia regina* Meigen, to stimulation of the tarsal chemoreceptors. AESA, **32**: 526–32.

DEONIER, C. C., and RICHARDSON, C. H. 1935 The tarsal chemoreceptor response of the housefly, *Musca domestica L.*, to sucrose and levulose. AESA, **28**: 467–74.

DERMER, O. C. 1947 The science of taste. POAS, **27**: 9–20.

DEROUET-BOISSIÈRE, H. M. E. H. 1839 Quelle est la valeur des signes fournis par les diverses saveurs perçues par le malade? (What is the value furnished by the different signs of taste perceived by an invalid?) Unpublished M.D. thesis, Paris, 37 pp. (see pp. 1–14).

DETHIER, V. G. 1937 Gustation and olfaction in *lepidopterous* larvae. BIBU, **72**: 7–23.

———. 1939 Taste thresholds in *lepidopterous* larvae. BIBU, **76**: 325–29.

———. 1951 Taste sensitivity to compounds of homologous series. AJPH, **165**: 247–50.

———. 1951–52 The limiting mechanism in tarsal chemoreception. JGPL, **35**: 55–65.

———. 1952 Adaptation to chemical stimulation of the tarsal receptors of the blowfly. BIBU, **103**: 178–89.

———. 1955 The physiology and histology of the contact chemoreceptors of the blowfly. QRBI, **30**: 348–71.

———. 1956 Chemoreceptor mechanisms, in *Molecular structure and functional activity of nerve cells*, R. G. Grenell and L. J. Mullins (eds.). American Institute of Biological Sciences, No. 1, 169 pp., (see pp. 1–33).

———. 1962 Chemoreceptor mechanisms in insects, in *Biological Receptor Mechanisms*, J. W. L. Beament (ed.). Academic Press, New York, 372 pp. (see pp. 180–96).

———. 1963 *The Physiology of Insect Senses*. John Wiley and Sons., New York, 266 pp.

DETHIER, V. G., and ARAB, Y. M. 1958 Effect of temperature on the contact chemoreceptors of the blowfly. JTPH, **2**: 153–61.

DETHIER, V. G., and CHADWICK, L. E. 1946–47 Rejection thresholds of the blowfly for a series of aliphatic alcohols. JGPL, **30**: 247–53.

———. 1948 Chemoreception in insects. PHRE, **28**: 220–54.

———. 1948–49 The stimulating effect of glycols and their polymers on the tarsal receptors of blowflies. JGPL, **32**: 139–51.

———. 1949–50 An analysis of the relationship between solubility and stimulating effect in tarsal chemoreception. JGPL, **33**: 589–99.

DETHIER, V. G., EVANS, D. R., and RHOADES, M. V. 1956 Some factors controlling the ingestion of carbohydrates by the blowfly. BIBU, **111**: 204–22.

DETHIER, V. G., and EVANS, D. R. 1961 The physiological control of water ingestion in the blowfly. BIBU, **121**: 108–16.

DETHIER, V. G., and HANSON, F. E. 1965 Taste papillae of the blowfly. JCCP, **65**: 93–100.

DETHIER, V. G., and RHOADES, M. V., 1954 Sugar preference-aversion functions for the blowfly. JEZO, **126**: 177–204.

DETHIER, V. G., and WOLBARSHT, M. L. 1956 The electron microscopy of chemosensory hairs. EXPE, **12**: 335–37.

DEUTSCH, J. A., and JONES, A. D. 1960 Diluted water: An explanation of the rat's preference for saline. JCPP, **53**: 122–27.

DE WARDENER, H. E., and HERXHEIMER, A. 1957 The effect of a high water intake on salt consumption, taste thresholds, and salivary secretion in man. JPHY, **139**: 53–63.

DIAMANT, H., ENFORS, B., and HOLMSTEDT, B. 1959 Salivary secretion in man elicited by means of stimulation of the chorda tympani. APSC, **45**: 293–99.

DIAMANT, H., FUNAKOSHI, M., STRÖM, L., and ZOTTERMAN, Y. 1963 Electrophysiological studies on human taste nerves, in *Olfaction and Taste*, Y. Zotterman (ed.). Macmillan, New York, 396 pp. (see pp. 193–203).

DIAMANT, H., OAKLEY, B., STRÖM, L., WELLS, C., and ZOTTERMAN, Y. 1965 A comparison of neural and psychophysical responses to taste stimuli in man. APSC, 64: 67–74.

DIAMANT, H., SKOOG, T., and ZOTTERMAN, Y. 1960 The taste of water. AOLA, 51: 308–11.

DICKER, S. E. 1958 The effects of methylpentynol on ethanol drinking and on water metabolism in rats. JPHY, 144: 138–47.

DIDIER, G. 1957 Anosmie et ageusie d'origine traumatique (Anosmia and ageusia of traumatic origin.) JSML, 75: 606–11.

DIEMAIR, W., and JANECKE, H. 1950 Sobre el reconocimiento de las sustancias amargas en la desecación de la avena. (Investigation of the bitter substances in the drying of oats.) ANBR, 2: 341–47. (English summary.)

DIETZEL, R. 1926 Saurer Geschmack und Wasserstoffionenkonzentration. (Sour taste and hydrogen ion concentration.) KOZE, 40: 240–48.

DIGIESI, V. 1961 Le variazioni della sensibilità gustativa per il sapore salato nell'uomo in particolari situazioni fisiologiche e sperimentali ed in alcuni stati morbosi. I: Il comportamento della soglia gustativa per le stimolazioni salato in particolari situazioni di ritenzione o deficit salino. (The variations of taste sensitivity for salt taste in man in special physiological and experimental situations and in various disease states. I: The behavior of the gustatory threshold for salt stimulation in special situations of saline retention and deficiency.) RNVE, 15: 303–19. (English summary.)

———. 1961 Le variazioni della sensibilità gustativa per il sapore salato nell'uomo in particolari situazioni fisiologiche e sperimentali ed in alcuni stati morbosi. II. Il comportamento della soglia gustativa per le stimolazioni salato e della preferenza per il sale nella insufficienza surrenale. (The variations in taste sensitivity for salt taste in man in special physiological and experimental situations and in various disease states. II. Taste thresholds and preference for salt in adrenal insufficiency.) RNVE, 15: 320–27. (English summary.)

———. 1961 Le variazioni della sensibilità gustativa per il sapore salato nell'uomo in particolari situazioni fisiologiche e sperimentali ed in alcuni stati morbosi. III. Il comportamento della soglia gustativa per le stimolazioni salato e della preferenza per il sale nell'obesità. (The variations of taste sensitivity for salt taste in man in special physiological and experimental situations and in various disease states. III. The behavior of the gustatory threshold for salt stimulation and preference for salt in obesity. RNVE, 15: 328–37. (English summary.)

———. 1962 L'appetito per il cloruro di sodio e l'acuità gustativa per il sapore salato nei soggetti affetti da ipertensione arteriosa. (Sodium chloride appetite and gustatory acuity for salty taste in subjects with arterial hypertension.) RNVE, 16: 54–62.

DIGIESI, V., and FROSECCHI, M. 1964 L'appetito per i quattro sapori fondamentali in soggetti obesi. Indagini preliminari. (Appetite for the four fundamental tastes in obese subjects. Preliminary investigation.) RNVE, 18 (Supplement): 551–55. (English summary.)

DIGIESI, V., and MORACE, G. 1963 Acuità gustativa per il sapore salato e concentrazione elettrolitica salivare. (Gustatory acuity to the salty taste and concentration of salivary electrolytes.) RNVE, 17: 67–72.

DIN, H. 1956 O reflektornkh vliianiiakh a retseptorov iazyka na dykhanie i krovoobrashchenie. (Chemoreceptors in muscles of the tongue.) FZLZ, 42: 1046–51. (English summary.)

DI STEFANO, G. 1940 Sulle proprietà chimico-fisiche della saliva parotidea umana studiate in rapporto con la qualità dello stimolo. (Chemical and physical properties of human parotid saliva in relation to the quality of the stimulus.) ASBI, 26: 418–30.

DITLEVSEN, J. G. 1872 Undersögele over smagslögene paa Tungen Hos pattedyrene og mennesket. (Research on taste buds on the tongue of mammals and man.) F. Hegel, Copenhagen, 91 pp.

DIX, K. W. 1912 Das Schmecken (Taste), in Körperliche und geistige Entwicklung eines Kindes. II: Die Sinne. (Physical and mental development of a child. II. The senses.) Wunderlich, Leipzig, 176 pp. (see pp. 152–63).

DIXON, A. F. 1897 On the course of the taste fibres. EMJO, 1: 395–401, 628–30.

———. 1899 The sensory distribution of the facial nerve in man. JAPH, 33: 471–92.

DJUPESLAND, G. 1962 Topisk diagnostikk ved perifere facialispareser. (Topical diagnosis of peripheral facial paralysis.) TNLA, 82: 1518–20.

DOBRIAKOVA, O. A. 1938 Issledovanie v oblasti elektricheskoĭ chuvstvitel' nosti zritel' nogo i vkusovogo retseptorov. (Studies on electric sensitivity of the visual and taste receptors.) BEMB, 6: 344–47.

———. 1939 O parallelizme v izmeneniĭakh elektricheskoi chuvstvitel' nosti organov ereniia i vkusovykh razdrazhiteleĭ. (Concerning the parallel in changes of electrical sensitivity of organs of vision and taste stimuli.) FZLZ, 26: 192–99. (French summary.)

*———. 1941 (On the influence of gustatory and thermal stimuli on color vision.) TFBE, 80–82.

———. 1944 Vliianie vkusovykh, temperaturnykh i slukhovykh razdrazhi-teleĭ na kritiueskuiu chastotu mel'kanii monokhromati-cheskikh luchei. (The influence of taste, temperature and sound stimuli on the critical flicker frequency of monochromatic light.) PFIO, 2: 81–84. (English summary.)

DODGE, H. W., JR., and CLARK, E. C. 1956 A test for savor (flavor) with report of a case of congenital anosmia. PRMC, 31: 312–15.

DOGIEL, A. S. 1897 Ueber die Nervenendingungen in den Geschmacksendknospen der Ganoideen. (On nerve endings in taste endbuds of Ganoidei.) AMAE, 49: 769–90.

DOMÁNSKIEGO, S. 1869 Kilka uwag nad przypadkiem porażenia nerwu twarzowego z zupełną utratą smaku. (Some remarks on accidental paralysis of facial nerve with complete loss of taste.) PRLK, 8: 255–57, 263–65, 279–81, 287–90.

D'ONOFRIO, F. 1923 La sensibilità gustativa nella meta anteriore della lingua dei malati di otite e di mastoidite. (Gustatory sensitivity in the anterior half of the tongue during otitis and mastoiditis.) CORL, 3: 45–61.

DOUGLAS, W. W. 1954 Is there chemical transmission at chemoreceptors? PARE, 6: 81–83.

DOVE, W. F. 1953 A universal gustometric scale in D-units. FORE, 18: 427–53.

DOWNEY, J. E. 1911 A case of colored gustation. AJPC, 22: 528–39.

DOX, A. W., and HOUSTON, B. 1924 Alkylchloromalonamides. The influence of homology on taste. JACS, 46: 1278–81.

DOX, A. W., and JONES, E. G. 1928 New derivatives of barbituric acid. JACS, 50: 2033–36.

DRASCH, O. 1883 Histologische und physiologische Studien über das Geschmacksorgan. (Histological and physiological studies on the taste organ.) SPAW, 88: 516–71.

———. 1887 Untersuchungen ueber die Papillae folliatae et circumvallatae des Kaninchen und Feldhasen. (Investigations on the foliate and circumvallate papillae in domesticated and field rabbits.) AMSA, 14: 229–68.

DRIELSMA, A. 1859 Onderzoek over den zetel van het smaakzintuig. (Investigations on the seat of the taste organ.) P. van Wicheren, Groningen, 115 pp.

DRUCE, J. G. F. 1929 Taste and chemical constitution. CHDR, 111: 775.

DRYDEN, E. C., and HILLS, C. H. 1959 Taste thresholds for sodium benzoate and sodium sorbate in apple cider. FOTE, 13: 84–86.

DÜBENDORFER, E. 1949 Über Geschmacksstörungen nach Otoskleroseoperationen. (On taste disturbances following otosclerosis operation.) AOLA, 37: 172–80. (English summary.)

DUBOIS, R. 1890 Sur la physiologie comparée des sensations gustatives et tactiles. (Comparative physiology of taste and tactile sensations.) CORE, 110: 473–75.

DUBRIEL, G., and VALETTE, M. 1931 Dispositifs vaso-sensoriels des organes de la gustation et du tact. (The vaso-sensory distributions supplying the organs of taste and touch.) CRSS, 107: 341–44.

DUCHENNE. 1850 Recherches électro-physiologiques et pathologiques sur les propriétés et les usages de la corde du tympan. (Research on the electrophysiological and pathological properties and their usage in the chorda tympani.) AGME, 24: 385–412.

DUGÈS, A. L. 1838 Du goût (Taste), in Traité de Physiologie Comparée de l'homme et des Animaux, I. Chez L. Castel, Montpellier, 526 pp. (see pp. 127–43).

DUKES, H. H. 1935 Taste, in The Physiology of Domestic Animals. Comstock Publishing Associates, Ithaca, 643 pp. (see pp. 553–55).

DUNCAN, C. J. 1960 Preference tests and the sense of taste in the feral pigeon (Columba livia var Gmelin). ANBE, 8: 54–60.

———. 1960 The sense of taste in birds. AABI, 48: 409–14.

———. 1962 Salt preferences of birds and mammals. PHZO, 35: 120–35.

———. 1963 Excitatory mechanisms in chemo- and mechanoreceptors. JTBI, 5: 114–26.

———. 1963 The response of the feral pigeon when offered active ingredients of commercial repellents in solution. AABI, 51: 127–34.

———. 1964 Synaptic transmission at taste buds. NATU, 203: 875–76.

———. 1964 The transducer mechanism of sense organs. NATW, 51: 172–73.

DURAND, V. J. 1955 Hallucinations olfactives et gustatives. (Olfactory and gustatory hallucinations.) AMPY, 113: 777–813.

DUSSIK, K. T., and KAUDERS, O. 1933 Untersuchungen zu einer neuen Methodik der Geruchs-und Geschmacksprüfung. (Research on a new method of smell and taste testing.) WKWO, 46: 745–47.

DUVAL, M. 1872 Goût. (Taste.) Nouveau Dict. de Medicine et de Chirurgie Pratiques (Paris), 16: 530–52.

DYER, W. T. T. 1887 A plant which destroys the taste of sweetness. NATU, 35: 557.

DYKGRAAF, S. 1933 Untersuchungen ueber die Funktion der Seitenorgane an Fischen. (Studies on the function of the side organs in fish.) ZVPH, 20: 162–212.

DYSON, G. M. 1938 Sweetness and sweetening agents. FLAV, 1(2): 40–48.

———. 1939 Saccharin. FLAV, 2(1): 24–27, 30–31.

———. 1939 Saccharin. FLAV, 2(3): 42–43.

———. 1939 Saccharin. FLAV, 2(4): 33–35.

DZENDOLET, E. 1957 Intensity-duration relations for taste using electrical stimulation. Unpublished Ph.D. thesis, Brown University, 71 pp.

———. 1962 Electrical stimulation of single human taste papillae. PMOS, 14: 303–17.

EBERSON, M., 1897 Über colorirten Geschmack. (On colored taste.) WMEP, 38: 1541–42.

EBLE, B. 1836 Der Geschmackssinn (Taste), in Versuch einer pragmatischen Geschichte der Anatomie und Physiologie vom Jahre 1800–1825. C. Gerold, Vienna, 355 pp. (see pp. 265–67).

EBNER, V. VON. 1873 *Die acinösen Drüsen der Zunge ihre Beziehungen zu den Geschmacksorganen.* (The acinous glands of the tongue and their relationship to the taste organs.) Leuschenr & Lubensky, Graz, 66 pp.

———. 1873 Über die traubenförmigen Drüsen der Zungenwurzel. (On the oval shaped glands of the roots of the tongue.) BNMV, 3: 58–59.

———. 1897 Über die Spitzen der Geschmacksknospen. (On the tip of the taste buds.) SWWA, 106: 73–82.

———. 1902 Von der Zunge (About the tongue), in *Handbuch der Gewebelehre des Menschen,* A. Kolliker (ed.). 6th ed. W. Engelmann, Leipzig, 1020 pp. (see pp. 10–31).

ECKARDT, F. 1938 Über die Geschmackswirkung einiger anorganischer Schwefel- und Stickstoff-Verbindungen. (On the effect of taste of some inorganic sulfur and nitrogen compounds.) Inaugural Dissertation, Jügelt, Jena, 18 pp.

ECKSTEIN, A. 1927 Zur Physiologie der Geschmacksempfindung und des Saugreflexes bei Säuglingen. (The physiology of taste preception and the sucking reflex in infants.) ZEKI, 45: 1–18.

———. 1927 Zur Physiologie der Geschmacksempfindung und des Saugreflexes bei Säuglingen. Über die Beziehungen des Saugreflexes zur Magentätigkeit. (The physiology of taste perception and the sucking reflex in infants. The relationship of the sucking reflex to the function of the stomach.) ZEKI, 45: 19–27.

———. 1928 Saugreflex und Geschmacksprüfung bei jungen Säuglingen. (Sucking reflex and taste tests in small infants.) MOKI, 38: 109–11.

ECONOMO, C. VON. 1911 Über dissoziierte Empfindungslähmung bei Ponstumoren und über die zentralen Bahnen des sensiblen Trigeminus. (Dissociable sensitive paralysis of the pons tumores and on the central pathways for trigeminal sensations.) JPNE, 32: 107–38.

ECTORS, L. 1936 Étude de l'activité électrique du cortex cérébral chez le lapin non narcotise ni curarise. (Study of the electrical activity of the cerebral cortex of the non-narcotised nor curarized rabbit.) AIPH, 43: 267–98.

EDINGER, L. 1903 Erkrankungen im Bereiche des N. glossopharyngeus. Störungen der Geschmacksempfindung. (Illness in the area of the N. glossopharyngeus. Disturbance of taste perception.) HTKR, 3 (5) : 626–27.

EDMONDS, C. J. 1960 Fluid intake and exchangeable body sodium of normal and adrenalectomized rats given various concentrations of saline to drink. QJEH, 45: 163–70.

EDWARDS, L. F. 1930 Origin of taste buds in the oro-pharyngeal cavity of the carp. OJSC, 30: 385–97.

EGER, H. 1937 Über den Geschmackssinn von Schmetterlingsraupen. (On the sense of taste of caterpillars.) BIZN, 57: 293–308.

EHLERS, H. 1932 Secretion of tears on gustatory stimulation. APNE, 7: 79–86.

EHRENBERG, R., and GÜTTES, H. J. 1949 Über die Wirkung von Rhodaniden und Sulfaten auf die Schwellenwerte des Geschmacks. (The effect of cyanates and sulphates on taste thresholds.) PAGP, 251: 664–71.

EHRENSVÄRD, G. 1942 Über die Primarvorgänge bei Chemorezeptorenbeeinflussung eine physikalischchemische Übersicht. Einige experimentelle Beiträge. Versuch einer Theorie. (The primary process of chemoreceptor influence. A physical-chemical general view. Some experimental contributions. An experiment of a theory.) APSS, 3 (9) : 1–151.

EHRHARDT, S. 1952 Vergleichende Geschmacksprüfung von PTC und Conteben. (Comparative taste testing of PTC and conteben.) HOMO, 3: 153–62.

EHRLICH, F. 1904 Über das natürliche Isomere des Leucins. I. (On the natural isomer of leucine. I.) BDCG, 37: 1809–40.

———. 1907 Über das natürliche Isomere des Leucins. II. (On the natural isomer of leucine. II.) BDCG, 40: 2538–62.

EHRMANN, O. 1894 Funktionsstörungen von Geschmackssinn, Sprache, Kau und Schluckbewegungen nach Totalexstirpation der Zunge. (Functional disturbances of the sense of taste, speech, chewing and swallowing movements after total extirpation of the tongue.) Inaugural Dissertation, H. Laupp, Tübingen, 38 pp.

EHRSAM, A. 1899 Über Substanzen, welche im Stande sind unsere Geschmacksempfindung zu beeinflussen. (On substances which influence our taste sensation.) Inaugural Dissertation, Würzburg, 19 pp.

EICKELBERG, E. W. 1940 How to use dextrose in canning. II. FOIN, 12: 50–51.

EIGLER, G. 1958 Regressanspruch wegen Geschmacksverlustes nach Tonsillektomie. (Compensation claim for loss of taste after tonsillectomy.) ZLRT, 37: 581–89.

EISIG, H. 1879 Die Seitenorgane und becherförmigen Organe der Capitelliden. (The side organs and goblet shaped organs of Capitellae.) MZSN, 1: 278–342.

EKMAN, G. 1961 Methodological note on scales of gustatory intensity. SJPS, 2: 185–90.

EKMAN, G., and AKESSON, C. 1964 Saltiness, sweetness, and preference: A study of quantitative relations in individual subjects. RPLS, 177: 1–13.

———. 1965 Saltiness, sweetness, and preference: A study of quantitative relations in individual subjects. SJPS, 6: 241–53.

ELEK, S. R. 1944 Altered taste in dengue. WAME, 6: 392–94.

ELLIOTT, R. 1937 Total distribution of taste

buds on the tongue of the kitten at birth. JCNE, **66**: 361–73.

————. 1944 Numerical and regional distribution of taste buds on the tongue of the opossum, with particular reference to those in the fungiform papillae. ANRE, **88**: 429. (Abstract.)

————. 1945 Distribution of taste buds in fungiform papillae on tongue of the opossum. JCNE, **82**: 205–13.

ELLIS, R. A. 1959 Cholinesterases in the mammalian tongue. JHCY, **7**: 156–63.

ELSBERG, C. A., and SPOTNITZ, H. 1938 The sense of taste. Formulas by which the relations between stimulus and reaction time can be foretold. BNIN, **7**: 174–77.

ELTRINGHAM, H. 1933 Olfactory and gustatory senses, in *The Senses of Insects*. Methuen, London, 126 pp. (see pp. 77–93).

ELTRINHAM, H. 1933 On the tarsal sense-organs of *lepidoptera*. TRES, **81**: 33–36.

EMMERS, R. 1964 Localization of modality specific thalamic units that respond to stimulation of the cat tongue. PYSO, **7**: 126.

————. 1964 Localization of thalamic projections of afferents from the tongue in the cat. ANRE, **148**: 67–74.

EMMERS, R., BENJAMIN, R. M., and ABLES, M. F. 1960 Differential localization of taste and tongue tactile afferents in the rat thalamus. FEPR, **19**: 286. (Abstract.)

EMMERS, R., BENJAMIN, R. M., and BLOMQUIST, A. J. 1962 Thalamic localization of afferents from the tongue in albino rat. JCNE, **118**: 43–48.

EMMERS, R., and NOCENTI, M. R. 1963 Role of the thalamic nucleus for taste in modifying calcium intake in rats maintained on a self-selection diet. PYSO, **6**: 176. (Abstract.)

ENGEL, R. 1928 Experimentelle Untersuchungen über die Abhängigkeit der Lust und Unlust von der Reizstärke beim Geschmackssinn. (Experimental investigations of the dependence of pleasantness and unpleasantness upon the strength of the stimulus in the case of taste.) PAGP, **64**: 1–36.

ENGELMANN, C. 1934 Versuche über den Geschmackssinn von Taube, Ente, und Huhn. (Experiments of the gustatory sense of pigeon, duck and chicken.) ZVPH, **20**: 626–45.

————. 1937 Vom Geschmackssinn des Huhns. (The gustatory sense of the fowl.) FOFO, **13**: 425–26.

————. 1937 Weitere Versuche über den Geschmackssinn des Huhns. (Further experiments on the gustatory sensitivity of the fowl.) ZVPH, **24**: 451–62.

————. 1940–41 Versuche über den Geschmackssinn des Huhns. IV: Der Einfluss von Korngrösse und Körnerform auf die Beliebtheit einiger Getreidearten bei Zwerghühnern. (Investigation on the sense of taste in the chicken. IV: Influence of size of grains

and form upon preference for certain kinds of cereals in dwarf hens.) ZTPS, **4**: 204–18.

————. 1940–41 Über den Geschmackssinn des Huhnes. V: Die Beliebtheit einzelner Körnerformen bei nur optischer Darbietung. (On the sense of taste in the chicken. V: The preference for certain forms of grains presented in a purely optical fashion.) ZTPS, **4**: 333–47.

————. 1942–43 Versuche über den Geschmackssinn des Huhnes. VI: Über angeborene Formvorlieben bei Hühnern. (Investigations on the sense of taste in the chicken. VI: On innate preferences for certain food forms.) ZTPS, **5**: 42–59.

————. 1942–43 Versuche über den Geschmackssinn des Huhnes. VII: Der Geschmack der Bitterstoffe und Zucker. (Investigations on the sense of taste in the chicken. VII: The taste for bitter and sweet substances.) ZTPS, **5**: 409–31.

————. 1942–43 Über den Geschmackssinn des Huhnes. VIII: Der Einfluss zusätzlichen Geschmacks auf die Annahmehäufigkeit fester Futterstoffe durch Zwerghühner. (The gustatory sense of the fowl. VIII: The influence of supplementary taste on the frequency of acceptance of solid food substances by dwarf hens.) ZTPS, **5**: 552–74.

ENGELMANN, T. W. 1868 Over de uiteinden der smaakzenuwen in de tong den kikvorsch. (On taste nerve endings in the tongue of frogs.) NAGN, **3**: 387–413.

————. 1868 Ueber die Endigungen der Geschmacksnerven in der Zunge des Frosches. (Taste nerve endings in the tongue of frogs.) ZWZA, **18**: 142–60.

————. 1872 Die Geschmacksorgane. (Taste organs.) HLGT, **2**: 822–38.

ENGSTRÖM, H., and RYTZNER, C. 1956 The fine structure of taste buds and taste fibres. AORH, **65**: 361–75.

————. 1956 The structure of taste buds. ANOL, **46**: 361–367.

EPSTEIN, A. N., and STELLAR, E. 1955 The control of salt preference in the adrenalectomized rat. JCPP, **48**: 167–72.

EPSTEIN, A. N., and TEITELBAUM, P. 1962 Regulation of food intake in the absence of taste, smell, and other oropharyngeal sensations. JCPP, **55**: 753–59.

ERB, W. 1870 Zur Casuistik der Nerven- und Muskelkrankheiten. (The case of nerve and muscle diseases.) DAKM, **7**: 246–55.

————. 1875 Ueber rheumatische Facialislähmung. (On rheumatic facial paralysis.) DAKM, **15**: 6–52.

*————. 1876 Neurosen der Geschmacksnerven, Paräthesien der Geschmacksnerven. (Neuroses of taste nerves, paraesthesia of taste nerves.) ZHPT, **2**: 229.

————. 1882 Über die Geschmacksfasern der

Chorda. (On the taste fibers of the chorda.) NEZE, 1: 73, 104–5, 149.

ERBENGI, T., and FERNER, H. 1964 Histochemische Untersuchungen der Geschmacksknospen des Kaninchens. (Histochemical studies on taste buds in rabbits.) ZZAC, 61: 673–87.

*ERICKSON, R. P. 1958 Responsiveness of single second order neurons in the rat to tongue stimulation. Unpublished Ph.D. dissertation, Brown University, 103 pp.

*———. 1959 Responsiveness of single second order neurons in the rat to tongue stimulation. DIAS, 19 (3) : 1835.

———. 1963 Sensory neural patterns and gustation, in Olfaction and Taste. Y. Zotterman (ed.). Macmillan, New York, 396 pp. (see pp. 205–13).

———. 1965 Duplexity theory of taste. SCIE, 147: 890.

ERICKSON, R. P., DOETSCH, G. S., and MARSHALL, D. A. 1965 The gustatory neural response function. JGPL, 49: 247–63.

ESAKOV, A. I. 1961 The efferent control of receptors (on the example of the chemoreceptors of the tongue). BEBM, 51: 257–62.

———. 1963 Efferent reactions in the sublingual nerve. BEBM, 56: 1184–86.

———. 1963 Reflex regulation of the "spontaneous" activity of the chemoreceptors of the tongue. BEBM, 56: 831–34.

———. 1964 Elektrofiziologicheskii analiz funktsional noi mobil' nosti i protsessov reguliatsii vkusovogo retseptornogo apparata. (Electrophysiological analysis of the functional mobility and processes of regulation of the taste receptor apparatus.) TIPF, 7: 43–44.

ESAKOV, A. I., and FILIN, V. A. 1964 Fiziologicheskaia kharakteristika funktsionirovaniia vkusovogo retseptornogo apparata. (Physiological characteristics of the functioning of taste-receptor apparatus.) FZLZ, 50: 169–76.

ESAKOV, A. I., and ZAIKO, N. S. 1963 Vliiani guanidina na funktsional'nuiu aktivnost' vkusovykh retseptorov. (Effect of guanidine on the functional activity of taste receptors.) FZLZ, 49: 984–89.

EVANS, D. A. P., KITCHIN, F. D., RINDING, J. E. 1962–1963 The metabolism of methyl thiouracil and thiopentone in tasters and nontasters of P.T.C. ANHG, 26: 123–33.

EVANS, D. R. 1961 Depression of taste sensitivity to specific sugars by their presence during development. SCIE, 133: 327–28.

———. 1963 Chemical structure and stimulation by carbohydrates, in Olfaction and Taste, Y. Zotterman (ed.). Macmillan, New York, 396 pp. (see pp. 165–76).

EVANS, D. R., and BROWNE, B. 1960 The physiology of hunger in the blowfly. AMNA, 64: 282–300.

EVANS, D. R., and DETHIER, V. G. 1957 The regulation of taste thresholds for sugars in the blowfly. JIPH, 1: 3–17.

EVANS, D. R., and MELLON, D. JR. 1962 Electro-physiological studies of a water receptor associated with the taste sensilla of the blowfly. JGPL, 45: 487–500.

———. 1962 Stimulation of a primary taste receptor by salts. JGPL, 45: 651–61.

EVANS, W. H., and KITCHIN, F. D. 1958 Taste threshold for P.T.C. in thyroid disease. HDTY, 12: 144. (Abstract.)

F., G. C. 1910 Un nuovo caso di sinestesia uditivo-gustativa. (A new case of auditory-gustatory synesthesia.) RIPS, 6: 101–4.

FABBI, F. 1954 Gustatory sense modifications in diabetes. AONK, 164: 543–46.

FABER, W., and JUNG, R. 1947 Über Geschmacksstörungen bei Hirnverletzten und das Syndrom Anosmie-Ageusie. (On taste disturbances in brain-injured and the anosmia-ageusia syndrome.) NERV, 18: 530–44.

FABIAN, F. M., and BLUM, H. B. 1943 Relative taste potency of some basic food constituents and their competitive and compensatory action. FORE, 8: 179–93.

FALCK, C. P. 1853 Das Verhalten der Geschmackswerkzeuge diabetischer Patienten. (Behavior of the taste mechanism of diabetic patients.) DEKL, 5: 419–20.

FALCONER, D. S. 1947 Sensory thresholds for solutions of phenyl thiocarbamide: Results of tests on a large sample, made by R. A. Fisher. ANEU, 13: 211–22.

FALK, J. L., and HERMAN, T. S. 1961 Specific appetite for NaCl without postingestional repletion. JCPP, 54: 405–8.

FALK, J. L., and TITLEBAUM, L. F. 1963 Saline solution preference in the rat: Further demonstrations. JCPP, 56: 337–42.

FALLIS, N., LASAGNA, L., and TETREAULT, L. 1962 Gustatory thresholds in patients with hypertension. NATU, 196: 74–75.

FARBMAN, A. I. 1965 Electron microscope study of the developing taste bud in rat fungiform papilla. DEBI, 11: 110–35.

———. 1965 Fine structure of the taste bud. JULR, 12: 328–50.

FASOLA, G. 1902 Contributo clinico alla conoscenza dell'innervazione gustatoria. (Clinical contribution to the knowledge of gustatory innervation.) RPNM, 7: 49–57.

FAVA, E., and GENTILLI, R. 1956 Sensibilità gustativa dei due terzi anteriori della lingua dopo alcoolizzazione del ganglio di Gasser. (Taste sensitivity of the anterior two thirds of the tongue after alcohol block of the Gasserian ganglion.) MIAN, 22: 407–13. (French, English, and German summaries.)

*FEHRER, P. 1935 Ueber Störungen der Geschmacksempfindungen. (Disturbances of taste sensations.) BONN, 31 pp.

FELDERMAN, L. 1935 The relationship of the gustatory to the olfactory systems. AORH, 44: 685–701.

FELDMANN, H. 1962 Die Geschmacksprüfung.

Praktische Durchführung und differential-diagnostische Auswertung. (Testing the taste sense. Practical methods and differential diagnostic evaluation.) DMWO, **87**: 1732–40.

FELLER, R. P., SHARON, I. M., CHAUNCEY, H. H., and SHANNON, I. L. 1965 Gustatory perception of sour, sweet, and salt mixtures using parotid gland flow rate. JAPY, **20**: 1341–44.

FÉRÉ, C. 1891 Gustation et vision colorée. (Taste and color vision.) CRSS, **43**: 769.

———. 1901 Note sur la fatigue par le excitation du goût. (Note on fatigue as a stimulation of taste.) CRSS, **11**: 722–24.

FÉRÉ, C., BATIGNE, P., and OUVRY, P. 1892 Recherches sur le minimum perceptible de l'olfaction et de la gustation chez les épileptiques. (Research on the minimal olfactory and gustatory perception in epileptics.) CRSS, **4**: 259–70.

FERGUSON, J. 1890 The nerve-supply of the sense of taste. MENP, **57**: 395–97.

FERGUSON, L. N., and LAWRENCE, A. R. 1958 Physicochemical aspects of the sense of taste. JCED, **35**: 436–44.

FERNANDES, J. L., JUNQUEIRA, P. C., KALMUS, H., OTTENSOOSER, F., PASQUALIN, R., and WISHART, P. 1957 P.T.C. thresholds, colour vision and blood factors of Brazilian Indians. I: Kaingangs. ANHG, **22**: 16–21.

FERNBERGER, S. W. 1932 A preliminary study of taste deficiency. AJPC, **44**: 322–26.

FERNER, H. 1952 Das Geschmacksorgan (The taste organ), in *Anatomie des Nervensystems und der Sinnesorgane des Menschen*. E. Reinhardt, Basel, 325 pp. (see pp. 294–97).

FERON, C. E. 1822 Dissertation sur le sens du goût, considéré physiologiquement et pathologiquement. (Dissertation on the sense of taste, physiological and pathological considerations.) Inaugural Dissertation, D. le Jeune, Paris, 25 pp.

FERRARI, A. 1951 Esquema rádio-electromagnético dos 4 sentidos específicos: vista, ouvido, olfato e paladar. (Radio-electromagnetic scheme of the four senses: sight, hearing, smell and taste.) RBME, **27**: 75.

FERRARI, P. 1904 Come si modifichi la sensibilità gustativa per le piccolissime dosi degli anestetici locali. (How taste sensitivity is modified by small doses of local anesthetics.) SBNP, **58**: 535–46.

———. 1905 Comment se modifie la sensibilité gustative pour les très petites doses des anesthésiques locaux. (How taste sensitivity is modified by very small doses of local anesthetics.) AIBL, **42**: 411–20.

FERRIER, D. 1875 Experiments on the brain of monkeys. PPRS, **23**: 409–32.

———. 1875 Experiments on the brain of monkeys. PTRS, **165**: 433–88.

———. 1890 Olfactory and gustatory centres, in *Croonian Lectures on Cerebral Localiza-tion*. Smith, Elder & Co., London, 152 pp. (see pp. 111–26).

FERRIER, D., and YEO, G. F. 1885 A record of the cerebral hemisphere. PTRS, **175**: 479–564.

FICK, A. 1864 Anatomie des Geschmacksorganes (Anatomy of the taste organs), in *Lehrbuch der Anatomie und Physiologie der Sinnesorgane*. M. Schauenburg & Co., Lahr, 351 pp. (see pp. 67–88).

FICKEN, M. S., and KARE, M. R. 1961 Individual variation in the ability to taste. POSC, **40**: 1402. (Abstract.)

FILDERMAN, J. 1962 Le sens du goût et protheses palatines. (The sense of taste and palatine prosthesis.) INDE, **44**: 1891–97.

FILIPELLO, F. 1956 A critical comparison of the two-sample and triangular binomial designs. FORE, **21**: 235–41.

FINCK, H. T. 1913 Sweet, sour, salt, and bitter, in *Food and Flavor*. The Century Co., New York, 594 pp. (see pp. 559–81).

FINCKS, H. T. 1886 The gastronomic value of odours. CORV, **50**: 680–95.

FINDLAY, J. P. 1933 Facial paralysis due to toxic inflammation of the geniculate ganglion. MJAU, **1**: 251–52.

FINK, H., and WILDNER, H. 1949 Über künstliche Süsstoffe. II (Synthetic sweeteners. II.) BRWS, **8**: 113–17; **9**: 133–37.

FINKE, J. 1962 Geschmacksschwitzen bei Syringomyelie. (Gustatory sweating in syringomyelia.) NERV, **33**: 133–35.

FINKELSTEIN, B., and PIPPITT, R. G. 1958 Effect of altitude and oxygen upon primary taste perception. AVMD, **29**: 386–91.

FINOCCHIARO, G. 1904 Contributo allo studio delle terminazioni nervose nelle papille circumvallate. (Contribution to the study of the neural termination of the circumvallate papillae.) AIAE, **3**: 288–97.

FINZI, C., and COLONNA, M. 1937 Constituzione chimica e sapore dolce. (Chemical constitution and sweet taste.) AANL, **26**: 19–24.

———. 1938 Constituzione chimica e sapore dolce. (Chemical constitution and sweet taste.) GCIT, **68**: 132–42.

*FISCHER, K., 1938 Über die Beeinflussung des Geschmacksfeldes auf der Zunge durch Anaesthetica. II. (On the effect on the area of taste of the tongue through anaesthesia. II.) Inaugural Dissertation.

FISCHER, R. 1960 "Taste-blindness" correlated with incidence of mongolism. PEHE, **1**: 6.

FISCHER, R., and GRIFFIN, F. 1959 On factors involved in the mechanism of "taste-blindness." EXPE, **15**: 447–48.

———. 1960 Factors involved in the mechanism of "taste-blindness." JOHE, **51**: 182–83.

———. 1960 Taste-blindness and variation in taste-threshold in relation to thyroid metabolism, in *Recent Advances in Biological Psychiatry, II*, J. Wortis (ed.). Grune & Stratton, New York, 417 pp. (see pp. 198–99).

————. 1961 Biochemical-genetic factors of taste-polymorphism and their relation to salivary thyroid metabolism in health and mental retardation. PWCP, 1: 542–47.

————. 1961 Quinine dimorphism among "non-tasters" of 6-n-propylthiouracil. EXPE, 17: 36–42.

————. 1961 "Taste-blindness" and variations in taste-threshold in relation to thyroid metabolism. JONE, 3: 98–104.

————. 1963 Taste thresholds in mothers of children with Down's syndrome. LANC, 1: 393–94.

————. 1963 Quinine dimorphism; A cardinal determinant of taste sensitivity. NATU, 200: 343–47.

*————. 1964 Chemoreception and gustatory memory formation, in Proceedings, 6th International Congress of Biochemistry, VIII, 651.

————. 1964 Pharmacogenetic aspects of gustation. ARZN,14: 673–86.

————. 1964 Pharmacogenetic aspects of taste and behavior, in Proceedings, 17th International Congress of Psychology. North Holland Publishing Co., Amsterdam, 426 pp. (see pp. 95–96).

FISCHER, R., GRIFFIN, F., ARCHER, R. C., ZINSMEISTER, S. C., and JASTRAM, P. S. 1965 Weber ratio in gustatory chemoreception; an indicator of systemic (drug) reactivity. NATU, 207: 1049–53.

FISCHER, R., GRIFFIN, F., ENGLAND, S., and GARN, S.M. 1961 Taste thresholds and food dislikes. NATU, 191: 1328.

FISCHER, R., GRIFFIN, F., ENGLAND, S., and PASAMANICK, B. 1961 Biochemical-genetic factors of taste-polymorphism and their relation to salivary thyroid metabolism in health and mental retardation. MEXP, 4: 356–61.

FISCHER, R., GRIFFIN, F., and KAPLAN, A. R. 1962 Taste thresholds in mothers of children with Down's syndrome. LANC, 2: 992.

FISCHER, R., GRIFFIN, F., and MEAD, E. L. 1962 Two characteristic ranges of taste sensitivity. MEXP, 6: 177–82. (German and French summaries.)

FISCHER, R., GRIFFIN, F., and PASAMANICK, B. 1965 The perception of taste: Some psychophysiological, pathophysiological, pharmacological and clinical aspects, in Psychopathology of Perception, P. Hoch & J. Zubin (eds.). Grune & Stratton, New York, London, 336 pp. (see pp. 129–63).

FISCHER, R., GRIFFIN, F., and ROCKEY, M. A. 1966 Gustatory chemoreception in man: Multidisciplinary aspects and perspectives. PBME, 9: 549–77.

FISCHER, R., KAPLAN, A. R., GRIFFIN, F., and STING, D. G. 1963 Abnormal congregation of insensitive ("non"-) tasters among parents of children with Down's syndrome. AJMD, 67: 849–55.

FISCHER, R., GRIFFIN, F., and KAPLAN, A. R.

1963 Taste thresholds, cigarette smoking, and food dislikes. MEXP, 9: 151–67.

————. 1963 Pharmacogenetic aspects of taste, in Genetics Today, I, S. J. Geerts (ed.). Pergamon Press, London, 332 pp. (see p. 292). (Abstract.)

*FISCHER, R., and KAELBLING, R. 1964 Increase in taste acuity with sympathetic stimulation: The relation of a just noticeable taste difference to systemic psychotropic drug dose, in Recent Advances in Biology and Psychiatry, IX. Plenum Press, New York, 278 pp.

FISCHER, R., KNOPP, W., and GRIFFIN, F. 1965 Taste sensitivity and the appearance of phenothiazine tranquilizer induced extrapyramidal symptoms. ARZN, 15: 1379–82. (German summary.)

FISH, H. S., MALONE, P. D., and RICHTER, C. P. 1944 The anatomy of the tongue of the domestic Norway rat. I: The skin of the tongue; the various papillae, their number and distribution. ANRE, 89: 429–40.

FISH, H. S., and RICHTER, C. P. 1946 Comparative numbers of fungiform and foliate papillae on tongues of domestic and wild Norway rats. PSEB, 63: 352–55.

FISHER, G. L. 1964 Measured saline preference in the albino rat: the role of non-gustatory factors. PSCI, 1: 45–46.

————. 1965 Measured sucrose preference in the albino rat: The influence of an auditory cue. PSCI, 2: 9–10.

————. 1965 Saline preference in rats determined by contingent licking. JEAB, 8: 295–303.

FISHER, G. L., PFAFFMANN, C., and BROWN, E. 1965 Dulcin and saccharin taste in squirrel monkeys, rats, and men. SCIE, 150: 506–7.

FISHMAN, I. Y. 1955 Single fiber studies on the chorda tympani nerves of rat and hamster. Unpublished Ph.D. thesis, Florida State University, 71 pp. DIAS, 22: 90.

————. 1957 Single fiber gustatory impulses in rat and hamster. JCCP, 49: 319–34.

————. 1959 Gustatory impulses of the white faced, ringtail monkey. FEPR, 18: 45. (Abstract.)

————. 1963 Gustatory responses of a tropical-frugivorous bat. JIAS, 70: 465–72.

FLASAROVA, B. 1959 Chutové cítí u novorozencu. (The sense of taste in newborns.) CEPE, 14: 526–29. (English summary.)

FLEISCHER, K. 1963 Hals-Nasen-Ohrenheilkunde Mundhöhle, Rachen, Speiseröhre. (Otorhinolaryngology. Oral cavity, pharynx, esophagus.) MMWO, 105: 153–60.

FLEISHER, L. 1956 The effects of maturation on the gustatory sensitivity of guinea pigs. Unpublished Master's thesis, Brown University, 55 pp.

FLEMING, J. K. 1939 Taste. FLAV, 2: 23–24.

FLEMMING, W. 1884 Ueber Organe vom Bau der Geschmacksknospen an den Tastern verschiedener Mollusken. (On the structure of taste buds on the different feelers of mollusks.) AMAE, **23**: 141–48.

FLOYD, H. H. 1936 Individual differences in gustation. TCOE, **155**: 1–12. (Abstract of Ph.D. thesis, George Peabody College for Teachers, Nashville.)

FODOR, K., and HAPPISCH, L. 1922 Über die Verschiedenheit der Unterschiedsschwellen für den Geschmacksinn bei Reizzunahme und Reizabnahme. (Variation of difference thresholds for the sense of taste with increased and decreased stimuli.) PAGP, **197**: 337–47.

FOLEY, J. O. 1945 The sensory and motor axons of the chorda tympani. PSEB, **60**: 262–67.

FOLSOM, N. 1863 The senses of smell and taste. BMSJ, **68**: 231–38.

FONTAN, M., LELIEVRE-LALLIGIER, A., STAN-KOWIAK, C., and DESMONS, F. 1964 Essais du 516 MD dans la cure de dégoût de 147 éthyliques. (Trials of MD-516 in the taste-aversion treatment of 147 alcoholics.) LIME, **9**: 294–96.

FONTANA, A. 1902 Influenza della eucaina-B sugli organi gustativi. (The influence of eucain-B on the taste organs.) GMDT, **45**: 105–14.

——. 1902 Ueber die Wirkung des Eucain B auf die Geschmacksorgane. (The effect of β-eucain on the taste organs.) ZPSI, **28**: 253–60.

FORBES, J. I., and DOY, R. W. 1963 Unilateral gustatory sweating. CAJM, **9**: 398–404.

FORCHHEIMER, L. 1916 Geruchs- and Geschmacksempfindungen nach intravenösen Injektionen von Salvarsan. (Smell and taste senses after intravenous injection of Salvarsan.) DECB, **19**: 98–101.

FORD, N., and MASON, A. D. 1941 Taste reactions of the Dionne quintuplets. JOHE, **32**: 365–68.

FOREL, A. 1908 Instinct of Direction—Smell—Taste, in *The Senses of Insects*. Translated from the French by M. Yearsley. Methuen, London, 324 pp. (see pp. 73–106).

——. 1910 Geruch und Geschmack (Smell and taste), in *Das Sinnesleben der Insekten*. E. Reinhardt, München, 393 pp. (see pp. 80–120).

——. 1921 Sense chimques—goût odorat (Chemical sense—taste, odor), in *Le Monde Social des Fourmis du Globe, II*. (Social World of Ants.) E. W. Heinrich, Geneva (see pp. 7–25).

FORNASARI, G. 1951 Variazioni della soglia gustativa in donne con ciclo mestruale normale. (Variation in taste response in women with normal menstrual cycles.) BMOG, **69**: 139–47. (English summary.)

FORSTER 1913 Anfälle von Geschmacksparästesien (Attacks of taste paraesthesia), in Verhandlungen ärztlicher Gesellschaften für Psy-chiatrie und Nervenkrankheiten. BKWO, **50**: 793.

FOX, A. L. 1931 Six in ten "tasteblind" to bitter chemical. SNLE, **19**: 249.

——. 1932 The relationship between chemical constitution and taste. PNAS, **18**: 115–20.

——. 1954 A new approach to explaining food preferences. ACAF, p. 14A. (Abstract.)

FRANCK, B. M. 1689 Dissertation de gusto atque experimentis et observationibus novissimis circa illum habitis. (Anatomical and physiological dissertation on the most recent experiments and observations on taste.) Inaugural Dissertation, Altdorf, 44 pp.

FRÄNKEL, S. 1906 Beziehungen zwischen Geschmack und Konstitution. (Relation between taste and constitution.) In *Die Arzneimittelsynthese*. 2nd ed. J. Springer, Berlin, 759 pp. (see pp. 137–58).

——. 1912 Beziehung zwischen Geschmack und Konstitution (Relation between taste and constitution), in *Die Arzneimittel—Synthese*. 3rd ed. J. Springer, Berlin, 823 pp. (see pp. 143–58).

——. 1927 Beziehung zwischen Geschmack und Konstitution (Relation between taste and constitution), in *Die Arzneimittel—Synthese*. 6th ed. J. Springer, Berlin, 935 pp. (see pp. 148–71).

FRANKL-HOCHWART, L. VON. 1896 Ueber die Innervation des Geschmackes. (On the innervation of taste.) ZEPH, **10**: 60–61.

——. 1897 Die nervösen Erkrankungen des Geschmacks (Nervous disorders of taste), in *Specielle Pathologie und Therapie, II*, H. Nothnagel (ed.). A. Hölder, Wien, pp. 1–42.

FRASER, G. R. 1961 Cretinism and taste sensitivity to phenylthiocarbamide. LANC, **1**: 964–65.

FREEMAN, G H. 1955 The selection and use of a panel for taste sensitivity tests with fruit. AEMR, **32**: 86–88.

FREEMAN, G. L. 1936 Relative adaptation times of the five senses. PYMO, **47**: 94–107.

FREGLY, M. J. 1955 Hypertension, NaCl aversion and polydipsia in rats: Time course and relation to age. AJPH, **182**: 139–44.

——. 1956 Effect of renal hypertension on the preference threshold of rats for sodium chloride. AJPH, **187**: 288–92.

——. 1957 Adrenal glands in the development of renal hypertension in rats. AJPH, **191**: 542–48.

——. 1957 The interaction of pregnancy and hypertension. APPN, **5**: 278–91.

——. 1958 NaCl appetite of adrenalectomized rats. PSEB, **97**: 144–48.

——. 1958 Specificity of the sodium chloride appetite of adrenalectomized rats: Substitution of lithium chloride for sodium chloride. AJPH, **195**: 645–53.

——. 1959 Specificity of sodium chloride aversion of hypertensive rats. AJPH, **196**: 1326–32.

FREIRE-MAIA, A. 1960 Smoking and P.T.C. sensitivity. ANHG, 24: 333–41.

FREIRE-MAIA, A., and QUELCE-SALGADO, A. 1960 Taste sensitivity to P.T.C. in samples from three Brazilian populations. ANHG, 24: 97–102.

FRENTZEL, J. 1896 Notiz zur Lehre von den Geschmacksempfindungen. (Note on the theory of taste sensations.) ZEPH, 10: 3–4.

FREUND, R. 1933 Ueber Strahlenwirkung insbesondere Geschmacksstörungen in der Mundhöhle. (On the effect of radiation, especially on disturbances of taste, in the oral cavity.) Inaugural Dissertation, Berlin, 27 pp.

*FREY, M. VON. 1903 Über das süssende Prinzip. (The sweet principle.) AAPA, pp. 113–19.

———. 1904 Ueber den laugigen und metallischen Geruch. (On the puckery and metallic odor.) VGNA, 75: 409–10.

*———. 1905 Die stickstoffhaltigen Süsstoffe. (The sweet substances that contain nitrogen.) AAPA, pp. 201–86.

———. 1910 Der laugige Geruch. (The alkaline odor.) PAGP, 136: 275–81.

FRIDERICI, M. V., and SEYLER, B. 1654 De sapore. (Taste.) Inaugural Dissertation, Leipzig, 16 pp.

FRINGS, H. 1945 Gustatory rejection thresholds for the larvae of the Cecropia moth, Samia Cecropia (Linnaean). BIBU, 88: 37–43.

———. 1946 Biological backgrounds of the "sweet tooth." TUNE, 24: 133–34.

———. 1946 Gustatory thresholds for sucrose and electrolytes for the cockroach, Periplaneta Americana (Linnaean). JEZO, 102: 23–50.

———. 1948 A contribution to the comparative physiology of contact chemoreception. JCPP, 41: 25–34.

———. 1951 Sweet taste in the cat and the taste-spectrum. EXPE, 7: 424–26.

FRINGS, H., and COX, B. L. 1954 The effects of temperature on the sucrose thresholds of the tarsal chemoreceptors of the flesh fly, Sarcophaga Bullata. BIBU, 107: 3, 360–63.

FRINGS, H. W. 1954 Gustatory stimulation by ions and the taste spectrum. ACAF, pp. 14A–15A. (Abstract.)

FRINGS, H. W., and O'NEAL, B. R. 1946 The location and thresholds of the contact chemoreceptors of the female horsefly, Tabanus sulcifrons Macquart CWS, Medical Division, Publications Board, No. 23851, U.S. Department of Commerce, Washington, D.C., 17 pp.

FRISCH, H. R. 1952 New synthetic compounds with a sweet taste. CHCA, 2: 22.

FRISCH, K. VON. 1926 Chemoreceptoren. I: Vergleichende Physiologie des Geruchs und Geschmackssinnes. (Chemoreceptors I: Comparative physiology of the odor and taste sense.) HNPP, 11: 203–39.

———. 1927 Versuche über den Geschmackssinn der Bienen. I. (Studies on the sense of taste in bees. I.) NATW, 15: 321–27.

———. 1928 Vesuche über den Geschmackssinn der Bienen. II. (Studies on the sense of taste in bees. II.) NATW, 16: 307–15.

———. 1930 Versuche über den Geschmackssinn der Bienen. (Investigations on the gustatory sense of bees.) NATW, 18: 169–74.

———. 1934 Berichtigung zu meiner Arbeit über den Geschmackssinn der Bienen. (A correction to my study on the gustatory sense of bees.) ZVPH, 21: 680.

———. 1934 Über den Geschmackssinn der Biene: Ein Beitrag zur vergleichenden Physiologie des Geschmacks. (On taste sensitivity in bees: A contribution to the comparative physiology of taste.) ZVPH, 21: 1–156.

*———. 1939 Tarsaler Geschmackssinn bei Fliegen. (Tarsal taste in flies.) Hochchulfilm-Nr. C 324, Reichsstelle für den Unterichts Film, Berlin.

FROMMER, G. P. 1961 Gustatory afferent responses in the thalamus, in The Physiological and Behavioral Aspects of Taste, M. R. Kare and B. P. Halpern (eds.). University of Chicago Press, 149 pp. (see pp. 50–65).

FROMMER, G. P., and PFAFFMANN, C. 1961 Electrophysiological analysis of gustatory, tongue temperature, and tactile representation in the thalamus of albino rat. PYSO, 4: 38. (Abstract.)

FUERST, W. F., JR., and KARE, M. R. 1962 The influence of pH on fluid tolerance and preference. POSC, 41: 71–77.

FUKUOKA, G. 1936 Frequency of taste-blindness among the Japanese and related races. EUNE, 21: 52–54.

FULLER, J. L., and JACOBY, G. A., JR. 1955 Central and sensory control of food intake in genetically obese mice. AJPH, 183: 279–83.

FUNAKOSHI, M., and ZOTTERMAN, Y. 1963 Effect of salt on sugar response. APSS, 57: 193–200.

FURCHTGOTT, E., and FRIEDMAN, M. P. 1960 The effect of hunger on taste and odor RLs. JCPP, 53: 576–81.

FURCHTGOTT, E., and WILLINGHAM, W. W. 1956 The effect of sleep-deprivation upon the thresholds of taste. AJPC, 69: 111–12.

FURSTNER, J. 1952 Examen des preceptions gustatives en relation avec les maladies d'oreilles et leurs operations. (Examination of taste perception in relation to diseases of the ear and their operation.) ANOL, 69: 48–53.

FURUKAWA, S. 1920 Relation between the chemical constitution and taste of perfumes (especially aldehydes, ketones, and their derivatives). A new perfume with sweet taste. NIKW, 41: 706–28.

FUSARI, R., and PANASCI, A. 1891 Les terminaisons des nerfs dans la muqueuse et dans les glandes sereuses de la langue des mammifères. (Nerve terminations in the mucosa and in the serous glands of the mammalian tongue.) AIBL, 14: 240–46.

GÄBELEIN, K. 1949 Nerverregung eine Resonanzerscheinung? (Nerve stimulation, a resonance phenomenon?) GRME, **2**: 521-24.

GAD, J. 1891 Ueber Beziehungen des Grosshirns zum Fressact beim Kaninchen. (The relationship of the cerebrum to food ingestion in the rabbit.) ARPI, pp. 541-42.

GAGLIO, M., and POMPEI, E. 1964 Studio di curve secretorie gastriche da stimoli gustativi nell'uomo. (Study of the gastric secretory curve from gustatory stimulation in man.) THEP, **5**: 168-73. (English summary.)

GAIRNS, F. W. 1953 Sensory nerve endings other than taste buds in the human tongue. JPHY, **121**: 33-34P.

———. 1954 Sensory nerve endings in the human palate. JPHY, **123**: 26-27P.

———. 1955 The sensory nerve endings of the human palate. QJEH, **40**: 40-48.

*GAL. 1846 Cas de paralysie du nerf facial avec perte complete du goût. (A case of facial nerve paralysis with complete loss of taste.) GMIT.

GALIOTO, G. B., and FARINA, E. 1961 Dispositivs per l'impiego dell-audiometro in ricerche di electrogeusimetria. (Apparatus for the use of the audiometer in research on the electrical measurement of taste.) BSIB, **37**: 145-46.

———. 1961 Valori di soglia gustativa con un nuovo elettro-geusimetro. (Threshold value of taste by means of a new electro-tastemeter.) BMOG, **79**: 147-53. (English summary.)

GALLUCCI, M. 1932 Ricerche sui riflessi vasomotori nel bambino neonato e lattante provocati a mezzo di stimoli gustativi. (Research on vasomotor reflexes in new-born and nursing infants, elicited by gustatory stimuli.) RCPI, **30**: 1396-1418. (French summary.)

GALVIN, S. L. 1948 The taste of monosodium glutamate and other amino acid salts in dilute solutions, in *Monosodium Glutamate: A Symposium*. Quartermaster Food & Container Institute, Chicago, 92 pp. (see pp. 39-44).

GAMBLE, E. A. M. 1910 Taste sensations. PSBU, **7**: 388. (Abstract.)

———. 1911 Taste and smell. PSBU, **8**: 147-49.

———. 1913 Taste and smell. PSBU, **10**: 116-17.

———. 1915 Taste and smell. PSBU, **12**: 112-13.

———. 1916 Taste and smell. PSBU, **13**: 134-37.

———. 1922 The psychology of taste and smell. PSBU, **19**: 297-306.

———. 1929 The psychology of taste and smell. PSBU, **26**: 566-69.

———. 1932 The psychology of taste and smell. PSBU, **29**: 249-59.

GAMNA, G., BESUSSO, P. C., CODA, G., FERRIO, L., and GANDIGLIO, G. 1958 Ricerche sul comportamento della sensibiltà gustativa alla P.T.C. in un gruppo di psicotici. (Research on taste sensitivity behavior to P.T.C. of a group of psychotics.) NEUS, **14**: 257-66. (French, English, and German summaries.)

GANDER, J. E., GRIFFIN, F., and FISCHER, R. 1964 A multiple site chemoreceptor model. AIPT, **151**: 540-51.

GÄNSHIRT, H. 1950 Über die Geschmacksleitung im Thalamus. (Disorders of taste sensation due to thalamic lesion.) APNV, **184**: 260-61.

GARAVIGLIA, B. 1828 De gustatu. (On taste.) Inaugural Dissertation, P. Bizzoni, Ticini Regii, 61 pp.

GARCIA, J., and KIMELDORF, D. J. 1957 Temporal relationship within the conditioning of a saccharin aversion through radiation exposure. JCPP, **50**: 180-83.

———. 1958 The effect of ophthalmectomy upon responses of the rat to radiation and taste stimuli. JCPP, **51**: 288-91.

GARCIA, J., KIMELDORF, D. J., and KOELLING, R. A. 1955 Conditioned aversion to saccharin resulting from exposure to gamma radiation. SCIE, **122**: 157-58.

GARCIN, R. 1935 Physiologie normale et pathologique des nerfs craniens. Trijumeau, facial, nerf vestibulaire, glosso-pharyngien, pneumogastrique, spinal et grand hypoglosse (Normal and pathological physiology of the cranial nerves. Trigeminal, facial, vestibular, glossopharyngeal, pneumogastric, spinal and grand hypoglossal), in *Traité de Physiologie Normale et Pathologique*, X. Masson et Cie, Paris, 981 pp. (see pp. 317-635).

GARDELLA, E. 1904 Azione dell'acido fenico sulla sensibilità gustativa. (Action of carbolic acid on taste sensitivity.) ARFI, **1**: 398-402.

*GARLOPEAU, F., and VALLAT, J. J. 1965 Que sait-on du goût? (What do we know about taste?) COME, **87**: 19-28.

GASPARINI, F. 1952 Beiträge zur Kenntniss der Entwicklung der Geschmacksknospen in den Papillae Vallatae des Menschen. (Development of the taste bud in the vallate papillae of man.) ACAT, **14**: 393-98. (French and English summaries.)

GASTAUT, H., ROGER, J., and GIOVE, C. 1955 Troubles de l'olfaction, de la gustation et de l'appétit chez les epileptiques psychomoteurs. (Olfactory, gustatory and appetite disorders in psychomotor epileptics.) AMPY, **113**: 177-206.

GATES, R. R. 1946 Taste and smell deficiencies, in *Human Genetics, II*. Macmillan, New York, 1518 pp. (see pp. 1066-1072).

GAUGER, M. E. 1929 The modifiability of response to taste stimuli in the preschool child. CUCE, No. 348, 53 pp.

GAUTIER, J. A. 1943 Saveur et constitution chimique: les molécules sucrées de synthèse. (Taste and chemical constitution: Synthesis of sugar molecules.) RESC, **81**: 121-32.

GAVAUDAN, P., POUSSEL, H., and SCHUTZENBERGER, M. P. 1948 Le mecanisme physico-chimique de l'excitation sapide et la notion d'excitant indifferent. (Physicochemical mechanism of taste stimulus and the idea of indifferent excitants.) CORE, **226**: 751–52.

GAVAUDAN, P., and SCHUTZENBERGER, M. P. 1950 Le problémé de la spécificité chimique dans les differences genétiques de sensible gustative. (The problem of chemical specificity in the genetic differences of taste sensitivity.) CORE, **230**: 1622–24.

GAVAUDAN, P., SCHUTZENBERGER, M. P., and POUSSEL, H. 1947 L'excitation des chimiorecepteurs de la langue par les substances du gruppe des narcotiques indifferents et la regle thermodynamique de la narcose. (The excitation of chemoreceptors of the tongue by substances of the group of indifferent narcotics and the thermodynamic regulation of narcosis.) CORE, **224**: 1525–27.

GAVAZZENI, S. 1903 Senso del gusto e funzioni gastriche. (The sense of taste and gastric function.) NRME, **2**: 145–75.

GAYDA, T. 1912 Sul rapporto fra proprietà chimico-fisiche dei sali e soglia di sensazione per il loro sapore. (The relation between correct chemical-physical salt threshold and taste sensation.) ARFI, **10**: 175–92.

GAZAGNIRE, J. 1886 Du siège de la gustation chez les insectes coleopteres. (The site of taste in the insects coleoptera.) CORE, **102**: 629–32.

GAZZOLA, G. 1952 Due casi di ageusia da insulino-terapia. (Two cases of ageusia caused by insulin shock.) APNP, **13**: 104.

GEGENBAUR, C. 1883 *Lehrbuch der Anatomie des Menschen.* (Handbook of Human Anatomy.) W. Engelmann, Leipzig, 984 pp. (see pp. 837–46).

GELDARD, F. A. 1950 Somesthesis and the chemical senses. ARPS, **1**: 71–86.

———. 1953 The sense of taste, in *The Human Senses.* John Wiley & Sons, New York, 364 pp. (see pp. 295–323).

*GENZMER, A. 1892 Untersuchungen über die Sinneswahrnehmungen des neugeborenen Menschen. (Investigations on the sense of taste in newborn babies.) Inaugural Dissertation, Halle.

GEREB, T. 1948 Beiträge zur Symptomatologie der Herderkrankungen des Rautenhirns (Contribution to the sypmtomatology of the basis of illness in the rhombencephalon.) MPNE, **115**: 103–11. (English summary.)

GEREBTZOFF, M. A. 1939 Le voies centrales de la sensibilité et du goût et leurs terminaisons thalamiques. (Central paths of sensation and of taste and their thalamic terminations.) CELL, **48**: 91–146.

———. 1941 Recherches oscillographiques et anatomo-physiologique sur le centres cortical et thalamic du goût. (Oscillographic and anatomicophysiologic studies on cortical and thalamic taste centers.) AIPH, **51**: 199–210.

GERMAIN, L. 1951 Impressions olfactives et gustatives. (Olfactory and gustatory impressions.) FRDE, **12**: 9–11.

GERTZ, E. 1923 Untersuchung über die Reizschwellen des Coffeins und Theobromins. (Studies on threshold stimulation with caffeine and theobromine.) SAPH, **44**: 129–42.

GERTZ, H. 1919 Une expérience critique relative à la théorie du goût électrique. (A critical study of the theory of electric taste.) AOLA **1**: 551–56.

GEYS, K. 1930 Ueber Geruchs- und Geschmackssinn. (Smell and taste.) WSBR, **47**: 193–98.

GIACALONE, A., and COLLESANO, G. 1935 Relazione fra costituzione chimica e sapore. (Relation between chemical constitution and taste.) GCIT, **65**: 129–31.

GIBSON, L., and HARTMAN, T. 1919 The comparative sapidity of hydrochloric, sulfuric and acetic acids. AJPC, **30**: 311–13.

GIDDON, D. B., DREISBACH, M. E., PFAFFMANN, C., and MANLY, B. S 1954 Relative abilities of natural and artificial dentition patients for judging the sweetness of solid foods. JPDE, **4**: 263–68.

GIERSBERG, H. 1926 Über den chemischen Sinn von *Octopus vulgaris.* (The chemical sense of *Octopus vulgaris*) ZVPH, **3**: 827–38.

GIERSBERG, H. K. 1920 Untersuchungen über den Geschmackssinn der Molche. (Investigation on the sense of taste in the salamander.) ZVPH, **3**: 377–88.

GILLESPIE, T. H. 1922 Taste or scent in the ostrich. SCTN, p. 168.

GILLILAND, A. R. 1921 Taste sensitivity of an anosmic subject. JEPS, **4**: 318–26.

GILMAN, H., and DICKEY, J. B. 1930 Attempted correlations of constitution with sweet taste in the furan series: The very high sweetening power of 5-benzyl-2-fururaldoxime. JACS, **52**: 2010–13.

GILMAN, H., and HEWLETT, A. P. 1929 Some correlations of constitution with sweet taste in the furan series. ISCJ, **4**: 27–33.

GIUROVSKI, A. 1960 Eksperimentalio-morofologichni danni otnosno nervnite iztochnitsi na vkusovopodobnite vetseptori v ligavitsata na larinksa. (Experimental morphological data on neurological origins of the gustatory receptors in the laryngeal mucosa.) NTVM, **39**: 89–102. (English summary.)

———. 1960 Kum vuprosa za razpredelenieto, lokalizatsiiata i otchasti morfologiiata na retseptorite v ligavitsata na larinksa u choveka, (On the distribution, the localization, and partly the morphology of the receptors in the human laryngeal mucosa.) NTVM, **39**: 103–16.

GLANVILLE, E. V., and KAPLAN, A. R. 1965 The

menstrual cycle and sensitivity of taste perception. AJOG, **92**: 189–94.

GLANVILLE, E. V., KAPLAN, A. R., and FISCHER, R. 1964 Age, sex, and taste sensitivity. JOGE, **19**: 474–78.

GLEY, E. 1886 Gustation. II. Physiologie. (Gustation. II. Physiology.) DSME, **11**: 580–653.

———. 1886 Note sur l'action gustative de la corde du tympan et sur l'origine réelle de ce nerf. (Note on the gustatory action of the chorda tympani and the actual origin of the nerve.) CRSS, **38**: 61–62.

———. 1890 Les nerfs du goût. (The taste nerves.) TRME, **22**: 453–56.

GLEY, E., and RICHET, C. 1885 Action chimique et sensibilité gustative. (Chemical action and gustatory sensitivity.) CRSS, **37**: 742–46.

———. 1885 De la sensibilité gustative pour les alcaloides. (Taste sensitivity to alcaloids.) CRSS, **37**: 237–39.

GLONING, I., and TSCHABITSCHER, H. 1956 Über einen Fall mit zentraler Geschmacksstörung und Gechmackshalluzination. (Central disorder of taste and gustatory hallucination.) WZND, **12**: 190–93.

GLUSCHKOFF, N. A. 1908 Undersuchung des Geschmacks und des Geruchs bei Epileptikern. (Investigations of taste and olfaction in epileptics.) RUMR, **6**: 525–36, 581–92, 645–49.

GMELIN, W. VON. 1892 Zur Morphologie der Papilla Vallata und Foliata. (The morphology of the vallate and foliate papilla.) AMAE, **40**: 1–28. (Abstract in ZEPH, **6**: 622–23, 1892.)

———. 1895 Die Geschmacksorgane der Thiere. (The taste organs of animals.) MPTI, **6**: 266–75.

GOETSCH, W. 1925 Neuere Untersuchungen über das Geruchs- und Geschmacksvermögen. (New discoveries about smell and taste capacities.) NTUR, **16**: 347–49.

GOETZL, F. R., AHOKAS, A. J., and GOLDSCHMIDT, M. 1951 Influence of sucrose in various concentrations upon olfactory acuity and sensations associated with food intake. JAPY, **4**: 30–36.

GOETZL, F. R., AHOKAS, A. J., and PAYNE, J. G. 1950 Occurrence in normal individuals of diurnal variations in acuity of the sense of taste for sucrose. JAPY, **2**: 619–26.

GOETZL, F. R., GOLDSCHMIDT, M., WHEELER, P., and STONE, F. 1949 Influence of sugar upon olfactory acuity and upon the sensation complex of appetite and satiety. GAST, **12**: 252–57.

GOIFFON, R. 1941 Essai sur la psychologie du goût (Introduction á l'etude de la dietétique). (Phychology of taste. [Introduction to a study of dietetics].) PRME, **49**: 537–39.

GOLDSCHEIDER, A., and SCHMIDT, H. 1891 Bemerkungen über den Geschmackssinn. (Comments on the sense of taste.) ZEPH, **4**: 10–12.

GOLDSCHMIDT, H. 1927 Zur Physiologie der Geschmacksempfindung und des Saugreflexes bei Säuglingen. Beobachtungen über die Verteilung der Geschmackspapillen bei Kindern in verschiedenen Lebensaltern. (Physiology of taste sensations and the sucking reflex of babies. Observations on the distribution of taste papillae in children of different ages.) ZEKI, **45**: 28–35.

GOODRICH, K. P. 1960 Running speed and drinking rate as functions of sucrose concentration and amount of consummatory activity. JCPP, **53**: 245–50.

GORDON, G., KITCHELL, R., STRÖM, L., and ZOTTERMAN, Y. 1959 The response pattern of taste fibres in the chorda tympani of the monkey. APSC, **46**: 119–32.

GORDON, J. 1965 Evaluation of sugar-acid-sweetness relationships in orange juice by a response surface approach. JFDS, **30**: 903–7.

GORMAN, W. 1964 Taste and chemical sense: A clinical review. EENT, **43**: 65–69.

———. 1964 Taste and the chemical sense, in *Flavor, Taste and the Psychology of Smell.* Charles C Thomas, Springfield, Ill., 106 pp. (see pp. 14–23).

*GORSCHKOFF, Y. P. 1901 Über die Lokalisation der Geruchs- und Geschmackszentren. (On the localization of the smell and taste centers.) Inaugural Dissertation, St. Petersburg.

———. 1902 O tsentral nykh provodnikakh vkusovykh oshtshushtshenii. (Central conductors of taste sensations.) NVKU, **10**: 11–34.

GOTTSCHAU, M. 1881 Ueber Geschmacknospen. (On taste buds.) VMGW, **15**: 41–44.

———. 1882 Über Geschmacksorgane der Wirbeltiere. (Taste organs in vertebrates.) BIZN, **2**: 240–48.

GOTTSCHICK, J. 1937 Erbliche Unterschiede der Geschmacksempfindungen auf P-Aethoxyphenylthioharnstoff. (Hereditary differences in taste sensations with P-ethoxyphenylthiourea.) ZMVK, **21**: 254–65.

GOUDRIAAN, J. C. 1925 Influence de la température sur la sensation gustative. (Influence of temperature on taste sensitivity.) ANPA, **10**: 411–17.

———. 1930 Über den Einfluss der Temperatur auf die Geschmacksempfindung. (The influence of temperature upon taste sensations.) ANPA, **15**: 253–82.

GOWERS, W. R. 1880 A case of loss of taste from disease of the fifth nerve. JPHY, **3**: 229–31.

———. 1897 A case of paralysis of the fifth nerve. EMJO, **1**: 37–45.

———. 1902 Taste and the fifth nerve. JPHY, **28**: 300–3.

GOY, K. 1896 Uber Substanzen welche die Geschmacksempfindungen beeinflussen. (On substances which influence taste sensations.) Inaugural Dissertation, K. Stahl, Würzburg, 20 pp.

GRÅBERG, J. 1898 Beiträge zur Genese des Geschmacksorgans des Menschen. (Contribution to the recovery of the taste organs in man.) MRAR, **8:** 117–34.

———. 1899 Zur Kenntnis des cellulären Baues der Geschmacksknospen beim Menchen. (Knowledge of the cellular structure of taste buds in man.) ANHE, **1, 12:** 337–68.

*GRACE, J. E. 1964 Neurological correlates of the specific hunger for salt in the rat. Unpublished Master's thesis, University of Waterloo.

GRAF, K. VON. 1961 Die Geruchs- und Geschmacksstörungen nach Schädelunfällen. (Odor and taste disturbances after cranial injuries.) PORL, **23:** 104–14.

GRAIN, G. O. 1943 Bilateral ageusia associated with unilateral Bell's palsy. ANPS, **49:** 926–27.

GRANDE, F., ALCALDE, V., and COLAS, A. 1952 Sensibilidad gustativa a la feniltiourea en un grupo de estudiantes. (Gustatory sensitivity to phenylthiourea in a group of students.) RPGA, **7:** 29–37.

GRANDJEAN, E., and FLEISCH, A. 1943 Neues Aesthesiometer. Vergleichende Messungen der Reizschwellen des Druck und Geschmackssinnes in Lauterbrunnen und auf Jungfraujoch. (A new aesthesiometer. Comparative measurements of the stimulus threshold of pressure and taste sense in Lauterbrunnen and in Jungfraujoch.) HPPA, **1:** 59–60.

GREEN, M. W. 1942 Sucrose octa acetate as a possible bitter stomachic. APBU, **10:** 131–33.

*GREEVES, A. F. A. 1828 An essay on the varieties and distinctions of tastes and smells and on the arrangement of the materia medica. Edinburgh.

GREGSON, R. A. M. 1962 A rating-scale method for determining absolute taste thresholds. JFDS, **27:** 4, 376–80.

———. 1964 Fitting a linear trace decay model to taste comparison and preference data. BJSP, **17:** 137–51.

———. 1964 Modification of perceived relative intensities of acid tastes by ambient illumination changes. ASJP, **16:** 190–99.

———. 1965 Representation of taste mixture cross-modal matching in a Minkowski R-metric. ASJP, **17:** 195–204.

———. 1965 The effect of disodium inosinate on the perception of relative sweetness. Research Project Report 8, Department of Psychology and Sociology, University of Canterbury, New Zealand, September, 22 pp.

———. 1966 Cross-modal matching of histograms, with one component fixed, under two pacing conditions. PMOS, **23:** 183–90.

———. 1966 Qualitative identification of the taste of weak sucrose-sodium chloride mixture stimuli. PEPS, **1:** 154–56.

———. 1966 Scaling perceived similarities between complex tastes which include ethanol. Research Project Report 9, Department of Psychology and Sociology, University of Canterbury, New Zealand, April, 46 pp.

———. 1966 Theoretical and empirical multidimensional scaling of taste mixture matchings. BJSP, **19:** 57–75.

GREGSON, R. A. M., and McCOWEN, P. J. 1963 The relative perception of weak sucrose-citric acid mixtures. JFDS, **28:** 371–78.

GREGSON, R. A. M., and RUSSELL, P. N. 1965 Problems and results in the scaling of intermodal and intramodal complex taste similarities by D* metrics. Research Project Report 7, Department of Psychology and Sociology, University of Canterbury, New Zealand, May, 30 pp.

———. 1965 Psychophysical power law exponent value for sucrose intensity. PMOS, **20:** 294.

GREGSON, R. A. M., and WILSON, G. D. 1966 Effects of illumination on the detection and perceived relative intensity of acid tastes. Research Project Report 10, Department of Psychology and Sociology, University of Canterbury, New Zealand, June, 28 pp.

GRESCHIK, E. 1917 Geschmacksknospen auf der Zunge des Amazonenpapageis. (Taste buds on the tongue of the Amazon parrot.) ANAN, **50:** 257–70.

GRIDGEMAN, N. T. 1957 Aspects of taste. WLCO, **20:** 203–15.

———. 1958 Application of quantal-response theory to the cross-comparison of taste-stimuli intensities. BIOM, **14:** 548–57.

*GRIFFIN, F. 1966 On the interaction of chemical stimuli with taste receptors. Unpublished Ph.D. thesis, Ohio State University.

GRIFFIN, F., and FISCHER, R. 1960 Differential reactivity of saliva from "tasters" and "nontasters" of 6-n-propylthiouracil. NATU, **187:** 417–19.

GRIFFINI, L. 1884 Sulla riproduzione degli organi gustatori. (On the reproduction of the gustatory organ.) GOCL, **5:** 124–25.

———. 1884 Sur la reproduction totale ou partielle de l'appareil folie du lapin et des papilles calyciformes. (Total or partial reproduction of the foliated structures of the rabbit and of the calyciform papillae.) AIBL, **5:** 106–7.

———. 1887 Sulla riproduzione degli organi gustatori. (On the reproduction of the gustatory organ.) RILR, **20:** 667–83.

GRINSTEAD, L. E., SPEER, V. C., CATRON, D. V., and HAYS, V. W. 1960 Comparison of sugar and artificial sweetness in baby pig diets. JANS, **19:** 1264. (Abstract.)

GRISANTI, G. 1959 Ricerche sulla sensazione gustativa relevata a mezzo del riflesso psicogalvanico. (Research on gustatory sensation relevant to psychogalvanic reflexes.) ACOR, 8: 49–62.

GRISOGANI, N. 1925 Ritmo della secrezione parotidea nell'uomo e sensazioni gustative e olfattive. (Effect on parotid secretion of gustatory and olfactory sensations in man.) AALB, 1: 602–4.

GRÖNBERG, J. 1919 Studien über die adstringierenden Wirkungen der Metallsalze. (Studies of astringent effects of metallic salts.) SAPH, 38: 256–79.

GROSS, A. O. 1917 Sense of taste in *Nereis virens*. ANRE, 12: 526–27.

GROSSMANN, B. 1921 Über das Vorkommen von Geschmacksknospen an der Vorderwand der Pars laryngea pharyngis beim Menschen. (The occurrence of taste buds on the front part of the pars larynx pharynx in humans.) MOLA, 55: 1174–86.

GROSSMAN, S. 1953 Loss of taste and smell due to propylthiouracil therapy. NYSJ, 53: 1236.

GRUENHAGEN, A. 1886 Geschmackssinn (Taste sense), in *Lehrbuch der Physiologie*. Voss, Hamburg, 662 pp. (see pp. 199–212).

GRÜNBERG, K. 1926 Geschmacksstörungen (Taste disturbances), in *Allgemeine Symptomatologie, Handbuch der Hals-, Nasen-, Ohrenheilkunde*, A. Denker and O. Kahler (eds.), VI (1), 1274 pp. (see pp. 903–4).

GRÜNWALD, M. 1933 Geruch und Geschmack. (Smell and taste.) RIEI, 8: 44–46.

GRÜNWALD, P., and HERMAN, C. 1962 Distribution of taste sensitivity for phenylthiocarbamide in Yugoslavia. NATU, 194: 95.

———. 1963 Study of several gene frequencies in Yugoslav population. NATU, 199: 830–31.

GRÜNWALD, P., and PFEIFER, S. 1962 Examination of taste sensitivity to bitterness (P.T.C. test). LIVJ, 34: 27–31.

GRÜTZNER, P. 1894 Über die chemische Reizung sensibler Nerven. (On the nerves stimulated by chemicals.) PAGB, 58: 69–104.

GRYLLUS, L. 1566 *De sapore dulci et amaro, libri duo in quibus non ex temere collectis autorum sententiis, sed rationibus ex ipsa verum natura sumptis ostenditur, quid de his saporibus sentiendum sit.* (Sweet and bitter taste, two books in which opinions of author have been collected, not by chance but as shown with reasons put forward from nature itself, what is to be thought of these tastes.) G. Melantrichum, Prague, 97 pp.

*GUASCHINO, G. 1923 Le alterazioni del gusto negli otopatici. (Alteration of taste during ear disorders.) ALOR, pp. 8–10.

GUIDIZI, S., and NOFERI, G. 1946 Le variazioni della sensibilità gustativa in particolari situazioni fisiologiche ed in alcuni stati morbosi. III: Le variazioni della soglia gustativa per il limone durante la gravidanza in rapporto al tasso ascorbico. (Variation in taste sensitivity in certain physiological situations and in some pathological states. III: Variation of gustatory threshold for lemon during pregnancy in relation to ascorbic acid level.) RCCM, 46 (5) : 76–88.

GUILLOT, M. 1964 Sur les problèmes du goût. (On problems of taste.) BSSH, 52: 231–35.

*GUINSBURG, S., and SALDANHA, P. H. 1953 Sobre a sensibilidade a finiltioureia em estudiantes da F.N.F. (On sensitivity to phenylthiourea in students of F.N.F.) RCIR, 4: 19.

GUITEL, F. 1891 Sur les organes gustatifs de la Baudroie (*L. piscatorius*). (On the taste organ of Baudroie-*L. piscatorius*.) CORE, 112: 879–82.

*GUSSEV, N. K. 1940 (Change of taste sensitivity in connection with a dynamic demand for food.) TIBI, 13: 156–80.

*———. 1941 (Gustatory perception as an indicator of the inner state of the organism.) SOPE, 10: 563–66.

GUSTAFSON, E. 1953 Exploratory methods for the study of children's taste preferences and discrimination. Unpublished Master's thesis, Florida State University, 43 pp.

GUTH, L. 1957 The effects of glossopharyngeal nerve transection on the circumvallate papilla of the rat. ANRE, 128: 715–31.

———. 1958 Taste buds on the cat's circumvallate papilla after reinnervation by glossopharyngeal, vagus, and hypoglossal nerves. ANRE, 130: 25–37.

GÜTTICH, H. 1965 Intravenös verabreichte Riechstoffe: Gustatorisches Riechen. (Intravenously administered scents: Gustatory capacity to perceive smell.) HNAO, 13: 42–45.

GUTTMAN, N. 1953 Operant conditioning, extinction, and periodic reinforcement in relation to concentration of sucrose used as reinforcing agent. JEPS, 46: 213–24.

———. 1954 Equal-reinforcement values for sucrose and glucose solutions compared with equal-sweetness values. JCPP, 47: 358–61.

GUYOT, J. 1837 Nouvelles expériences sur le sens du goût chez l'homme, suivies d'un examen succinct des travaux principaux publiés récemment sur le même sujet. (New experiments on the sense of taste in man followed by a brief examination of the principle work published recently on the same subject.) AGME, 13: 51–69.

———. 1856 Note sur l'anesthésie du sens du goût. (Note on the anesthesia of the sense of taste). CORE, 42: 1143.

GUYOT, J., and ADMYRAULT. 1830 Expériences sur le goût. (Taste experiences.) JCHM, 6: 426–31.

———. 1830 Extrait d'un mémoire sur le siège du goût chez l'homme. (Abstract of an article on the taste center in man.) JCHM, 6: 169–75.

———. 1830 Mémoire sur le siège du goût chez l'homme. (Memoire on the origin of taste in man.) BUUV, 21: 18–22.

———. 1830 Über den Sitz des Geschmackssinns beim Menschen. (On the origin of the sense of taste in man.) NGNH, **27**: 133–37.

———. 1831 Seat of the sense of taste. JRIB, **1**: 425.

GUYOT, J., and CAZALIS, E. 1839 Expériences sur les nerfs glosso-pharyngien, lingual et hypoglosse. (Studies of the glossopharyngeal, lingual and hypoglossal nerves.) CORE, **8**: 84–85.

HAAGEN-SMIT, A. J. 1952 Smell and taste. SCAM, **186**: 28–32.

HAAS, E. 1953 Kasuistischer Beitrag zum Thema: Geschmacksstörungen nach Tonsillektomie. (Causal contribution to the subject: Disorders of sensation following tonsillectomy.) ZLRT, **32**: 413–14.

HABS, H. 1938 Zwillingsphysiologische Untersuchungen über die Erbbedingtheit der alveolaren CO_2-Spannung, der Geschmacksschwellen und der Dunkeladaptation nebst einem Überblick über die bisherigen zwillingsphysiologischen Arbeiten. (Twin physiology studies on inheritance of alveolar CO_2-pressure, taste thresholds and dark adaptation besides an overview of work to the present on twin physiology.) ZMVK, **21**: 447–75.

HADDEN, J. W. 1965 An exploratory experiment into the physiological basis of sour taste. JGPL, **73**: 307–16.

HAEMELINCK, M. 1905 Étude sur l'asymétrie du sens gustatif. (Study of the asymmetry of the sense of taste.) ANPQ, **11**: 116–27.

HAGER, N. 1893 Dulcin, ein neuer Süsstoff. (Dulcin, a new sweetener.) PAPO, **26**: 233–34.

*HAGSTROM, E. C. 1954 The response of taste receptors to stimulation by sugars and non-carbohydrate "sweetening agents." Unpublished Master's thesis, Brown University, 41 pp.

———. 1957 Nature of taste stimulation by sugar. Unpublished Ph.D. thesis, Brown University, 55 pp.

———. 1958 Nature of taste stimulation by sugar. DIAS, **18**: 676.

HAGSTROM, E. C., and PFAFFMANN, C. 1959 The relative taste effectiveness of different sugars for the rat. JCPP, **52**: 259–62.

HAHN, H. 1932 Einige für den Geschmackssinn neue Gesetzmässigkeiten. (Newly discovered laws on the sense of taste.) KLWO, **11**: 1504–8.

———. 1934 Die Adaptation des Geschmackssinnes. (Taste adaptation.) ZPSI, **65**: 105–45.

———. 1936 Über die Ursache der Geschmacksempfindung. (The reason for the sensation of taste.) KLWO, **15**: 933–35.

———. 1937 Sobre algunos problemas de la fisiología de los sentidos. (On some problems on the physiology of the senses.) RMGI, pp. 91–102.

———. 1943 Geschmackssinnes- und Permeabilitätsforschung. I. Teil: Die Geschmacks-erregenden und- vermittelnden Kräfte. (Taste sense and permeability study. Part I: The taste stimulating and supplying power.) KLWO, **22**: 245–49.

———. 1943 Geschmackssinnes- und Permeabilitätsforschung. II. Teil: Die Anpassung an die Geschmacksreize. (Taste sense and permeability study. Part II. The adaptation of the taste stimulus.) KLWO, **22**: 269–73.

———. 1951 Kurvenmässige Darstellung der Adaptation des Geschmackssinnes. (Diagrammatic representation of adaptation of the sense of taste.) VORT, **8**: 27–28.

HAHN, H., and GÜNTHER, H. 1933 Über die Reize und die Reizbedingungen des Geschmackssinnes. (Concerning the stimulus and stimulus conditions of the gustatory sense.) PAGP, **231**: 48–67.

HAHN, H., KUCKULIES, G., and BISSAR, A. 1940 Ein systematische Untersuchung der Geschmacksschwellen. II. (A systematic investigation of taste thresholds. II.) ZESI, **68**: 185–260.

HAHN, H., KUCKULIES, G., and TAEGER, H. 1938 Eine systematische Untersuchung der Geschmacksschwellen I. (A systematic investigation of taste thresholds. I.) ZESI, **67**: 259–306.

HAHN, H., and ULRICH, L. 1948 Eine systematische Untersuchung der Geschmacksschwellen. (A systematic investigation of taste thresholds.) PAGP, **250**: 357–84.

HALBAN, J. 1896 Zur Physiologie der Zungennerven. (The physiology of the nerves of the tongue.) WIKR, **10**: 51–53.

HALDANE, J. B. S. 1941 Physiological properties of some common gases at high pressures. CPCN, **4**: 83–84.

HALL, A. R., and BLAKESLEE, A. F. 1945 Effect of smoking on taste thresholds for phenyl-thio-carbamide (PTC). PNAS, **31**: 390–96.

HALLENBERG, B. A. 1914 Beiträge zur Kenntnis der alkoholhaltigen Getränke. I: Untersuchungen über die Geschmacks- und Geruchsschwelle einiger einatomiger Alkohole. (Contribution to the knowledge of alcoholic beverages. I: Studies on taste and odor thresholds of some mono-atomic alcohols.) SAPH, **31**: 75–80.

HALLER, A. VON. 1762 Par octavum, ejusque ramus glossopharyngeus (Pair eight, and its glossopharyngeal branch), in *Elementa Physiologie, IV*. F. Grasset, Lausanne, 596 pp. (see pp. 231–33).

———. 1763 Gustus (Taste), in *Elementa Physiologie, V*. F. Grasset, Lausanne, 646 pp. (see pp. 99–124).

HALLER, B. 1909 Die phyletische Entfaltung der Sinnesorgane der Säugetierzunge. (The phyletic development of sense organs in the tongue of mammals.) AMAE, **74**: 368–466.

HALLMAN, B. L., and HURST, J. W. 1953 Loss of taste as toxic effect of methimazole (tapazole) therapy: Report of 3 cases. JAMA, **152**: 322.

HALPERN, B. P. 1959 Gustatory responses in the medulla oblongata of the rat. Unpublished Ph.D. thesis, Brown University, 73 pp.
———. 1959 Gustatory responses in the medulla oblongata of the rat. DIAS, 20: 2, 2397.
———. 1962 Gustatory nerve responses in the chicken. AJPH, 203: 541–44.
———. 1962 Neural-behavioral interrelationships in taste. BPSS, 1: 22–28.
———. 1963 Chemical coding in taste—temporal patterns, in Olfaction and Taste, Y. Zotterman (ed.). Macmillan, New York, 396 pp. (see pp. 275–84).
HALPERN, B. P., BERNARD, R. A., and KARE, M. R. 1962 Amino acids as gustatory stimuli in the rat. JGPL, 45: 681–701.
HALPERN, B. P., and KARE, M. R. 1961 Physiological and behavioral aspects of taste. SCIE, 133: 216–19.
HALPERN, B. P., and NELSON, L. M. 1965 Bulbar gustatory responses to anterior and to posterior tongue stimulation in the rat. AJPH, 209: 105–10.
HAMBLOCH, H., and PÜSCHEL, J. 1928 Über die sinnlichen Erfolge bei Darbietung von Geschmacksmischungen. (The sensory results of the presentation of taste mixtures.) ZPSI, 50: 136–50.
HAMMER, F. J. 1951 The relation of odor, taste, and flicker-fusion thresholds to food intake. JCPP, 44: 403–11.
HAMOR, G. H. 1961 Correlation of chemical structure and taste in the saccharin series. SCIE, 134: 1416.
*HANAOKA, T. 1955 Mikaku to kyokaku (Gustation and olfaction), in Kankaku no Seirigaku. (Physiology of sensations.) K. Motokawa (ed.). Kawaideshobo, Tokyo (see pp. 67–77).
HÄNIG, D. P. 1901 Zur Psychophysik des Geschmackssinnes. (The psychophysics of the sense of taste.) PHST, 17: 576–623. (Abstract in ZPSI, 29: 134–37, 1902.)
HANSEN, R., and LANGER, W. 1935 Über Geschmacksveränderungen in der Schwangerschaft. (Changes in sense of taste during pregnancy.) KLWO, 14: 1173–76.
HANSTRÖM, B. 1926 Einige Experimente und Reflexionen über Geruch, Geschmack und den allgemeinen chemischen Sinn. (Experiments and observations on smell, taste, and the general chemical senses.) ZWBC, 4: 528–44.
HARA, S. 1955 Interrelationship among stimulus intensity, stimulated area and reaction in the human gustatory sensation. BTMD, 2: 147–58.
HARBERT, F., WAGNER, S., and YOUNG, I. M. 1962 The quantitative measurement of taste function. AROT, 75: 138–43.
HARO, F. G. 1963 Relation between the blood groups of the ABO system and the taste sensibility to phenylthiourea (P.T.C.), in Genetics Today, I, S. J. Geerts (ed.). Pergamon

Press, London, 332 pp. (see p. 293). (Abstract.)
HARPER, A. R. 1961 On testing the sense of taste by a simple electrical gustatory probe. SMDJ, 6: 381–83.
HARRIMAN, A. E. 1955 The effect of a preoperative preference for sugar over salt upon compensatory salt selection by adrenalectomized rats. JONU, 57: 271–76.
HARRIMAN, A. E., and KARE, M. R. 1964 Preference for sodium chloride over lithium chloride by adrenalectomized rats. AJPH, 207: 941–43.
———. 1966 Aversion to saline solutions in starlings, purple grackles, and herring gulls. PHZO, 39: 123–26.
———. 1966 Tolerance for hypertonic saline solutions in herring gulls, starlings, and purple grackles. PHZO, 39: 117–22.
HARRIMAN, A. E., and MACLEOD, R. B. 1953 Discriminative thresholds of salt for normal and adrenalectomized rats. AJPC, 66: 465–71.
HARRIS, E. K. 1960 Analysis of experiments measuring threshold taste. BIOM, 16: 245–60.
HARRIS, H., and KALMUS, H. 1949 Chemical specificity in genetical differences of taste sensitivity. ANEU, 15: 32–45.
———. 1949 Genetic differences in taste sensitivity to phenylthiourea and to anti-thyroid substances. NATU, 163: 878–79.
———. 1949 The measurement of taste sensitivity to PTC. ANEU, 15: 24–31.
———. 1951 The distribution of taste threshold for phenylthiourea of 384 sib pairs. ANEU, 16: 226–30.
HARRIS, H., KALMUS, H., and TROTTER, W. R. 1949 Taste sensitivity to phenylthiourea in goiter and diabetes. LANC, 257: 1038–39.
HARRIS, L. J., CLARY, J., HARGREAVES, F. J., and WARD, A. 1933 Appetite and choice of diet: The ability of the vitamin B deficient rat to discriminate between diets containing and lacking the vitamin. PRLB, 113: 161–90.
HARRIS, W. 1952 The fifth and seventh cranial nerves in relation to the nervous mechanism of taste sensation. BMJO, 1: 831–36.
HARRIS, W., and NEWCOMB, W. D. 1926 Case of pontine glioma, with special reference to paths of gustatory sensation. PRSM, 19: 1–5.
HARRISON, G. R. 1956 Taste, in What Man May Be—The Human Side of Science. Wm. Morrow and Co., New York, 278 pp. (see pp. 134, 137, 143–45).
HARRISON, W. H. 1965 The effect of palatal coverage on taste perception. Unpublished Master's thesis, Ohio State University, 39 pp.
HART, H. R. 1938 Bad taste (cacogeusia). ANPS, 39: 771–79.
HARTLINE, H. K. 1942 Sense organs. ARPH, 4: 445–64.
HARTMANN, G. 1939 Application of individual taste difference toward phenyl-thio-carbamide in genetic investigations. ANEU, 9: 123–35.

HARTMANN, R. 1863 Ueber die Endigungsweise der Nerven in den Papillae fungiformes der Froschzunge. (The endings of nerves in the fungiform papillae in the tongue of the frog.) AAPA, pp. 634–48, 710–16.

HARTMANS, H. M. A. 1946 Derivatives of 1-chloro-2-cyano-4-nitrobenzene. RTCP, 65: 468–76.

HARTRIDGE, H. 1945 The importance of taste and smell in nutrition. JOPH, 103: 34–35P.

HARVEY, R. B. 1920 The relation between the total acidity, the concentration of hydrogen ion, and the taste of acid solutions. JACS, 42: 712–14.

HARVEY, R. B., and FULTON, R. R. 1935 Relation of pH and total acidity to the taste of tomatoes. FPJV, 14: 238–39.

HASAMA, B. 1935 Hirnrinderregung durch Reizung des peripheren Geschmacksorgans im Aktionsstrombild. (Cerebral cortex excitation by stimulation of peripheral taste organs recorded by means of action currents.) PAGP, 236: 36–44.

HASLER, A. D. 1957 The sense organs: Olfactory and gustatory senses of fishes, in The Physiology of Fishes, II, M. E. Brown (ed.). Academic Press, New York, 526 pp. (see pp. 187–209).

HASLINGER, F. 1935 Über den Geschmackssinn von Calliphora Erythrocephala Meigen und über die Verwertung von Zuckern und Zuckeralkoholen durch diese Fliege. (The sense of taste and the utilization of sugars and sugar alcohols by the fly, Calliphora Erythrocephala.) ZVPH, 22: 614–40.

HASSETT, C. C., DETHIER, V. G., and GANS, J. 1950 A comparison of nutritive values and taste thresholds of carbohydrates for the blowfly. BIBU, 99: 446–53.

HAUSMANN, M. F. 1933 The behavior of albino rats in choosing foods. II: Differentiation between sugar and saccharin. JCPP, 15: 419–28.

HAYCRAFT, J. B. 1885 A new theory of the sense of taste. NATU, 32: 562. (Abstract.)

———. 1885–86 On the objective cause of sensation. Part II: Taste. PREB, 13: 961–75.

———. 1888 The nature of the objective cause of sensation. II: Taste. BRAI, 10: 145–63.

———. 1900 The sense of taste, in Textbook of Physiology, E. A. S. Schafer (ed.). Y. J. Pentland, Edinburgh, 1365 pp. (see pp. 1237–45).

HAYES, E. R., and ELLIOTT, R. 1942 Distribution of the taste buds on the tongue of the kitten, with particular reference to those innervated by the chorda tympani branch of the facial nerve. JCNE, 76: 227–38.

HEIDENHAIN, M. 1914 Ueber die Sinnesfelder und die Geschmacksknospen der Papilla foliata des Kaninchens. Beiträge zur Teilkörpertheorie. III. (The sensitivity area and the taste bud of the papillae foliata in the rabbit. Contributions to the structural theory III.) AMAE, 85: 365–479.

———. 1914 Untersuchungen über die Teilkörpernatur der Geschmacksknospen in der Papilla Foliata des Kaninchens. (Studies on the structure of taste buds of the papillae foliata in the rabbit.) ANAN, 45: 385–405.

———. 1918 Ueber die Geschmacksknospen als Objekt einer allgemeinen Theorie der Organisation. (Taste buds as the object of an overall theory of organization.) MMWO, 75: 579–81.

HEIDERICH, F. 1906 Die Zahl und die Dimension der Geschmacksknospen der Papilla Vallata des Menschen in den verschiedenen Lebensaltern. (The number and dimension of taste buds of the vallate papillae in man in different ages.) NAKG, 1: 54–64.

———. 1906 Über das Vorkommen von Flimmerepithel an menschlichen Papillae Vallatae. (The occurrence of flicker epithel on the human vallate papillae.) ANAN, 28: 315–16.

HEIDUSCHKA, A., and KOMM, E. 1925 Beziehungen zwischen Konstitution und Geschmack von α-Aminosäuren. II. Mitteilung: über die Abhängigkeit des Süssungsgrades wässeriger Aminosäurelösungen von der Konzentration. (Relation between constitution and taste of alpha-amino acids. II: The dependence of degree of sweetness of aqueous amino acid solutions on concentration.) ZACH, 38: 941–45. (See also pp. 291–94.)

HEINEMANN, G. 1937 Ueber die Geschmackswirkung von anorganischen Doppelsalzen. II. (On the effect of taste of inorganic salts. II.) Inaugural Dissertation, Stadtroda, Jena, 28 pp.

HEINTZE, K. VON, and BRAUN, F. 1958 Beziehungen zwischen der geschmacklichen Wahrnehmung von Glutamat und dem pH-Wert. (Relationship between perceived taste of glutamate and pH-value.) DLRU, 54: 25–28.

HEITLER, M. 1904 Pulsveränderung durch Erregung des Gehörs, Geruchs und Geschmacks. (Pulse changes through excitation of hearing, smell, and taste.) ZIME, 25: 401–7.

HELGREN, F. J., LYNCH, M. J., and KIRCHMEYER, F. J. 1955 A taste panel study of the saccharin "off-taste." JPMS, 44: 353–55.

HELLEKANT, G. 1965 Electrophysiological investigation of the gustatory effect of ethyl alcohol. I: The summated response of the chorda tympani in the cat, dog and rat. APSC, 64: 392–97.

———. 1965 Electrophysiological investigation of the gustatory effect of ethyl alcohol. II: A single fibre analysis in the cat. APSC, 64: 398–406.

———. 1965 The effect of ethyl alcohol on non-gustatory receptors of the tongue of the cat. APSC, 65: 243–50.

HELLMAN, T. J. 1921 Die Genese der Zungenpapillen beim Menschen. (The origin of tongue papillae in man.) ASUP, 26: 1–72.

HELSMOORTEL, J., JR. 1929 Les troubles de

l'olfaction et du goût. (Disorders of olfaction and taste.) JONP, 29: 298–301.

HELSMOORTEL, J., JR., and NYSSEN, R. 1935 Asociación de anosmia y ageusia completa en un traumatismo craneocerebral. (Association of complete anosmia and ageusia in craniocerebral injuries.) RVOO, 10: 171–75.

———. 1936 Zusammentreffen von vollständiger Anosmie und Ageusie bei der Schädelhirnverletzung. (The occurrence of complete anosmia and ageusia by brain injury.) ZHNG, 26: 284. (Abstract.)

HELSMOORTEL, J., JR., NYSSEN, R., and THIENPONT, R. 1934 À propos d'un cas d'anosmie et d'ageusie complète d'origine traumatique. (A case of complete anosmia and ageusia of traumatic origin.) JBEN, 34: 226–30.

———. 1935 Un nouveau cas d'anosmie et d'ageusie complète d'origine traumatique. (A new case of complete anosmia and ageusia of traumatic origin.) JBEN, 35: 656–62.

———. 1936 Six cas d'anosmie—ageusie d'origine traumatique. (Six cases of anosmia and ageusia of traumatic origin.) APNE, 11: 251–66.

HENCKEL, K. O., and PANTOJA, A. 1939 Zur Entwicklungsgeschichte der Papillae Circumvallatae beim Hausschwein. (The developmental history of the circumvallate papillae in the pig.) ANAN, 87: 355–60.

HENKIN, R. I., GILL, J. R., JR., and BARTTER, F. C. 1963 Studies on taste thresholds in normal man and in patients with adrenal cortical insufficiency; the role of adrenal cortical steroids and of serum sodium concentration. JCIN, 42: 727–35.

HENKIN, R. I., GILL, J. R., JR., BARTTER, F. C., and SOLOMON, D. H. 1962 On the presence and character of the increased ability of the Addisonian patient to taste salt. JCIN, 41: 1364–65.

HENKIN, R. I., and KOPIN, I. J. 1964 Abnormalities of taste and smell thresholds in familial dysautonomia: Improvement with methacholine. LIFS, 3: 1319–25.

HENKIN, R. I., and POWELL, G. F. 1962 Increased sensitivity of taste and smell in cystic fibrosis. SCIE, 138: 1107–8.

HENKIN, R. I., and SOLOMON, D. H. 1962 Salt-taste threshold in adrenal insufficiency in man. JCEM, 22: 856–58.

HENLE, J. 1880 Über den Geschmackssinn. (On the sense of taste.) ANVO, 2: 1–24.

HENNIES, E. 1933 Über die Beeinflussung der Mischungsgleichungen durch Umstimmung des Geschmackswerkzeuges. (The influence of adaptation of the organ of taste upon compound equations.) ZPSI, 64: 115–25.

HENNING, H. 1916 Die Qualitätenreihe des Geschmacks. (The quality range of taste.) ZEPS, 74: 203–19.

———. 1921 Physiologie und Psychologie des Geschmacks. (Physiology and psychology of taste.) ERPH, 19: 1–78.

———. 1925 Ausgeprägte Anschauungsbilder der beiden Arten von Geschmackssinn. (Typical illustration of two kinds of gustatory sense.). ZEPS, 95: 137–41.

———. 1927 Psychologische Studien am Geschmackssinn. (Psychological studies on the sense of taste.) HBAM, 6A: 627–740.

*HENNRICH, W. 1955 Über die Rolle der Blutzusammensetzung bei Geschmacksleistungen. (The importance of the blood components in taste performances.) Inaugural Dissertation, Berlin.

HENRY, C. 1894 Le temps de réaction a des impressions gustatives, measuré par un compteur a secondes. (Reaction time to gustatory stimuli measured by a computer in seconds.) CRSS, 46: 682.

HENSCHEN, S. E. 1919 Über die Geruchs- und Geschmackszentren. (On the smell and taste centers.) MPNE, 45: 121–65.

HERLITZKA, A. 1908 Sul "sapore metallico," sulla sensazione astringente e sul sapore dei sali. (On the "metallic taste," on astringent sensations and on the taste of salt.) ARFI, 5: 217–42.

———. 1909 Contributo all'analisi fisico-chimica del sapore dei sali. (Contribution to the physico-chemical analysis of the taste of salt.) ARFI, 7: 557–78.

HERMANN, F. 1884 Beitrag zur Entwicklicklungsgeschichte des Geschmacksorgans beim Kaninchen. (Contribution to the developmental history of taste organs in the rabbit.) M. Cohen & Son, Bonn, 16 pp.

———. 1885 Beitrag zur Entwicklungsgeschichte des Geschmacksorgans beim Kaninchen. (Contribution to the developmental history of taste organs in the rabbit.) AMAE, 24: 216–29.

———. 1886 Ueber einige neuere Arbeiten zur Morphologie und Physiologie der Geschmacksorgane. (Some new works on the morphology and physiology of taste organs.) BIZN, 5: 12–17.

———. 1887 Studien über den feineren Bau des Geschmacksorgans. (Studies on the delicate structure of the taste organs.) E. T. Jacob, Erlangen, 41 pp.

———. 1888 Studien über den feineren Bau des Geschmacksorganes. (Studies on the delicate structure of taste organs.) SMPB, 18: 277–318.

HERMANN, L. 1891 Beiträge zur Kenntniss des electrischen Geschmacks. (Contribution to the knowledge of the electric taste.) PAGP, 49: 519–38.

———. 1905 Der Geschmackssinn (The taste sense), in Lehrbuch der Physiologie. Hirschwald, Berlin, 762 pp. (see pp. 341–45).

HERMANN, R. 1899 Haben Vögel Geschmack? (Have birds taste?) DEVO, 24: 59–68.

HERRICK, C. J. 1902 The organ and sense of taste in fishes. USFC, **22**: 239–72.

———. 1905 The central gustatory paths in the brains of bony fishes. JCNP, **15**: 375–456.

———. 1906 On the centers for taste and touch in the medulla oblongata of fishes. JCNP, **16**: 403–39.

———. 1907 The central reflex connections of cutaneous taste buds in the codfish and the catfish: An illustration of the functional adaptation in the nervous system. SCIE, **25**: 736–37.

———. 1908 On the phylogenetic differentiation of the organs of smell and taste. JCNP, **18**: 157–66.

———. 1922 Organs of taste, in *An Introduction to Neurology*. W. B. Saunders Co., Philadelphia, 395 pp. (see pp. 96–98).

HERRICK, C. L. 1893 Contributions to the comparative morphology of the central nervous system. II: Topography and histology of the brain of certain reptiles. JCNE, **3**: 77–106.

HERRING, J. P. 1930 The measurement of liking and disliking. JLEP, **21**: 159–96.

HERTEL, H. 1933 Über den Geschmack einiger organischer Salze. (The taste of some organic salts.) ZESI, **64**: 152–60.

HERXHEIMER, A., and WOODBURY, D. M. 1959 The effect of deoxycorticosterone acetate (DOCA) on salt and sucrose taste preference thresholds in rats. JPHY, **149**: 42–43P. (Abstract.)

———. 1960 The effect of deoxycorticosterone on salt and sucrose taste preference thresholds and drinking behavior in rats. JPHY, **151**: 253–60.

HERZFELD, A., and SCHMIDT, T. 1887 Vergleich der Süssigkeit von Stärkezucker und Rohrzucker. (Comparison of sweetness of corn sugar with cane sugar.) DTZU, **12**: 579.

HERZFELD, J. 1897 Ueber Ursachen und Behandlung widerlicher Geschmacks-Empfindungen. (On causes and treatment of disagreeable taste sensations.) THMO, **11**: 27–31.

HERZOG, F. 1912 Zur Kenntnis der zentralen Vaguslähmungen, zugleich ein Beitrag zur Kenntnis des Verlaufs der Geschmacksfasern. (On the knowledge of vagus paralysis, also a contribution to the knowledge of the course of taste fibers.) Inaugural Dissertation, E. Lehmann, Leipzig, 52 pp.

———. 1927 Az izérzés és a szaglás agykérgi központjának helyéről. (Cortical localization of senses of taste and smell.) ORHE, **71**: 1488–92.

———. 1928 Über die corticalen Zentren des Geschmacks und des Geruchs auf Grund von Beobachtungen bei Hypophysentumoren. (Cortical centers of taste and smell as basis for observation in hypophyseal tumors.) DZNE, **102**: 221–38.

HESSE, R. 1926 Ueber die Mündungen der Drüsen an den Geschmackspapillen. (The opening of the glands on the taste papillae.) DCNN, **82**: 35–39.

HEÜMAN, G. 1911 Einige Untersuchungen betreffend den elektrischen Geschmack. (Investigations on the electric taste.) ZMEE, **13**: 133–44.

———. 1911 Quelques recherches concernant le goût électrique. (Investigations on the electric taste.) AEMP, **19**: 298–99.

———. 1941 Några undersöknigar angående den elektriska smaken. (Investigation on the electric taste.) UPSF, **17**: 130–40.

HEUSNER, L. 1886 Eine Beobachtung über den Verlauf der Geschmacksnerven. (An observation on the course of taste nerves.) BKWO, **23**: 758–59.

HEYMANS, G. 1899 Untersuchungen über psychische Hemmung. (Studies on physical inhibition.) ZEPH, **21**: 321–59.

HILGARD, T. C. 1854 Experimental observations on taste and smell. PAAS, **8**: 248–57.

HILLIX, W. A. 1959 Volume ingested as a function of deprivation, taste, and nutrition. DIAS, **19**: 3, 2162–63.

HILTON, W. A. 1943 Gustatory receptors. JENZ, **35**: 66–76.

HINCHCLIFFE, R. 1958 Clinical quantitative gustometry. AOLA, **48**: 453–66.

HINREINER, E., FILIPELLO, F., BERG, H. W., and WEBB, A. D. 1955 Evaluation of thresholds and minimum difference concentrations for various constituents of wines. IV: Detectable differences in wine. FOTE, **9**: 489–90.

HINREINER, E., FILIPELLO, F., WEBB, A. D., and BERG, H. W. 1955 Evaluation of thresholds and minimum difference concentrations for various constituents of wines. III: Ethyl alcohol, glycerol and acidity in aqueous solution. FOTE, **9**: 351–53.

HINTZE, K. 1890 Ueber die Entwicklung der Zungenpapillen beim Menschen. (On the development of papillae on the tongue in man.) Inaugural Dissertation, Heintz & Mündel, Strasburg, 18 pp.

HIRSCH, C. 1932 Ueber die klinische Prüfung des Geruchs- und Geschmackssinns. (On clinical tests of smell and taste.) MMWO, **79**: 1234–38.

———. 1936 Investigations of smell and taste in diagnostic localization. JAIH, **29**: 166–69.

Ho, W. Y. H. 1937 Disturbances of taste of otitic origin with special reference to operations on the ear. AROT, **26**: 146–69.

HOAGLAND, H. 1933 Specific nerve impulses from gustatory and tactile receptors in catfish. JGPL, **16**: 685–93.

HÖBER, R. 1899 Über einige Beziehungen zwischen den Geschmacksqualitäten und dem physikalisch-chemischen Verhalten der Schmeckstoffe. (Some relationships between taste qualities and the physical-chemical behavior of taste substances.) BIZN, **19**: 491–96.

HÖBER, R., and KIESOW, F. 1898 Ueber den

Geschmack von Salzen und Laugen. (On the taste of salts and lye.) ZPCL, **27**: 601–16.

HODGSON, E. S. 1953 A study of chemoreception in aqueous and gas phases. BIBU, **105**: 115–27.

———. 1955 Problems in invertebrate chemoreception. QRBI, **30**: 331–47.

———. 1955 The comparative physiological approach to the study of chemoreception. VJSC, **6**: 22–26.

———. 1956 Temperature sensitivity of primary chemoreceptors of insects. ANRE, **125**: 560–61.

———. 1957 Electrophysiological studies of arthropod chemoreception. II: Responses of labellar chemoreceptors of the blowfly to stimulation by carbohydrates. JIPH, **1**: 240–47.

———. 1958 Chemoreception in arthropods. AREN, **3**: 19–36.

———. 1958 Electrophysiological studies of arthropod chemoreception. III: Chemoreceptors of terrestrial and fresh-water arthropods. BIBU, **115**: 114–25.

———. 1961 Taste receptors. SCAM, **204**: 135–44.

———. 1964 Chemoreception, in *The Physiology of Insects, I*, M. Rockstein (ed.). Academic Press, New York, 640 pp. (see pp. 363–96).

———. 1965 The chemical senses and changing viewpoints in sensory physiology, in *Viewpoints in Biology, IV*, J. D. Carthy and C. L. Duddington (eds.). Butterworths, London, 256 pp. (see pp. 83–124).

HODGSON, E. S., and BARTON-BROWNE, L. 1960 Electrophysiology of blowfly taste receptors. ANRE, **137**: 365. (Abstract.)

HODGSON, E. S., LETTVIN, J. Y., and ROEDER, K. D. 1955 Physiology of a primary chemoreceptor unit. SCIE, **122**: 417–18.

HODGSON, E. S., and ROEDER, K. D. 1956 Electrophysiological studies of arthropod chemoreception. I: General properties of the labellar chemoreceptors of diptera. JCCP, **48**: 51–75.

HOFFMANN, A. 1875 Ueber die Verbreitung der Geschmacksknospen beim Menschen. (The distribution of taste buds in man.) VAPA, **62**: 516–30.

HOFFMANN, C. 1961 Vergleichende Physiologie des Temperatursinnes und der chemischen Sinne. (Comparative physiology of the temperature and chemical senses.) FOZO, **13**: 190–256.

HOFMANN, F., and BUNZEL, R. 1897 Untersuchungen über den elektrischen Geschmack. (Studies on electrical taste.) PAGP, **66**: 215–32.

HOGBEN, L., and POLLACK, R. 1935 A contribution to the relation of the gene loci involved in the isoagglutinin reaction, taste blindness, Friedreich's ataxia, and major brachydactyly of man. JOGN, **31**: 353–61.

HOLBROOK, F. 1950 Taste sensitivity of grasshoppers to sugars. JCOQ, **4**: 81. (Abstract.)

HOLLEMAN, A. F. 1923 On some derivatives of saccharin. RTCP, **42**: 839–45.

HOLLIDAY, J. C. 1940 Total distribution of taste buds on the tongue of the pup. OJSC, **40**: 337–44.

HOLLINGSWORTH, D. R. 1963 Phenylthiourea taste testing in Hiroshima subjects with thyroid disease. JCEN, **23**: 961–63.

HOLLINGWORTH, H. L., and POFFENBERGER, A. T., JR. 1917 *The Sense of Taste.* Moffat, Yard, & Co., New York, 200 pp.

HOLWAY, A. H., and HURVICH, L. M. 1937 Differential gustatory sensitivity to salt. AJPC, **49**: 37–48.

———. 1938 On the psychophysics of taste. I: Pressure and area as variants. JEPS, **23**: 191–98.

HOLZLÖHNER. 1956 Geschmacksstörungen nach Operationen im Mund- und Rachenbereich. (Taste disturbances after operations in the mouth and throat area.) HNOK, **6**: 91–92. (Abstract.)

*HÖNIG. 1900 Zur Psychophysik des Geschmackssinns. (The psychophysics of the sense of taste.) PHST, **17**: 576.

HÖNIGSCHMIED, J. 1873 Beiträge zur mikroskopischen Anatomie über die Geschmacksorgane der Säugethiere. (Contribution to the microscopic anatomy of the sense of taste in mammals.) ZWZA, **23**: 414–34.

———. 1877 Kleine Beiträge zur Vertheilung der Geschmacksknospen bei den Säugethieren. (Small contribution on the distribution of taste buds in mammals.) ZWZA, **29**: 255–62.

———. 1888 Kleine Beiträge, betreffend die Anordnung der Geschmacksknospen bei den Säugethieren. (Small contribution, with respect to the arrangement of taste buds in mammals.) ZWZA, **47**: 190–200.

HOOPER, D. 1887 An examination of the leaves of gymnema sylvestre. NATU, **35**: 565–67.

HOOVER, E. F. 1956 Reliability of phenylthiocarbamide-sodium benzoate method of determining taste classifications. JAFC, **4**: 345–48.

HOPF, K., and EDZARD, D. 1910 Beobachtungen über die Verteilung der Zungenpapillen bei verschiedenen Menschenrassen. (Observation on the distribution of tongue papillae in different human races.) ZEMA, **12**: 548–58.

HOPKINS, A. E. 1932 Chemical stimulation by salts in the oyster, *Ostrea virginica*. JEZO, **61**: 13–28.

———. 1932 Sensory stimulation of the oyster, *Ostrea virginica* by chemicals. USFB, **47**: 247–261.

HOPKINS, C. Y. 1942 Taste differences in compounds having the NCS linkage. CNRB, **20**: 268–73.

HOPPE, J. B. 1710 De organo gustus. (Taste organs.) Inaugural Dissertation, C. Schrödter, Wittenberg, pp. 105–20.

HORN, W. VON. 1825 *Ueber den Geschmackssinn des Menschen, ein Beitrag zur Physiologie desselben.* (The sense of taste in man, a contribution to the physiology of the sense of taste.) K. Groos, Heidelberg, 104 pp.

HOROWITZ, H. 1953 Le role du goût et de l'odorat dans l'alimentation du nourrison. (The role of taste and olfaction in the nutrition of nurslings.) Unpublished M.D. Thesis, University of Geneva. J. Perroud, S. A. Bulle, 34 pp.

HOSHISHIMA, K., YOKOYAMA, S., and SETO, K. 1962 Taste sensitivity in various strains of mice. AJPH, **202:** 1200–4.

HOU-JENSEN, H. M. 1933 Die Papillae foliatae des Menschen. (The foliate papillae in man.) ZAEN, **102:** 348–88.

HOUSSAY, B. A. 1955 Chemical senses, smell and taste, in *Human Physiology.* 2nd ed. McGraw-Hill, New York, 1177 pp. (see pp. 919–30).

HOWELL, W. H. 1906 Sensations of taste and smell, in *A Text-book of Physiology for Medical Students and Physicians.* W. B. Saunders Co., Philadelphia, 905 pp. (see pp. 270–75).

———. 1922 Sensations of taste and smell, in *Textbook of Physiology.* 8th ed. W. B. Saunders Co., Philadelphia, 1053 pp. (see pp. 290–95).

HOWELL, W. H., and KASTLE, J. H. 1887 Note on the specific energy of the nerves of taste. JBLS, **4:** 13–17.

HOYER, H. 1859 Mikroskopische Untersuchungen über die Zunge des Frosches. (Microscopical studies on the tongue of the frog.) AAPA, pp. 481–514.

HOYME, L. E. 1955 Genetics, physiology and phenylthiocarbamide. JOHE, **46:** 167–75. (Abstract in AJPN, **12:** 289–90, 1954.)

HUARD, P., BOURLIÈRE, F., VY, T., and CAN, N. H. 1953 Sur la sensibilité gustative des Vietnamiens à la thiourée. (Taste sensitivity for thiourea in Vietnamese.) CORE, **237:** 1034–36.

HUBER, G. C., and EGGERTH, A. H. 1917 On the morphogenesis of the papilla foliata of the rabbit. ANRE, **13:** 341–57.

HUDSON, A. 1958 The effect of flight on the taste threshold and carbohydrate utilization of *Phormia regina* Meigen. JIPH, **1:** 293–304.

HUGHES, L. H. 1957 Saccharine reinforcement in a T maze. JCPP, **50:** 431–35.

HUMBOLDT, F. A. VON. 1797 *Versuche über die gereizten Muskel- und Nervenfasern nebst Vermutungen über den chemischen Prozess des Lebens in der Tier- und Pflanzenwelt, I.* (Studies on stimulated muscle and nerve fibers and speculation on the chemical process of life in the animal and plant kingdoms.) Decker & Co., Posen, 493 pp. (see pp. 224–26, 320–23, 445–46).

HUNT, E. L., CARROLL, H. W., and KIMELDORF, D. J. 1965 Humoral mediation of radiation-induced motivation in parabiont rats. SCIE, **150:** 1747–48.

HURD, C. D., and KHARASCH, N. 1946 The di- polar ion structures of the 2-thiazolylsulfamic acids. JACS, **68:** 653–58.

HURWITZ, H. M. B., WALKER, S. F., SALMON, E. A., and PACKHAM, D. 1965 The effects of two sucrose solutions on rate of response under a fixed ratio schedule. PYRC, **15:** 145–50.

HUTT, F. B. 1947 Odd familial P.T.C. reaction: an unusual sensitivity to phenylthiocarbamide. JOHE, **38:** 377–78.

IAKOVLEVA, I. I. 1957 K voprosu o vkusovoi chuvstvitel'nosti pri bolezni Men'era i kokhleo-vestibuliarnykh narusheniiakh pri sosudistykh zabolevaniiakh i travme cherepa. (Sense of taste in Ménière's disease and cochleovestibular disorders during vascular diseases and brain trauma.) VORL, **19:** 51–53. (English summary.)

ICHIOKA, M., and HARA, S. 1955 On the reaction time of the human gustatory sensation. BTMD, **2:** 159–165.

ICHIOKA, M., OHBA, A., and SHIMIZU, H. 1963 Versuche über den elektrischen Geschmack. (Experiments on electrical taste sensations.) ZEBL, **113:** 461–71. (English summary.)

IKEDA, K. 1912 On the taste of the salt of glutamic acid. ICAC (8th), **18:** 147.

IKEDA, S., FURUKAWA, H., and YAMAGUCHI, S. 1962 (An attempt to establish scales of taste measurement of delicious taste intensity by Thurstone-Mosteller's method.) STOC, **13:** 76–79. (In Japanese, English summary.)

IMBRIANO, A. E. 1963 La actividad sensorial. (Sensory activity.) SEME, **123:** 1249–63.

INANAGA, K., NAKAO, H., and FUCHIWAKI, H. 1953 Electrical excitation on the cerebral cortex by gustatory stimulation. Report I: Widespread evocation type of potentials of the cerebral cortex by gustatory stimulation. FPNJ, **7:** 1–16.

INZANI, G., and LUSSANA, F. 1862 Sui nervi del gusto. (On the taste nerve.) AUMM, **181:** 282–322.

IRIKI, T. 1960 Electron microscopic observation on the taste buds of the rabbit. AMUK, **2:** 78–94.

IRIUCHIJIMA, J., and ZOTTERMAN, Y. 1961 Conduction rates of afferent fibres to the anterior tongue of the dog. APSC, **51:** 283–89.

IRVIN, D. L., and GOETZL, F. R. 1952 Diurnal variations in acuity of sense of taste for sodium chloride. PSEB, **79:** 115–18.

ISHIKAWA, S. 1963 Responses of maxillary chemoreceptors in the larva of the silkworm, *Bombyx mori,* to stimulation by carbohydrates. JCCP, **61:** 99–107.

ISHIKO, N., and AMATSU, M. 1964 Effects of stretch of the tongue on taste responses in glossopharyngeal and chorda tympani nerves of cat. KUMJ, **17:** 5–17.

ISON, J. R. 1964 Acquisition and reversal of a

spatial response as a function of sucrose concentration. JEPS, **67**: 495–96.

IUR'FVA, G. I. 1958 O roli reaktivngkh grupp belkvoykh kampleksov v vozbuzhdenii vkusovogo retseptora. (Influence of reactive protein complexes on stimulation of the taste receptors.) BIOF, **2**: 665–69.

———. 1960 The role of the reactive groups of protein in taste reception. FZLZ, **46**: 1250–55.

———. 1961 New data on the role of sulfhydryl protein groups on the gustatory sensitivity. BIOP, **6**: 29–32.

JACKSON, H. 1874 Remarks on loss of smell and loss of taste. LANC, **2**: 622.

*JACOBOWITSCH. 1872 Zur Geschmacksempfindung. (On taste perception.) MEVI.

JACOBS, B. B. 1962 Propylthiouracil taste inheritance in mice. JOHE, **53**: 183–86.

*JACOBS, H. L. 1955 The motivation of sugar preferences in the albino rat. Unpublished Ph.D. thesis, Cornell University, 176 pp.

———. 1958 Studies on sugar preference. I: The preference for glucose solutions and its modification by injections of insulin. JCPP, **51**: 304–10.

———. 1962 Some physical, metabolic, and sensory components in the appetite for glucose. AJPH, **203**: 1043–54.

———. 1964 Observations on the ontogeny of saccharine preference in the neonate rat. PSIC, **1**: 105–6.

———. 1964 The interaction of hunger and thirst: Experimental separation of osmotic and oral-gastric factors in the regulation of caloric intake, in *Thirst*, A. J. Wayner (ed.). Macmillan, New York, 570 pp. (see pp. 117–37).

JACOBS, H. L., and SHARMA, K. N. 1964 Energy balance and palatability: The effect of food deprivation on the intake of positively and negatively flavored solutions. PYSO, **7**: 166. (Abstract.)

———. 1964 The modulating influence of flavor on food preferences in hypothalamic obese rats. FEPR, **23**: 448. (Abstract.)

JACOBS, M. B. 1951 Structure of artificial sweeteners. APEO, **57**: 49, 51.

———. 1951 Sweetness and molecular structure. APEO, **57**: 129–30, 137.

———. 1955 The sweetening power of stevioside. APEO, **66**: 44, 46.

JACQUES, P. 1893 Terminaisons nerveuses dans l'organe de la gustation (Neural terminations of the taste organs), in *Bibliographie Antomique*, I. Berger-Levrault et Cie, Paris, 203 pp. (see pp. 200–2).

JAEGER, G. 1876 Ueber die Bedeutung des Geschmacks- und Geruchsstoffes. (The significance of taste and odor substances.) ZWZA, **27**: 319–31.

JAFFE, N. B. 1955 Dyspepsia caused by artificial dentures. MVMJ, **77**: 160, 178.

JAHN, T. L., and WULFF, V. J. 1950 Chemoreception, in *Comparative Animal Physiology*, C. L. Prosser (ed.). W. B. Saunders Co., Philadelphia, 888 pp. (see pp. 447–70).

JALESKI, T. C. 1926 Some studies on taste and chemical constitution. JAPM, **15**: 461–63.

JAMPEL, R. S., and TITONE, C. 1962 Congenital paradoxical gustatory-lacrimal reflex and lateral rectus paralysis: Case report. AROP, **67**: 123–26.

JANOWITZ, H. D., and GROSSMAN, M. I. 1949 Gusto-olfactory thresholds in relation to appetite and hunger sensation. JAPY, **2**: 217–22.

JAUME Y MÁTAS, P 1890 Nervosismo crónico con perversión del gusto. (Chronic nervousness with perversion of taste.) RBCM, **6**: 449–54.

JENKINS, G. N. 1960 The intimate nature of taste, in *The Physiology of the Mouth*. 2nd ed. Blackwell, Oxford, 355 pp. (see pp. 323–24).

JENSEN, K. 1932 Differential reactions to taste and temperature stimuli in newborn infants. GPMO, **12**: 361–479.

JODL, F. 1896 Geschmack und Geruch (Taste and smell), in *Lehrbuch der Psychologie*. J. G. Cotta, Stuttgart, 767 pp. (see pp. 270–81).

———. 1903 Geschmack und Geruch (Taste and smell), in *Lehrbuch der Psychologie*. J. G. Cotta, Stuttgart, 435 pp. (see pp. 316–29).

JOHNSTON, J. B. 1906 Special visceral or gustatory system, in *The Nervous System of Vertebrates*. P. Blakiston's Son & Co., Philadelphia, 370 pp (see pp. 164–74).

———. 1909 The limit between ectoderm and entoderm in the mouth and the origin of the taste buds. ANRE, **3**: 261–62.

JOHNSTON, J. W., JR. 1955 Concepts of contact chemoreception in mammals and man. VJSC, **6**: 27–32.

———. 1955 Physiological aspects of testing contact chemoreception. VJSC, **6**: 14–15.

JONAS, A. D. 1964 Olfactory-gustatory mentation: A link between thinking mechanisms and infantile feeding. ARGP, **10**: 36–42.

JONES, F. N. 1956 A forced-choice method of limits. AJPC, **69**: 672–73.

JONES, F. N., and MARCUS, M. J. 1961 The subject effect in judgments of subjective magnitude. JEPS, **61**: 40–44.

JONES, L. E. 1941 Taste and smell. CHIN, **60**: 248–50.

JONES, L. E. 1941 Taste and smell. FLAV, **4**: 18–20.

JONES, M. H., and JONES, F. N. 1952 Critical frequency of taste. APEO, **59**: 379.

———. 1952 The critical frequency of taste. SCIE, **115**: 355–56.

JONES, P. E., and THOMASON, F. G. 1951 Sweetness, in *Competitive Relationships between Sugar and Corn Sweeteners*. XAAI, **48**: 245 pp. (see pp. 48–50, 53).

JONG, W. W. W. DE. 1964 Smaakproeven met

phenylthiocarbamide (PTC) bij nederlandse schoolkinderen. Het verband met endemische krop. (Taste tests with phenylthiocarbamide in Dutch school children. Relation to endemic goiter.) GBKL, **50**: 349–84.

JØRGENSEN, M. B., and BUCH, N. J. 1961 Sense of smell and taste in pregnant diabetics. PORL, **23**: 390–96.

———. 1961 Studies on the sense of smell and taste in diabetics. AOLA, **53**: 539–45.

JORDAN, S. 1940 How one sugar compares with another. FOIN, **12**: 45–47.

JOSEPH, G. 1877 Zur Morphologie des Geschmacksorgans bei den Insecten. (Morphologie of taste organs in insects.) ABNA, **50**: 227–28.

JOSLYN, M. A., and GOLDSTEIN, J. L. 1964 Astringency of fruits and fruit products in relation to phenolic content. AFRE, **13**: 179–217.

JOURDAN, E. 1881 Sur les organes du goût des poissons osseux. (On taste organs of bony fish.) CORE, **92**: 743–45.

JULIEN, P. F. J. A. 1938 De verdeeling van den Phenylthio-ureum-smaakdrempel in Nederland en West Equatoriaal Afrika. (Distribution of the taste threshold for phenylthiourea in the Netherlands and in western equatorial Africa.) MENM, **14**: 364–65.

JULLIAN, H. 1900 Troubles du goût et de l'odorat dans le tabes. (Disorders of taste and smell in tabes.) Unpublished M.D. thesis, A. Maloine, Paris, 60 pp.

JUNQUEIRA, P. C., KALMUS, H., and WISHART, P. 1957 P.T.C. thresholds, colour vision and blood factors of Brazilian Indians. II: Carajas. ANHG, **22**: 22–25.

JURISCH, A. 1922 Studien über die Papillae valvatae beim Menschen. (Studies on the vallate papillae in man.) ZAEN, **66**: 1–149.

KADANOV, D. 1954 Prinos kŭm izuchavane morfologiĭata na atipchnite na vkusovite retseptory na grŭkliana. (Contribution to the morphological study of the atypical forms of taste receptors in the larynx.) NTMA, **1**: 29–42.

KAHLENBERG, L. 1898–1901 The action of solutions on the sense of taste. UWIB, **2**: 1–31.

———. 1900 The relation of the taste of acid salts to their degree of dissociation. I, II. JPCH, **4**: 33–37, 533–37.

KAHN, S. G. 1951 Taste perception—individual reactions to different substances. TISA, **44**: 263–69.

KALJEVITCH, T. 1921 Ueber die Geschmacksknospen in den umwallten Zungenpapillen des Pferdes und des Rindes. (On taste buds on the circumvallate papillae of the horse and cattle.) Inaugural Dissertation, P. Haupt, Bern, 24 pp.

KALLIUS, E. 1901 Beiträge zur Entwickelung der Zunge. I: Amphibien und Reptilien. (Contribution to the development of the tongue.

I: Amphibian and reptiles.) ANHE, **16**: 531–760.

———. 1905 Beiträge zur Entwickelung der Zunge. II: Vögel (*Anas Bochas* L. *passer Domesticus* L.). (Contribution to the development of the tongue. II: Birds.) ANHE, **28**: 307–580.

———. 1905 Geschmacksorgan (Taste organ), in *Handbuch der Anatomie des Menschen*, K. von Bardeleben (ed.), V, 243–70.

———. 1910 Beiträge zur Entwickelung der Zunge. III: Säugetiere, *Sus scrofa dom.* (Contribution to the development of the tongue. III: Mammals, *Sus scropha dom.*) ANHE, **41**: 177–337.

KALMUS, H. 1957 Defective colour vision, P.T.C. tasting and drepanocytosis in samples from fifteen Brazilian populations. ANHG, **21**: 313–17.

———. 1957 Physiology and genetics of organoleptic perception, in *Molecular Structure and Organoleptic Quality*, S.C.I. Monograph No. 1, 124 pp. (see pp. 13–28).

———. 1957–58 Improvements in the classification of the taster genotypes. ANHG, **22**: 222–30.

———. 1958 The chemical senses. SCAM, **198**: 97–102, 104, 106.

———. 1962 Taste thresholds in mothers of children with Down's syndrome. LANC, **2**: 1120.

KALMUS, H., DE GARAY, A. L., RODARTE, U., and COBO, L. 1964 The frequency of PTC tasting, hard ear wax, colour blindness and other genetical characters in urban and rural Mexican populations. HUBI, **36**: 134–45.

KALMUS, H., and FARNSWORTH, D. 1959 Impairment and recovery of taste following irradiation of the oropharynx. JLOT, **73**: 180–82.

KALMUS, H., and HUBBARD, S. J. 1960 *The Chemical Senses in Health and Disease.* Charles C Thomas, Springfield, Ill., 95 pp.

KALMUS, H., and TROTTER, W. R. 1962 Direct assessment of the effect of age on P.T.C. sensitivity. ANHG, **26**: 145–49.

KAMEI, T. 1936 (Experimental studies on taste. I: The course of the peripheral sensory surface of the taste organ. II: Studies on the electrical taste.) OIZA, **48**: 124–31, 339–45. (In Japanese; German summary.)

KAMEN, J. 1959 Interaction of sucrose and calcium cyclamate on perceived intensity of sweetness. FORE, **24**: 279–82.

KAMEN, J. M., PILGRIM, F. J., GUTMAN, N. J., and KROLL, B. J. 1961 Interactions of suprathreshold taste stimuli. JEPS, **62**: 348–56.

KAMENETZKY, J., and PILGRIM, F. J. 1958 The effect of sucrose upon the perceived intensity of salt and bitter. AMPS, **13**: 420. (Abstract.)

KAMRIN, R. P., and SINGER, M. 1953 Influence of sensory neurons isolated from central nervous system on maintenance of taste buds and regeneration of barbels in the catfish, *Ameiurus nebulosus.* AJPH, **174**: 146–48.

KANDER, L. 1906 Die Störungen der Geschmacksempfindung bei chronischen Mittelohreiterungen insbesondere nach operativen Eingriffen. (Disturbances of taste sensations in chronic middle ear infections especially after an operative intervention.) AONK, **68**: 69–100.

KANE, F., and LAW, M. E. 1950 Nerve connexions of taste-buds. NATU, **165**: 978.

KANEKO, T. 1938 (Taste and constitution of α-amino acids.) JCSJ, **59**: 433–39. (In Japanese.)

———. 1939 (Taste and constitution of α-amino acids. II: Stereochemistry of α-amino acids.) JCSJ, **60**: 531–38. (In Japanese.)

KANZ, E. 1951 Wetterwirkungen auf die menschliche Physis und Psyche als Ergebnis experimenteller Untersuchungen. I. Teil. (Experimental studies of the physical and mental effects of weather on man.) AHBA, **135**: 83–149. (French and English summaries.)

KAPLAN, A. R., and FISCHER, R. 1965 Taste sensitivity for bitterness: Some biological and clinical implications, in *Recent Advances in Biological Psychiatry, VII*, J. Wortis (ed.). Plenum Press, New York (see pp. 183–96).

KAPLAN, A. R., FISCHER, R., GLANVILLE, E., POWELL, W., KAMIONKOWSKI, M., and FLESHLER, B. 1964 Differential taste sensitivities in duodenal and gastric ulcer patients. GAST, **47**: 604–9.

KAPLAN, A. R., FISCHER, R., ZSAKO, S., GRIFFIN, F., and GLANVILLE, E. V. 1965 Research in the etiology of Down's syndrome, intricacies and pitfalls. AGMG, **14**: 93–96.

KAPLAN, A. R., GLANVILLE, E. V., and FISCHER, R. 1964 Taste thresholds for bitterness and cigarette smoking. NATU, **202**: 1366.

———. 1965 Cumulative effect of age and smoking on taste sensitivity in males and females. JOGE, **20**: 334–37.

KAPLAN, A. R., POWELL, W., FISCHER, R., and MARSTERS, R. 1963 Re-examination of genetic aspects of taste thresholds for thiourea-type compounds, in *Genetics Today, I*, S. J. Geerts (ed.). Pergamon Press, London, 332 pp. (see pp. 292–93). (Abstract.)

KAPLAN, H., and SPRING, P. N. 1960 Gustatory hyperhidrosis associated with subcondylar osteotomy. JAHD, **18**: 50–53.

KAPLAN, M. F., and SINGER, E. 1963 Dogmatism and sensory alienation: An empirical investigation. JCPH, **27**: 486–91.

KAPLICK, M. 1953 Über Vorkommen, Verteilung und histologische Beziehungen der Geschmacksknospen am Munddach einiger Säuger, besonders der Nagetiere. (The occurrence, distribution and histological relations of taste buds in the roof of the mouth of several mammals, especially rodents.) ZZAC, **38**: 571–90.

KAPPAUF, W. E., BURRIGHT, R. G., and DEMARCO, W. 1963 Sucrose-quinine mixtures which are isohedonic for the rat. JCPP, **56**: 138–43.

KARASHIMA, N. 1934 Ueber die Wärmebildung der Submaxillardrüse durch verschiedene Geschmacksreize. (Increase in temperature of submaxillary glands in response to various gustatory stimuli.) NAGZ, **12**: 650–51.

KARASHIMA, N., and KUMAMI, S. 1934 Über die Temperatursteigerung und die Speichelsekretion der Sumaxillardrüse unter dem Einfluss verschiedener Geschmacksreize. (Increase in temperature and salivary secretion of submaxillary glands due to various gustatory stimuli.) NAGZ, **12**: 793–94.

KARE, M. R. 1960 Senses of animals differ from man's. FARR, **26**: 8–9.

———. 1965 Special senses, in *Avian Physiology*, P. D. Sturkie (ed.). 2nd ed. Comstock Publishing Associates, Ithaca, N. Y., 766 pp. (see pp. 433–46).

———. 1966 Taste perception in animals. AGSW, **4**(1): 10–15.

KARE, M. R., BLACK, R., and ALLISON, E. G. 1957 The sense of taste in the fowl. POSC, **36**: 129–38.

KARE, M. R., and FICKEN, M. S. 1963 Comparative studies on the sense of taste, in *Olfaction and Taste*, Y. Zotterman (ed.). Macmillan, New York, 396 pp. (see pp. 285–97).

KARE, M. R., and HALPERN, B. P. 1961 *The Physiological and Behavioral Aspects of Taste*. The University Press, Chicago, 149 pp.

KARE, M. R., HALPERN, B. P., and JONES, C. C. 1961 The influence of caloric deficiency on taste preference. POSC, **40**: 1419. (Abstract.)

KARE, M. R., and MALLER, O. 1964 Taste and caloric regulation in the bird. FEPR, **23**: 449. (Abstract.)

KARE, M. R., and MEDWAY, W. 1959 Discrimination between carbohydrates by the fowl. POSC, **38**: 1119–26.

KARE, M. R., and PICK, H. L., JR. 1960 The influence of the sense of taste on feed and fluid consumption. POSC, **39**: 697–706.

KARE, M. R., POND, W. C., and CAMPBELL, J. 1965 Observations on the taste reactions in pigs. ANBE, **13**: 265–69.

KASTLE, J. H. 1898 On the taste and affinity of acids. ACJO, **20**: 466–71.

KATO, M., and TAZIMA, O. 1956 (The threshold test. Part 3: For ethyl alcohol.) JSBJ, **51**: 64–65. (In Japanese; English summary.)

KATO, S. 1960 Studies on the sense of taste. I: The sense of taste in normal individuals and in patients. The relationship between taste and coated tongue, favourite taste and appetite. II: Changes in the threshold for taste in various diseases and in various conditions. JPGA, **57**: 729–36, 737–46.

KATSUMI, K., and BEIDLER, L. M. 1961 Microelectrode study of taste receptors of rat and hamster. JCCP, **58**: 131–39.

KATZ, D. 1934 The tongue as a primitive sense organ. MLPS, **78**: 56–72.

————. 1935 Psychophysiologische Untersuchungen an der Zunge. (Psychophysical studies of the tongue.) KWPS, 6: 237–59.

————. 1938 Un appareil sensoriel primitif: La langue recherches psychophysiologiques. (A primary sensory apparatus: Psychophysiological studies of the tongue.) JPNP, 35: 457–71.

————. 1953 Psychologische Untersuchungen an der Zunge. Ein Beitrag zur Entwicklungspsychologie (Psychological investigation of the tongue. A contribution to developmental psychology), in *Studien zur Experimentellen Psychologie*. B. Schwabe & Co., Basel, 130 pp. (see pp. 39–74).

KAWAMURA, Y., and ADACHI, A. 1965 (Single taste nerve responses to the chemical taste enhancers.) JPSJ, 27: 279–84. (In Japanese; English summary.)

KAWAMURA, Y., ADACHI, A., OHARA, M., and IKEDA, S. 1964 Neurophysiological studies on taste effectiveness of flavor enhancing substances. AACD, 10: 168–78.

KAWAMURA, Y., FUNAKOSHI, M., ADACHI, A., and OKAMOTO, J. 1964 (Electrophysiological analysis of taste of beer.) JPSJ, 26: 286–91. (In Japanese; English summary.)

KAWAMURA, Y., FUNAKOSHI, M., NISHIYAMA, T., MAJIMA, T., and KAMADA, A. 1964 (Relations between taste qualities and parotid gland secretion rate.) JPSJ, 26: 495–502. (In Japanese; English summary.)

KAWASHIMA, K., NAKAMURA, K., and INOUE, H. 1956 (The threshold test. Part 4: For sour taste.) JSBJ, 51: 68–73. (In Japanese; English summary.)

KEASTER, J. 1940 Studies on the anatomy and physiology of the tongue. LARY, 50: 222–58.

KEKCHEEV, K. 1942 Mechanism of sensitivity changes of sense organs. NATU, 150: 491–92.

KEKCHEEV, K. K., and ORLUIK, A. G. 1936 Vliîanie sensornikh razdrazhenii na chuvstvitel' nost'perifericheskogo zreniia. (The influence of gustatory stimulation on sensitivity of peripheral vision.) BEBM, 2: 361–62.

*KELLOGG, W. N., and KELLOGG, L. A. 1945 Facial expressions of a human and a chimpanzee infant following taste stimuli (film), State College, Pennsylvania, Psychological Film Register, 192 feet, 16 mm. silent, $12.00.

KENRICK, F. B. 1931 The sour taste of acids. TRCM, 25: 227–228.

KEPPLER, F. 1869 Das Unterscheidungsvermögen des Geschmacksinnes für Concentrations-differenzen der schmeckbaren Körper. (The ability of the sense of taste to differentiate taste substances of different concentrations.) Inaugural Dissertation, C. Georgi, Bonn, 12 pp.

————. 1869 Das Unterscheidungsvermögen des Geschmacksinnes für Concentrations-differenzen der schmeckbaren Körper. (The ability of the sense of taste to differentiate between concentrations of taste substances.) PAGP, 2: 449–58.

KERR, F. W. L. 1962 Facial, vagal and glossopharyngeal nerves in the cat. ARNE, 6: 264–81.

KEY, E. A. 1861 Om smaknervernas ändningssatt i grodtungan jemte anmärkningar öfver nervernas likartade ändningssätt i de öfriga högre sinnesorganerna. (On the terminal arrangement of gustatory nerves in the tongue of the frog, with remarks on homogenous terminal disposition in other higher organs.) B. Boktryckeriet, Lund, 31 pp.

————. 1861 Ueber die Endigungsweise der Geschmacksnerven in der Zunge des Frosches. (On the taste nerve endings on the tongue of frogs.) AAPA, pp. 329–49.

KHAIRUSHEV, E. A. 1961 Osobennosti funktsional'nogo sostoianiia oboniatel' nogo vkusovogo i kozhonogo analizatorov v razlichnyk vozrastnykh gruppakh. (Characteristics of the functional status of the olfactory, gustatory and cutaneous analyzer in various age groups.) IKAD, 2: 15–17.

KHARITONOV, S. A. 1940 K fiziologicheskoǐ kharakteristike vkusovogo analizatora. (On the physiological characteristics of the gustatory analyzer.) FZLZ, 29: 472. (Abstract.)

————. 1940 K metodike khronaksimetrii vkusovogo apparata. (On the methods of the chronaximetry of the taste apparatus.) NEPS, 19: 89–90.

*————. 1941 (Interaction of the afferent systems of the gustatory apparatus.) TSPP, pp. 271–73.

KIESOW, F. 1894 Beiträge zur physiologischen Psychologie des Geschmackssinnes. (Contribution to the physiological psychology of the sense of taste.) PHST, 10: 329–68, 523–61.

————. 1894 Über die Wirkung des Cocain und der Gymnemasäure auf die Schleimhaut der Zunge und des Mundraums. (On the effect of cocain and gymnemic acid on the mucous membrane of the tongue and the oral cavity.) PHST, 9: 510–27.

————. 1896 Beiträge zur physiologischen Psychologie des Geschmackssinnes. (Contribution to the physiological psychology of the sense of taste.) PHST, 12: 255–78, 464–73.

————. 1898 Expériences gustatives sur diverses papilles isolément excitées. (Taste experiments on different isolated papillae.) AIBL, 30: 399–425.

————. 1898 Schmeckversuche an einzelnen Papillen. (Taste tests on individual papillae.) PHST, 14: 591–615.

————. 1898 Zur Psychophysiologie der Mundhöhle. (Psychophysiology of the oral cavity.) PHST, 14: 567–88.

————. 1902 Sur la présence de boutons gustatifs à la surface linguale de l'epiglotte humaine, avec quelques réflexions sur les mêmes organs qui se trouvent dans la muqueuse de larynx. (On the presence of taste buds on the surface of the human tongue and epiglottis, with some reflections on these same organs present in the mucosa of the larynx.) AIBL, 38: 334–36.

———. 1903 Ein Beitrag zur Frage nach den Reacktionszeiten der Geschmacksempfindungen. (A contribution to the question of reaction times in taste perception.) ZPSI, 33: 453–61.

———. 1903 Zur Psychophysiologie der Mundhöhle nebst Beobachtungen über Funktionen des Tast- und Schmerzapparates und einigen Bemerkungen über die wahrscheinlichen Tastorgane der Zungenspitze und des Lippenrots. (The psychophysiology of the oral cavity and observations on function of touch and pain apparatus and some comments on probability of touch organs on the tip of the tongue and lips.) ZPSI, 33: 424–443.

———. 1904 Zur Frage nach den Schmeckflächen des hinteren kindlichen Mundraumes. I: Die Uvula. (The question of the taste area in the back part of the oral cavity in a child. I: The uvula.) ZPSI, 36: 90–92.

———. 1904 Zur Kenntniss der Nervenendigungen in den papillen der Zungenspitze. (Knowledge of nerve endings in the papillae on the tip of the tongue.) ZPSI, 35: 252–59.

———. 1905 Ueber Geschmacks- und Geruchsträume. (Taste and odor dreams.) ICPY, 5: 282–86.

———. 1929 Sulla frequenza dei sogni gustativi ed olfattivi. (On the frequency of gustatory and olfactory dreams.) AOIP, 7: 226–31.

KIESOW, F., and HAHN, R. 1901 Beobachtungen über die Empfindlichkeit der hinteren Theile des Mundraumes für Tast-, Schmerz-, Temperatur- und Geschmacksreize. (Studies on the sensitivity of the posterior part of the oral cavity for touch, pain, temperature and taste stimuli.) ZPSI, 26: 383–417.

———. 1901 Sulla sensibilità gustativa di alcune parti della retrobocca, e dell'epiglottide. (Taste sensitivity in the back part of the mouth and of the epiglottis.) AAMT, 7: 497–502.

———. 1902 Ueber Geschmacksempfindungen im Kehlkopf. (Taste perception in the larynx.) ZPSI, 27: 80–94.

KIESOW, F., and NADOLECZNY, M. 1900 Sulla fisiologia della corda del timpano. (On the physiology of the chorda tympani.) AIOR, 10: 297–304.

———. 1900 Sur la physiologie de la corde du tympan. (Physiology of the chorda tympani.) AIBL, 34: 277–84.

———. 1900 Zur Psycho-physiologie der Chorda tympani. (The psycho-physiology of the chorda tympani.) ZPSI, 23: 33–59.

KILBURN, R. W. 1958 The taste of citrus juice. I: Relationship between Brix, acid and pH. PFSH, 71: 251–54.

KILBURN, R. W., and DAVIS, T. T. 1959 The taste of citrus juice. II: Citrate salts and pH. PFSH, 72: 271–76.

KIMELDORF, D. J., GARCIA, J., and RUBADEAU, D. O. 1960 Radiation-induced conditioned avoidance behavior in rats, mice, and cats. RARE, 12: 710–18.

KIMMEL, D. L. 1941 Development of the afferent components of the facial, glossopharyngeal and vagus nerves in the rabbit embryo. JCNE, 74: 447–72.

KIMURA, K. 1961 Adaptation of chemoreceptors of frog, as analyzed by activity in single gustatory fibers. KUMJ, 14: 149–56.

———. 1961 Factors affecting the response of taste receptors of rat. KUMJ, 14: 95–99.

———. 1962 Effects of temperature on the response of chemoreceptors in frog tongue. KUMJ, 15: 73–82.

KIMURA, K., and BEIDLER, L. M. 1956 Microelectrode study of taste bud of the rat. AJPH, 187: 610–11. (Abstract.)

———. 1961 Microelectrode study of taste receptors of rat and hamster. JCCP, 58: 131–39.

KIONKA, H., and STRÄTZ, F. 1922 Setzt der Geschmack eines Salzes sich susammen aus dem Geschmack der einzelnen Ionen oder schmeckt man jedes Salz als Gesamtmolekul? (Does the taste of a salt depend upon the tastes of the individual ions or upon the entire molecule?) AEPP, 95: 241–57.

KISELEV, K. V. 1936 K issledovaniiu vkusa i normalnykh liudeĭ. (Study of sense of taste in normal persons.) SOPE, 10: 44–48.

KISSILEFF, H. R., and EPSTEIN, A. N. 1962 Loss of salt preference in rats with lateral hypothalamic damage. AMZO, 2: 116.

*KITAMURA, K. 1936 Histo-embryological study on the lingual papilla and the innervation of taste bud in mice. JJSS, 10: 12–13.

———. 1939 Die elektroencephalographische Untersuchung der Geschmacksempfindlichkeit. (The electroencephalographic study of taste sensitivity.) TPSF, 7: 13–32.

KITCHELL, R. L. 1963 Comparative anatomical and physiological studies of gustatory mechanisms, in Olfaction and Taste, Y. Zotterman (ed.). Macmillan, New York, 396 pp. (see pp. 235–55).

———. 1965 Taste perception. FRPD, 1: 4–5.

KITCHELL, R. L., STRÖM, L., and ZOTTERMAN, Y. 1959 Electrophysiological studies of thermal and taste reception in chickens and pigeons. APSC, 46: 133–51.

KITCHIN, F. D., and HOWEL-EVANS, W. 1959 The PTC taste response in thyroid disease. JOEN, 18: 22–23. (Abstract.)

KITCHIN, F. D., HOWEL-EVANS, W., CLARKE, C. A., McCONNELL, R. B., and SHEPPARD, P. M. 1959 P.T.C. taste response and thyroid disease. BMJO, 1: 1069–74.

KLAATSCH, and STICH, A. 1858 Ueber den Ort

der Geschmacksvermittlung. (The region of taste transmission.) VAPA, 14: 225–43.

KLEIN, H. 1952 Die gerichtsmedizinische Bedeutung der Geschmacksdifferenz für Phenylthiocarbamid. Grundlagen, Probleme, Erfahrungen. (Medicolegal significance of differences in taste of phenyl thiocarbamide. Bases, problems, experiences.) DZGG, 41: 83–95.

KLEINER, M. 1894 Paraguesia with report of a case. GMCB, 2: 149–50.

KLEIST, K. 1934 Geschmacksstörungen. (Taste disturbances) and Gehirn Pathologie, vornehmlich auf Grund der Kriegserfahrungen (Brain pathology, especially based on war experiences), in Handbuch ärztlichen Erfahrungen im Weltkriege. J. A. Barth, Leipzig, 1408 pp. (see pp. 1278–95).

*KLEMM, B. 1924 Die chemischen Grundlagen des Süssens von Lebensmitteln mit Saccharin und Dulcin. (The chemical composition of foods sweetened with saccharin and dulcin.) Inaugural Dissertation, München, 81 pp.

KLENK, F. 1930 Untersuchungen über die Geschmackswirkung von Säuren bei Fischen mit einem Vergleich am Menschen. (Studies on the gustatory action of acid in fish as compared with man.) ZVPH, 13: 359–96.

KLIPPEL, M. 1897 Des troubles du goût et de l'odorat dans le tabes. (Disorders of taste and smell in tabes.) ANEF, 3: 257–81.

KLOEHN, N. W., and BROGDEN, W. J. 1948 The alkaline taste: a comparison of absolute thresholds for sodium hydroxide on the tip and mid-dorsal surfaces of the tongue. AJPC, 61: 90–93.

KNAPP, H. 1884 Hydrochlorate of cocaine—experiments and application. MERC, 26: 461–63.

KNARR, F. A., and COLLIER, G. 1962 Taste and consummatory activity in amount and gradient of reinforcement functions. JEPS, 63: 579–88.

KNEELAND, S. 1853 Case of an affection of the olfactory nerve, with total loss of smell and taste; with remarks on the probable identity of the two senses. TBMI, 1: 102–6.

KNOWLES, D., and JOHNSON, P. E. 1941 A study of the sensitiveness of prospective food judges to the primary tastes. FORE, 6: 207–16.

KNÜCHEL, W. 1950 Beziehungen zwischen Geschmack und Verträglichkeit von Conteben (p-acetamino-benzaldhyd-thiosemicarbazon). (Relation between taste and tolerance for conteben.) NEUM, 1: 1487.

KODAMA, S. 1919 Leucic acid and Walden's transformatiōn of leucic acid. JTKC, 40: 825–62.

———. 1920 Taste. JTKC, 41: 495–534.

KOEHLER, O. 1932 Beiträge zur Sinnesphysiologie der Süsswasserplanarien. (Contribution on the sensory physiology of fresh water planaria.) ZVPH, 16: 606–756.

KOEPPE, H. 1939 Der Geschmack von Erwach-

senen und von Kindern. (Taste in adults and in children.) ARKI, 116: 68–71.

KOH, S. D. 1958 Absolute taste thresholds of rats obtained by a psychophysical method. Unpublished Ph.D. thesis, Harvard University, 49 pp.

KOH, S. D., and TEITELBAUM, P. 1961 Absolute behavioral taste thresholds in the rat. JCPP, 54: 223–29.

KOIZUMI, H. 1953 On innervation of taste-buds in larynx in dog. TJEM, 58: 211–15.

KOKETSU, K. 1951 Impulses from receptors in the tongue of a frog. KMMS, 2: 53–61.

KOKETSU, K., and KIMURA, K. 1953 Effect of some salt-ions upon chemoreceptors in the mucous membrane of a frog's palate. KMMS, 3: 233–41.

KOLMER, W. 1910 Ueber Strukturen im Epithel des Sinnesorgane. (On the epithelial structures of the sense organs.) ANAN, 36: 281–99.

———. 1927 Geschmacksorgan. (Taste organ.) HMAM, 3: 154–96.

———. 1927 Ueber das Vorkommen von Geschmacksknospen im Ductus naso-palatinus der Ratte. (Occurrence of taste buds in the ductus naso-palatinus of the rat.) ANAN, 63: 248–51.

KOMM, E., and LÄMMER, H. 1940 Über die Stärke des sauren Geschmacks von in der Süsswarenindustrie gebräuchlichen organischen Säuren. I, II. (The strength of the sour taste of organic acids for use by the candy industry.) ZULE, 79: 433–53; 541–61.

KOMURO, K. 1921 Le sens du goût a-t-il un coefficient de température? (Has the sense of a taste a temperature coefficient?) ANPA, 5: 572–79.

KONIKOV, A. L. 1941 Vliyanie razdrazheniya vkusovogo retseptora na uroven' motornoĭ khronaksii u cheloveka. (Effect of stimulation of the gustatory receptor on the level of motor chronaxy in man.) BEBM, 11: 364–67.

KONISHI, J. 1958 On the sweet taste sensation. RFFM, 3: 101–3.

KONISHI, J., and NIWA, H. 1964 Some properties of taste receptors in freshwater fish: Responses to weak solutions. JJPH, 14: 328–43.

KONISHI, J., and ZOTTERMAN, Y. 1961 Function of taste fibres in the carp. NATU, 191: 286–87.

———. 1961 Taste functions in the carp: An electrophysiological study on gustatory fibres. APSC, 52: 150–61.

———. 1963 Taste functions in fish, in Olfaction and Taste. Y. Zotterman (ed.). Macmillan, New York, 396 pp. (see pp. 215–33).

KOPERA, A. 1931 Untersuchungen über die Unterschiedsempfindlichkeit im Bereiche des Geschmacksinns. (Studies on sensory discrimination in the gustatory field.) PAGP, 82: 273–307.

KÖRNER, O. 1899 Die Neurosen den Schlundes. (Neurosis of the throat.) HHLR, 2: 321–40.

KORNFELD, J. 1836 De functionibus nervorum linguae experimenta. (Experiments on function of lingual nerves.) Inaugural Dissertation, Nietackianis, Berlin, 37 pp.

KORNFELD, S., and BIKELES, G. 1892 Untersuchungen über das Verhalten der Hautsensibilität sowie des Geruchs- und Geschmackssinnes bei Paralytikern. (Studies on the behavior of the skin sensibility, also of odor and taste sense of paralytics.) JPNE, 11: 195–235.

KOSHTOIANTS, K. S., and KATALIN, R. 1958 The enzymatic basis of tasting. BIOP, 3: 652–54.

KÖSTER, G. 1900 Klinischer und experimenteller Beitrag zur Lehre von der Lähmung des Nervus facialis, zugleich ein Beitrag zur Physiologie des Geschmackes, der Schweiss-, Speichel- und Tränenabsonderung. (Clinical and experimental contribution to the theory of the paralysis of the facial nerve, and a contribution to the physiology of taste, sweat-, saliva-, and tear secretion.) DAKM, 68: 343–82.

———. 1902 Ein zweiter Beitrag zur Lehre von der Facialislähmung, zugleich ein Beitrag zur Physiologie des Geschmacks, der Schweiss-, Speichel- und Tränenabsonderung. (A second contribution to the theory of facial paralysis, a further contribution to the physiology of taste, sweat-, and tear secretion.) DAKM, 72: 327–65, 518–52.

———. 1904 Eine merkwürdige zentrale Störung der Geschmacksempfindung. (An odd central disturbance of taste sensations.) MMWO, 51: 333–35, 392–97.

KOSTSOVA, A. G. 1941 Issledovanie v oblasti khimii zhirnykh sul'fokislot. I: Sintez i svoistva atsilamidov zhirnykh sul'fokislot. (Aliphatic sulfonic acids. I: Synthesis and properties of acylamides of sulfonic acids.) ZOKH, 11: 63–66.

———. 1948 Issledovanie v oblasti zhirnykh sul'fokislot. II: Sintez i svoistva atsilamidov sul'fokislot. (Aliphatic sulfonic acids. II: Synthesis and properties of acylamides of sulfonic acids.) ZOKH, 18: 729–32.

KOTTMEYER, G. 1961 Plethysmographische Untersuchungen nach schwellennahen sensorischen und sensiblen Reizen. Zugleich ein Beitrag zum objektiven Nachweis einer Gehörs-, Geruchs- und Geschmackswahrnehmung. (Plethysmographic investigations after threshold sensory and sensible stimulations. With a contribution to the objective demonstration of a hearing, smell and taste perception.) AONK, 177: 297–352.

KOVATS, L. T. 1962 Über Organoleptik. (On the organoleptic concept.) ERNF, 7: 395–401.

KRAKAUER, D., and DALLENBACH, K. M. 1937 Gustatory adaptation to sweet, sour, and bitter. AJPC, 49: 469–75.

KRAMER, G. 1933 Geruch und Geschmack (Smell and taste), in Untersuchungen über die Sin-

nesleitungen und das Orientierungsverhalten von Xenopus laevis Daudin. (Research on the sense functioning and orientation behavior of Xenopus laevis Daudin.) ZJZP, 52: 629–76.

KRARUP, B. 1958 Electro-gustometry: A method for clinical taste examinations. AOLA, 49: 294–305.

———. 1958 On the technique of gustatory examinations. AOLA, 140 (Supplement): 195–200.

———. 1958 Smagsforstyrrelser efter mandibularanestesi. (Taste investigation after anesthetization of the mandibula.) TAND, 62: 313–16.

———. 1958 Taste fibres and the chorda tympani. AOLA, 140 (Supplement): 201–5.

———. 1958 Taste reactions of patients with Bell's palsy. AOLA, 49: 389–99.

———. 1959 Electrogustometric examinations in cerebellopontine tumors and on taste pathways. NEUR, 9: 53–61.

KRAUPA-RUNK, M. 1916 Perverse Geruchs- und Geschmacksempfindungen nach Neosalvarsaninjektionen. (Perversion of smell and taste after injections of neosalvarsan.) MMWO, 63: 46.

KRAUSE, F. 1895 Die Physiologie des Trigeminus, nach Untersuchungen an Menschen, bei denen das Ganglion Gasseri entfernt worden ist. (The physiology of the trigeminus after investigation in humans in whom the ganglion gasseri was removed.) MMWO, 42: 577–81, 602–4, 628–31.

———. 1896 Geschmacksempfindung (Taste perception), in Die Neuralgie des Trigeminus nebst der Anatomie und Physiologie der Nerven. F. C. W. Vogel, Leipzig, 260 pp. (see pp. 82–91).

KRAUSE, G. 1908 Über die Papillae filiformes des Menschen. (On filiform papillae in man.) Inaugural Dissertation, O. Kümmel, Königsberg. 34 pp.

KRAUSE, W. 1863 Ueber die Nerven-Endigung in den Papillae circumvallatae der menschlichen Zunge. (On nerve endings in the circumvallate papillae of the human tongue.) NAKG, pp. 144–46.

———. 1870 Die Nerven-Endigung in der Zunge des Menschen. (Nerve endings in the tongue of man.) NAKG, 18: 423–26.

———. 1876 Geschmacksorgan (Taste organ), in Allgemeine und microscopische Anatomie. Hahn, Hannover, 581 pp. (see pp. 179–95).

———. 1879 Handbuch der menschlichen Anatomie. (Handbook of Human Anatomy.) Hahn, Hannover, 1954 pp. (see pp. 385, 404–7, 738).

KRAUSS, R. M., and MAYER, J. 1964 Autoregulation of intake of amino-acids: Reversal of an "unwise" dietary preference in rats under conditions favourable for learning. NATU, 202: 463–64.

KREIBIG, J. K. 1917 Der Schmecksinn (Taste

sense), in *Die Sinne des Menschen*. B. G. Teubner, Leipzig, 116 pp. (see pp. 35–38).

KREMER, J. H. 1917 Influence de sensations du goût sur d'autres spécifiquement différentes. (Influence of taste on certain other sensations which differ specifically.) ANPA, 1: 625–34.

———. 1917 Smaakgewaarwordingen, waarop door andere specifiek ongelijke smaakgewaarwordingen invloed wordt uitgeoefend. (Sensations of taste influenced by other specifically dissimilar taste sensations.) NTGE, 2: 1284–86.

KRINNER, M. 1934 Über die Geschmacksempfindlichkeit der Elritzen. (The taste sensitivity of minnows.) ZVPH, 21: 317–42.

*KROLL. 1942 Verwendung des künstlichen Süsstoffes bei Heissgetränken. (The use of artificial sweeteners in hot drinks.) DDZE, 63: 319.

KROL'-LIFSHITS, D. E. 1933 Izmenenie vysoty porogov razdrazheniia vkusa u sobak pod vliianiem vozdeistviia vysokoi vneshnei temperatury. (Changes of thresholds of taste stimuli in dogs under influence of high external temperature.) ARBN, 33: 503–8. (German summary.)

———. 1934 Vliianie myshechnoi raboty na vysotu porogov razdrazheniia vkusa u sobaki. (The influence of muscular activity on the magnitude of gustatory thresholds in dogs.) TVEM, 1: 47–51. (German summary.)

———. 1935 Vliianie temperatury rastvorov na vysotu porogov razdrazheniia vkusa u sobaki. (Effect of temperature of solution on taste threshold in dogs.) FZLZ, 18: 115–22. (German summary.)

KROL'-LIFSHITS, D. E., and TIMOFEEV, N. V. 1935 Biologicheskii metod opredeleniia kontsentratsii beshchestv, vyzyvaiushchikh solenyi i kislyi vkusy. (Biologic method for determination of concentration of substances provoking salty and sour taste.) FZLZ, 18: 108–14. (German summary.)

———. 1935 Vliianie vkusovykh razdrazhenii na reflektornuiu fazu zheludochnogo sokootdeleniia i ezofagotomirovannoi sobaki. (Effect of gustatory stimuli on reflex phase of gastric secretion in esophagotomized dogs.) FZLZ, 18: 664–71. (German summary.)

KRON, J. 1901 Ein Beitrag zur Lehre über den Verlauf der Geschmacksfasern. (Course of the fibers of taste.) NEUZ, 20: 549–61.

———. 1902 Kucheniyn o khodie vkusovikh volokon. (Course of the fibers of taste.) OPEP, 7: 435–45.

KRONECKER, H. 1914 Kompensationen der Geschmackempfindungen. (Compensation in taste perception.) ZEMA, 18: 351–56.

KRONER, T. 1882 Ueber die Sinnesempfindungen der Neugeborenen. (Taste sensations in the new-born.) BAZE, 4: 37–41.

KRÜGER, F. VON. 1928 Physiologie: Reizaufnahme und ihre Topographie. (Physiology:

Topography of organs which transmit taste sensations.) FOZA, 4: 632–50.

KRÜGER, K. H. R. 1936 Qualitative Untersuchungen über den Adaptationsvorgang im Bereich des Geschmackssinnes. (Qualitative investigations on the adaptation reactions in the area of taste.) Inaugural Dissertation, R. Pfau, Berlin, 16 pp.

KRUT, L. H., PERRIN, M. J., and BRONTE-STEWART, B. 1961 Taste perception in smokers and non-smokers. BMJO, 1: 384–87.

KUBOTA, K., and HAYAMA, S. 1964 Comparative anatomical and neurohistological observations on the tongues of pigmy and common marmosets. ANRE, 150: 473–85.

KUBOTA, K., and KUBOTA, J. 1960 Contribution to the development of so-called gustatory papillae in human tongue. BTMD, 7: 475–505.

KUBOTA, K., KUBOTA, J., FUKUDA, N., ASAKURA, S., NAKAGAWA, S., and MASUI, M. 1963 Comparative anatomical and neurohistological observations on the tongue of the marsupials. ANRE, 147: 337–53.

KUCKULIES, G. 1936 Experimentelle Untersuchungen über die spezifische Qualität des Bittergeschmackes. (Experimental studies on the specific quality of the bitter taste.) Inaugural Dissertation, Pfau, Berlin, 18 pp.

KUHN, R., and GIRAL, F. 1935 Einfluss der Kettenlänge auf den Geschmack aliphatischer w-Betaine. (Effect of a chain length on the taste of aliphatic w-Betaine.) ZPCH, 231: 208–9.

KUHN, R., and ZILLIKEN, F. 1950 Über den Geschmack von p-Acetamino-benzaldehydthiosemicarbazon. (On the taste of p-acetamino-benzaldehydethiosemicarbazon.) NATW, 37: 167.

KUKITA, K. 1932 Beiträge zur physischen Anthropologie der Ainu. Über die Papillae vallatae der Ainu. (Contribution to the physical anthropology of the Ainu. The papillae vallata of the Ainu.) FUIZ, 25: 169–70. (Abstract.)

KULAKOVSKAJA, E. 1929 Beobachtungen über Geschmack und Geruch bei Neugeborenen. (Observation on taste and smell in the new-born.) ZRVD, 9: 15–20.

KÜLPE, O. 1893 Die Geschmacksqualitäten (Taste qualities), in *Grundriss der Psychologie auf Experimenteller Grundlage Dargestellt*. W. Engelmann, Leipzig, 478 pp. (see pp. 99–103).

*KUMAR, N. 1955 Taste, middle-phalangeal hair and occipital hair whorls among Nokte Naga. BUDI, 4: 61–67.

KÜNCKEL, J. 1878 Terminaisons nerveuses, tactiles et gustatives de la trompe des Diptères. (Neural terminations, tactile and gustatory in the mouth of Dipteres.) AFAS, pp. 771–73.

KÜNCKEL, J., and GAZAGNAIRE, J. 1881 Du siège de la gustation chez les insectes diptères. Constitution anatomique et valeur physiologique de l'epipharynx et de l'hypopharynx. (Distribution of taste in dipteral insects. Anatomical constitution and physiological values of the cpipharynx and the hypopharynx.) CRSS, 93: 347–50.

———. 1881 Rapport du cylindre-axe et des cellules nerveuses périphériques avec les organes des sens chez les insectes. (Relationship of the cylindraxile and the peripheral nerve cells with the sense organs of insects.) CRSS 33: 30–31, 48–50.

*Kuninaka, A. 1960 Studies on the taste of ribonucleic acid derivatives. JSOJ, 24: 489–92.

———. 1961 (Tasting effects and production methods of 5′-nucleotides: Biochemical considerations.) TKKO, 6: 403–10. (In Japanese.)

Kunitomo, K. 1912 Über die Zungenpapille und die Zungengrösse der Japaner. (On the lingual papillae and the size of the tongue of the Japanese.) ZEMA, 14: 339–66.

Kunitomo, F., and Kikuchi, K. 1935 Über die Zungenpapillen und die Zungengrösse des Japanischen Embryos. (On the lingual papillae and the size of the tongue of the Japanese embryos.) OFAJ, 13: 147–61.

Kunze, G. 1915 Die Zungenpapillen der Primaten. (The lingual papillae of primates.) GEMJ, 49: 569–679.

———. 1915 Ueber die Beziehungen der Papillae vallatae zu den Papillae fungiformes. (The relationship of the vallate papillae to the fungiform papillae.) Inaugural Dissertation, H. Fleischmann, Breslau, 67 pp.

———. 1927 Einige Versuche über den Geschmackssinn der Honigbiene. (Experiments on the sense of taste in the honey bee.) ZJZP, 44: 287–314.

———. 1933 Einige Versuche über den Antennengeschmackssinn der Honigbienen. (Some experiments on the antenna taste sense in honey bees.) ZJZP, 52: 465–511.

Kupalov, P. S. 1939 O funktsional'noi strukture kory bol'shikh polusharii. (The functional structure of the cortex of the great hemispheres.) ARBN, 54: 5–13.

Kuraoka, K. 1928 (Studies on human salivary secretion as taste reflex.) SMEJ, 47: 65–77. (In Japanese.)

———. 1928 Über die Ermüdung des Geschmackssinnes. (On fatigue of sense of taste.) SMEJ, 47: 3.

———. 1929 Ueber die Latenzzeit der Geschmacksempfindung. (Latent period of taste perception.) SMEJ, 48: 2–3.

———. 1929 Ueber die Unterdrueckungserscheinung im Gebiete des Geschmackssinnes. (On the suppression of the area of the taste sense.) SMEJ, 48: 13.

Kuroda, R. 1932 Preliminary studies on the gustatory response in fishes. APKY, 1: 157–61.

Kurta, L. 1934 Ueber die Ursache des sauren Geschmackes. (The origin of the sour taste.)

Inaugural Dissertation, G. Hoffmann, Charlottenburg, 18 pp.

Kusano, K. 1958 The influence of cations on the activity of gustatory receptors. I: Effect of KCl. II: Effects of NaCl, ▮Cl, NH₄Cl and CsCl. KUMJ, 11: 174–83, 240–50.

———. 1959 The influence of cations on the activity of gustatory receptors. III: Effects of CaCl₂, SrCl₂ and BaCl₂. KUMJ, 12: 28–38.

———. 1959 The influence of narcotics on the activity of gustatory receptors. KUMJ, 12: 236–43.

———. 1960 Analysis of the single unit activity of gustatory receptors in the frog tongue. JJPH, 10: 620–33.

Kusano, K., and Sato, M. 1957 Properties of fungiform papillae in frog's tongue. JJPH, 7: 324–38.

———. 1958 The influence of anions on the activity of gustatory receptors. JJPH, 8: 254–74.

Kussmaul, A. 1896 Von Geschmackssinne und dem Ekelgefühle des Neugeborenen (Taste sense and nausea in the newborn), in *Untersuchungen über das Seelenleben des neugeborenen Menschen*. 3rd ed. F. Pietzcker, Tübingen, 58 pp. (see pp. 22–28) .

*Kuwabara, M. 1963 Tarsal chemoreception in the butterfly, *Vanessa indica*. PCZO, 3: 96–97.

Kuznetsova, I. V. 1960 Vkusovaîa i̅ oboni̅atel'naia chuvstvitel'nost'u lits, rabotaiushchikh Ma betatronakh. (Senses of taste and smell in persons working on betatrons.) MERA, 5: 82–84. (English summary.)

Laird, D. A. 1939 Does denture wearing affect the sense of taste? JADS, 26: 1518–19.

———. 1939 The effect of smoking on taste preferences. MERC, 149: 404.

Laird, D. A., and Breen, W. J. 1939 Sex and age alterations in taste preference. JADA, 15: 549–50.

Lalonde, E. R., and Eglitis, J. A. 1961 Number and distribution of taste buds on the epiglottis, pharynx, larynx, soft palate and uvula in a human newborn. ANRE, 140: 91–93.

Landa, J. S. 1945 Practical full denture prosthesis. XXV: The sense of taste in patients wearing full dentures. DIIN, 67: 537–42.

Landacre, F. L. 1907 On the place of origin and method of distribution of tastebuds in *Ameiurus melas*. JCNP, 17: 1–66.

Landau, H. 1904 Drei Fälle von halbseitiger Atrophie der Zunge (Hemiatrophia linguae) . (Three cases of unilateral atrophy of the tongue.) DZNE, 26: 102–27.

Landgren, S. 1957 Convergence of tactile, thermal, and gustatory impulses on single cortical cells. APSC, 40: 210–21.

———. 1959 Thalamic units responding to cooling of the cat's tongue. JPHY, 147: 12–13P.

LANDGREN, S., LILJESTRAND, G., and ZOTTERMAN, Y. 1954 Chemical transmission in taste fibre endings. APSC, **30**: 105–14.

LANGE, N. A., EBERT, H. L., and YOUSE, L. K. 1929 Some ureas and thioureas derived from vanillylamine. Relations between constitution and taste of pungent principles. JACS, **51**: 1911–14.

LANGE, N. A., and REED, W. R. 1926 Some para-phenoxy-ureas and thio-ureas derived from para-phenoxy-aniline. The effect of the phenoxy group on the taste. JACS, **48**: 1069–74.

LANGER, W. 1936 Über den Geschmackssinn in der Schwangerschaft. (The taste sense in pregnancy.) Inaugural Dissertation, Hinstorff, Rostock, 19 pp.

LANGTON, H. M. 1938 Bitterness. FLAV, 1 (4): 55–57.

———. 1938 Sourness. FLAV, 1 (2): 51–61.

LANGWILL, K. E. 1948 Women more sensitive to taste than the men. FRFF, **7**: 2, 4.

———. 1949 Taste perception and taste preference of the consumer. FOTE, **3**: 136–39.

LANGWORTHY, O. R. 1924 A study of the innervation of the tongue musculature with particular reference to the proprioceptive mechanism. JCNE, **36**: 273–97.

LANNEGRACE, P. J. J. 1878 *Terminaisons Nerveuses dans les Muscles de la Langue et dans sa Membrane Muqueuse.* (Neural termination of the tongue muscles and its mucous membrane.) J. B. Bailliere & Fils, Paris, 88 pp.

LAPICQUE, L. 1941 Quelques remarques sur l'emploi de la saccharine. (Some remarks on the use of saccharin.) BAME, **124**: 116–17.

LAPINA, I. A. 1960 Differentiation of chemical substances by the taste analyser in the dog with the use of food reinforcement. (Translated by R. Crawford.) ZVND, **10**: 742–46.

LARGUIER DES BANCELS, J. 1908 Les sensations gustatives. (Taste sensations.) ANPQ, **15**: 273–99.

———. 1912 *Le Goût et L'Odorat.* (Taste and Olfaction.) A. Hermann & Fils, Paris. 94 pp.

LARSEN, J. R. 1962 The fine structure of the labellar chemosensory hairs of the blowfly, *Phormia regina* Meigen. JIPH, **8**: 683–91.

LARSEN, J. R., and DETHIER, V. G. 1963 The fine structure of the labellar and antennal chemoreceptors of the blowfly. *Phormia regina.* PCZO, **3**: 81–83.

LASAREFF, P. 1922 Untersuchungen über die Ionentheorie der Reizung. III: Ionentheorie der Geschmacksreizung. (Investigations of the ion theory of stimulation. III: Ion theory of taste stimulation.) PAGP, **194**: 293–97.

———. 1922 V. Vliianie temperaturey na otnositel'noe polozhenie krivykh nasyshcheniia dyukh veshchestv: krivaia nasyshcheniia dvumia veshchestvami. (Influence of temperature on the curvilinear relationship of two substances.) ZRKO, **54**: 106–9.

LASERSTEIN, S., and HERMANN, L. 1891 Beiträge zur Kenntniss des elektrischen Geschmacks. (Contribution to the electric taste.) PAGP, **49**: 519–38.

LASKIEWICZ, A. 1954 Some clinical observations of disturbances of the taste sensation. RLOR, **75**: 448–66.

LASSCHE, J. B., HARTOG, C. DEN, and WEITS, J. 1962 Invloed van licht van verschillende golflengte op de beoordeling van smaak en geur. (Effect of light of different wave lengths on evaluation of taste and smell.) VOED, **23**: 98–103.

LATERZA, A., and MORENO, M. 1953 Ageusia in miastenico. (Ageusia in myasthenia.) RINE, **23**: 338.

LATTES, L. 1952 Osservazioni sull'ereditarietà della "cecità gustativa." (Observations on heredity of "gustatory blindness.") MMAA, **72**: 85–86.

LAVERACK, M. S. 1960 Tactile and chemical perception of earthworms. I: Responses to touch, sodium chloride, quinine and sugars. CBCP, **1**: 155–63.

———. 1961 Tactile and chemical perception in earthworms. II: Responses to acid pH solutions. CBCP, **2**: 22–34.

———. 1963 Aspects of chemoreception in crustacea. CBCP, **8**: 141–51.

———. 1963 Aspects of chemoreception in crustacea. PCZO, **3**: 72–74.

LAVIN, A., ALCOCER-CUARÓN, C., and HERNANDEZ-PEÓN, R. 1959 Centrifugal arousal in the olfactory bulb. SCIE, **129**: 332–33.

LAWRENCE, A. R., and FERGUSON, L. N. 1959 Exploratory physicochemical studies on the sense of taste. NATU **183**: 1469–71.

LAWRENTIEVA, N. B. 1960 K voprosu o strukture pericheskogo kontsa vkusovogo analizatora cheloveka. (Structure of peripheral end of the gustatory analyser in man. AAGE, **38** (Section A): 57–63. (English summary.)

———. 1961 Histofiziologiia vkusovikh sosochkov iazyka mlekopita iushchikh zhivotnykh. (Histophysiology of gustatory papillae of the tongue in mammals.) AAGE **41** (Section A): 70–77. (English summary.)

LAZZARONI, A. 1962 Modificazioni dell'ARN negli organuli gustativi del palato di "Rana esculenta" trattati con soluzioni sapide. (Modification of RNA in the taste organs of the palate of "Rana esculenta" treated with sapid solutions.) BILM, **15**: 685–92. (English, Spanish, French, and German summaries.)

LE CAT, C. N. 1740 Du goût (Taste), in *Traité des Sens*, A. Rouen, Paris, 523 pp. (see pp. 219–28).

LEE, B. F. 1934 A genetic analysis of taste deficiency in the American Negro. OJSC, **34**: 337–42.

LEE, T. S. 1954 Physiological gustatory sweating in a warm climate. JPHY, **124**: 528–42.

LEGUEBE, A. 1960 A phenylthiocarbamide test. NATU, **186**: 970.

——. 1960 Génétique et anthropologie de la sensibilité a la phenylthiocarbamide I: Fréquence due gène dans la population belge. (Genetics and anthropology of the sensitivity to phenylthiocarbamide. I: Gene frequency in a Belgian population.) BABS, **36**: 1–27. (English and German summaries.)

——. 1963 Sex differences in tasting P. T. C. LIFS, **2**: 337–42

LEHMANN, K. B. 1884 Ein Beitrag zur Lehre vom Geschmacksinn. (A contribution to the theory of the sense of taste.) PAGP, **33**: 194–98.

LEIDERITZ, H. 1957 Vital-Ökonomie und -Ökologie der Geschmacks- und Geruchsstoffe: Grundlagenforschung. (Vital, economic, and ecologic taste and odor substances; fundamental research.) PAKO, **38**: 499–501.

——. 1958 Vital-Ökonomie und Ökologie der Geschmack- und Geruchstoffe. II. Teil. (Vital economic and ecologic taste and odor substances. Part II. PAKO, **39**: 193–96.

LEIGH, A. D. 1943 Defects of smell after head injury. LANC, **1**: 38–40.

LE MAGNEN, J. 1945 L'indépendance fonctionnelle des saveurs. (Functional independence of flavors.) CRSS, **139**: 265–66.

——. 1953 Activité de l'insuline sur la consommation spontanée des solutions sapides. (Influence of insulin on the spontaneous consumption of sapid solutions.) CRSS, **147**: 1753–56.

——. 1953 Régulation immédiate de la prise spontanée d'eau et de sel chez le rat blanc dans des états imposés de déséquilibre hydro-minéral. (Immediate regulation of spontaneous intake of water and salt in the white rat in imposed states of hydro-mineral imbalance.) CRSS, **147**: 619–23.

——. 1954 Le processus de discrimination par le rat blanc des stimuli sucrés alimentaires et non alimentaires. (The process of discrimination by the white rat of nutritive and non-nutritive sweet stimuli.) JOPH, **46**: 414–18.

——. 1955 Le rôle de la réceptivité gustative au chlorure de sodium dans le mécanisme de régulation de la prise d'eau chez le rat blanc. (The role of the gustatory receptivity to sodium chloride in the mechanism of regulation of water intake in the white rat.) JOPH, **47**: 405–18.

——. 1956 Le rôle des stimulations oflacto-gustatives dans les méchanismes de régulation de la prise alimentaire. (The effect of olfactory-gustatory stimuli on the regulatory mechanism of food intake.) ANAI, **10**: 153–88.

——. 1959 Le rôle des stimuli olfacto-gustatifs dans la régulation du comportement alimentaire du mammifère. (The role of smell and taste stimuli in the regulation of feeding behavior of mammals.) JPNP, **56**: 137–60.

——. 1963 Le controle sensoriel dans la régulation de l'apport alimentaire. (Sensory control in the regulation of food intake.) PAEN, **7**: 147–71.

LE MAGNEN, J., and MARFAING-JALLAT, P. 1961 Le rôle des afférences buccales dans le déterminisme des consommations spontanées d'alcool chez le rat. (The role of sensory information from the mouth in determination of spontaneous drinking of alcohol in the rat.) JPPG, **53**: 407–8.

LEMBERGER, F. 1908 Psychophysische Untersuchungen über den Geschmack von Zucker und Saccharin (Saccharose und Krystallose). (Psychophysical studies on taste of sucrose and saccharin.) PAGP, **123**: 293–311.

LENHOFF, H. M. 1963 On the mechanism of the glutathione-receptor of *Hydra littoralis*. PCZO, **3**: 69–71.

LENHOSSÉK, M. VON. 1892 Les nerfs des corpuscules du goût. (The nerves of the taste buds.) BIUN, **28**: 573–78.

——. 1892 Ursprung, Verlauf und Endigung der sensibeln Nervenfasern bei Lumbricus (Origin, course and endings of sensory nerve fibers in lumbricus.) AMAE, **39**: 102–36.

——. 1893 Der feinere Bau und die Nervenendigungen der Geschmacksknospen. (The delicate structure and nerve endings of taste buds.) ANAN, **8**: 121–27.

——. 1893 Die Geschmacksknospen in den blattförmigen Papillen des Kaninchens. (The taste buds of the leaf-shaped papillae in the rabbit.) VMGW, **27**: 191–266.

——. 1894 Die Endknospen der Barbe und des Aales (End buds of barbel and eel), in *Beiträge zur Histologie des Nervensystems und der Sinnesorgane*. J. F. Bergmann, Wiesbaden, 190 pp. (see pp. 95–126).

——. 1895 Die Nervenendigungen in den Endknospen der Mundschleimhaut der Fische. (The nerve endings in the terminal buds of the mucosal membrane in fish.) VNGB, **10**: 92–100.

LESSA, A., DESSAI, M., and FRAZÃO, V. 1953 Um novo sistema cromosómico: a "sensibilidade gustative" para a F.T.C. com um comentário sobre o interesse patogénico, semiológico e terapêutico da fenil- tio- carbamida. (New chromosomal system: Taste sensitivity to phenyl-thio-carbamide; pathogenic, semeiologic and therapeutic interest.) BCHL, **17**: 613–42.

LESTER, D., and GREENBERG, L. A. 1952 Nutrition and the etiology of alcoholism; the effect of sucrose, saccharin and fat on self-selection of ethyl alcohol by rats. QJSA, **13**: 553–60.

LETZERICH, L. 1869 Ueber die Endapparate der Geschmacksnerven. (The end apparatus of taste nerves.) VAPA, **45**: 9–19.

LEUCHS, H. 1905 Synthese von oxy-pyrrolidin-carbonsäuren (Oxy-prolinin). (Synthesis of hydroxlpyrolidine carbonic acid.) BDCG, **38**: 1937–43.

LEUCHS, H., and FELSER, H. 1908 Zur Kenntniss der oxy-proline und über die Synthese von Oxyhygrinsäuren. (Knowledge of hydroxl-proline and the syntheses of hydroxy grinic acid.) BDCG, **41**: 1726–34.

LEVANDOWSKY, M., and HODGSON, E. S. 1965 Amino acid and amine receptors of lobsters. CBCP, **16**: 159–61.

LEVINE, P., and ANDERSON, A. S. 1932 Observations on taste blindness. SCIE, **75**: 497–98.

LEWIN, L. 1894 II. Ueber die Geschmacksverbesserung von Medicamenten und über Saturationen. (On improvement of taste and medicaments and on saturation.) BKWO, **31**: 644–46.

LEWIS, D., and DANDY, W. E. 1930 The course of the nerve fibers transmitting sensation of taste. ARSU, **21**: 249–88.

LEWIS, D. R. 1948 Psychological scales of taste. JOPS, **26**: 437–46.

LEWIS, M. 1960 Behavior resulting from sodium chloride deprivation in adrenalectomized rats. JCPP, **53**: 464–67.

LEYDIG, F. 1872 II. Die becherförmigen Sinnesorgane: Ihr Vorkommen bei Schlangen. (II. The goblet shaped sense organs: Their existence in snakes.) AMAE, **8**: 329–49.

LICHTENSTEIN, A. 1893–94 Über die Geschmacksempfindung gesunder und rachitischer Kinder. (On taste perception of healthy and rachitic children.) JAKI, **37**: 76–90.

LICHTENSTEIN, P. E. 1948 The relative sweetness of sugars: Sucrose and dextrose. JEPS, **38**: 578–86.

LICHTWITZ, L. 1887 Recherches cliniques sur les anesthésis hystériques des muqueuses et de quelques organes des sens (goût, odorat, ouie), et sur le zones hystérogènes des muqueuses. (Clinical research on hysteria anesthesias of the mucous membranes and the sense organs —taste, olfaction, hearing—and on the hysterogenous zones of the mucous membranes.) Inaugural Dissertation, A. Bellier & Cie., Bordeaux, 184 pp.

LILJESTRAND, G. 1922 Über den Schwellenwert des sauren Geschmacks. (The threshold value of acid taste.) ANPA, **7**: 532–37.

———. 1954 VI. The problem of transmission at chemoreceptors. PARE, **6**: 73–78.

———. 1955 Etude sur les récepteurs gustatifs. (Study of taste receptors.) RMLI, **10**: 687–97.

LILJESTRAND, G., and ZOTTERMAN, Y. 1954 The water taste in mammals. APSC, **32**: 291–303.

———. 1956 The alkaline taste. APSC, **35**: 380–89.

———. 1957 The effect of certain demulcents on the taste nerve endings, in *Festschrift Arthur Stoll—Arbeiten aus dem Gebiete der Naturstoffchemie.* Birkhäuser, Basel, 911 pp. (see pp. 806–13).

LINDENMAIER, P., and KARE, M. R. 1959 The taste end-organs of the chicken. POSC, **38**: 545–50.

LINDSLEY, O. R. 1950 Neural components of the chorda tympani of the rat. Unpublished Master's thesis, Brown University, 48 pp.

LINKER, E., MOORE, M. E., and GALANTER, E. 1964 Taste thresholds, detection models, and disparate results. JEPS, **67**: 59–66.

LIPMANN, O. 1917 Psychische Geschlechtsunterschiede. (Psychic sex differences.) ZAPB, **17A**: 34.

LIPPMNN, E. O. von. 1895 *Die Chemie der Zuckerarten.* (The Chemistry of Sweetness.) Vieweg und Sohn, Braunschweig, 1174 pp.

LISZT, E. R. VON. 1917 Ueber den Geschmack- und Geruchsinn des Haussperlings. (On taste and olfactory senses in house sparrows.) ORBE, **14**: 213–16.

LIVINGSTON, R. M. 1956 Some observations on the natural history of the tongue. ARCS, **19**: 185–200.

LOCKHART, E. E., and GAINER, J. M. 1950 Effect of monosodium glutamate on taste of pure sucrose and sodium chloride. FORE, **15**: 459–64.

LOCKHART, E. E., and STANFORD, J. E. 1952 The taste interrelationship of monosodium glutamate and sucrose. FORE, **17**: 404–8.

LOCKHART, E. E., TUCKER, C. L., and MERRITT, M. C. 1955 The effect of water impurities on the flavor of brewed coffee. FORE, **20**: 598–605.

*LOEB, J. M. 1961 The role of taste stimulation in the prefeeding effect. DIAS, **22**: 2080–81.

LOEWENSTEIN, W. R., and ISHIKO, N. 1962 Sodium chloride sensitivity and electrochemical effects in a lorenzinian ampulla. NATU, **194**: 292–94.

LOGINOV, N. E. 1941 Novyi metod izmereniia sladosti sakharinstykh veshchestv. (A new method for measuring the sweetness of sugars.) PPEZ, **1**: 32.

———. 1943 O sladkikh veshcehstvakh. (Sweet substances.) PPEZ, **1–2**: 22–25.

LÖHNER, L. 1916 Über Geschmacks-physiologische Versuche mit Blutegeln. (On taste physiological experiments with leeches.) PAGP, **163**: 239–46.

LOMBROSO, C., and FERRERO, G. 1923 Gusto (Taste), in *La Donna Deliquenta, la Prostituta e la Donna Normale.* F. Bocca, Torino, 508 pp. (see p. 239).

LOMBROSO, C., and OTTOLENGHI, S. 1891 Die Sinne der Verbrecher. (The senses of criminals.) ZEPH, **2**: 337–60.

LONGET, A. 1843 Influence sur le goût (Influence on taste), in *Anatomie et physiologie du système nerveux. Documents et recherches sur quelques points douteux de l'anatomie et de la physiologie du nerf facial.* AMPY, **1**: 232–55.

LONGET, F. A. 1850 Sens du goût (Sense of

taste), in *Traité de Physiologie, II.* Masson, Paris, 187 pp. (see pp. 163–174) .

LORANG, H. F. J. 1928 The relationship between the constitution and taste of some urea derivatives. RTCP, **47**: 179–90.

LORIAN, V. 1960 Estudo de sensibilidade gustativa e olfativa dos tuberculosos pulmonares. (Study of gustatory and olfactory sensitivity in pulmonary tuberculosis.) RBTU, **28**: 373–76.

LOTKA, A. J. 1914 The sense of taste. SCAM, **78**: 275.

*LOUBIMOW, N. 1896 Der elektrische Geschmack. (The electric taste.) NAOZ.

LOVELAND, A. E. 1897 A study of the organs of taste. TAMS, **19**: 129–74.

LOVELL, M. R. C., GROSS, C. G., and WEISKRANTZ, L. 1961 A note on the effects of gymnemic acid on taste perception. ANBE, **9**: 31–33.

LOVEN, C. 1868 Bedrag till kännedomen om tungans smakpapiller. (Contribution to the structure of taste buds on the tongue.) MEDS, **3**: 1–14.

———. 1868 Beiträge zur Kenntniss vom Bau der Geschmackswärzchen der Zunge. (Contribution to the knowledge of structure of taste buds on the tongue.) AMAE, **4**: 96–110.

LUCHTMANS, P. 1758 Saporibus et Gustu. (Flavor and taste.) Inaugural Dissertation, Leiden, 82 pp.

LUCIANI, F. 1952 Il sapore e la sua correzione nei medicinali. (Correction of taste of medicine.) CLTE, **2**: 79–89.

LUCIANI, L. 1917 The sense of taste, in *Human Physiology, IV.* Translated by F. A. Welby. Macmillan, London, 519 pp. (see pp. 126–59) .

LUDWIG, C. 1858 Geschmackssinn (Taste) , in *Lehrbuch der Physiologie des Menschen.* C. F. Winter, Leipzig and Heidelberg, 612 pp. (see pp 389–94) .

LUGG, J. W. H. 1955 Some notably high acuities of taste for phenylthiocarbamide. NATU, **176**: 313–14.

———. 1956–57 Taste-thresholds for phenylthiocarbamide of some population groups. II: The thresholds of two uncivilized ethnic groups living in Malaya. ANHG, **21**: 244–53.

———. 1962 Some extremely high acuities of taste for P. T. C. NATU, **194**: 980.

LUGG, J. W. H., and WHYTE, J. M. 1954–55 Taste thresholds for phenylthiocarbamide of some population groups. I: The thresholds of some civilized ethnic groups living in Malaya. ANHG, **19**: 290–311.

LUMIA, V. 1959 Diabete senile e sensibilità gustativa assoluta e differenziale per il sapore dolce. (Senile diabetes and absolute and differential gustatory sensitivity for sweet taste.) GIGE, **7**: 961–63.

———. 1959 Sulla sensibilità gustativa dell'uomo in età senile. Variazioni della soglia in rap-

porto all'età. (On the gustatory sensitivity of man in old age. Variations of the threshold in relation to age.) ARFI, **59**: 69–84. (English summary.)

———. 1960 Ricerche sulla sensibilità gustativa differenziale per il sapore salato in soggetti di diversa età. (Research on differential gustatory sensitivity to the taste of salt in subjects of various ages.) ARFI, **59**: 279–87.

———. 1961 Ricerche sulla sensibilità gustativa differenziale per il sapore acido in soggetti di diversa età. (Research on differential gustatory sensitivity to sour in persons of different ages.) ARFI, **60**: 240–46. (English summary.)

———. 1961 Ricerche sulla sensibilità gustativa differenziale per il sapore amaro in soggetti di diversa età. (Research on differential gustatory sensitivity in bitter in persons of different ages.) ARFI, **60**: 387–94. (English summary.)

———. 1961 Ricerche sulla sensibilità gustativa differenziale per il sapore dolce in soggetti di diversa èta. (Research on differential gustatory sensitivity to sweet in persons of different ages.) ARFI, **60**: 232–39. (English summary.)

LUNEDEI, A. 1946 Sulla regolazione umorale della sensibilità gustativa e sue variazioni patologiche. (Humoral regulation of taste sensitivity and its pathological variation.) RCCM, **46**(5): 3–9.

LUSSANA, F. 1862 Abolizione del gusto nella parte anteriore della lingua per taglio della corda del timpano. (Obliteration of taste on the anterior part of the tongue as a result of section of the chorda tympani.) AUMM, **182**: 307–13.

———. 1869 Recherches expérimentales et observations pathologiques sur les nerfs du goût. (Experimental research and pathology observations on the taste nerves.) APHP, **2**: 20–32, 197–209.

———1869 Sui nervi del gusto. Ricerche sperimentali ed osservazioni patologiche. (On the taste nerve. Experimental research and pathology observations.) GMPV, **12**: 105–9.

———. 1870 Sui nervi del gusto. Novelle osservazioni ed esperienze. (On the taste nerve. New observations and experience.) GMPV, **12**: 345–49.

———. 1872 Sur les nerfs du goût. Observations et expériences nouvelles. (On the nerves of taste. New observations and experiences.) APHP, **4**: 150–67, 334–50.

LUSTIG, A. 1884 Beiträge zur Kenntniss der Entwickelung der Geschmacksknospen. (Contribution to the knowledge of the development of taste buds.) SWWA, **89**: 308–24.

LUTHER, W. 1930 Versuche über die Chemorezeption der Brachyuren. (Experiments on chemoreception of brachyura.) ZVPH, **12**: 177–205.

———. 1931 Zur Frage der Chemorezeption der

Brachyuren und Anomuren. (On the question of chemoreception of brachyura and anomure.) ZOAN, **94**: 147–53.

MacCarthy-Leventhal, E. M. 1959 Post-radiation mouth blindness. LANC, **2**: 1138–39.

MacDonald, G. 1888 On the mechanism of the nose as regards respiration, taste, and smell. BMJO, p. 1210.

Macht, M. B. 1951 Subcortical localization of certain "taste" responses in the cat. FEPR, **10**: 88. (Abstract.)

Mackenzie, I. C. K. 1955 A simple method of testing taste. LANC, **268**: 377–78.

Mackey, A. 1958 Discernment of taste substances as affected by solvent medium. FORE, **23**: 580–83.

Mackey, A. O., and Jones, P. 1954 Selection of members of a food tasting panel: Discernment of primary tastes in water solution compared with judging ability for foods. FOTE, **8**: 527–30.

Mackey, A. O., and Valassi, K. 1956 The discernment of primary taste in the presence of different food textures. FOTE, **10**: 238–40.

MacLeod, S. 1950 A construction and attempted validation of sensory sweetness scales. Unpublished Ph.D. thesis, Brown University, 46 pp.

———. 1952 A construction and attempted validation of sensory sweetness scales. JEPS, **44**: 316–23.

MacRoberts, M. H. 1964 Taste sensitivity to phenylthiocarbamide (PTC) among the Papago Indians of Arizona. HUBI, **36**: 28–31.

Maddox, R. L. 1869 A contribution to the minute anatomy of the fungiform papillae and terminal arrangement of nerve to striped muscular tissue in the tongue of the common frog. (*Rana temporaria*). MOMJ, **1**: 1–14.

Maestrini, D. 1912 La sensazione dell'amaro nei Ditteri. (The sensation of bitterness in diptera.) AFMC, **2**: 259–64.

Magendie, F. 1826 Vom Schmecken (On taste), in *Lehrbuch der Physiologie, I.* Translated from French by D. Hofacker. E. F. Osiander, Tübingen, 432 pp. (see pp. 104–9).

———. 1831 Of taste, in *An Elementary Compendium of Physiology.* Translated from French by E. Milligan. 4th ed. J Carfrae & Son, Edinburgh, 648 pp. (see pp. 79–83).

———. 1845 The sense of taste, in *An Elementary Treatise on Human Physiology.* Translated from French by J. Revere. Harper & Brothers, New York, 539 pp. (see pp. 100–7).

Magidson, O. J., and Gorbatschow, S. W. 1923 Zur Frage der Süssigkeit des Saccharins. Das o-Benzoylsulfimid und seine elektrolytische Dissoziation. (The question of sweetness of saccharin. The o-benzoyl sulfonimide and its electrolytic dissociation.) BDCG, **56B**: 1810–17.

Mahner, P. 1909 Vergleichende psycho-physio-logische Versuche über die Unterscheidungs-fähigkeit im Gebiete des inneren und äussern Tastsinns, des Geschmack- und Geruchssinnes an taubstummen, blinden, normalsinnigen, schwachsinnigen, und taub-stumm-blinden Kindern. (Comparative psycho-physiological studies of the power of discrimination of the inner and outer tactile sense, the gustatory and olfactory senses of deaf and dumb, blind, normal, feebleminded, and of blind-deaf-dumb children.) Inaugural Dissertation, O. Wiegand, Leipzig, 60 pp.

Maier, E. 1904 Über Geschmackstörungen bei Mittelohrerkrankungen. (Taste disturbance in middle ear infections.) ZHNO, **48**: 178–209.

Mainland, R. C. 1945 Absence of olfactory sensation. JOHE, **36**: 143–44.

Makepeace-Lott, R. 1941 Taste and smell. CHIN, **60**: 246–48.

Makous, W., Nord, S., Oakley, B., and Pfaffmann, C. 1963 The gustatory relay in the medulla, in *Olfaction and Taste*, Y. Zotterman (ed.). Macmillan, New York, 396 pp. (see pp. 381–93).

Malcke, J. F. 1728 De gustu atque loquela. (A discourse on taste.) Inaugural Dissertation, T. J. Schreiber, Gedani, 16 pp.

Maller, O. 1964 The effect of hypothalamic and dietary obesity on taste-preference in rats. LIFS, **3**: 1281–91.

Maller, O., and Kare, M. R. 1965 The selection and intake of carbohydrates by wild and domesticated rats. PSEB, **119**: 199–203.

Malloizel, L. 1903 Dégénérescence et régénération de la chorde du tympan chez un chien, a fistule sous-maxillaire permanente. (Degeneration and regeneration of the chorda tympani in a dog with a permanent sub-maxillary fistula.) CORE, **55**: 630–31.

Malmo, R. B., and Ellis, M. M. 1941 Sour thresholds as a function of the pH of hydrochloric and sulphuric acids. AJPC, **54**: 410–12.

Mameli, E. 1929 Sulle relazioni fra costituzione chimica e azione fisiologica. (Relation between chemical constitution and physiological action.) BCFA, **68**: 861–66.

Mangold, E. 1909 Die Geschmacksorgane (The taste organ), in *Unsere Sinnesorgane und ihre Function.* Quelle and Meyer, Leipzig, 147 pp. (see pp. 117–24).

Manlapas, F. C., Stein, A. A., and Pagliara, A. S. 1965 Phenylthiocarbamide taste sensitivity in cystic fibrosis. JOPD, **66**: 8–11.

Manly, R. S., Pfaffmann, C., Lathrop, D. D., and Keyser, J. 1952 Oral sensory thresholds of persons with natural and artificial dentitions. JDRE, **31**: 305–12.

Mannessier-Mameli, A. 1935 Anilidi dell'acido o-solfamido-tiobenzoico. (Anilides of o-sulfamylthiobenzoic acid.) GCIT, **65**: 69–77.

———. 1935 Azione della aniline sulla saccarina

e sulla tiosaccarina. (Action of anilines on saccharin and on thiosaccharin.) GCIT, **65**: 51–69.

——. 1935 Sulla pirolisi della saccarionossima. (The pyrolysis of saccharin oxime.) GCIT, **65**: 77–84.

——. 1941 Azione della semicarbazide sulla saccarina, sulla tiosaccarina e sulla acetilsaccarina. (The action of semicarbazide on saccharin, on thiosaccharin and on acetylsaccharin.) GCIT, **71**: 25–40.

MARCHAND, L. 1902 Développement des papilles gustatives chez le foetus humain. (Development of taste papillae in the human fetus.) CORE, **54**: 910–12.

——. 1903 *Le Goût.* (Taste.) O. Doin, Paris, 331 pp.

——. 1903 Mesure des sensations gustatives. (Measurement of taste sensations.) RPPE, pp. 245–54.

MARCUS, H. 1934 Die Lokalisation des Geschmackszentrums. (The localization of the center of taste.) APNE, **9**: 85–116.

——. 1934 Epilepsie mit Geschmacksaura. (Epilepsy with taste aura.) ZGNP, **149**: 711–22.

MARGOLIN, G. I. 1941 Effect of visual and taste stimuli upon the muscular tonus in man. (Translated by T. Rogalina.) DANK, **33**: 125–28.

MARGULIES, B. A., and GOETZL, F. R. 1950 The effect of alcohol upon the acuity of the sense of taste for sucrose and the sensation complex of appetite and satiety. PFMB, **8**: 102–6.

MARIAU, A. 1900 Le voile du palais, organe de gustation. (The covering of the palate, organ of taste.) BSCT, **4**: 63–70.

——. 1900 Le voile du palais, organe de gustation. (The covering of the palate, organ of taste.) CORE, **52**: 255–56.

MARK, J. 1943 Salt, carbohydrate and water appetite of adrenalectomized rats before and after treatment with desoxycorticosterone pellets. JHHB, **72**: 243–45.

MÄRK, W. 1940 Besonderheiten im Vorkommen von Flimmerepithel, Drüsen und Geschmacksknospen in der menschlichen Mundhöhle. (Peculiarities in occurrence of ciliated epithelium, glands and taste buds in human buccal cavity.) ZMAF, **49**: 82–107.

MARLOW, C. D., WINKELMANN, R. K., and GIBILISCO, J. A. 1965 General sensory innervation of the human tongue. ANRE, **152**: 503–11.

——. 1965 Special sensory innervation of the human tongue. JDRE, **44**: 1381–85.

MARLOWE, R. H. 1942 A laboratory method for evaluating feeding preference of fruitflies. JEEN, **35**: 799–802.

MAROTTE, 1869 Névralgie accompagnée d'un goût sucré dans la bouche. (Neuralgia accompanied by a sweet taste in the mouth.) UMSP, **3**: 106.

——. 1879 Névralgie accompagnée d'un goût sucré dans la bouche. (Neuralgia accompanied by a sweet taste in the mouth.) AMPY, **4**: 137.

MARTIN, J. P. 1946 Epileptiform attacks of sensations of taste and smell: Unilateral Parkinsonian tremor (undiagnosed) . PRSM, **39**: 597. (Abstract.)

MARTIN DU PAN, R. 1955 Le rôle du goût et de l'odorat dans l'alimentation du nourrisson. (Role of taste and smell in feeding of nurslings.) PEDR, **10**: 169–176. (English summary.)

MARTINES, C. DE. 1900 Recherches sur les troubles du goût et de l'odorat dans la paralysie générale progressive. (Research on disorders of taste and smell in progressive general paralysis.) RMSR, **20**: 405–23, 453–71.

MASHANSKII, F. N. 1956 Simptom otvrasheniya k sladkomu i zhiromu pri tsistitserkoze IV zheludochka golovnogo mozga. (The symptom of aversion for sweet and fatty foods in cysticercosis of the fourth ventricle.) VONE, **6**: 41–43.

MASSLER, M., and SCHOUR, I. 1946 Dorsum of the tongue, in *Atlas of the Mouth and Adjacent Parts in Health and Disease.* American Dental Associations, Chicago, Plate 20.

MATA, F. 1963 Effect of dextro-amphetamine on bitter taste threshold. JNEU, **4**: 315–320.

MATOT, C. 1961 Les troubles du goût en odontostomatologie. (Taste disorders in odontostomatology.) RBSD, **16**: 185–200.

MATTEI, E. DI. 1901 Le sensibilità nei fanciulli in rapporto al sesso ed all'età. (The sensitivity of children with respect to sex and age.) AACL, **22**: 207–28.

MATTHES, E. 1938 Olfacto e gosto no reino animal. (Smell and taste in the animal kingdom.) AMNL, **9**: 17–46.

——. 1938 Über einige Besonderheiten der Pinnipedierzunge. (The peculiarities of the tongue of the Pinnipedia.) ZAEN, **108**: 52–60.

MATSON, G. A. 1938 Blood groups and ageusia in Indians of Montana and Alberta. AJPN, **27**: 81–89.

——. 1940 Blood groups and ageusia in Indians of North Alberta. AJPN, **27**: 263–67.

MAURIZI, M., and CIMINO, A. 1961 L'influenza delle variazioni termiche sulla sensibilità gustativa. (The influence of thermal variations on gustatory sensitivity). BMOG, **79**: 626–34. (English summary.)

MAURO, G., CARNEVALE-SCHIANCA, S., and ALLIOD, R. 1963 Ricerche sul comportamento della sensibilità gustative alla feniltiocarbamide. (Research on the behavior of taste sensitivity to phenylthiocarbamide.) ASME, **116**: 234–45.

MAY, R. M. 1925 The relation of nerves to degenerating and regenerating taste buds. JEZO, **42**: 371–410.

MAYBEE, G. R. 1939 Flavor in food. SPML, **62**: 40–44.

——. 1939 Flavour in food. Classification and comparison of tastes. CCPI, **23**: 115–18.

MAYER. 1843 Über die Zunge als Geschmacksorgan. (The tongue as a taste organ.) NOAL,
20: 721–48.

MAYER, B. 1927 Messende Untersuchungen über
die Umstimmung des Geschmackswerkzeugs.
(Quantitative studies of the adaptation of the
sense of taste.) ZESI, 58: 133–52.

———. 1935 Diabetes und Geschmack (Diabetes
and taste), in Die Beziehungen des Diabetes
mellitus zu den oberen Luftwegen. MOLA, 69:
564–82.

MAYER-GROSS, W. 1928 Pathologie der Wahrnehmung. II: Geruch und Geschmack (Pathology of perception. II: Smell and taste), in
Handbuch der Geisteskrankheiten, I. O.
Bumke, J. Springer, Berlin, 732 pp. (see pp.
488–89).

MAYER-GROSS, W., and WALKER, J. W. 1946 Taste
and selection of food in hypoglycaemia. BJEP,
27: 297–305.

MAYR, K. 1904 Beiträge zur Physiologie und
Pathologie des Geschmackssinnes. (Contribution to the physiology and pathology of the
sense of taste.) Inaugural Dissertation, F.
Scheiner, Würzburg, 68 pp.

McBURNEY, D. H., and PFAFFMANN, C. 1963
Gustatory adaptation to saliva and sodium
chloride. JEPS, 65: 523–29.

McCANCE, R. A., and LAWRENCE, R. D. 1933 An
investigation of quebrachitol as a sweetening
agent for diabetics. BIJO, 27: 986–89.

McCLEARY, R. A. 1951 A physiological mechanism of sugar preference. Unpublished Ph.D.
thesis, The Johns Hopkins University, 46 pp.

———. 1953 Taste and post-ingestion factors in
specific-hunger behavior. JCPP, 46: 411–21.

McCREESH, A. H., and MANN, D. E. JR. 1958
Effect of orally administered sodium iodide
and sodium iodate on blood sugar response to
thiourea in rats. JAPM, 47: 56–57.

McCUTCHEON, N. B. 1963 The effect of sodium
deficiency on the recognition threshold for
sodium chloride. Unpublished Master's thesis,
Brown University, 46 pp.

McDONNELL. 1875 On a case of double facial
palsy, with observations on the physiology of
the nerves supplying the fore part of the
tongue. MCTR, 58: 369–75.

McFADDEN, H. B. 1937 The influence of temperature and solution concentration on reaction
time to taste stimuli (sodium chloride). JOPS,
4: 349–63.

McGINTY, D., EPSTEIN, A. N., and TEITELBAUM,
P. 1965 The contribution of oropharyngeal
sensations to hypothalamic hyperphagia.
ANBE, 13: 413–18.

McGREGOR, G. 1937 Comparative anatomy of the
tongue. TALA, 59: 33–44.

———. 1938 Comparative anatomy of the
tongue. AORH, 47: 196–211.

McINDOO, N. E. 1927 Smell and taste and their
applications. SCMO, 25: 481–503.

———. 1928 Responses of insects to smell and
taste and their value in control. JEEN, 21:
903–13.

———. 1934 Chemoreceptors of blowflies. JOMO,
56: 445–75.

McLAURIN, W. A. 1964 Postirradiation saccharin
avoidance in rats as a function of the interval
between ingestion and exposure. JCPP, 57:
316–17.

MEE, A. J. 1934 Taste and chemical constitution.
SCPR, 29: 228–35.

MEINHOLD, W. 1935 Kettengleichungen im Gebiete des Geschmackssinnes. Gleich sauer
schmeckende Lösungen. (Serial equations in
the field of gustation; equally sour tasting
solutions.) Inaugural Dissertation, B. Sporn,
Zeulenroda, Jena, 40 pp.

MELLO, M. DE. 1940 Parosmia e parageustia consecutiva a trauma cerebral. (Parosmia and
parageusia following cerebral trauma.) RBOR,
8: 467–72.

MELLO, N. K., and MENDELSON, J. H. 1964 Operant performance by rats for alcohol reinforcement: A comparison of alcohol-preferring and
nonpreferring animals. QJSA, 25: 226–34.

MELLON, F., DE, and EVANS, D. R. 1961 Electrophysiological evidence that water stimulates a
fourth sensory cell in the blowfly taste receptor. AMZO, 1: 372–73. (Abstract.)

MERKEL, F. 1880 Über die Endigungen der sensiblen Nerven in der Haut der Wirbelthiere.
(On sensory nerve endings on the skin of
vertebrates.) H. Schmidt, Rostock, 214 pp.

MERTON, B. B. 1958 Taste sensitivity to P. T. C.
in 60 Norwegian families with 176 children.
Confirmation of the hypothesis of single gene
inheritance. AGSM, 8: 114–28.

METZNER, C. A. 1943 Investigation of odour and
taste. Psychological principles. WLCO, 6: 5–18.

———. 1960 Investigation of odour and taste.
Psychological principles. BRGI, 46: 532–56.

MEYER, D. R. 1952 The stability of human
gustatory sensitivity during changes in time
of food deprivation. JCPP, 45: 373–76.

MEYER, H. 1959 Thalamussyndrom mit Sensi-
bilitatsstörungen in Gesicht und Mund ohne
Geschmacksstörungen. (Thalamic syndrome
with sensory disturbances of face and mouth
without taste impairment.) PNMP, 11: 129–32.
(Russian summary.)

MEYER, S. 1896 Durchschneidungsversuche am
Nervus Glossopharyngeus (Experiments to cut
the glossopharyngeal nerve.) Inaugural Dissertation, Berlin, 30 pp.

———. 1897 Durchschneidungsversuche am
Nervus Glossopharyngeus. (Experiments to cut
the glossopharyngeal nerve.) AMAE, 48: 143–
45.

MHASKAR, K. S., and CAIUS, J. F. 1930 A study
of Indian medicinal plants. II: Gymnema sylvestre, Brown. IJMR, 17, 49 pp. (see pp. 3–8,
14–15).

MICHAEL, S. 1932 Ueber die Beziehungen des Geschmacks zur chemischen Konstitution. (The relationships of taste to chemical constitution.) BIZE, **255**: 351–77.

MICHAEL, S., and LIMMER, G. 1933 Physiologische und termische Versuche an Geschmacksstoffen. (Thermal and physiological studies on taste substances.) PAGP, **233**: 645–51.

MICHELSON, P. 1891 Ueber das Vorhandensein von Geschmacksempfindung im Kehlkopf. (On the existence of taste perception in the larynx.) VAPA, **123**: 389–401.

MIGNOT, H., and LEMPERIERE, T. 1955 Crises olfacto-gustatives. La crise uncinée. (Olfactory-gustatory crises. Uncinate crisis.) EMCP, **1**: 7.

MIKAMI, M. 1931 Ueber den Binnen-netz-apparat der verschiedenen Zellen der Geschmacks-knospe. (The internal net apparatus of the different cells in the taste buds.) DAJK, **36**: 56. (Abstract.)

MIKI, T., TANAKA, T., and FURUHTA, T. 1960 On the distribution of the ABO blood groups and the taste ability for phenyl-thio-carbamide (P.T.C.) of the Lepchas and the Khasis. PRJA, **36**: 78–80.

MILLER, R. E. 1965 Barium sulfate suspensions. RADL, pp. 241–51.

MILLER, W. T. 1946 Sweetening powers of sugars compared. FOPA, **27**: 50, 54.

MILLOT, J. 1936 Le sens du goût chez les araignées. (The sense of taste in spiders.) BSZF, **61**: 27–38.

MILLS, C. K. 1908 The cerebral centers for taste and smell and the uncinate group of fits, based upon the study of a case tumor of the temporal lobe with necropsy. JAMA, **51**: 880–85.

MILLS, F., WEIR, C. E., and WILSON, G. D. 1960 The effect of sugar on the flavor and color of smoked hams. FOTE, **14**: 94–97.

MINGAZZINI, G. 1894 Sui disturbi del gusto negli alienati. (Disturbances of taste in the lunatic.) AACL, **15**: 75–95.

MINNICH, D. E. 1921 An experimental study of the tarsal chemoreceptors of two nymphalid butterflies. JEZO, **33**: 173–203.

———. 1922 A quantitative study of tarsal sensitivity to solutions of saccharose, in the red admiral butterfly, *Pyrameis atalanta* Linnaean. JEZO, **36**: 445–57.

———. 1922 The chemical sensitivity of the tarsi of the red admiral butterfly, *Pyrameis atalanta* Linnaean. JEZO, **35**: 57–81.

———. 1926 The chemical sensitivity of the tarsi of certain muscid flies (*Phormia regina, Phormia terrae novae* R. D. and *Lucilia sericata* Meigen. BIBM, **51**: 166–78.

———. 1926 The organs of taste on the proboscis of the blowfly, *Phormia regina* Meigen. ANRE, **34**: 126. (Abstract.)

———. 1929 The chemical senses of insects. QRBI, **4**: 100–12.

———. 1929 The chemical sensitivity of the legs of the blowfly. *Calliphora vomitoria* Linnaean, to various sugars. ZVPH, **11**: 1–55.

———. 1931 The sensitivity of the oral lobes of the proboscis of the blowfly, *Calliphora vomitora* Linnaean, to various sugars. JEZO, **60**: 121–39.

———. 1932 The contact chemoreceptors of the honey bee, *Apis mellifera* Linnaean. JEZO, **61**: 375–93.

MINTZ, B., and STONE, L. S. 1934 Transplantation of taste organs in adult *Triturus viridescens*. PSEB, **31**: 1080–82.

MIYAJI, N., and UTSUNOMIYA, S. 1956 (The threshold test. Part 6: Salty). JSBJ, **51**: 41–42. (In Japanese.)

MIYASHITA, K. 1935 Ueber die umwallte Zungen-papille der Chinesen. (On the circumvallate papillae of the tongue of Chinese.) JOOM, **22**: 17–18.

MIYAZAKI, H. 1933 Pigment in den Geschmacks-papillen des Menschen. (Pigment in taste papillae of man.) JPMA, **3**: 241–43.

MOCHIZUKI, Y. 1937 An observation on the numerical and topographical relations of taste buds to circumvallate papillae of Japanese. OFAJ, **15**: 595–608.

———. 1938 (Studies on the circumvallate papillae of the Japanese.) SHGO, **18**: 221–41. (In Japanese.)

MOCHIZUKI, Y. 1939 Studies on the papilla foliata of Japanese. 1: The number of papillae foliatae. 2: The number of taste buds. OFAJ, **18**: 337–54, 355–69.

MODRZEWSKA, K. 1952 Reakcje smakowe na fenyltiokarbamid. (Taste reaction to phenyl-thiocarbamide.) APYP, **3**: 206–7. (Russian and English summaries.)

MODRZEWSKA, K. 1953 Badania nad uczuleniem ludzi na fenltiomocznik. (Investigations on sensitivity of people to phenylthiocarbamide.) AUSK, **52**: 522–26.

MOHR, J. 1951 Taste sensitivity to phenylthiourea in Denmark. ANEU, **16**: 282–86.

MÖNCH, P. H. 1916 Beitrag zur Kenntnis der Geschmacksinnervation der Zunge. (Contribution to the knowledge of taste innervation of the tongue.) Inaugural Dissertation, O. Lerner, Leipzig, 28 pp.

MONCRIEFF, R. W. 1944 Gustation. I, II, III. FOMA, **19**: 203–5, 275–79, 356–61.

———. 1944 *The Chemical Senses*. John Wiley & Sons, New York, 424 pp.

———. 1948 Relative sweetness. FLAV, **11** (5): 5–8; (6) 5–11.

———. 1949 Taste differences in individuals. FOMA, **24**: 257–61.

———. 1949 The sweetness of synthetics. FOMA, **24**: 29–32.

——. 1950 The sense of taste. PEOR, 41: 259–63.

——. 1950 The tastes. Part I: The salt taste. Part II: The sour taste. PEOR, 41: 367–71, 415–19

——. 1951 *The Chemical Senses*. 2nd ed. Leonard Hill Ltd., London, 538 pp.

——. 1951 The tastes. Part III: The sweet taste. Part IV: The bitter taste. PEOR, 42: 25–30, 51–55.

——. 1955 Taste, smell and molecular weight. CPCN, 18: 131–33.

——. 1962 The first international conference on olfaction and taste. APEO, 77: 17–18.

——. 1964 The metallic taste. PEOR, 55: 205–7.

MONES, J. 1950 Jacobson's organ. Why do full upper denture wearers experience loss of taste and smell? DESU, 26: 185–86.

MONTENEGRO, L. 1964 P.T.C. tasting among Tucano Indians. ANHG, 28: 185–87

MOOK, D. G. 1963 Oral and postingestional determinants of the intake of various solutions in rats with esophageal fistulas. JCPP, 56: 645–50.

MOON, C. N., and PULLEN, E. W. 1963 Effect of chorda tympani section during middle ear surgery. LARY, 73: 392–405.

MOORE, C. A., and ELLIOTT, R. 1944 Numerical and regional distribution of taste buds on the tongue of the pigeon. ANRE, 88: 449. (Abstract.)

——. 1946 Numerical and regional distribution of taste buds on the tongue of the bird. JCNE, 84: 119–31.

MOORE, M. E., LINKER, R., and PURCELL, M. 1965 Taste-sensitivity after eating: A signal-detection approach. AJPC, 78: 107–11.

MOOS, S. 1867 Innervationsstörungen durch Applikation des künstlichen Trommelfells. (Innervation disturbances through application of an artificial tympanic membrane.) ZMWI, 5: 721. (Abstract.)

——. 1869 Ueber Störungen des Geschmacks und Tastsinnes der Zunge in Folge von Applikation des künstlichen Trommelfells bei grossen Trommelfell-Perforationen. (On disturbances of the senses of taste and touch on the tongue as a result of artificial application of a tympanic membrane due to severe tympanic membrane perforation.) AAOH, 1: 207–16.

——. 1879 Ein Fall von Geschmackslähmung nach Exstirpation eines von der Steigbügelregion entspringenden Polypen. (A case of taste paralysis after extirpation of polyps in the region of the stapes.) ZHNO, 8: 222–23.

MORGAN, C. T., and STELLAR, E. 1950 Gustation, in *Physiological Psychology*. 2nd ed. McGraw-Hill, New York, 623 pp. (see pp. 116–22).

MORGANE, P. J. 1961 The effects of taste-abolishing thalamic lesions on the exaggerated reactivity of static phase hypothalamic obese rats to dietary sensory qualities. PYSO, 4: 77. (Abstract.)

MORITA, H. 1959 Initiation of spike potentials in contact chemosensory hairs of insects. III: D. C. stimulation and generator potential of labellar chemoreceptor of calliphora. JCCP, 54: 189–204.

——. 1963 Generator potential of insect chemoreceptors. PCZO, 3: 105–6.

MORITA, H., DOIRA, S., TAKEDA, K., and KUWABARA, M. 1957 Electrical response of contact chemoreceptor on tarsus of the butterfly, *Vanessa indica*. FKFS, 2: 119–39.

MORITA, H., and TAKEDA, K. 1959 Initiation of spike potentials in contact chemosensory hairs of insects. II: The effect of electric current on tarsal chemosensory hairs of Vanessa. JCCP, 54: 177–87.

MORITA, H., and YAMASHITA, S. 1959 Generator potential of insect chemoreceptor. SCIE, 130: 922.

——. 1959 The back-firing of impulses in a labellar chemosensory hair of the fly. FKFS, 3: 81–87.

MORRIS, D. D., and SMITH, J. C. 1964 X-Ray-conditioned saccharin aversion induced during the immediate postexposure period. RARE, 21: 513–19.

*MORRISON, G. R. 1959 The rhinencephalic representation of taste in the albino rat. Unpublished Ph.D. thesis, Brown University.

MORRISON, G. R., and NORRISON, W. 1966 Taste detection in the rat. CJPS, 20: 208–17.

MORSE, R. L. D. 1954 Exploratory studies of preschool children's taste discrimination and preference for selected citrus juices. FSHS, 66: 292–301.

MORTON, N. E., MOLONEY, W. C., and FUJII, T. 1954 Linkage in man: Pelger's nuclear anomaly, taste, and blood groups. AJHG, 6: 38–43.

MORUYAMA, Y. 1935 On the papillae vallatae of the Formosan-Chinese. TWIZ, 34: 1608–11.

MORUZI, A., and LECHINTSKI. 1938 Quelques observations au sujet des voies de transmission des sensations gustatives chez l'homme. (Observations on transmission pathways of taste sensations in man.) RENE, 70: 478–83.

MOSEL, J. N., and KANTROWITZ, G. 1952 The effect of monosodium glutamate on acuity to the primary tastes. AJPC, 65: 573–79.

——. 1954 Absolute sensitivity to the glutamic taste. JGPS, 51: 11–18.

MOTTA, G. 1959 I centri corticali del gusto. (The cortical taste centers.) BOSM, 131: 480–93.

MOTTA, G., and BARAVELLI, P. 1961 Indagini sulla sensibilità gustativa in soggetti con esiti di encefalopatie prenatali, neonatali o della prima infanzia. (Investigation on the gustatory sensitivity in subjects with prenatal, neonatal and early childhood encephalopaties.) RNSA, 7: 59–66. (English and German summaries.)

Motta, G., Nucci, C., and Alvisi, C. 1964 Contributo alla conoscenza delle vie nervose periferiche del gusto. (Contribution to the knowledge of the peripheral nerve pathways of taste.) COUR, 33: 175–98. (English and French summaries.)

Müller, A. 1911 Geschmacksparästesie auf arteriosklerotischer Grundlage (Taste parasthesia based on arteriosclerosis.) ZIME, 32: 689–91.

Müller, G. P. 1964 Zur Klinik, Prognose und Therapie der kryptogenetischen peripheran Facialisparese unter besonderer Berücksichtigung der prednison-Behandlung. Klinische Studie anhand von 278 nachkontrollierten Fällen. (On the clinical picture, prognosis and therapy of cryptogenetic peripheral facial paralysis with special reference to prednisone therapy. Clinical studies based on 278 follow-up cases.) SANP, 93: 35–71. (French and English summaries.)

Müller, J. 1837 Historisch-anatomische Bemerkungen. (Historical-anatomical comments.) AAPA, pp. 273–96.

——. 1838 Vom Geschmackssinn (Taste sense), in Handbuch der Physiologie des Menschen. J. Hölscher, Coblenz, 502 pp. (see pp. 489–94).

——. 1840 Vom Geschmackssinn (Taste sense), in Handbuch der Physiologie des Menschen, II. J. Hölscher, Coblenz, 780 pp. (see pp. 489–94).

——. 1844 Von den Sinnesnerven (Sense nerves), in Handbuch der Physiologie des Menschen. J. Hölscher, Coblenz, 741 pp. (see pp. 667–72.)

Münch, F. 1896 Die Topographie der Papillen der Zunge des Menschen und der Säugethiere. (The topography of the papillae on the tongue of humans and mammals.) MRAR, 6: 605–90.

Murray, A. 1961 Two gustatory cell types of rabbit taste buds. ANRE, 139: 331. (Abstract.)

Murray, E. J., Wells, H., Kohn, M., and Miller, N. E. 1953 Sodium sucaryl: A substance which tastes sweet to human subjects but is avoided by rats. JCPP, 46: 134–37.

Murray, R. G., and Murray, A. 1960 The fine structure of the taste buds of rhesus and cynomolgus monkeys. ANRE, 138: 211–19.

*Murskii, L. I. 1959 Opyt izucheniya vosstanovleniya analizatorov u ozhuvlennykh zhivotnykh. (Recovery of analyzer function in resuscitated animals.) UPIY, 32.

Müssle, H. 1891 Vergleichende Geschmacksprüfungen zwischen Alkoholen, Glykosen und Saccharosen. (Comparative taste tests between alcohols, glycols and saccharose.) Inaugural Dissertation, F. Fromme, Würzburg, 28 pp.

Myers, C. S. 1903 Taste, in Reports of the Cambridge Anthropological Expedition to Torres Straits, II (2). The University Press, Cambridge, 223 pp. (see pp. 186–88).

——. 1904 The taste-names of primitive peoples. BJSG, 1: 117–26.

Myers, R. D., and Carey, R. 1961 Preference factors in experimental alcoholism. SCIE, 134: 469–70.

Nachman, M. 1957 The influence of diet and age on saccharine preference in rats. AMPS, 12: 461. (Abstract.)

——. 1959 The inheritance of saccharin preference. JCPP, 52: 451–57.

——. 1962 Taste preferences for sodium salts by adrenalectomized rats. JCPP, 55: 1124–29.

——. 1963 Learned aversion to the taste of lithium chloride and generalization to other salts. JCPP, 56: 343–49.

——. 1963 Taste preferences for lithium chloride by adrenalectomized rats. AJPH, 205: 219–21.

Nachman, M., and Pfaffmann, C. 1963 Gustatory nerve discharge in normal and sodium-deficient rats. JCPP, 56: 1007–11.

Nagaki, J., Yamashita, S., and Sato, M. 1964 Neural response of cat to taste stimuli of varying temperatures. JJPH, 14: 67–89.

Nagel, W. 1892 Der Geschmackssinn der Actinen. (The taste sense of actinia.) ZOAN, 15: 334–38.

——. 1904 Einige Bemerkungen über nasales Schmecken. (Some remarks on nasal taste.) ZPSI, 35: 268–89.

——. 1905 Bemerkungen zu der vorstehenden Arbeit von Zwaardemaker "Riechend Schmecken." (Remarks on the previous work by Zwaardemaker; "Nasal taste.") ZPSI, 38: 196–99.

——. 1905 Der Geschmackssinn. (The taste sense.) HPME, 3: 621–46.

Nagel, W. A. 1894 Ergebnisse vergleichend-physiologischer und anatomischer Untersuchungen über den Geruchs- und Geschmackssinn und ihre Organe. (Comparison of physiological and anatomical investigations of the olfactory and taste senses and their organs.) BIZN, 14: 543–55.

——. 1894 Vergleichend physiologische und anatomische Untersuchungen über den Geruchs- und Geschmackssinn und ihre Organe, mit einleitenden Betrachtungen aus der allgemeinen vergleichenden Sinnesphysiologie. (Comparative physiological and anatomical studies on the sense of smell and taste, and their organs, with introductory considerations of general comparative physiology of the senses.) BIZO, 18: 1–208.

——. 1896 Über die Wirkung des chlorsauren Kali auf den Geschmackssinn. (The effect of potassium chloride on the sense of taste.) ZPSI, 10: 235–39.

Nageotte, J. 1906 The pars intermedia or nervus intermedius of Wrisberg, and the bulbopontine gustatory nucleus in man. RNPS, 4: 473–88.

NAIDUS, D. I. 1940 Problema zapakha i vkusa, cviaz' mezhdu nimi i khimicheskim stroenium veshchestva. (The problem of smell and taste: The connection between them and the chemical structure of matter.) PRIR, 29: 29–37.

NAKAJIMA, A. 1959 (Distribution and inheritance of taste ability for phenyl-thio-carbamide [P.T.C.], with special reference to difference in threshold values between homo- and heterozygotes.) HAZA, 25(5) II: 28–41. (In Japanese.)

NAKHMINOVICH, I. M. 1952 U roli dieteticheskogo faktora v patogeneze i terapii skrofuleznykh zabolevanii glaz (opyt nevrogennoi interpretatsii etiologii skofuleza glaz.) (Role of dietetic factor in pathogenesis of scrofulous eye disease [neurogenic interpretation of ocular scrofulous].) VEOF, 31: 35–45.

NAVARRO, R. 1897 Interpretación hipotética de algunos síntomas del gusto. (Hypothetical interpretations of some symptoms of taste.) GMES, 44: 802–5.

NEJAD, M. S. 1962 Factors involved in the mechanism of stimulation of gustatory receptors and bare nerve endings of the tongue of the rat. DIAS, 22 (3) : 2855–56.

NELSON, A. K. 1928 The reactions of infants to thermal, gustatory, and olfactory stimuli. Unpublished Ph.D. thesis, Ohio State University, 173 pp.

NELSON, D. 1947 Do rats select more sodium chloride than they need? FEPR, 6: 169.

NEMANOVA, T. P. 1941 Uslovnye refleksy na vkusovye razdrazheniia u detei pervykh mesiatsev zhizni. (Conditioned reflexes to taste stimuli in infants.) FZLZ, 30: 478–83. (English summary.)

NEMETSCHEK-GANSLER, H., and FERNER, H. 1964 Über die Ultrastruktur der Geschmacksknospen. (On the ultrastructure of the taste buds.) ZZAC, 63: 155–78.

NERI, A. 1937 Contributo allo studio del rapporto tra sapore e costituzione chimica. Ricerche nel gruppo delle nafthoisotriazine. Nota II, III, IV. (Contribution to the study of the relation between taste and chemical constitution. Research on the naphtoisotriazine group. Note II, III, IV.) GCIT, 67: 282–88; 289–93; 448–53.

———. 1940 Contributo allo studio del rapporto tra sapore e costituzione chimica. Ricerche nel gruppo delle naftoisotriazine. Nota X, XI, XII. (Contribution to the study of the relation between taste and chemical constitution. The naphthoisotriazine group. Note X, XI, XII.) GCIT, 70: 311–17, 317–22; 323–27.

———. 1941 Contributo allo studio del rapporto tra sapore e costituzione chimica. Ricerche nel gruppo delle naftoisotriazine. Nota XIII. (Contribution to the study of the relation between taste and chemical constitution. Research on the naphthoisotriazine group. Note XIII.) GCIT, 71: 201–8.

———. 1941 Le sostanze sapide naturali e artificiali.- Rapporto tra costituzione chimica e sapore. Sintesi scientifica e technica. (Natural and artificial taste substances. Relations between chemical constitution and taste. Scientific and technical synthesis.) CINM, 23: 11–19.

NERI, A., and GRIMALDI, G. 1937 Contributo allo studio del rapporto tra sapore e costituzione chimica. Ricerche nel gruppo delle naftoisotriazine. Nota I, V. (Contribution to the study of the relation between taste and chemical constitution. Research on the naphthoisotriazine group. Note I, V.) GCIT, 67: 273–82; 453–60.

NEUBERG, C., and WOLFF, H. 1903 Über α- und β-2-amino-d-glucoheptonsäure. (On α- and β-2-amino-d-glucoheptone acid.) BDCG, 36: 618–20.

NEUFFER, E. 1925 Der Bau der Papillae filiformes der menschlichen Zunge. (The structure of the filiform papillae on the human tongue.) ZAEN, 75: 319–60.

NEUMAN, F. J. 1943 Studies on the psychophysics of taste: The determination of stimulus and difference limens for sucrose, dextrose and saccharin. Unpublished Ph.D. thesis, Ohio State University, 166 pp.

NEUMANN, E. 1864 Die Elektrizität als Mittel zur Untersuchung des Geschmackssinnes im gesunden und kranken Zustande und die Geschmacksfunktion der Chorda tympani. (Electricity as a means of studying the sense of taste in healthy and pathological conditions and the taste function of the chorda tympani.) KMJB, 4: 1–22.

———. 1864 Partieller Verlust des Geschmackssinnes als Folge einer Otitis interna, ein neuer Beitrag zur Kenntnis der Chorda tympani. (Partial loss of the sense of taste as a result of internal otitis: A new contribution to the knowledge of the chorda tympani.) KMJB, 4: 340–44.

NEUMANN, H. 1896 Bemerkung über die Geschmacksempfindung bei kleinen Kindern. (Comments on taste perception of small children.) JAKI, 41: 155–59.

NEVILLE-JONES, D. 1957 Taste and smell. NATU, 180: 274–75.

NEVRAEVA, O. G. 1959 Izmeneniia vkusovoi chuvstvitel'nosti pri bolezni botkina i tsirrozakh pecheni. (Changes in the gustatory sensitivity in patients with infectious hepatitis and cirrhosis of the liver.) SOME, 6: 67–74. (English summary.)

NEWBRUN, E. 1962 Amylase content and flow rate of saliva. IADR, 40: 14. (Abstract.)

NICKLES, J. 1861 Sur la théorie physique des

odeurs et des saveurs. (On the physical theory of odors and flavors.) MSTA, **30**: 365–85.

NICOL, H. 1960 Towards a theory of tastes. BRGI, **46**: 588–98.

NIEMAN, C. 1958 Relative Süsskraft von Zuckerarten. (Relative sweetness of sugars.) ZUSU, **11**: 420–22, 465–67, 505–7, 632–33, 670–71, 752–53, 791–92, 840–42, 878–79, 933–34, 974, 1012, 1051, 1089.

———. 1960 Sweetness of glucose, dextrose, and sucrose. AIFC, pp. 3–22.

NIKITINA, I. P. 1960 Fiziologiia vysshei nervnoi deiatel'nosti. Eksterotseptivnye uslovnye refleksy pri razlichnykh solevykh rezhimakh. (Exteroceptive conditioned reflexes in the presence of sodium-chloride restriction and supplementation.) NSLF, **2**: 115–21.

NINOMIYA, K., IKEDA, S., YAMAGUCHI, S., and YO-SHIKAWA, S. 1965 (Relation of various amino acids to taste.) RSEC, **6**: 16–37. (In Japanese.)

NIOSI, C., and VENSI, E. 1958 Contributo allo studio del sapore metallico. (Contribution to the study of metallic tastes.) MIOT, **8**: 489–93.

*NISHI, K. 1924 Über die Papillae vallatae beim Japaner. (On the vallate papillae of Japanese.) CHIZ, **2**: 4.

———. 1927 (The circumvallate papillae of the Japanese.) CHIZ, **5**: 1635–51. (In Japanese.)

NISHIDA, I. 1943 On the summation of the gustatory stimulation. JPSJ, **8**(52): 521. (Abstract.)

NISHIDA, I., TORIGOE, H., HAMAMURA, H., and MIYAHARA, M. 1958 (Effect of alkali metal ions on the taste receptors.) YOIZ, **9**: 619–23. (In Japanese.)

NISHIDA, I., TORIGOE, H., and MIYOSI, Z. 1958 (Interference in the taste sensation.) YOIZ, **9**: 609–15. (In Japanese.)

NIXON, C. J. 1876 Double facial paralysis, with some remarks upon the nerves of taste. IJMS, **62**: 105–12.

NOFERI, G., and GUIDIZI, S. 1946 Le variazioni della sensibilità gustativa in particolari situazioni fisiologiche ed in alcuni stati morbosi. Nota IV: Le variazioni della soglia gustativa per l'acido e della soglia olfattiva per l'odore limone durante la gravidanza. (Variation in gustatory sensitivity in specific psysiological states and in disease. Note IV: Variation in taste response to acid and olfactory response of lemon odor during pregnancy.) RCCM, **46**(5): 89–100.

NONNIS-MARZANO, C., MARCUCCI, L., and MARCATO, D. 1961 Comportamento di alcune attività enzimatiche nella funzione gustativa in condizioni normali e durante lo stato gravidico. (Behavior of some enzymatic activities in the gustatory function in normal conditions and during pregnancy.) AOGI, **83**: 236–48. (English, German, and French summaries.)

NONOYAMA, J. 1936 The distribution of the taste-buds on the tongue of some reptilia. JSHU, **5**: 57–66.

*NOSEDA, M. 1944 Contribution à l'étude des hallucinations olfactives et gustatives et de leur valeur pronostique. (Contribution to the study of olfactory and gustatory hallucinations and their prognostic value.)

NOYCE, W. K., COLEMAN, C. H., and BARR, J. T. 1951 Vinology in sweetening agents. I: A vinology of dulcin. JACS, **73**: 1295–96.

NUCCI, P. 1959 Sensibilità gustativa nei portatori di protesi totale in resina. (Taste sensitivity in patients with total dentures that have been treated with resin.) CLOP, **6**: 338–48.

NÜNDEL, R. B. 1936 Kettengleichungen in Gebiete des Geschmackssinnes: gleich bitter schmeckende Lösungen. (Chain equations in the area of taste: solutions of equal bitterness.) Inaugural Dissertation, K. Triltsch, Jena, 27 pp.

NYQUIST, G. 1949 The influence of prosthetic and operative restorations on bitter taste-testing ability. AOSC, **8**: 221–35.

NYSSEN, R., and HELSMOORTEL, J., JR. 1936 Ageusie traumatique et auto-suggestion. (Traumatic ageusia and auto-suggestion.) BUME, **50**: 161–62.

O, T. 1905 Inversity of taste. BMJO, **1**: 516.

OAKLEY, B. 1960 Electrophysiologically monitored lesions in the gustatory thalamic relay of the albino rat. Unpublished Master's thesis, Brown University, 153 pp.

———. 1962 Microelectrode analysis of second order gustatory neurons in the albino rat. DIAS, **23**: 2593–94.

———. 1965 Impaired operant behavior following lesions of the thalamic taste nucleus. JCPP, **59**: 202–10.

OAKLEY, B., and BENJAMIN, R. M. 1966 Neural mechanisms of taste. PHRE, **46**: 173–211.

OAKLEY, B., and PFAFFMANN, C. 1962 Electrophysiologically monitored lesions in the gustatory thalamic relay of the albino rat. JCPP, **55**: 155–60.

ODDO, B., and PEROTTI, A. 1937 Variazioni sul potere dolcificante della saccarina. Nota IV: Influenze relative all'associazione della saccarina con sostanze ad aggruppamento ureidico. (Variation in the sweetening power of saccharin. Note IV: Influence of the ureide group.) GCIT, **67**: 543–52.

———. 1940 Variazioni sul potere dolcificante della saccarina. Nota V: Influenze relative all'associazione della saccarina con sostanze ad aggruppamento ureidico. (Variation in the sweetening power of saccharin. Note V: Influence of the ureide group.) GCIT, **70**: 567–74.

OEFELE, VON. 1894 Gymnema silvestre bei unan-
genehmen Geschmacksempfindungen. (The unpleasant taste sensations of Gymnema sylvestre.) AMCZ, 63: 121–23.

OERTLY, E., and MYERS, R. G. 1919 A new theory
relating constitution to taste. (Preliminary
paper) Simple relations between the constitution of aliphatic compounds and their sweet
taste. JACS, 41: 855, 867.

———. 1920 A new theory relating constitution
to taste. (Preliminary paper) Simple relations
between the constitution of aliphatic compounds and their sweet taste. CNEW, 121:
159–65.

OGATA, M., URATA, Y., TOYOTA, B., and KISHI-
HARA, K. 1960 The lingual papillae of a red
panda. KSGZ, 14: 293–94.

OGAWA, H. 1940 Studien über die umwallten
Zungenpapillen bei japanischen Zwillingsfeten.
(Studies on the circumvallate papillae in Jap-
anese twin foetus.) OFAJ, 19: 377–90.

OGILVIE, J. P. 1922 Comparative sweetness of re-
fined and direct consumption of cane sugar.
ISUJ, 24: 288–90.

OGNIBENE, S. 1940 Ageusia produzida por ins-
tilacão medicamentosa no ouvido. (Ageusia
produced by medication inserted in the ear.)
RBOR, 8: 54–56.

*OHARA, M. 1966 Shokuhin no agi. (Taste of
foods.) Korinshoin, Tokyo, 286 pp.

ÖHRVALL, H. A. 1889 Studier och undersökningar
öfver smaksinnet. (Studies and investigations
on the sense of taste.) UPSF, 24: 353–439.

———. 1891 Untersuchungen über den Geschmacksinn. (Investigations on the sense of taste.)
SAPH, 2: 1–69.

———. 1901 Die Modalitäts- und Qualitätsbe-
griffe in der Sinnesphysiologie und deren
Bedeutung. (The modality and quality concepts in sensory physiology and their significance.) SAPH, 11: 245–72.

OKADA, S. 1931 Über die Geschmacksknospe der
Papilla foliata der Maus. (On the taste buds of
the foliate papilla of the mouse.) DAJK, 37:
86.

———. 1932 (On the foliate papillae of the rat.)
(In Japanese.) AIIZ, 39: 720–31.

O'KELLY, L. I., and FALK, J. L. 1958 Water regulation in the rat. II: The effects of preloads of
water and sodium chloride on the bar-pressing
performance of thirsty rats. JCPP, 51: 22–25.

OLANO, G. 1910 Alucinaciones del sentido del
gusto, precursoras (aura) de ataques histero
epileptiformes, curados por autosugestión. (Hallucinations of the sense of taste, precursors
[aura] of hysterical epileptic attacks, cured by
autosuggestion.) CRME, 27: 315–17.

OLEA HERRAIZ, I. 1940 Sugerencias para en estudio del sabor. (Suggestions on the study of
taste.) MCGU, 5: 291–98.

OLMSTED, J. M. D. 1920 The nerve as a forma-
tive influence in the development of taste-
buds. JCNE, 31: 465–68.

———. 1920 The results of cutting the seventh
cranial nerve in Amiurus nebulosus Lesueur.
JEZO, 31: 369–401.

———. 1921 Effects of cutting the lingual nerve
of the dog. JCNE, 33: 149–54.

———. 1922 Taste fibers and the chorda tympani nerve. JCNE, 34: 337–41.

———. 1939 Smell and taste. ARPH, 1: 465–66.

———. 1940 Taste and smell. ARPH, 2: 304.

———. 1945 Smell and taste. ARPH, 7: 522.

OLMSTED, J. M. D., and PINGER, R. R. 1936 Regeneration of taste buds after suture of the
lingual and hypoglossal nerves. AJPH, 116:
225–27.

OMM, P. 1958 Have you a blind sense of taste?
DRRE, 6: 111–15.

OPPEL, A. 1899 Ueber die Zunge der Mono-
tremen, Marsupialier und von Manis javanica.
(On the tongue of monotremata, marsupials
and of Javanese manis.) SZFA, 4: 105–70.

———. 1899 Zur Topographie der Zungendrüsen des Menschen und einiger Säugetiere
(The topography of the glands of the tongue
in man and some mammals), in Festschrift
zum 70 Geburtstag von Kupffers. G. Fischer,
Jena, 750 pp. (see pp. 11–32).

OPPENHEIMER, W. 1932 Die Zunge des Orang-
Utans. (The tongue of orangutans.) GEMJ, 69:
62–97.

OSEPIAN, V. A. 1958 Razvitie funktsii vkusovogo
(khimicheskogo) analizatora u detei pervogo
goda zhizni. (Development of the function of
the gustatory [chemical] analyzer in children
in the first year of life). ZVND, 8: 828–34.
(English summary.)

———. 1959 Development of the function of the
taste analyzer in puppies. (Translated by R.
Crawford.) FZLZ, 45: 137–42.

OSTER, R. H., PROUT, L. M., SHIPLEY, E. R., POL-
LACK, B R., and BRADLEY, J. E. 1953 Human
salivary buffering rate measured in situ in
response to an acid stimulus in common
beverages. JAPY, 6: 348–54.

OSTWALD, W., and KUHN, A. 1921 Zur Kenntniss
des sauren Geschmacks. (Causes of the sour
taste.) KOZE, 29: 266–71.

OTTOLENGHI, S. 1889 Il gusto nei criminali in
rapporto ai normali. (Gustation in criminals
compared with the normal.) GMDT, 37: 218–
22.

———. 1889 Il gusto nei criminali in rapporto
coi normali. (Taste in criminals in comparison
with the normal.) APSI, 10: 332–38.

———. 1890 L'olfatto ed il gusto nei criminali
in rapporto ai normali. (Olfaction and gustation in criminals compared to the normal.)
ARCP, 2: 138–42.

OUGH, C. S. 1963 Sensory examination of four

organic acids added to wine. JFDS, **28**: 1, 101–6.

———. 1964 Die sinnenmässige Erkennung von Sorbinsäure im Wein. (The sensory detection of sorbic acid in wines.) MKAR, **14**: 260–65.

PACKARD, A. S. 1889 On the occurrence of organs probably of taste in the epipharynx of the Mecaptera (*panorpa* and *boreus*). PSHE, **5**: 159–64.

PALEANI, O. 1910 Esame clinico metodico del senso del gusto negli ammalati del sistema nervoso. (Methodical clinical examination of the sense of taste in diseases of the nervous system.) CMIA, **49**: 557–87.

PALMBERG, A. G. 1860 *Några ord om smaksinnet jemte försök att medelst elektrisk retning bestämma gränsorna för detsamma.* (On the organ of taste, and experiment to ascertain its limits by means of electricity.) J. C. Freuckell & Son, Helsingfors, 57 pp.

PANEBIANCO, G. 1950 Le variazioni della sensibilità gustativa in gravidanze. II. (Variation in gustatory sensitivity in pregnancy. II.) VALS, **26**: 306–16. (French and English summaries.)

PANGBORN, R. M. 1959 Influence of hunger on sweetness preferences and taste thresholds. AJCN, **7**: 280–87.

———. 1960 Influence of color on the discrimination of sweetness. AJPC, **73**: 229–38.

———. 1960 Taste interrelationships. FORE, **25**: 245–56.

———. 1961 Taste interrelationships. II: Suprathreshold solutions of sucrose and citric acid. JFDS, **26**: 648–55.

———. 1962 Taste interrelationships. III: Suprathreshold solutions of sucrose and sodium chloride. JFDS, **27**: 495–500.

———. 1963 Relative taste intensities of selected sugars and organic acids. JFDS, **28**: 726–33.

PANGBORN, R. M., BERG, H. W., and HANSEN, B. 1963 The influence of color on discrimination of sweetness in dry table-wine. AJPC, **76**: 492–95.

PANGBORN, R. M., and CHRISP, R. B. 1964 Taste interrelationships. VI: Sucrose, sodium chloride, and citric acid in canned tomato juice. JFDS, **29**: 490–98.

PANGBORN, R. M., and GEE, S. C. 1961 Relative sweetness of α- and β-forms of selected sugars. NATU, **191**: 810–11.

PANGBORN, R. M., and HANSEN, B. 1963 The influence of color on discrimination of sweetness and sourness in pear-nectar. AJPC, **76**: 315–17.

PANGBORN, R. M., OUGH, C. S., and CHRISP, R. B. 1964 Taste interrelationship of sucrose, tartaric acid, and caffeine in white table wine. AJEV, **15**: 154–61.

PANGBORN, R. M., and SIMONE, M. 1958 Body size and sweetness preference. JADA, **34**: 924–28.

PANGBORN, R. M., and TRABUE, I. M. 1964 Taste interrelationships. V: Sucrose, sodium chloride, and citric acid in lima bean purée. JFDS, **29**: 233–40.

PANIZZA, B. 1834 *Ricerche Sperimentali Sopra i Nervi* (Experimental Research on the Nerve.) Bizzoni, Pavia, 58 pp.

PARISELLA, R. M., and PRITHAM, G. H. 1964 Effect of age on alcohol preference by rats. QJSA, **25**: 248–52.

PARISER, E. R. 1961 How physical properties of candy affect taste. MACO, **41** (5) : 47–50.

PARKER, G. H. 1908 The sense of taste in fishes. SCIE, **27**: 453.

———. 1912 The relations of smell, taste, and the common chemical sense in vertebrates. JACP, **15**: 221–34.

———. 1922 *Smell, Taste, and Allied Senses in the Vertebrates.* J. P. Lippincott, Philadelphia, 192 pp.

———. 1929 Smell and taste, in *Encyclopedia Britanica*, XX. 14th ed. New York, 819–20.

PARKER, G. H., and CROZIER, W. J. 1929 The chemical senses, in *Foundations of Experimental Psychology*, C. Murchison (ed.). Clark University Press, Worcester, Mass., 907 pp. (see pp. 350–91).

PARKER, G. H., and METCALF, C. R. 1906 The reactions of earthworms to salts: A study in protoplasmic stimulation as a basis of interpreting the sense of taste. AJPH, **17**: 55–74.

PARKER, G. H., and STABLER, E. M. 1913 On certain distinctions between taste and smell. AJPH, **32**: 230–40.

PARKER, G. H., and VAN HEUSEN, A. P. 1917 The responses of the catfish, *Amiurus nebulosus*, to metallic and non-metallic rods. AJPH, **44**: 405–20.

PARKES, A. S. 1963 Olfactory and gustatory discrimination in man and animals. PRSM, **56**: 47–51.

PARR, L. W. 1934 Taste blindness and race. JOHE, **25**: 187–90.

PARTRIDGE, L., SUNDERLAND, E., and ZEKI, S. M. 1962 Taste blindness to P.T.C. in the Black Mountain area of Carmarthenshire, Wales. MANA, **62**: 38–39.

PASCUCCI, F., and WEISS VALBRANCA, G. 1947 Le variazioni della sensibilità gustativa in particolari situazioni fisiologiche ed in alcuni stati morbosi. VI: Le modificazioni della soglia di percezione del cosidetto "sapore metalico" dei sali di ferro negli stati anemici. (Variation in gustatory sensitivity in particular physiological situations and in some pathological states. VI: Modification of threshold for so-called "metallic taste" of ferrous salts in the anemic state.) RCCM, **47**(3): 551–58.

PASTEUR, F. 1936 Electrophysiologie de la fonction sensorielle du goût. (The electrophysiology of the sensory function of taste.) CRSS, **121**: 332–34.

PATRICK, G. T. W. 1899 On the analysis of perception of taste. IUST, **2**: 85–127. (Abstract in ZPSI, **26**: 124–27, 1901.)

———. 1899 On the confusion of tastes and odors. PSRV, **6**: 160–62. (Abstract.)

PATTON, H. D. 1950 Physiology of smell and taste. ARPH, **2**: 469–84.

———. 1955 Taste, olfaction, in *A Textbook of Physiology*, J. F. Fulton (ed.). 17th ed. W. B. Saunders Co., Philadelphia, 1275 pp. (see pp. 371–98).

———. 1960 Taste, olfaction and visceral sensation, in *Medical Physiology and Biophysics*, T. C. Ruch and J. F. Fulton (eds.). 18th ed. W. B. Saunders Co., Philadelphia, 1232 pp. (see pp. 369–85).

PATTON, H. D., and AMASSIAN, V. E. 1950 Cortical receptive of the chorda tympani. FEPR, **9**: 99. (Abstract.)

———. 1952 Cortical projection zone of chorda tympani nerve in the cat. JONE, **15**: 245–50.

PATTON, H. D., and RUCH, T. C. 1944 Preference thresholds for quinine hydrochloride in chimpanzee, monkey and rat. JCPO, **37**: 35–49.

———. 1946 Taste, in *Howell's Textbook of Physiology*, J. F. Fulton (ed.). W. B. Saunders Co., Philadelphia, 1304 pp. (see pp. 370–84).

PATTON, H. D., RUCH, T. C., and FULTON, J. F. 1946 The relation of the foot of the pre- and postcentral gyrus to taste in the monkey and chimpanzee. FEPR, **5**: 79. (Abstract.)

PATTON, H. D., RUCH, T. C., and WALKER, A. E. 1944 Experimental hypogeusia from Horsley-Clarke lesions of the thalamus in *Macaca mulatta*. JONE, **7**: 171–84.

PAUL, T. 1916 Beziehung zwischen saurem Geschmack und Wasserstoffionen-Konzentration. (Relation between sour taste and hydrogen ion concentration.) BDCG, **49**: 2124–37.

———. 1917 Physikalische Chemie der Lebensmittel. IV: Wissenschaftliche Weinprobe zur Feststellung der Beziehungen swischen der Stärke des sauren Geschmacks und der Wasserstoffionenkonzentration. (Physical chemistry of foodstuffs. IV: Scientific tasting of wine to establish the relation between the strength of the sour taste and the hydrogen ion concentration.) ZEEL, **23**: 87–93.

———. 1921 Der Süssungsgrad von Dulcin und Saccharin. (The degree of sweetness of dulcin and saccharin.) CMKZ, **45**: 38.

———. 1921 Begriffsbestimmungen und Masseinheiten in der Süsstoff-Chemie. (Definitions and units of measure in the chemistry of sweeteners.) CMKZ, **45**: 705–6.

———. 1921 Physikalische Chemie der Lebensmittel. V: Der Süssungsgrad der Süsstoffe. (Physical chemistry of foodstuffs. V: Degree of sweetness of sugars.) ZEEL, **27**: 539–46.

———. 1922 Der Süssungsgrad der Süsstoffe.

(The degree of sweetness of sweet substances.) ZNGE, **43**: 137–49.

———. 1922 Die saure Geschmacksempfindung. (The sour taste sensation.) UMSC, **39**: 610–12.

———. 1922 Physikalische Chemie der Lebensmittel. VI: Physikalisch-chemische Untersuchungen über die saure Geschmacksempfindung. (Physical chemistry of foods. VI: Physical-chemical studies on the sour taste sensation.) ZEEL, **28**: 435–46.

PAULI, R. 1920 Bestimmung der Süsskraft von künstlichen Süsstoffen. (Determination of sweetness of artificial sweeteners.) UMSC, **24**: 592.

———. 1921 Über die Messung der Süsskraft von künstlichen Süsstoffen. (The measurement of sweetness of artificial sweeteners.) BIZE, **125**: 97–105.

———. 1923 Geruchs- und Geschmacksempfindungen (Odor and taste perception), in *Psychologisches Praktikum, Leitfaden für Experimentell-phychologische Übungen*. G. Fischer, Jena, 247 pp. (see pp. 67–74).

PAULY, . 1901 Troubles du goût dans le domaine de la corde du tympan par lésion basilaire. (Taste disturbances in the region of the chorda tympani from basal lesions.) LYME, **97**: 799–802.

PEARSON, A. M., and BATEN, W. D. 1958 The influence of salt upon panel scores of irradiated and unirradiated beef roasts. FORE, **23**: 384–87.

PEARSON, L. K. 1919 A comparative study of the pungency of synthetic aromatic ketones related to zingerone. PHJO, **103**: 78–80.

PEIRCE, A. W. 1957 Salt tolerance of sheep. I: The tolerance of sheep for sodium chloride in the drinking water. AJAE, **8**: 711–22.

———. 1959 Studies on salt tolerance of sheep. II: The tolerance of sheep for mixtures of sodium chloride and magnesium chloride in the drinking water. AJAE, **10**: 725–35.

———. 1960 Studies of salt tolerance of sheep. III: The tolerance of sheep for mixtures of sodium chloride and sodium sulphate in the drinking water. AJAE, **11**: 548–56.

PENFIELD, W., and BOLDREY, E. 1937 Somatic motor and sensory representation in the cerebral cortex of man as studied by electrical stimulation. BRAI, **60**: 389–443.

PERRIN, M. J., and KRUT, L. H. 1961 Smoking and food preferences. BMJO, **1**: 387–88.

PERRINO, A., and GESSINI, L. 1961 Disturbi permanenti del gusto dopo tonsillectomia. (Permanent disorders of taste after tosillectomy.) COUR, **13**: 624–29. (English and French summaries.)

PERRITT, R. A. 1936 The histology of the tongue. AROT, **24**: 404. (Abstract.)

PERYAM, D. R. 1960 The variable taste perception of sodium benzoate. FOTE, **14**: 383–86.

*———. 1961 Variability of gustatory response to sodium benzoate and other compounds.

Unpublished Ph.D. thesis, Illinois Institute of Technology, Chicago.

——. 1963 Variability of taste perception. JFDS, **28**: 734–40.

PETERS, R. 1931 Geruchs- und Geschmacksstörungen und ihre erwerbsvermindernde Bedeutung. (Olfactory and gustatory disturbances and their significance in decreasing efficiency.) Inaugural Dissertation, Trapp, Bonn, 52 pp.

PETERS, W., and RICHTER, S. 1963 Morphological investigations on the sense organs of the labella of the blowfly, *Calliphora erythrocephala* Meigen. PCZO, **3**: 89–92.

PETERSEN, S., and MÜLLER, E. 1948 Über eine neue Gruppe von Süsstoffen. (On a new group of sweet substances.) CHBE, **81**: 31–38.

PETERSON, F. 1890 A note upon disturbance of the sense of taste after amputation of the tongue. MERC, **38**: 230–31.

PETRI, A. 1935 Ueber die Geschmacksreizwirkung des Glykokolls. (Effect of aminoacetic acid on taste stimulation.) ZPSI, **66**: 137–45.

PETROSELLI, F. 1923 Sopra un caso di anosmia, ageusia e vasta anestesia cutanea. (On a case of anosmia, ageusia and wide-spread cutaneous anesthesia.) MORG, **65**: 153–62.

PEVZNER, R. A. 1964 Raspredelenie aktivnosti suktsindegidrazy (suktsinat-NST-reduktazy) vo vkusovykh lukovitsakh naktorykh pozvonochnykh. (Determination of the succinate dehydrogenase [succinate-NST-reductase] activity in taste buds of some vertebrate animals.) DANK, **155**: 191–93.

PFAFF, C. H. 1794 Abhandlung über die sogenannte thierische Elektrizität. (Transactions on so-called animal electricity.) JOPK, **8**: 196–201.

——. 1795 *Über thierische Elektrizität und Reizbarkeit* (On animal electricity and sensitivity.) S. L. Crusius, Leipzig, 398 pp. (see pp. 304–5).

PFAFFMANN, C. 1934 An experimental comparison of the absolute and constant stimulus methods of gustation. PSBU, **31**: 622–23. (Abstract.)

——. 1935 An experimental comparison of the method of single stimuli and the method of constant stimuli in gustation. AJPC, **47**: 470–76.

——. 1935 Apparatus and technique for gustatory experimentation. JGPS, **12**: 446–47.

——. 1935 Differential responses of the newborn cat to gustatory stimuli. PSBU, **32**: 697. (Abstract.)

——. 1936 Differential responses of the newborn cat to gustatory stimuli. JGPY, **49**: 61–67.

——. 1938 Action potentials elicited by gustatory stimulation. PSBU, **35**: 718. (Abstract.)

——. 1939 Specific gustatory impulses. JPHY, **96**: 41–42P. (Abstract.)

——. 1941 Gustatory afferent impulses. JCCP, **17**: 243–58.

——. 1948 Studying the senses of taste and smell, in *Methods of Psychology*, T. G. Andrews (ed.). John Wiley & Sons, New York, 716 pp. (see pp. 268–88).

——. 1949 The effect of thirst on salt preference. AMPS, **4**: 224.

——. 1950 The afferent neural determinants of the specific hunger for salt. AMPS, **5**: 272–73.

——. 1951 Somesthesis and the chemical senses. ARPS, **2**: 79–94.

——. 1951 Taste—A monitor of diet? OFRR, pp. 16–21.

——. 1951 Taste and smell, in *Handbook of Experimental Psychology*, S. S. Stevens (ed.). John Wiley & Sons, New York, 1436 pp. (see pp. 1143–71).

——. 1952 Taste preference and aversion following lingual denervation. JCPP, **45**: 393–400.

——. 1953 Species differences in taste sensitivity. SCIE, **117**: 470.

——. 1954 Sensory mechanisms in taste discrimination. ACAF, pp. 17A–18A. (Abstract.)

——. 1955 Gustatory nerve impulses in rat, cat, and rabbit. JONE, **18**: 429–40.

——. 1956 Taste and smell. ARPS, **7**: 391–408.

——. 1957 Taste mechanisms in preference behavior. AJCN, **5**: 143–47.

——. 1958 Behavioral responses to taste and odor stimuli, in *Flavor Research and Food Acceptance*, A. D. Little (ed.). Reinhold Publishing Corp., New York, 391 pp. (see pp. 29–44).

——. 1959 The afferent code for sensory quality. AMPS, **14**: 226–32.

——. 1959 The sense of taste, in *Handbook of Psyiology-Neurophysiology, I,* J. Field (ed.), 779 pp. (see pp. 507–33).

——. 1960 The pleasures of sensation. PSRV, **67**: 253–68.

——. 1961 Preface, in *The Physiological and Behavioral Aspects of Taste*, M. R. Kare and B. P. Halpern (eds.). The University of Chicago Press, Chicago, 149 pp. (see pp. vii–xi).

——. 1961 The sensory and motivating properties of the sense of taste, in *Nebraska Symposium on Motivation*, M. R. Jones (ed.). University of Nebraska Press, Lincoln, 210 pp. (see pp. 71–110).

——. 1962 On the code for gustatory sensory quality. PUPC, **3**: 267–72.

——. 1962 Sensory processes and their relation to behavior: studies on the sense of taste as a model S–R system, in *Psychology: A Study of a Science*, S. Koch (ed.). McGraw-Hill, New York, 731 pp. (see pp. 380–416).

——. 1963 Taste stimulation and preference behavior, in *Olfaction and Taste*, Y. Zotterman (ed.). Macmillan, New York, 396 pp. (see pp. 257–73).

——. 1964 On the code for gustatory sensory quality, in *Information Processing in the Ner-*

vous System, R. W. Gerard and J. W. Duyff (eds.). Excerpta Medica Foundation, Amsterdam and New York, 458 pp. (see pp. 267–72).

———. 1964 Taste, its sensory and motivating properties. AMSC, **52**: 187–206.

———. 1965 De gustibus. AMPS, **20**: 21–33.

———. 1966 Taste—its sensory and motivating properties, in *Science in Progress,* W. R. Brode (ed.). Yale University Press, New Haven, Conn., 417 pp. (see pp. 233–62).

PFAFFMANN, C., and BARE, J. K. 1948 Salt preference following denervation of the tongue. AMPS, **3**: 254. (Abstract.)

———. 1950 Gustatory nerve discharges in normal and adrenalectomized rats. JCPP, **43**: 320–24.

PFAFFMANN, C., ERICKSON, R. P., FROMMER, G. P., and HALPERN, B. P. 1961 Gustatory discharges in the rat medulla and thalamus, in *Sensory Communication,* W. A. Rosenblith (ed.). M.I.T. Press and John Wiley & Sons, New York, 844 pp. (see pp. 455–73).

PFAFFMANN, C., and HAGSTROM, E. C. 1955 Factors influencing taste sensitivity to sugar. AJPC, **183**: 651 (Abstract.)

PFAFFMANN, C., HALPERN, B. P., and ERICKSON, R. P. 1959 Gustatory afferent discharges in the medulla. FEPR, **18**: 120. (Abstract.)

PFAFFMANN, C., and McBURNEY, D. H. 1962 Gustatory adaptation to saliva and NaCl. ICPS, p. 1. (Abstract.)

PFAFFMANN, C., YOUNG, P. T., DETHIER, V. G., RICHTER, C. P., and STELLAR, E. 1954 The preparation of solutions for research in chemoreception and food acceptance. JCPP, **47**: 93–96.

PFEIFER, B. 1907 Verspätete Geschmacksempfindung bei vorwiegend cerebraler mit bulbarparalytischen Symptomen beginnender Tabes. (Delayed taste perception in predominantly cerebral bulbar paralytic symptoms in beginning tabes.) DZNE, **33**: 246–304.

PICHT, F. 1829 De gustus et olfactus nexu praesertim argumentis pathologicis et experimentis illustrato. (Arguments on pathology and illustrated experiments on the relation between taste and olfaction.) Inaugural Dissertation, Brüschckianis, Berlin, 31 pp.

PICK, H. L., JR. 1961 Research on taste in the Soviet Union, in *The Physiological and Behavioral Aspects of Taste,* M. R. Kare and B. P. Halpern (eds.). The University of Chicago Press, Chicago, 149 pp. (see pp. 117–26).

PICK, H. L., JR., and KARE, M. R. 1959 Certain aspects of taste preference in chickens and calves. AMPS, **14**: 572. (Title only.)

———. 1962 The effect of artificial cues on the measurement of taste preference in the chicken. JCPP, **55**: 342–45.

PICKERILL, H. P. 1914 *The Prevention of Dental Caries and Oral Sepsis.* 2nd ed. Bailliere, Tindall and Cox, London, 374 pp. (see pp. 165–69).

PICKERT, I. 1955 Über die Sicherheit, mit der sich eine Geschmacksspur verfolgen lässt. (The reliability of following the gustatory tracks.) ZEBL, **107**: 149–60.

PIERCE, A. H. 1907 Gustatory audition; a hitherto undescribed variety of synaesthesia. AJPC, **18**: 341–52.

PIÉRON, H. 1914 Recherches sur les lois de variation des temps de latence sensorielle en fonction des intensités excitatrices. (Research on the laws of variation in time of sensory latency as a function of exciting intensities.) ANPQ, **20**: 17–96.

———. 1945 L'excitation gustative (Taste stimulation), in *La Sensation, Guide de Vie, Série No. 3.* Gallimard, Paris, 420 pp. (see pp. 113–21).

———. 1952 The tastes, in *The Sensations, their Functions, Processes and Mechanisms.* Translated by M. H. Pirenne and B. C. Abbott. Yale University Press, New Haven, Conn., 469 pp. (see pp. 191–99).

*———. 1953 *La Sensation.* (Sensation.) Presses Universitaires de France, Paris, 136 pp.

PIERREL, R. 1955 Taste effects resulting from intermittent electrical stimulation of the tongue. JEPS, **49**: 374–80.

PILGRIM, F. J. 1957 The components of food acceptance and their measurement. AJCN, **5**: 171–75.

———. 1961 Interactions of suprathreshold taste stimuli, in *The Physiological and Behavioral Aspects of Taste,* M. R. Kare and B. P. Halpern (eds.), 149 pp. (see pp. 66–78).

PILGRIM, F. J., SCHUTZ, H. G., and PERYAM, D. R. 1955 Influence of monosodium glutamate on taste perception. FORE, **20**: 310–14.

PIUTTI, A. 1886 Ein neues Asparagin. (A new asparagine.) BDCG, **19**: 1691–95.

———. 1886 Sur une nouvelle espèce d'asparagine. (On a new species of asparagine.) CORE, **103**: 134–37.

PLANK, R. 1944 Der gegenwärtige Stand der Klassifikation und objectiven Bewertung von Geschmacks und Geruchsempfindung. Auszug. (The present status of the classification and objective evaluation of taste and smell sensitivity. A condensation.) CHMI, **57**: 154–56.

PLATE, W. P. 1929 Een Bruikbaar smaakcorrigens bij zoutloos diëet. (Valuable corrective of taste in salt-free diets.) NTGE, **2**: 5867–71.

PLOHR, J. A. 1698 Disputatio physica de saporibus eorumque differentiis. (Discussion of the natural science of taste and differences.) Inaugural Dissertation, Brandenburger, Leipzig, 42 pp.

*POCCOS, S. A. 1908 Ai anomaliai tes geuseos. (Taste anomalies.) IAME, **8**: 74–00.

PODIAPOLSKY, P. 1896 Opyty s gimnemovoi kislotoi. (Experiences with gymnemic acid.) BLPY, 1: 49–60.

Podwisotzky, V. 1878 Anatomische Untersuchungen über die Zungendrüsen des Menschen und der Säugethiere. (Anatomical investigation of the glands of the tongue of man and mammals.) Inaugural Dissertation, C. Mattiesen, Dorpot, 144 pp.

Polimanti, O. 1907 Contribution a la physiologie des sensations gustatives subséquentes. (Contribution to the physiologie of subsequent taste sensations.) JPNP, 4: 24–28.

Pons, J. 1955 Taste sensitivity to phenylthiourea in Spaniards. HUBI, 27: 153–60.

———. 1960 A contribution to the heredity of the P.T.C. taste character. ANHG, 24: 71–76.

———. 1961 Capacidád gustativa a la fenilthiocarbamida en Araneses. (Taste threshold to P.T.C. in Aranese people.) TIAE, 15: 143–53.

Ponzo, M. 1905 Sulla presenza di calici gustativi in alcune parti della retrobocca e nella parte nasale della faringe del feto umano. (The presence of taste buds on certain parts of the anterior mouth and in the nasal part of the pharynx of human fetus.) GMDT, 68 (4): 122–27.

———. 1905 Sur la présence de bourgeons gustatifs dans quelques parties de l'arrièrebouche et dans la partie nasale du pharynx du foetus humain. (On the presence of taste buds on certain parts of the anterior mouth and in the nasal part of the pharynx of human fetus.) AIBL, 43: 280–86.

———. 1907 Intorno alla presenza di organi gustativi sulla faccia infiore della lingua del feto umano. (Investigation on the presence of taste organs on the lower side of the tongue of the human fetus.) ANAN, 30: 529–32.

———. 1907 Sulla presenza di organi del gusto nella parte laringea della faringe nel tratto cervicale dell'esofago e nel palato duro del feto umano. (On the presence of taste organs in the laryngeal part of the pharynx, the cervical tract of the esophagus, and the hard palate of the human fetus.) ANAN, 31: 570–75.

———. 1909 Über die Wirkung des Stovains auf die Organe des Geschmacks, der Hautempfindungen, des Geruchs und des Gehörs, nebst einigen weiteren Beobachtungen über die Wirkung des Kokains, des Alipins und der Karbolsäure im Gegiete der Empfindungen. (Effect of stovain on organs of taste, cutaneous sensation, smell and hearing, with additional observation on the effect of cocain, alipin and carbolic acid on the sphere of sensation.) PAGP, 14: 385–436.

———. 1913 Dei rapporti fra i dati anatomici, fisiologici e psicologici nei processi gustativi. (Report on anatomical, physiological and psychological data on the gustatory processes.) RIPS, 9: 513–39.

———. 1914 Rapports entre les données anatomiques, physiologiques, et psychologiques dans les processus gustatifs. (Relationship between anatomical, physiological, and psychological studies of the gustatory processes.) AIBL, 61: 355–68.

———. 1926 Signification et importance des mouvements automatiques et réflexes dans les fonctions gustatives et olfactives. (Significance and importance of automatic movements and reflexes in gustatory and olfactory functions.) AIBL, 77: 93–103.

———. 1927 Significato ed importanza dei movimenti automatici e riflessi negli avvenimenti gustative ed olfattivo. (Significance and importance of automatic and reflex movements in gustatory and olfactory acts.) AIBL, 5: 19–30.

Pope, F. M. 1889 Taste function of the glossopharyngeal nerve. LANC, 2: 458.

———. 1889 Thrombosis of vertebral artery pressing on glosso-pharyngeal nerve: Unilateral loss of taste at back of tongue. BMJO, 2: 1148–49.

Popelski, L. B. 1903 Vkus i potrebnosti organizma. (Taste and the needs of the organism.) RUVR, 2: 1737–40.

Popielski, B. 1956 Wrażliwość smakowa jako nowa cecha grupowa czlowieka. (Taste sensitivity as a new group characteristic of man.) POLE, 11: 3–5. (Russian and English summaries.)

Poritsky, R. L., and Singer, M. 1963 The fate of taste buds in tongue transplants to the orbit in the urodele, Triturus. JEZO, 154: 211–18.

Port, T. 1962 Geschmack und Geschmacksstörungen. (Taste and taste disorders.) MEWE, 6: 314, 317–19.

Portmann, A. 1960 Taste, in Biology and Comparative Physiology of Birds, I, A. J. Marshall (ed.). Academic Press, New York, 468 pp. (see pp. 41–42).

Portugal, J. R. 1942 A sensibilidade gustative dos dois têrcos anteriores da língua. (Taste sensitivity of the anterior two thirds of the tongue.) ABME, 32: 139–50.

Potts, C. S., and Spiller, W. G. 1903 A case of solitary tubercle of the pons. Remarks on the pathway for sensations of taste from the anterior portion of the tongue. With pathological report and remarks on palsy of associated ocular movements. CPCM, pp. 1–11.

Poulton, E. B. 1883 The tongue of Perameles nasuta, with some suggestions as to the origin of taste buds. QJMS, 23: 69–86.

Pousson, A. 1886 Gustation. I: Anatomie. (Gustation. I: Anatomy.) DSME, 11: 569–80.

Power, F. B., and Tutin, F. 1904 Chemical examination of gymnema leaves. PHJO, 19: 234–39.

PRADINES, M. 1929 Sur l'objectivité des odeurs et des saveurs. (Objectivity of odors and tastes.) JPNP, **26**: 16–73.

PRESSMAN, T. G., and DOOLITTLE, J. H. 1966 Taste preferences in the Virginia opossum. PYRI, **18**: 875–78.

PREVOST, J. L. 1869 Note relative aux fonctions gustatives du nerf lingual. (Note relative to the gustatory function of the lingual nerve.) CRSS, **21**: 234–35.

———. 1869 Note relative aux fonctions gustatives du nerf lingual. (Note relative to the gustatory function of the lingual nerve.) GAMP, **24**: 494, 506–7.

———. 1870 Note relative aux fonctions gustatives du nerf lingual. (Note relative to the gustatory function of the lingual nerve.) CRSS, **22**: 76–78.

———. 1872 Sur la distribution de la corde du tympan. (On the distribution of the chorda tympani.) CRSS, **75**: 1828–30.

———. 1873 Nouvelles expériences relatives aux fonctions gustatives du nerf lingual. I, II. (New experiences relative to the taste functions of the lingual nerve. I, II.) APHP, **5**: 253–80, 375–88.

PREYER, W. 1870 *Die Fünf Sinne des Menschen.* (The Five Senses of Man.) R. Reisland, Leipzig, 75 pp. (see pp. 15–20).

———. 1890 Das Schmecken (Taste), in *Die Seele des Kindes.* T. Grieben, Leipzig, 539 pp. (see pp. 91–101).

PRONKO, N. H., and HILL, H. 1949 A study of differential stimulus function in hypnosis. JOPS, **27**: 49–53.

PROSSER, C. L. 1961 Chemoreception, in *Comparative Animal Physiology,* C. L. Prosser and F. A. Brown, Jr. (eds.). 2nd ed. W. B. Saunders Co., Philadelphia, 688 pp. (see pp. 319–34).

PRUETT, B. S. 1939 Parageusia as a symptom of kidney disease. AJSU, **43**: 145–46.

PRÜFER, J. 1963 Genusswert der Nahrung. (Enjoyment of food.) THGE, **102**: 1142–50.

PUIG Y ROIG, P. 1962 Factores cósmicos, telúricos, meteorológicos y sensoriales en el problema de la fertilidad matrimonial. (Cosmic, terrestrial, meteorological and sensory factors in the problem of conjugal fertility.) REOG, **21**: 247–62.

PULEC, J. L., and HOUSE, W. F. 1964 Special tests in the early diagnosis of acoustic neuromas. LARY, **74**: 1183–93.

———. 1964 Special tests in the early diagnosis of acoustic neuromas. TALR, **68**: 323–33.

PULEC, J. L., URBAN, J., and HOUSE, W. F. 1964 A new taste tester. TAAO, **68**: 890–92.

PULLIN, E. W., and SUNDERLAND, E. 1963 A survey of phenylthiocarbamide (P.T.C.)-tasting and colour-blindness in Pembrokeshire, Wales. MANA, **63**: 52–55.

PUMPHREY, R. J. 1935 Nerve impulses from receptors in the mouth of the frog. JCCP, **6**: 457–67.

PURDUM, W. A. 1942 Method of evaluating relative efficacy of disguising agents for distasteful drugs. JAPM, **31**: 298–305.

PYKE, M. 1944 Nutrition and a matter of taste. NATU, **154**: 229–31.

QUEVENNE, M. 1847–48 On the effect of coffee in diminishing the bitter taste of sulphate of quinine. PHJO, **7**: 352–53.

QUIRINI, A. 1891 Gymnesinsay. (Gymnemic acid.) GYHE, pp. 370–71.

QUIX, F. H. 1903 Een nieuwe methode om den smaakzin te onderzoeken. (A new method on the investigation of the sense of taste.) NTGE, **39**: 283–85.

———. 1903 Eine neue Methode zur Untersuchung des Geschmacksinnes. (A new method on the investigation of the sense of taste.) MOLA, **37**: 572.

———. 1903 Nouvelle méthode de gustatométrie. (New method of gustometry.) POBB, **2**: 581–84.

———. 1910 Die Störungen des Geschmackssinnes. (The disturbances of the sense of taste.) HBNE, **1**: 959–66.

RABL, H. 1895 Notiz zur Morphologie der Geschmacksknospen auf der Epiglottis. (Note on the morphology of taste buds on the epiglottis.) ANAN, **11**: 153–56.

RAKHAWY, M. T. E. 1962 Succinic dehydrogenase in the mammalian tongue with special reference to gustatory epithelia. ACAT, **48**: 122–36.

———. 1962 The histochemistry of the lymphatic tissue of the human tongue and its probable function in taste. ACAT, **51**: 259–70.

———. 1963 Alkaline phosphatases in the epithelium of the human tongue and a possible mechanism of taste. ACAT, **55**: 323–42.

RAKHAWY, M. T. E., and BOURNE, G. H. 1960 Cholinesterases in the human tongue. BIAN, **2**: 243–55.

———. 1964 The histochemistry of the human foetal tongue. ACAT, **56**: 93–102.

*RAMON Y CAJAL, S. 1891 Pequeñas contribuciones al conocimiento del sistema nervioso. (Small contribution to the knowledge of the nervous system.)

RAMON Y CAJAL, S., and TELLO-MUÑOZ, J. F. 1933 Gustatory nerve terminations, in *Histology.* Translated from 10th ed. by M. Fernán-Nuñez. William Wood & Co., Baltimore, 738 pp. (see pp. 350–53).

RANCKE-MADSEN, E., and KROGH, J. A. 1956 On the use of the senses of taste and smell in determining the end point of an acid-base titration. ACSA, **10**: 495–99.

RANNER, K. 1956 Zur sensorischen und sensiblen Innervation der Zunge. (Gustatory and sensory innervation of the tongue.) WKWO, **68**: 245–47.

RANVIER, L. 1884 De l'éléidine et de la répartition de cette substance dans la peau, la muqueuse buccale et la muqueuse oesophagienne des vertébrés. (The epidermis and its distribution on the skin, and the mucous of the bucal cavity and esophagus of vertebrates.) APHP, **3**: 125–41.

———. 1889 Organs du goût (Organs of taste), in *Traité Technique D'Histologie.* F. Savy, Paris, 871 pp. (see pp. 724–32).

RAPAPORT, A. 1952 Recherche du mécanisme sensoriel de l'activité du glutamate de soude comme "améliorant" des saveurs alimentaires. Glutamate de soude et réceptivité gustative. (Research on the sensory mechanism of the activity of sodium glutamate as an improver of food flavors; sodium glutamate and taste perception.) CRSS, **146**: 378–80.

———. 1954 Recherche d'un effet de la castration sur la réponse du rat blanc au stimulus amer. (Research on an effect of castration on the response of the white rat to bitter stimulus.) CRSS, **148**: 2000–2.

———. 1956 Effet du salicylate de soude sur la réponse primaire du rat blance aux stimuli amers. (Effect of sodium salicylate on the primary response of the white rat to bitter stimuli.) CRSS, **150**: 2182–86.

RAPUZZI, G. 1961 Azione inibitoria di alcuni sali sui ricettori linguali di rana. (Inhibitory action of some salts on tongue receptors of frog.) BSIB, **37**: 49–53.

RAPUZZI, G., and CASELLA, C. 1962 The effect of $BaCl_2$ on the tactile and chemical response of the fungiform papillae in frog's tongue. ICPS, **2**: 1027. (Abstract.)

———. 1965 Innervation of the fungiform papillae in the frog tongue. JONE, **28**: 154–65.

RAPUZZI, G., CASELLA, C., and TACCARDI, B. 1961 La sensibilité au Ca++ des récepteurs de la langue de Grenouille. (The sensitivity to Ca++ of the receptors in the frog tongue.) JOPH, **53**: 455–56.

RAPUZZI, G., and PEDRINI, A. 1963 Importanza dell'acetilcolina sull'attivazione dei ricettori linguali di rana. (Importance of acetylcholine in the activation of frog lingual receptors.) BSIB, **39**: 1851–53.

———. 1963 La sensibilità gustativa della rana. (Gustatory sensitivity of the frog.) ASBI, **47**: 73–82.

RAPUZZI, G., RICAGNO, G., and VENTURA, U. 1963 Influenza di alcuni aminoacidi sulla sensibilità dei ricettori gustativi di rana. (Influence of some amino acids on the sensitivity of gustatory receptors in the frog.) BSIB, **39**: 1853–55.

RAPUZZI, G., and TACCARDI, B. 1960 La risposta al $CaCl_2$ dei ricettori linguali di rana derivata da singole fibre del nervo glossofaringeo. (The response to $CaCl_2$ of tongue receptors of the frog derived from single fibers of the glossopharyngeal nerve.) BSMP, **74**: 827–30.

RAPUZZI, G., TACCARDI, B., and CASELLA, C. 1960 Azione del $BaCl_2$ sui ricettori linguali della rana. (Action of $BaCl_2$ on the lingual receptors of the frog.) BSIB, **36**: 1758–61.

———. 1961 L'action du $BaCl_2$ sur les récepteurs de la langue de grenouille. (The action of $BaCl_2$ on the tongue receptors of the frog.) JOPH, **53**: 669–78. (English summary.)

RASPAIL, F. V. 1838 Das Organ des Geschmacks. (The organ of taste.) NGNH, **5**: 149–52.

RATCLIFF, J. D. 1954 Are you bitter-sweet or bitter-bitter? COLS, **134**: 44–48.

RAUHLFS, K. 1932 Sinnesphysiologische Untersuchungen des Geschmackssinnes mit Hilfe von Stammbetäubung des N. lingualis und unter Verwendung spezifisch unterschneelligen Schmecklösungen. (Investigations on the sensory physiology of the sense of taste, with the aid of narcosis of the lingual nerve and with the application of specifically subliminal taste solutions.) DMZK, **14**: 637–52.

RAUTENBERG, E. 1898 Beiträge zur Kenntniss der Empfindungs und Geschmacksnerven der Zunge. (Contribution to the knowledge of perception and taste nerves of the tongue.) Inaugural Dissertation, R. Leupold, Königsberg, 45 pp.

REBIERRE, P. 1930 Hydrorhée faciale gustative paraissant correspondre à une région de distribution sympathique, avec divers autres troubles végétatifs, chez un opere du cou. (Facial, gustatory hydrorrhea apparently corresponding to region of sympathetic distribution with other sympathetic disturbances after operation on neck.) RONO, **8**: 23–27.

REDOGLIA, F. 1941 Reazioni riflesse resporatorie e circolatorie dopo stimolazioni gustative. (Respiratory and circulatory reflex responses during gustatory stimulation.) MSAI, **9**: 211–28. (German, French, and English summaries.)

REGNAULT, F. 1921 Philies et phobies du goût. (Likes and dislikes in taste.) PRME, **29**: 145–48.

REICHERT, F. L. 1934 Neuralgias of the glossopharyngeal nerve with particular reference to the sensory, gustatory and secretory functions of the nerve. ANPS, **32**: 1030–37.

REICHERT, F. L., and POTH, E. J. 1933 Recent knowledge regarding the physiology of the glossopharyngeal nerve in man with an analysis of its sensory, motor, gustatory and secretory functions. JHHB, **31**: 131–39.

REID, A. W., and BECKER, C. H. 1956 A study of cocoa syrups for taste preference. JAPM, **45**: 160–62.

———. 1956 The use of cocoa syrups for masking the taste of quinine hydrochloride. JAPM, 45: 151–52.

REID, C. 1943 The higher centres and the blood sugar curve. JPHY, 102: 20P. (Abstract.)

REILLY, T. R. 1914 Parageusia and its treatment. NYMJ, 100: 1061–63.

REINICKE, R. 1943 Ueber die chemischen Vorbedingungen für das Zustandekommen der Geschmacksempfindung "Süss." (The chemical procedure for initiation of "sweet" taste perception.) ZUIN, 1: 79–82.

REMAGGI, P. L. 1937 Sulla partecipazione della chorda tympani e del trigemino alla sensibilità gustativa dei due terzi anteriori della lingua. (On the participation of the chorda tympani and the trigeminus in gustatory sensitivity in the anterior two-thirds of the tongue.) VALS, 13: 657–70.

———. 1938 Nuove ricerche sulla partecipazione della chorda tympani e del trigemino alla sensibilità gustativa dei due terzi anteriori della lingua. (New research on the participation of the chorda tympani and the trigeminal on gustatory sensitivity of the anterior two-thirds of the tongue.) AIMS, 3: 727–50. (French, English, and German summaries.)

———. 1959 Gusto e vitamina B$_6$. (Taste and vitamin B$_6$.) BMOG, 77: 361–85. (English summary.)

RENAULT, A. 1913 Une observation d'hyperestésie et de perversion gustative de la langue d'origine spécifique. (An observation of hyperaesthesia and of gustatory perversion of the tongue of specific origin.) ANMV, 8: 824–27.

RENNER, H. D. 1939 Some distinctions in the sweetness of sugars. CNFP, 5: 255–56.

RENQVIST, Y. 1919 Über den Geschmack. (On taste.) SAPH, 38: 97–201.

———. 1920 Der Schwellenwert des Geschmackreizes bei einigen homologen und isomeren Verbindungen. (The threshold value of taste stimulus of some homologous and isomeric compounds.) SAPH, 20: 117–24.

———. 1922 Ein Versuch, den Geschmacksreiz des Wassertoffsuperoxydes als einen im Geschmackssystem stattfindenden chemischen Prozess aufzufassen. (A study of perception of hydrogen superoxide as a taste stimulus that occurs as a chemical process in the taste system.) SAPH, 42: 273–80.

RENSCH, B. 1925 Experimentelle Untersuchungen über den Geschmackssinn der Vögel. (Experimental studies on the sense of taste in birds.) JORN, 73: 1–8.

RENSCH, B., and EISENTRAUT, M. 1927 Experimentelle Untersuchungen über den Geschmackssinn der Reptilien. (Experimental studies on the taste sense in reptiles.) ZVPH, 5: 607–12.

RENSCH, B., and NEUNZIG, R. 1925 Experimentelle Untersuchungen über den Geschmackssinn der Vögel. II. (Experimental studies on the sense of taste in birds. II.) JORN, 73: 633–45.

RENSHAW, S. 1933 The influence of solution temperature on the gustatory stimulus limens. PSBU, 30: 684–85. (Abstract.)

———. 1934 Studies on taste: the neutral temperature range of the tongue and the RLs for NaCl solutions from 3°C. to 52°C. PSBU, 31: 683. (Abstract.)

RETZIUS, G. 1892 Die Nervenendigungen in dem Geschmacksorgan der Säugetiere und Amphibien. (Nerve endings in the taste organs of mammals and amphibians.) BIOU, 4: 19–32.

———. 1893 Ueber Geschmacksknospen bei Petromyzon. (On taste buds of petromyzon.) BIOU, 5: 69–70.

———. 1905 Zur Kenntniss der Nervenendingungen in den Papillen der Zunge der Amphibien. (Knoweldge of nerve endings in the papillae of the tongue of amphibians.) BIOU, 12: 61–64.

———. 1913 Zur Kenntnis des Geschmacksorgans beim Kaninchen. (Knowledge of taste organs in the rabbit.) BIOU, 17: 72–80.

REY, A., and PERROT, L. 1953 Note sur l'évolution des sensations gustatives. (Note on the evolution of gustatory sensations.) APSY, 34: 64–71. (German and English summaries.)

RIBOT, T. 1920 Le goût et l'odorat. (Taste and smell.) JPNP, 17: 5–15.

RICCOMANNI, C. 1924 Relazioni fra costituzione chimica e sapore. (Relation between chemical constitution and taste.) AALB, 33: 145–48.

RICE, K. K., and RICHTER, C. P. 1943 Increased sodium chloride and water intake of normal rats treated with desoxycorticosterone acetate. ENDO, 33: 106–15.

RICHARDS, R. K., TAYLOR, J. D., O'BRIEN, J. L., and DUESCHER, H. O. 1951 Studies on cyclamate sodium (sucaryl sodium), a new noncaloric sweetening agent. JAPM, 40: 1–6.

RICHARDS, T. W. 1898 The relation of the taste of acids to their degree of dissociation. ACJO, 20: 121–26.

———. 1900 The relation of the taste of acids to their degree of dissociation. II. JPCH, 4: 207–11.

RICHET, C. 1884 De l'action comparée de quelques métaux sur les nerfs du goût. (The comparative action of some metals on the taste nerves.) CRSS, 35: 687–89.

RICHTER, C. P. 1936 Increased salt appetite in adrenalectomized rats. AJPH, 115: 155–61.

———. 1939 Salt taste thresholds of normal and adrenalectomized rats. ENDO, 24: 367–71.

———. 1939 Transmission of taste sensation in animals. TANA, 65: 49–50.

———. 1941 Decreased carbohydrate appetite of adrenalectomized rats. PSEB, 48: 577–79.

———. 1941 Sodium chloride and dextrose appetite of untreated and treated adrenalectomized rats. ENDO, 29: 115–25.

———. 1942 Increased dextrose appetite of normal rats treated with insulin. AJPH, **135**: 781–87.

————. 1942 13 Total self-regulatory function in animals and human beings. HALE, **38**: 63–103.

————. 1947 Carbohydrate appetite of normal and hyperthyroid rats as determined by the taste threshold method. ENDO, **40**: 455. (Abstract.)

————. 1950 Taste and solubility of toxic compounds in poisoning of rats and man. JCPP, **43**: 358–74.

————. 1954 Behavioral regulators of carbohydrates homeostasis. ACNE, **9**: 247–59.

————. 1956 Salt appetite in mammals: its dependence on instinct and metabolism, in *L'Instinct dans le Comportement des Animaux et de l'Homme.* Masson et Cie, Paris, 796 pp. (see pp. 577–632).

RICHTER, C. P., and BARELARE, B., JR. 1938 Nutritional requirements of pregnant and lactating rats studied by the self-selection method. ENDO, **23**: 15–24.

————. 1939 Further observations on the carbohydrate, fat, and protein appetite of vitamin B deficient rats. AJPH, **126**: 607–8P. (Abstract.)

RICHTER, C. P., and CAMPBELL, K. H. 1940 Alcohol taste thresholds and concentrations of solution preferred by rats. SCIE, **91**: 507–8.

————. 1940 Sucrose taste thresholds of rats and humans. AJPH, **128**: 291–97.

————. 1940 Taste thresholds and taste preferences of rats for five common sugars. JONU, **20**: 31–46.

RICHTER, C. P., and CLISBY, K. H. 1941 Phenylthiocarbamide taste. Thresholds of rats and human beings. AJPH, **134**: 157–64.

————. 1942 Toxic effects of the bitter-tasting phenylthiocarbamide. ARPA, **33**: 46–57.

RICHTER, C. P., and ECKERT, J. F. 1937 Increased calcium appetite of parathyroidectomized rats. ENDO, **21**: 50–54.

————. 1938 Mineral metabolism of adrenalectomized rats studied by the appetite method. ENDO, **22**: 214–24.

————. 1939 Mineral appetite of parathyroidectomized rats. AJMS, **198**: 9–16.

RICHTER, C. P., and HAWKES, C. D. 1941 The dependence of the carbohydrate, fat and protein appetite of rats on the various components of the vitamin B complex. AJPH, **131**: 639–49.

RICHTER, C. P., HOLT, L. E., JR., and BARELARE, B., JR. 1937 Vitamin B₁ craving in rats. SCIE, **86**: 354–55.

RICHTER, C. P., HOLT, L. E., JR., BARELARE, B., JR., and HAWKES, C. D. 1938 Changes in fat, carbohydrate and protein appetite in vitamin B deficiency. AJPH, **124**: 596–602.

RICHTER, C. P., and MACLEAN, A. 1939 Salt taste threshold of humans. AJPH, **126**: 1–6.

RICHTER, C. P., and MOSIER, H. D. 1954 Maximum sodium chloride intake and thirst in domesticated and wild Norway rats. AJPH, **176**: 213–22.

RICHTER, C. P., and SCHMIDT, E. C. H., JR. 1941 Increased fat and decreased carbohydrate appetite of pancreatectomized rats. ENDO, **28**: 179–92.

RICHTER, C. P., SCHMIDT, E. C. H., JR., and MALONE, P. D. 1945 Further observations on the self-regulatory dietary selection of rats made diabetic by pancreatectomy. JHHB, **76**: 192–219.

RIDDELL, W. J. B., and WYBAR, K. C. 1944 Taste of thiouracil and phenylthiocarbamide. NATU, **154**: 669.

RIFE, D. C. 1953 An investigation of genetic variability among Sudanese. AJPN, **11**: 189–202.

————. 1954 Distributions of skin pigmentation, dermatoglyphics, tasting ability, and ABO blood groups within mixed Negro-white populations. AGMG, **3**: 259–69.

RIFE, D. C., and SCHONFELD, M. D. 1944 A comparison of the frequencies of certain genetic traits among Gentile and Jewish students. HUBI, **16**: 172–80.

RIKIMARU, J. Y. 1934 A study of "taste-blindness." I: The incidences among Japanese and Formosans, and divergences in race, age and sex. JJPS, **9**: 11–12.

————. 1934 A study of the individual and racial differences in taste reaction using the same stimulus compound. JJPS, **9**: 59–61.

————. 1936 Taste deficiency of Japanese and other races in Formosa. AJPC, **48**: 649–53.

————. 1937 (Taste deficiency for P.T.C., with special reference to its hereditary nature.) JJPS, **12**: 33–54. (In Japanese.)

RITTER, E. 1936 Untersuchungen über den chemischen Sinn beim schwarzen Kolbenwasserkäfer *Hydrous piceus.* (Investigations on chemical sensitivity in the black water beetle, *Hydrous piceus.*) ZVPH, **23**: 543–70.

RITTMEYER, K. 1885 Geschmackspruefungen. (Taste testing.) Inaugural Dissertation, J. C. Schmidt, Helmstedt, 28 pp.

RIVA, A. 1879 Anosmia e conseguente ageusia da nevrosi dell'olfattorio. (Anosmia and consequent ageusia from the olfactory nerve.) GISM, **1**: 584–92.

RIVERS, W. H. R. 1900 Über die Sinne der primitiven Menschen. (On the senses of primitive men.) UMSC, **25**: 491–93.

————. 1905 Observations on the senses of the Todas. BJSG, **1**: 321–96.

ROASENDA, G. 1932 Nuovo processo di esame della sensibilità gustativa nelle paralisi facciali periferiche. (New procedure of testing of gustatory sensitivity during peripheral facial paralysis.) PSMD, **29**: 509–18.

ROASENDA, J. 1925 Sur une nouvelle méthode

d'examen de la sensibilité gustative. Contribution à la sémiologie de la corde du tympan. (On a new method of examination of gustatory sensitivity. Contribution to the semiology of the chorda tympani.) RENE, **32**: 1062–69.

ROBY, T. B. 1950 The effect of primary reinforcement in acquisition of taste preferences. Unpublished Ph.D. dissertation, Yale University, 50 pp.

ROCÉN, E. 1920 Contributions to the localisation of "sweet smell." SAPH, **40**: 129–44.

ROCKWELL, A. D. 1881 A case of complete and prolonged loss of the sense of both taste and smell; rapid recovery under the influence of galvanism. MERC, **19**: 120.

RODGERS, D. A., and McCLEARN, G. E. 1964 Sucrose versus ethanol appetite in inbred strains of mice. QJSA, **25**: 26–35.

ROEDERER, H. 1952 Verdickungsvermögen und Süsskraft von Stärkesirup. (Thickening power and degree of sweetness of glucose.) STRK, **4**: 19–22.

ROESKE, H. 1897 Ueber die Nervenendigungen in den Papillae fungiformes der Kaninchenzunge. (On the nerve endings in the fungiform papillae of the tongue of the rabbit.) IMAP, **14**: 247–60.

ROGER, W. 1931 Taste deficiency for creatine. SCIE, **74**: 597–98.

ROLLE, S. D. 1955 Issledovanie vkusovoi i oboniatel'noi funktsii metodom sosudistykh refleksov u bol'nykh s narusheniem mozgovogo krovoobrashcheniia. (Investigations on gustatory and olfactory functions using vascular reflexes in disorders of cerebral circulation.) BEBM, **39**: 32–35.

———. 1955 Naruzheniia funktsii vkusovogo i obniatel'nogo analizatorov posle rasstroistva mozgovogo krovoobrashcheniia i ikh vosstanovlenie. (Disturbance of functions of gustatory and olfactory analyzers following disorder of cerebral circulation and their restoration.) ZNPP, **55**: 912–15.

ROLLETT, A. 1897 Über Geruch und Geschmack. (On odor and taste.) MNVS, **34**: 10–39.

———. 1899 Beiträge zur Physiologie des Geruchs, des Geschmacks, der Hautsinne und der Sinne im Allgemeinen. (Contribution to physiology of olfactory, gustatory and tactile senses, and of the senses in general.) PAGP, **74**: 383–465.

RONCORONI, L. 1892 Esame dell'odorato, del gusto e dell'udito in 15 donna e 20 uomino borghesi, senza precedenti criminali ne psicopatici. Confronto coi pazzi. (Examination of olfaction, gustation, and hearing in 15 women and 20 men of the middle class, without previous criminal nor psychopathic records. Comparison with the mentally ill.) ASPI, **13**: 108–9.

ROSEN, S. 1952 Effect of stimulation and section of the chorda tympani nerve. NEUR, **2**: 244–47.

ROSENBAUM, H. 1925 Über den Schwellenwert des sauren Geschmacks. (Threshold value of acid taste.) PAGP, **208**: 730–31.

ROSENTHAL, J. 1860 Über den elektrischen Geschmack. (On the electric taste.) AAPM, pp. 217–23.

*ROSHUPKINA, A. I. 1954 (Experimental material on the physiology of the taste analyzer.) Inaugural Dissertation, Lenin Library, Moscow.

ROSS, S., and VERACE, J. 1953 The critical frequency for taste. AJPC, **66**: 496–97.

ROTCH, T. M. 1878 A case of traumatic anosmia and ageusia, with partial loss of hearing and sight; recovery in six weeks. BMSJ, **99**: 130–32.

*ROTHE, K. G. 1918 Geruch und Geschmack. (Smell and taste.) LEFO, **3**.

ROUSSEAU, M. 1956 À propos d'un cas de fracture du crane avec anosmie et ageusie. (A case of cranial fracture with anosmia and ageusia.) RONO, **28**: 168–70.

ROVIDA, C. 1903–04 Di un particolare disturbo di gusto di natura isterica. (A particular disturbance of taste from natural hysteria.) STON, **2**: 463–65.

ROWINSKI, P., and MANUNTA, G. 1953 Influenza delle gonadi sulla sensibilità gustativa del ratto albino. (Effect of the gonads of gustatory sensitivity in the albino rat.) ARFI, **53**: 117–30. (English summary.)

ROYS, C. C. 1958 A comparison between taste receptors and other nerve tissues of the cockroach in their responses to gustatory stimuli. BIBU, **115**: 490–507.

RUBIN, E. 1936 Taste. BJSG, **27**: 74–85.

RUBIN, T. R., GRIFFIN, F., and FISCHER, R. 1962 A psysico-chemical treatment of taste thresholds. NATU, **195**: 362–64.

*RUBNER, M. 1902 Die hygienische Beurteilung der anorganischen Bestandteile des Trink- und Nutzwassers. (The hygienic judgment of the inorganic composition of drinking water.) VGMS, **24**: 29–119.

RUCH, T. C. 1953 Somesthesis and the chemical senses. ARPS, **4**: 111–36.

RUCH, T. C., and PATTON, H. D. 1946 The relation of the deep opercular cortex to taste. FEPR, **5**: 89–90.

RUCH, T. C., PATTON, H. D., and BROBECK, J. R. 1942 Hyperphagia and adiposity in relation to disturbances of taste. FEPR, **1**: 76.

RUCHHOFT, C. C., MIDDLETON, F. M., BRAUS, H., and ROSEN, A. A. 1954 Taste and odor-producing components in refinery gravity oil separator effluents. INEW, **46**: 284–89.

RUDBERG, J. 1786 Sapor medicamentorum (Taste of medicine), in *Amoenitates Academicae, II*, K. von Linne (ed.). J. J. Palm, Erlangen, 472 pp. (see pp. 365–87).

RUDOLPHI, K. A. 1823 *Grundriss der Physiologie*. (Basis of Physiology.) F. Dümmler, Berlin, 407 pp. (see pp. 87–100).

RUITER, L. DE, and OTTER, C. J. DEN. 1963 Taste

hair stimulation and proboscis response in *Calliphora erythrocephala*. PCZO, **3**: 98.

RULLIER. 1836 Goût (Tastc), in *Dictionnaire de Medicine ou Repertoire General des Sciences Medicales*. J. Bechet, Paris, XIV, 536 pp. (see pp. 195–210).

*RÜMLER, P. 1943 Die Leistungen des Geschmackssinnes bei Zwillingen. (Taste sensitivity in twins.) Inaugural Dissertation, Jena.

RUSHWORTH, G. 1960 Parageusia following Bell's palsy: A result of faulty reinnervation. JNNP, **23**: 250–52.

RUSSELL, P. N., and GREGSON, R. A. M. 1966 A comparison of intermodal and intramodal methods in the multi-dimensional scaling of three component taste mixtures. ASJP, **18**: 244–54.

RUSSO, S. 1957 Sulle allucinazioni olfattive e gustative. (Olfactory and gustatory hallucinations.) RANE, **11**: 41–72.

SACCONE, G. 1902 Sulla localizzazione corticale del centro dell'odorato e del gusto. (Cortical localization of the centers of smell and taste.) AMDN, **8**: 261–75.

SACHS, E., SCHWARTZ, H., and WEDDELL, G. 1937 Pathways transmitting sensation. TANA, **63**: 160.

SAIDULLAH, A. 1927 Experimentelle Untersuchungen über den Geschmacksinn. (Experimental investigations on the sense of taste.) PAGP, **60**: 457–84.

SAKAGUCHI, K., and FUKUMITSU, H. 1956 (The threshold test. Part 5: On MSG.) JSBJ, **51**: 42–43. (In Japanese.)

SAKAI, K. 1964 Studies on chemical transmission in taste fibre endings. I: The action of acetylcholinesterase on bitter taste. CPBT, **12**: 1159–64.

SAKHIULINA, G. T. 1945 Kharakter elektrocheskikh potentsialov iazykoglotochnogo nerva pri vkusovom razdrazhenii iazyka. (Character of electrical potentials of the glossopharyngeal nerve under taste stimulation of the tongue.) BEBM, **19**: 66–68.

SALDANHA, P. H. 1956 Apparent pleiotropic effect of genes determining taste thresholds for phenylthiourea. LANC, **271**: 74.

———. 1958 Taste thresholds for phenylthiourea among Japanese. ANHG, **22**: 380–84.

———. 1962 Taste sensitivity to phenylthiourea among Brazilian Negroes and its bearing on the problem of white Negro intermixture in Brazil. HUBI, **34**: 179–86.

SALDANHA, P. H., and BECAK, W. 1959 Taste thresholds for phenylthiourea among Ashkenazic Jews. SCIE, **129**: 150–51.

SALDANHA, P. H., and GUINSBURG, S. 1954 Taste thresholds for phenylthiourea among students in Rio de Janeiro. RBBI, **14**: 285–90.

SALDANHA, P. H., and NACRUR, J. 1963 Taste thresholds for phenylthiourea among Chileans. AJPN, **21**: 113–19.

SALE, J. W., and SKINNER, W. W. 1922 Relative sweetness of invert sugar. JIEC, **14**: 522–25.

SALMON, T. N., and BLAKESLEE, A. F. 1935 Genetics of sensory thresholds: variations within single individuals in taste sensitivity for PTC. PNAS, **21**: 78–83.

SALOMONSOHN, H. 1888 Ueber den Weg der Geschmacksfasern zum Gehirn. (The path of taste fibers to the brain.) Inaugural Dissertation, G. Schade, Berlin, 30 pp.

SALVERDA-TER LAAG, P. B. 1936 L'eau que préfèrent les oiseaux pour boire et pour se baigner. (Water preference of birds for drinking and for bathing.) ANPA, **21**: 294–308.

SANCTIS, S. DE, and VESPA, B. 1898 Modificazione delle percezioni visive sotto l'influenza di sensazioni gustative simultanée. Ricerche sperimentali su adulti e bambini. (Modification of visual perception under the influence of simultaneous taste variations. Experimental research on adults and children.) RQPP, pp. 369–88.

SANDERS, R. 1948 The significance of thresholds of taste acuity in seasoning with glutamate, in *Flavor and Acceptability of Monosodium Glutamate*. Proceedings of the Symposium, Quartermaster Food and Container Institute, Chicago, 92 pp. (see pp. 70–72).

SANDMEYER, W. 1895 Ueber das Verhalten der Geschmacksknospen nach Durchschneidung des N. glossopharyngeus. (The behavior of taste buds after cutting of the glossopharyngeal nerve.) AAPA, pp. 269–76.

SANFORD, E. C. 1897 Sensations of taste and smell, in *A Course in Experimental Psychology*. D. C. Heath & Co., Boston, 183 pp. (see pp. 47–53).

SAPOLINI. 1883 Études anatomiques par le nerf de Wrisberg et le corde du tympan ou un treizieme nerf cranien. (Anatomical studies on the nerve of Wrisberg and the chorda tympani or the thirteenth cranial nerve.) JMCP, **77**: 337–44.

SATO, M. 1959 (Receptive mechanisms of taste.) KAGT, **29**: 124–31. (In Japanese.)

———. 1963 The effect of temperature change on the response of taste receptors, in *Olfaction and Taste*, Zotterman, Y. (ed.). Macmillan, New York, 396 pp. (see pp. 151–64).

*——— 1965 Mikaku (Gustation), in *Shin Seirigaku* (New Physiology), C. Toida and K. Uchizono (eds.). 2nd ed. Igakushoin, Tokyo.

SATO, M., and AKAIKE, N. 1965 5'Ribonucleotides as gustatory stimuli in rats. Electrophysiological studies. JJPH, **15**: 53–70.

*SATO, M., and KUSANO, K. 1960 Electrophysiology of gustatory receptors, in *Electrical Activity of Single Cells*, Igakushoin, Hongo, Tokyo (see pp. 75–95).

SATO, M., and YAMASHITA, S. 1965 5'Ribonucleotides as gustatory stimuli in rats. Effects of temperature. JJPH, 15: 570–78.

———. 1965 The effect of temperature on the taste response of rats. KUMJ, 18: 41–43.

SATO, S. 1956 (The threshold test. Part I: Bitterness.) JSBJ, 51: 44–47. (In Japanese; English summary.)

SCHÄFER, E. A. 1888 Experiments on special sense localisations in the cortex cerebri of the monkey. BRAI, 10: 362–80.

SCHAFFER, J. 1897 Beiträge zur Histologie menschlicher Organe. IV: Zunge. (Contribution to the histology of human organs. IV: Tongue.) SWWA, 3(106): 353–64.

SCHAFFER, K. 1914 Ueber ein paariges Geschmacksorgan am Eingang der Speiseröhre bei Spitzmäusen. (A pair of taste organs at the entrance of the esophagus in mice.) ZEWA, 28: 97–99.

SCHAMBERG, J. C. 1689 Disputatio physica de gustation ex recentiorum philosophorum hypothesi explicato. (Physical disputation of taste explained from the hypotheses of recent philosophers.) Inaugural Dissertation, Wittig, Leipzig, 19 pp.

SCHARRER, E., SMITH, S. W., and PALAY, S. L. 1947 Chemical sense and taste in the fishes, *Prionotus* and *Trichogaster*. JCNE, 86: 183–98.

SCHEIBER, S. H. 1904 Beitrag zur Lehre von der Tränensekretion am Anschlusse an drei Fälle von Fazialislähmung mit Tränenmangel, nebst Bemerkungen über den Geschmacksinn und über Sensibilitätsstörungen bei Fazialislähmangen. (Contribution to the theory of tear secretion in connection with three cases of facial paralysis, in addition on the sense of taste and on sensitivity disturbances by facial paralysis.) DZNE, 27: 45–70.

———. 1904 Ueber drei Fälle von Fazialislähmung mit Thränenmangel, nebst Bemerkungen über den Geschmackssinn und über Sensibilitätsstörungen bei Fazialislähmungen. (Three cases of facial paralysis with lack of tears, in addition comments on the sense of taste and on disturbances in sensitivity by facial paralysis.) PMCB, 40: 711–75.

SCHEIER, M. 1893 Zwei Fälle von Verletzung des Trigeminus an der Basis. (Two cases of injury of the trigeminus at its base.) BKWO, 30: 1082–83.

———. 1894 Verletzung des Trigeminus an der Basis. (Injury of the trigeminus at its base.) APNV, 26: 897–99.

———. 1895 Beitrag zur Kenntniss der Geschmacksinnervation und der neuroparalytischen Augenentzündung. (Contribution to the knowledge of innervation of taste and neuroparalytic eye infection.) ZKME, 28: 441–60.

———. 1895 Beitrag zur Kenntniss der neuroparalytischen Augenentzündung und der Innervation des Geschmacks. (Contribution to the knowledge of neuroparalytic eye infection

and the innervation of taste.) VGNA, pp. 185–89.

SCHELLING, J. L., TETRAULT, L., LASAGNA, L., and DAVIS, M. 1965 Abnormal taste threshold in diabetes. LANC, 1: 508–12.

SCHETTINO, A. 1925 Riflessi e sensibilità subbiettiva nella donna gravida. (Reflexes and subjective sensitivity of pregnant women.) RAOG, 34: 289–98.

*———. 1926 Riflessi e sensibilità subbiettiva nella donna gravida. (Reflexes and subjective sensitivity of pregnant women.) PRMD, 26: 7.

SCHIFF, M. 1867 Du sens du goût (The sense of taste), in *Leçons sur la Physiologie de la Digestion, I.* H. Loescher, Florence and Turin, 414 pp. (see pp. 78–124).

———. 1867 Neue Untersuchungen über die Geschmacksnerven des vorderen Theiles der Zunge. (New studies on the taste nerves of the anterior part of the tongue.) UNMT, 10: 406–22.

———. 1872 Sull'origine dei nervi gustatori della parte anteriore della lingua. (On the origin of the gustatory nerve of the anterior portion of the tongue.) IMPZ, 12: 422–26.

———. 1886 Nouvelles recherches sur la section intracranienne du trijumeau. (New research on the intracranial section of the trigeminus.) SEMD, 6: 394–95.

———. 1894 Nerfs gustatifs (Gustatory nerves.), in *Recueil des Memoires Physiologiques de Maurice Schiff, III.* Brugg, Lausanne, 597 pp. (see pp. 182–83.)

SCHILDER, P. 1913 Über Störungen der Geschmacksempfindung bei Läsionen der inneren Kapsel und des Thalamus opticus. (On disturbances of taste perception by lesion of the inner capsule and the optic thalamus.) DZNE, 46: 472–82.

SCHINKELE, O. 1942 Über das Vorkommen von Geschmacksknospen im kranialen Drittel des Oesophagus. (On the occurrence of taste buds on the cranial third of the esophagus.) ZMAF, 51: 498–501.

SCHINZ, H. R. 1942 Geschmackstüchtigkeit, Geschmacksschwäche, und Geschmacksblindheit gegen Phenylthioharnstoff und deren Deutung als Polyallelie. (Taste efficiency, taste impairment, and taste blindness to phenylthiourea and its significance as a polyallele.) ERBA, 10: 171–75.

SCHIRMAN, A. 1896 Case of absolute loss of smell and taste. MERC, 49: 372–73.

SCHIRMER, R. 1856 Nonnullae de gustu disquisitiones. (Some investigations on taste.) Inaugural Dissertation, F. G. Kunike, Gryphiae, 45 pp.

———. 1859 Einiges zur Physiologie des Geschmacks. (Something on the physiology of taste.) DEKL, 11: 131–32, 156–58, 184–86.

SCHLICHTING, H. 1898 Klinische Studien über die Geschmackslähmungen durch Zerstörung der

Chorda tympani und des Plexus tympanicus. (Clinical studies of taste paralysis through injury of the chorda tympani and flexus sympaticus.) ZHNO, **32**: 388–401.

SCHMID, L., and DOBRÝ, E. 1952 Vysetrování chuti po svalové námaze. (Examination of gustatory sense following physical exercise.) CLCE, **37**: 1058–62. (Russian and French summaries.)

SCHMIDT, A. 1895 Ein Fall vollständiger isolirter Trigeminuslähmung nebst Bemerkungen über den Verlauf der Geschmacksfasern der Chorda tympani und über trophische Störungen. (A case of complete isolated trigeminus paralysis and comments on the course of taste fibres of the chorda tympani and on trophic disturbances.) DZNE, **6**: 438–56.

———. 1938 Geschmacksphysiologische Untersuchungen an Ameisen. (Physiological taste studies on ants.) ZVPH, **25**: 351–78.

———. 1925 Vorübergehende Anosmie und Ageusie in der Schwangerschaft. (Anosmia and ageusia in pregnancy.) BKWO, **4**: 1967–68.

———. 1937 Über die Geschmackswirkung von Alkaliverbindungen einiger organischer Säuren. (The gustatory effects of alkali compounds of some organic acids.) Inaugural Dissertation, Jügelt, Jena (Thüringen), 21 pp.

SCHNEEBERG, N. G. 1952 Loss of sense of taste due to methylthiouracil therapy. JAMA, **149**: 1091–93.

SCHNEIDER, D. E. 1947 The growth concept of nervous integration. VI. B: On imagined hearing; second contribution to a new theory of hearing. A proposed solution for the dilemma of taste-physiology. The integrative function of the tractus solitarius and its relation to the ego, super-ego, and id systems. Summary of the growth concept of nervous integration. JNMD, **105**: 255–82.

———. 1952 Psychosomatic implications of a new theory of taste and hearing: Psychosurgical perspectives. HIHJ, **1**: 156–65.

———. 1953 The psychophysiology of the sonic system. JNMD, **118**: 494–515.

SCHNEIDER, K. E. 1937 Ueber die Geschmackswirkung von anorganischen Eisen- und Kobaltverbindungen. (Taste effects of inorganic iron and cobalt compounds.) Inaugural Dissertation, Erlangen-Bruck, Jena, 26 pp.

SCHOFIELD, R. H. A. 1876 Observations on taste-goblets in the epiglottis of the dog and cat. JAPH, **10**: 475–77.

SCHOLL, F. M., and MUNCH, J. C. 1937 Taste tests. IV. Relative bitterness. JAPM, **26**: 127–29.

SCHOLZ, B. 1911 Über Geschmacksstörungen bei Tumoren der hinteren Schädelgrube. (Taste disturbances from tumors of the anterior cranium.) MGMC, **23**: 637–58.

SCHREIBER, G. A. 1887 Zavisimosti vkusovykh oshchushchenii ot territorii vkusovago organa i temperatury vkusovykh veshchestv. (The dependence of taste sensation on the site of the taste organ and the temperature of the taste substances.) Unpublished M.D. dissertation, Physiological Institute, Imperial Moscow University, 131 pp.

SCHREIBER, P. J. 1889–90 Abnorme Geschmacksempfindung bei Neurasthenia sexualis. (Abnormal taste sensations in neurasthenia sexualis.) MEZE, **1**: 206–10.

SCHRIER, A. M. 1965 Response rates of monkey (*Macaca mulatta*) under varying conditions of sucrose refinement. JCPP, **59**: 378–84.

SCHRIJVER, F. 1933 Über das Bezeichnen von Geschmacksempfindungen. (The labeling of taste sensations.) ZPSI, **130**: 385–92.

———. 1933 Über die Erforschung erblicher Abweichungen beim Geschmacksinn. (On the investigation of hereditary deviation of the sense of taste.) ZERA, **6**: 177–79.

SCHTSCHERBACK, A. 1892 Zur Frage über die Localisation der Geschmackscentren in der Hirnrinde. (Question of the localization of taste centers in the cortex.) ZEPH, **5**: 289–98.

SCHULTE, E. 1885 Die Beziehungen der Chorda tympani zur Geschmacksperception auf den zwei vorderen Dritteln der Zunge. (The relationship of the chorda tympani to taste perception on the anterior two-thirds of the tongue.) ZHNO, **15**: 67–78.

SCHULTE, M. J. 1942 Over smaak en smaakcorrigentia. (Taste and taste corrigents.) PHWE, **79**: 161–64.

SCHULZ, H. 1937 Ueber die Geschmackswirkung von anorganischen Strontium-, Barium- und Nickelsalzen. (Taste effects of inorganic strontium, barium, and nickel salts.) Inaugural Dissertation, B. Sporn, Zeulenroda, Jena, 20 pp.

SCHULZ, R. 1909 Über Geschmacksstörungen bei Mittelohraffektionen. (Taste sensations in middle ear disorders.) AONK, **79**: 220–45.

SCHULZE, F. E. 1863 Ueber die becherförmigen Organe der Fische. (On the goblet shaped organs of fish.) ZWZA, **12**: 218–22.

———. 1870 Die Geschmacksorgane der Froschlarven. (Taste organs of frog larva.) AMAE, **6**: 407–9.

SCHULZE, W. 1937 Über die Geschmackswirkung von organischen Magnesium und Kalciumsalzen. (The taste effects of inorganic magnesium and calcium salts.) Inaugural Dissertation Würzburg, Jena, 19 pp.

SCHUMACHER, S. 1927 Die Zunge (The tongue), in *Möllendorff's Handbuch der Mikroskopischen Anatomie der Menschen*. J. Springer, Berlin, 374 pp. (see pp. 35–60).

SCHUR, H. 1937 Grundlagen, Bedeutung und Leistungsgrenzen der automatischen Regulierung der Nahrungsaufnahme durch Instinkt, Appetit und Geschmacksinn. (Principles, significance and limits of automatic regulation of food intake by instinct, appetite and sense of taste.) KLWO, **16**: 185–88, 217–22.

SCHÜRGER, J. 1937 Ueber die Geschmackswirkung von organischen Strontium-, Eisen- und Mangansalzen. (On the effect of taste of organic strontium, iron and manganese salts.) Inaugural Dissertation, B. Sporn, Zeulenroda, Jena, 26 pp.

SCHUTZ, H. G. 1952 The influence of an olfactory stimulus upon a gustatory threshold. Unpublished Master's thesis, Illinois Institute of Technology, 58 pp.

SCHUTZ, H. G., and PILGRIM, F. J. 1957 Differential sensitivity in gustation. JEPS, 54: 41–48.

———. 1957 Sweetness of various compounds and its measurement. FORE, 22: 206–13.

SCHWALBE, G. A. 1867 Das Epithel der Papillae vallatae. (The epithelium of the vallate papillae.) AMAE, 3: 504–8.

———. 1868 Ueber die Geschmacksorgane der Säugethiere und des Menschen. (On taste organs of mammals and humans.) AMAE, 4: 154–87.

———. 1868 Zur Kenntniss der Papillae fungiformes der Säugetiere. (Knowledge of the fungiform papillae of mammals.) ZMWI, 6: 433–34.

SCHWANKE, W. 1936 Geschmacksstörungen bei Grippe. (Taste disturbances in influenza.) KLWO, 15: 93.

SCHWARTZ, H. G., and WEDDELL, G. 1938 Observations on the pathways transmitting the sensation of taste. BRAI, 61: 99–115.

SCHWARTZ, M. J., HOPEWELL, W. S., and PIOTROWSKI, S. F. 1962 Prepared saccharin solution for study of circulation time. NYSJ, 63: 3086–88.

SCHWARTZBAUM, J. S., and WILSON, W. A., JR. 1961 Taste-discrimination in the monkey. AJPC, 74: 403–9.

SCOFIELD, E. S. 1934 Studies in taste: The effect of solution temperature on the stimulus thresholds of sodium chloride. Unpublished Master's thesis, Ohio State University, 40 pp.

———. 1939 An experimental study of some factors influencing the determination of gustatory thresholds. Unpublished Ph.D. dissertation, Ohio State University, 185 pp.

SCOTT, E. M. 1946 Self-selection of diet. I: Selection of purified components. JONU, 31: 397–406.

———. 1948 Self-selection of diet. TAAC, 6: 126–33.

SCOTT, E. M., and QUINT, E. 1946 Self-selection of diet: Effect of flavor. JONU, 32: 113–19.

———. 1946 Self-selection of diet. III: Appetites for B vitamins. JONU, 32: 285–91.

———. 1946 Self-selection of diet. IV: Appetite for protein. JONU, 32: 293–301.

SCOTT, E. M., SMITH, S. J., and VERNEY, E. L. 1948 Self-selection of diet. VII: The effect of age and pregnancy on selection. JONU, 35: 281–86.

SCOTT, E. M., and VERNEY, E. L. 1947 Self-selection of diet. V: Appetite for carbohydrates. JONU, 34: 401–7.

———. 1947 Self-selection of diet. VI: The nature of appetite for B vitamins. JONU, 34: 471–80.

———. 1948 Self-selection of diet. VIII: Appetite for fats. JONU, 36: 91–98.

———. 1949 Self-selection of diet. IX: The appetite for thiamine. JONU, 37: 81–91.

SCOTT, E. M., VERNEY, E. L., and MORISSEY, P. D. 1950. Self-selection of diet. X: Appetites for sodium, chloride and sodium chloride. JONU, 41: 173–86.

———. 1950 Self-selection of diet. XI: Appetites for calcium, magnesium and potassium. JONU, 41: 187–201.

———. 1950 Self-selection of diet. XII: Effects of B vitamin deficiencies on selection of food components. JONU, 41: 373–81.

SCOTT, P. J. 1960 Glossitis with complete loss of taste sensation during Dindevan treatment. Report of a case. NZMJ, 59: 296.

SCOTT-MONCRIEFF, R. 1939 The sense of taste. BUVM, 15: 218–20.

SCOW, R. O., and CORNFIELD, J. 1954 Quantitative relations between the oral and intravenous glucose tolerance curves. AJPH, 179: 435–38.

SEGALL, G. 1948 Taste-blind identical twins; with diabetes and other striking pathological characteristics. JOHE, 39: 228–32.

SEGUNDO, J. P., and GALEANO, C. 1960 Somatic functions of the nervous system. ARPH, 22: 433–72.

SEIDLER, W. 1938 Über die Beeinflussung des Geschmacksfeldes auf der Zunge durch Anaesthetica. I. (The effect of anaesthetics on the taste area of the tongue. I.) Inaugural Dissertation, E. Richter, Jena, 46 pp.

SEIFTER, E. 1960 Vitamin A affects taste, too. CENE, 38: 81.

*SEMERIA, C. 1957 Le alterazioni della sensibilità olfattiva e gustativa consecutive a traumi cranici. (Changes in olfactory and gustatory sensitivity caused by cranial injuries.) MIOT, 7: 111–15.

———. 1957 Studio delle modificazioni della sensibilità olfattiva e gustativa in condizioni di ipossiemia sperimentale nell'uomo. (Olfactory and gustatory changes in experimental hypoxemic conditions in man.) MIOT, 7: 354–58.

SENATOR, H. 1882 Ein Fall von Trigeminusaffection. Beitrag zur Kenntniss von der neuroparalytischen Ophthalmie, dem Verlauf der Geschmacksfasern der Chorda und den intermittirenden Gelenkschwellungen. (A case of trigeminus affection. Contribution to the knowledge of neuroparalytic ophthalmy, the course of taste fibers of the chorda and of intermittent joint swellings.) APNV, 13: 590–601.

SEO, A. 1932 Vergleichende physiologische Studien über die Chemoreceptoren des Frosches. (Comparative physiological studies concerning the chemical receptors of frogs.) JPMP, 2: 249–55.

SERRA, F., and COSTA, A. 1950 La sensibilità gustativa verso la fenil-tio-carbamide. Suoi riflessi nella patologia e fisiologia umana. (Taste sensitivity to phenyl-thio-carbamide. Its reflection on human pathology and physiology.) CLOD, 5: 358–76.

SERTOLI, E. 1874 Osservazioni sulle terminazioni dei nervi del gusto. (Observations on the terminations of the taste nerve.) GAMV, 4: 129–42.

——. 1875 Osservazioni sulle terminazioni dei nervi del gusto. (Observations on the terminations of the taste nerve.) SPER, 36: 69.

——. 1876 Beiträge zur Kenntniss der Endigungen der Geschmacksnerven. (Contributions to the knowledge of taste nerve endings.) UNMT, 11: 403–15.

SETO, H. 1963 *Studies of the Sensory Innervation (Human Sensibility.)* 2nd ed. Charles C Thomas, Springfield, Ill., 522 pp. (see pp. 443–51).

SETTERFIELD, W., SCHOTT, R. G., and SNYDER, L. H. 1936 Studies in human inheritance. XV: The bimodality of the threshold curve for the taste of phenyl-thio-carbamide. OJSC, 36: 231–35.

SEWALL, K. W. 1939 Blood, taste, digital hair, and colour of eyes in Eastern Eskimo. AJPN, 25: 93–99.

SHAFAR, J. 1965 Dysageusia in the elderly. LANC, 1: 83–84.

SHALLENBERGER, R. S. 1963 Hydrogen bonding and the varying sweetness of the sugars. JFDS, 28: 584–89.

SHALLENBERGER, R. S., ACREE, T. E., and GUILD, W. E. 1965 Configuration, conformation, and sweetness of hexose anomers. JFDS, 30: 560–63.

SHEBA, C., ASHKENAZI, I., and SZEINBERG, A. 1962 Taste sensitivity to phenylthiourea among the Jewish population groups in Israel. AJHG, 14: 44–51.

SHEFFIELD, F. D., and ROBY, T. B. 1950 Reward value of a non-nutritive sweet taste. JCPP, 43: 471–81.

SHELDON, R. E. 1909 The reactions of the dogfish to chemical stimuli, JCNP, 1: 273–311.

SHENKIN, H. A., and LEWEY, F. H. 1944 Taste aura preceding convulsions in a lesion of the parietal operculum. JNMD, 100: 352–54.

SHEPARD, T. H. 1961 Phenylthiocarbamide nontasting among congenital athyrotic cretins; further studies in an attempt to explain the increased incidence. JCIN, 40: 1751–57.

SHEPARD, T. H., and GARTLER, S. M. 1960 Increased incidence of nontasters of phenythio-

carbamide among congenital athyreotic cretins. SCIE, 131: 929.

SHEPARD, T. H., LORINCZ, A. E., and GARTLER, S. M. 1963 Desulfuration of thiourea by saliva. PSEB, 112: 38–42.

SHERWOOD, P. 1949 The sense of taste. WIVI, 30(6): 18.

SHIGA, A., and HOZUMI, T. 1956 (The threshold test. Part 7. Sweetness and astringency.) JSBJ, 51: 40–41. (In Japanese.)

*SHIMAZU, K. 1953 Mikaku (Gustation), in *Jukkenshinrigaku-teijo, III.* (Manual of Experimental Psychology.) Iwanami-shoten, Tokyo (see pp. 175–223).

*SHIMIZU, M. 1957 Cellular physiology of taste. II: Bitter taste and sulfhydryl groups in the taste epithelium. JPMP, 19: 491–97.

——. 1958 (Cellular physiology of taste. III: Phosphatase and taste substances in the taste epithelium especially concerning sweet and bitter taste.) JJPH, 20: 422–24. (English summary.)

——. 1958 (Relative quantitative measurement of sulfhydryl groups in the taste epithelium.) JJPH, 20: 425–29. (English summary.)

SHINJO, T. 1950 Salivary secretion in relation to facilitation and inhibition in the sense of taste. TJEM, 52: 241–48.

SHINN, M. W. 1905 Der Geschmack (Taste), in *Körperliche und Geistige Entwicklung eines Kindes in Biographischer Darstellung.* F. G. L. Gressler, Langensalza, 645 pp. (see pp. 238–62).

SHORE, L. E. 1892 A contribution to our knowledge of taste sensations. JPHY, 13: 191–217. (Abstract in ZEPH, 6: 625–27, 1892.)

SHOWALTER, H. A. 1945 Taste and flavors. FOCN, 5(1): 9–11.

*SHUFORD, E. H., JR. 1955 Relative acceptability of sucrose and glucose solutions in the white rat. Unpublished Ph.D. thesis, University of Illinois, 63 pp.

——. 1959 Palatability and osmotic pressure of glucose and sucrose solutions as determinants of intake. JCPP, 52: 150–53.

SIEDLER, P. 1916 Über künstliche Süsstoffe insbesondere Dulcin. (Artificial sweeteners, especially dulcin.) CMKZ, 40: 853–55.

SIGERSON, G. 1880 Contributions to the study of nerve-action in connexion with the sense of taste. I: Function of the trigeminus. II: Functions of the chorda tympani. PRIB, 13: 257–71.

SILBERPFENNIG, I., and URBAN, H. 1937 Hémihyperpathie du goût. (Hemihyperpathy of taste.) RENE, 68: 613–18.

——. 1937 Zur Frage der Hyperpathie. Ein fall von sensibler und Geschmackshyperpathie bei einem medullären Herd. (Sensory and gustatory hyperpathia with medullary focus.) DZNE, 142: 120–52.

SILIMBANI, A. 1954 Chorda tympani e sensibilità gustative dei ⅔ anteriori della lingua. (Chorda tympani and gustatory sensitivity of anterior ⅔ of the tongue.) ORLI, 22: 51–66..

SIMMONS, R. T., GRAYDON, J. J., SEMPLE, N. M., and D'SENA, G. W. L. 1953 A genetical survey in Chenchu, South India; blood, taste and secretion. MJAU, 1: 497–503.

SIMMONS, R. T., GRAYDON, J. J., SEMPLE, N. M., and TAYLOR, C. N. D. 1951 Blood, taste and secretion: A genetical survey in Maoris. MJAU, 38: 425–31.

SIMONETTA, B. 1928 Presenza di calici gustativi nella porzione laringea della faringe di topo bianco. (Presence of taste buds in the larynx and pharynx of the white rat.) ATNV, 37: 129–34.

SIMONS, R. D. G. 1927 Over de doseering van arseen. (On the dosages of arsenic.) PHWE, 74: 315–21. (English summary.)

SINGER, F. 1963 Disgeusie e odontostomatopatie. (Dysgeusia and dental diseases.) MOOD, 5: 321–24. (French, English, and German summaries.)

SINGER, H. D. 1923 An unusual syndrome. Anosmia and ageusia. ANPS, 9: 262–63.

SINNOT, J. J., and RAUTH, J. E. 1937 Effect of smoking on taste thresholds. JGPS, 17: 151–53.

*SIQUELAND, E. R. 1963 An experimental modification of preference. Unpublished Ph.D. thesis, University of Washington.

———. 1965 Experimental modification of taste preference. JCPP, 59: 166–70.

SIVETZ, M. 1949 Acids play important roles in flavor. FOIN, 21: 1384–85.

SJÖSTRÖM, K. E. 1953 En smaksinnesundersökning på ett psykiatriskt klientel. (Study of gustatory sense of psychiatric patients.) SVLA, 50: 473–76.

SKOUBY, A. P., and ZILSTORFF-PEDERSEN, K. 1955 The influence of acetylcholine, menthol, and strychnine on taste receptors in man. APSC, 34: 250–56.

SKRAMLIK, E. VON. 1921 Geschmacksreize und Zungenkreislauf. (The relation between taste and circulation in the tongue.) ZGEM, 12: 50–54.

———. 1921 Ueber die Lokalisation der Geschmacksempfindungen. (On localization of taste perception.) DMWO, 47: 1414.

———. 1922 Mischungsgleichungen im Gebiete des Geschmackssinns. (Equivalent mixtures in the area of taste.) ZPSI, 53: 36–78.

———. 1922 Mischungsgleichungen im Gebiete des Geschmacksinns. II. (Equivalent mixtures in the area of taste. II.) ZPSI, 53: 219–33.

———. 1925 Über die Lokalisation der Empfindungen bei den niederen Sinnen. (On the localization of perception in the lower senses.) ZESI, 56: 69–140.

———. 1926 Handbuch der Physiologie der Niederensinne. I. Der Physiologie des Geruchs und Geschmackssinnes. Georg Thieme, Leipzig, 532 pp. (see pp. 346–520).

———. 1926 Physiologie des Geschmackssinnes (Physiology of the taste sense), in Handbuch der Normalen und Pathologischen Physiologie. J. Springer, Berlin, 1062 pp. (see pp. 306–92).

———. 1937 Neue Verfahren zur Prüfung des Leistungen des Geschmackssinnes. (New methods for the investigation of the taste sense.) HBAM, 5: 1727–74.

———. 1943 Vererbungsforschungen auf dem Gebiete des Geschmackssinnes. (Hereditary investigations in the area of taste.) JEZN, 76: 50-80.

———. 1948 Über die zur minimalen Erregung des menschlichen Geruchs, Geschmackssinnes notwendigen Molekulmengen. (The minimum concentrations necessary to arouse sensations of smell and taste.) PAGP, 249: 702–16.

———. 1954 Vergleichende Untersuchungen über die Geschmackswirkung von Gemüse- und Obstpressäften. (Comparison of the taste effects of vegetable and fruit juices.) PHAR, 10: 843–51.

———. 1955 Organoleptik. Wesen, Wege, Ziele. (Organoleptic analysis, compounds, pathways, objectives.) ZGIM, 10: 3–17.

———. 1955 Sinnesphysiologische Untersuchung von Gerwürzen in Pulverform. (Sensory physiological investigations of spices in powderform.) DLRU, 51: 173–79.

———. 1955 Sinnesphysiologische Untersuchung von Obstpressäften. (Sensory and physiological studies of fruit juices.) DLRU, 51: 75–80.

———. 1956 Über die Bedeutung der Verbesserung der sinnlichen Wirkungen von Arzneimitteln. (On the significance of improving the sensitivity effect of drugs.) PHZI, 101: 1037–43.

———. 1957 Ein neuer Kochsalzersatz. (A new table salt substitute.) PHAR, 12: 580–82.

———. 1957 Die Psychophysiologie der Arzneiwirkungen, Arzneiverordnungen einst und jetzt. (The psychophysiological effect of drugs, drug prescriptions before and now.) ZGIM, 8: 7–40.

———. 1957 Kritik der Diätsalze. (Critique of salt substitutes.) PHZI, 102: 863–66.

———. 1957 Über Diätsalze im allgemeinen und einen neuen Ersatz für Kochsalz im besonderen. (Salt substitutes in general and special emphasis on a new substitute for NaCl.) ZGIM, 10: 433–42.

———. 1962 Die Beinflussung der Substrate für die Geschmacksgrundempfindungen. (Control of media for basic taste sensations.) ZEBL, 113: 293–322.

———. 1962 Über die Erscheinungen der positiven und negativen Unterdrückung beim Geschmackssinn. (On the phenomenon of positive and negative suppression in the sense of taste.) ZEBL, 113: 266–92.

———. 1962 Über Geruchs- und Geschmacksstärke. (On odor and taste intensity.) ZEBL, 113: 227–40.

———. 1963 The fundamental substrates of taste, in *Olfaction and Taste,* Zotterman, Y. (ed.). Macmillan, New York, 396 pp. (see pp. 125–32).

———. 1963 Über die Zahl der Emfindungsqualitäten im Gebiete der chemischen Sinneswerkzeuge (Geruchs- und Geschmackssinn.) (On the number of sensory qualities in the area of chemical sense organs [olfactory and taste sense].) ZEBL, 113: 329–39.

SKRAMLIK, E. VON, and KLOSA, J. 1957 Ein Kochsalzersatz auf organischer Grundlage. (An organic table salt substitute.) NATU, 44: 268.

SKRAMLIK, E. VON, and SCHWARZ, G. 1959–60 Über die sinnlichen Wirkungen von Geschmackslösungen in der Mundhöhle. (Sensory effects of taste solutions in the mouth cavity.) ZEBL, 111: 99–127.

SKUDE, G. 1959 Sweet taste perception for phenylthiourea (P.T.C.). HERE, 45: 597–622.

———. 1960 Complexities of human taste variation. JOHE, 51: 259–63.

———. 1960 Consistency of sweet taste perception for P.T.C. AGMG, 9: 325–33.

———. 1960 On sweet taste perception for P.T.C. AGMG, 9: 99–102.

———. 1961 Saliva and sweet taste perception for phenylthiourea (P.T.C.). AGMG, 10: 316–20.

———. 1963 Some factors influencing taste perception for phenylthiourea (P.T.C.). HERE, 50: 203–10.

———. 1963 Studies in sweet taste perception for phenylthiourea (P.T.C.). HERE, 50: 196–202.

SLIFER, E. H., PRESTAGE, J. J., and BEAMS, H. W. 1959 The chemoreceptors and other sense organs on the antennal fagellum of the grasshopper (Orthoptera, *Acrididae*). JOMO, 105: 145–66.

SLOSSON, E. E. 1890 The relative sweetness of different alcohols. TSAS, 12: 104–5.

SMITH, A. A., and DANCIS, J. 1964 Taste discrimination in familial dysautonomia. PEDI, 33: 441–43.

SMITH, A. A., FARBMAN, A., and DANCIS, J. 1965 Absence of taste-bud papillae in familial dysautonomia. SCIE, 147: 1040–41.

SMITH, J. C., and MORRIS, D. D. 1963 Effects of atropine sulfate on the conditioned aversion to saccharin fluid with X-rays as the unconditioned stimulus. RARE, 18: 186–90.

SMITH, J. C., MORRIS, D. D., and HENDRICKS, J. 1964 Conditioned aversion to saccharin solution with high dose rates of X-rays as the unconditioned stimulus. RARE, 22: 507–10.

SMITH, M., and DUFFY, M. 1957 Consumption of sucrose and saccharine by hungry and satiated rats. JCPP, 50: 65–69.

———. 1957 Evidence for a dual reinforcing effect of sugar. JCPP, 50: 242–47.

SMITH, M., and KINNEY, G. C. 1956 Sugar as a reward for hungry and nonhungry rats. JEPS, 51: 348–52.

SMITH, M., POOL, R., and WEINBERG, H. 1958 Evidence for a learning theory of specific hunger. JCPP, 51: 758–63.

SMITH, M. P., and CAPRETTA, P. J. 1956 Effects of drive level and experience on the reward value of saccharine solutions. JCPP, 46: 553–57.

SMITH, M. P., and ROSS, S. 1960 Acceptance of sodium sucaryl by C57 black mice. JGPY, 96: 101–4.

SMITH, R. M. 1889 The sense of taste, in *The Physiology of the Domestic Animals.* F. A. Davis, Philadelphia, 938 pp. (see pp. 893–97).

SNIAKIN, P. G., and ZAIKO, N. S. 1956 Znachenie issledovanii chuvestvitel'nosti slizistoi obolochki polosti rta. (The significance of examinations of the sensitivity of the oral mucosa.) STMM, 11: 11–15.

SNOW, J. H. 1909 Effect of sugar and temperature on fruit juices. JHOE, 1: 261–66.

SNYDER, L. H. 1931 Inherited taste deficiency. SCIE, 74: 151–52.

———. 1932 Studies in human inheritance. IX: The inheritance of taste deficiency in man. OJSC, 32: 436–40.

SNYDER, L. H., BAXTER, R. C., and KNISELY, A. W. 1941 Studies in human inheritance. XIX: The linkage relations of the blood groups, the blood types, and taste deficiency to P.T.C. JOHE, 32: 22–25.

SNYDER, L. H., and DAVIDSON, D. F. 1937 Studies in human inheritance. XVIII: The inheritance of taste deficiency to di-phenyl-guanidine. EUNE, 22: 1–2.

SOBEL, S. P. 1929 Chronic pancreatitis and the metallic taste. MJRE, 130: 682–83.

SOEDARMO, D., KARE, M. R., and WASSERMAN, R. H. 1961 Observations on the removal of sugar from the mouth and the crop of the chicken. POSC, 40: 123–28.

SOEMMERRING, S. T. 1806 *Abbildungen der Menschlichen Organe des Geschmackes und der Stimme.* (Illustrations of human organs of taste and the voice.) Varrentrapp and Wenner, Frankfurt, 21 pp.

———. 1808 *Icones Organorum Humanorum Gustus et Vocis.* (Illustrations of the human taste and vocal organs.) Varrentrapp and Wenner, Frankfurt, 6 pp.

SOLLIER, P. 1891 Gustation colorée. (Colored gustation.) CRSS, 3: 763.

SOLLMANN, T. 1921 Astringency and protein-precipitation by masked tannin compounds. JPET, 17: 63–104.

SOLMS, J., VUATAZ, L., and EGLI, R. H. 1965 The taste of L- and D-amino acids. EXPE, 21: 692–97.

SOLTAN, H. C., and BRACKEN, S. E. 1958 The relation of sex to taste reactions for P.T.C., sodium benzoate and four "standards." JOHE, **49**: 280–84.

SOLUMIN, P. M. 1935 Krovosnabzhenie iazyka cheloveka. (The blood supply of the human tongue.) VRRA, **15**: 183–92. (French and English summaries.)

SONNTAG, C. F. 1920 The comparative anatomy of the tongue of the mammalia. I. General description of the tongue. PZSL, pp. 115–29.

——. 1921 The comparative anatomy of the tongues of mammalia. II. Family 1. Simiidae. PZSL, **1**: 1–29.

——. 1921 The comparative anatomy of the tongue of the mammalia. III. Family 2. Cercopithecidae: With notes on the comparative physiology of the tongues and stomachs of the langurs. PZSL, **2**: 277–322.

——. 1921 The comparative anatomy of the tongues of the mammalia. IV. Families 3 and 4. Cebidae and Hapalidae. PZSL, **2**: 497–524.

——. 1921 The comparative anatomy of the tongues of the mammalia. V. Lemuroidea and Tarsioidea. PZSL, **2**: 741–55.

——. 1921 The comparative anatomy of the tongues of the mammalia. VI. Summary and classification of the tongues of the primate. PZSL, **2**: 757–67.

——. 1922 The comparative anatomy of the tongues of the mammalia. VII. Cetacea, Sirenia, and Ungulata. PZSL, **2**: 639–57.

——. 1923 The comparative anatomy of the tongues of the mammalia. VIII. Carnivora. PZSL, **1**: 129–53.

——. 1923 The comparative anatomy of the tongues of the mammalia. IX. Edentata, Dermoptera, and Insectivora. PZSL, **2**: 515–29.

——. 1924 The comparative anatomy of the tongues of the mammalia. X. Rodentia. PZSL, **2**: 725–41.

——. 1924 The comparative anatomy of the tongue of the mammalia. XI. Marsupialia and Montremata. PZSL, **2**: 743–55.

——. 1925 The comparative anatomy of the tongues of the mammalia. XII. Summary, classification and phylogeny. PZSL, **1**: 701–62.

SONOHARA, T. 1934 Systematic studies on psychology of human neonates. I (3). Reactions to bitter stimuli. JJPS, **1**: 127–41.

SOTTNER, L. 1964 Diabetes mellitus a chutnání fenylthiokarbamidu. (Diabetes mellitus and the taste of phenylthiocarbamide.) CLCE, **103**: 1308–13. (English, Russian, French, and Spanish summaries.)

SOULAIRAC, A. 1943 Action de l'acetate de désoxycorticostérone sur le choix des solutions salines par la souris. (Action of desoxycorticosterone acetate on the choice of saline solutions by the mouse.) BSZF, **68**: 39–41.

——. 1944 Action de l'insuline sur la consommation de différents glucides chez la souris. (Action of insulin on ingestion of different glucides by the mouse.) CRSS, **138**: 119–20.

——. 1944 Action de l'insuline sur le choix spontané et combiné de différents glucides par la souris. (Action of insulin on spontaneous selection and combination of different glucides by the mouse.) BSZF, **69**: 134–41.

——. 1945 Action de la cortico-surrénale sur la consummation spontanée des glucides. (Action of the adrenal cortex on spontaneous consumption of glucosides.) ANEN, **6**: 51–54.

——. 1946 Action de la thyroíde sur la consommation spontanée du glucose. (Action of thyroid on spontaneous consumption of glucose.) CRSS, **140**: 859–61.

——. 1947 Importance de l'absorption intestinale dans la régulation de l'appétit glucidique. (Importance of intestinal absorption in the regulation of glucosidic appetite.) CORE, **224**: 961–63.

——. 1947 La physiologie d'un comportement; l'appétit glucidique et sa regulation neuro-endocrinienne chez les rongeurs. (The physiology of behavior; glucose appetite and its neuro-endocrine regulation in rodents.) BUBF, **81**: 272–432. (English summary.)

——. 1947 Le rôle du complexe hypothalamo-hypophysaire dans la régulation centrale de l'appétit glucidique. (The role of the hypothalamic-hypophysis complex on the central regulation of the glucosidic appetite.) CORE, **224**: 757–60.

——. 1947 Modifications du seuil gustatif du glucose à la suite de perturbations endocriniennes. (Changes in the taste threshold for glucose following endocrine disturbances.) CRSS, **141**: 745–47.

SOULAIRAC, A., and SOULAIRAC, M. L. 1958 Modifications de la consommation alimentaire et du seuil gustatif pour le glucose, à la suite de lésions du cortex cérébral, chez le rat. (Modifications of food intake and gustatory threshold for glucose, following lesions of the cerebral cortex in the rat.) JOPH, **50**: 520–23.

SOUTHERDEN, F. 1903 The bearing of recent discoveries on the physics of taste and smell. NATU, **67**: 486–87.

SPECKAN, C. 1922 Untersuchungen über Geschmacksveränderungen des Süsstoffs Dulcin (p-Phenetolcarbamid) infolge chemischer Eingriffe bzw. über die Süsskraft von Derivaten des p-Oxyphenylharnstoffs. (Investigations on taste changes in the sweet substance, dulcin [p-phenetol-carbamide] on account of chemical action on the strength of sweetness of derivatives of p-oxyphenylurea.) BERP, **32**: 83–107.

SPENGLER, O., and TRAEGEL, A. 1927 Vergleichende Versuche, betreffend Feststellung des Süssungsgrades von Saccharose und Fructose. (Comparative experiments to establish the degree of sweetness of sucrose and fructose.) ZVDZ, **77**: 1–12.

——. 1928 Vergleichende Versuche, betreffend Feststellung des Süssungsgrades von Saccharose und Fructose. (Comparative experiments to establish the degree of sweetness of sucrose and fructose.) ZVDZ, **78**: 334–40.

SRINIVASAN, M. 1955 Has the ear a role in registering flavour? BUCT, **4**: 136.

SRIVASTAVA, R. P. 1959 Measurement of taste sensitivity to phenylthiourea (P.T.C.) in Uttar Pradesh. EAAN, **12**: 267–72.

———. 1961 Frequency of non-tasters among the Danguria Tharu of Uttar Pradesh. EAAN, **14**: 258–59.

STAHR, H. 1901 Über die Papillae fungiformes der Kinderzunge und ihre Bedeutung als Geschmacksorgan. (On the fungiform papillae of the child's tongue and its meaning as organ of taste.) ZEMA, **4**: 199–260.

———. 1902 Über die Papilla foliata beim wilden und beim domesticirten Kaninchen. (On the papilla foliate of the wild and domesticated rabbit.) ANAN, **21**: 354–61.

———. 1903 Über die Ausdehnung der Papilla foliata und die Frage einer einseitigen "kompensatorischen Hypertrophie" im Bereiche des Geschmacksorgans. (On the expansion of the foliate papillae and the question of a unilateral compensatory hypertrophy in the area of taste organs.) AREO, **16**: 179–99.

———. 1903 Zur Aetiologie epithelialer Geschwülste. I: Epithelperlen in den Zungenpapillen des Menschen. II: Eine experimentell erzeugte Geschwulst der Rattenvallata. (The etiology of epithelia tumors. I: Epithelpearls in the tongue papillae of men. II: An experimentally produced tumor in the rat vallata.) ZAPP, **14**: 1–6.

———. 1906 Ueber die Zungenpapillen des Breslauer Gorillaweibchens. (On the taste papillae of the female gorilla in Breslau.) JEZN, **41**: 618–31.

———. 1906 Vergleichende Untersuchungen an den Geschmackspapillen der Orang-utan-Zunge. (Comparative investigations on the taste papillae of the orangutan tongue.) ZEMA, **9**: 344–60.

———. 1910 Über gewebliche Umwandlungen an der Zunge des Menschen im Bereiche der Papilla foliata. (On tissue change on the tongue of man in the area of the foliate papillae.) AMAE, **75**: 375–413.

STAMM, 1839 Beobachtung eines Falles von theilweiser krebsiger Zerstörung des Keilbeines, des Gaumenbeines, des Rachens und von Skirrhus am Nervus trigemins dexter, nebst dem Beweise, dass der Nervus lingualis nicht der Geschmacksnerve ist. (Observation of a case of partial cancer destruction of the sphenoid bone, the palate bone, the pharynx and the right trigeminal nerve; evidence that the lingual nerve is not the taste nerve.) MEAL, **5**: 70–80.

STANNIUS, 1848 Versuche über die Funktion der Zungennerven. (Studies on the function of taste nerves.) AAPM, pp. 131–38.

STANOJEVIC, L. 1924 O poremečenoj gustatoricnoj inervaciji jezika ili parcijalnoj bilateralnoj povrjedi "chorda tympani" kod jednog slucaja sclerosis polyinsularis sa diabetes insipidus. (On disturbances of gustatory innervation of the tongue or on partial bilateral lesions of the chorda tympani in diabetes insipidus in combination with multiple sclerosis.) LIVJ, **46**: 551–56. (German summary.)

STARLING, F. H. 1962 Sensations of taste and smell, in *Principles of Human Physiology*, H. Dawson and M. G. Eggleton (eds.). Lea and Febiger, Philadelphia, 1579 pp. (see pp. 1350–63).

STAUB, H. 1942 Künstliche Süsstoffe. (Synthetic sweetener.) SMWO, **23**: 983–86.

STEGGERDA, M. 1937 Testing races for the threshold of taste, with PTC. JOHE, **28**: 309–10.

STEGNER, K. 1937 Über die Geschmackswirkung von anorganischen Beryllium-, Cadmium- und Manganverbindungen. (Taste effects of inorganic beryllium, cadmium, and manganese compounds.) Inaugural Dissertation, B. Sporn, Zeulenroda, Jena, 20 pp.

STEIN, W. 1960 Proba zastrosowania srodków przeciwhistaminowych w smakowym poceniu się twarzy i w smakowym lzawieniu. (Attempted application of antihistamine drugs in gustatory sweating of the face and in gustatory lacrimation.) NNPP, **10**: 433–40. (French and Russian summaries.)

STEINBUCH, J. G. 1811 Geschmack (Taste), in *Beytrag zur Physiologie der Sinne*. J. L. Schrag, Nürnberg, 312 pp. (see pp. 300–3).

STEINER, G. 1956 Fortschritte und Probleme in der Analyse der chemischen Sinne. (Progress and problems in the analysis of the chemical senses.) NARS, **9**: 13–17.

*STEINHARDT, R., MORITA, H., and HODGSON, E. S. 1963 Electrophysiological analysis of inhibition and specificity in labellar chemoreceptors of the blowfly. PCZO, **3**: 99–101.

———. 1966 Mode of action of straight chain hydrocarbons on primary chemoreceptors of the blowfly, *Phormia regina*. JCCP, **67**: 53–62.

STEINHARDT, R. G., JR., CALVIN, A. D., and DODD, E. A. 1962 Taste-structure correlation with α-D-mannose and β-D-mannose. SCIE, **135**: 367–68.

STELLAR, E., HYMAN, R., and SAMET, S. 1954 Gastric factors controlling water- and salt-solution-drinking. JCPP, **47**: 220–26.

STERNBERG, W. 1898 Beziehungen zwischen dem chemischen Bau der süss und bitter schmeckenden Substanzen und ihrer Eigenschaft zu schmecken. (Relation between the chemical structure of the sweet and bitter tasting substances and their individual taste.) AAPM, pp. 451–83.

———. 1899 Geschmack und Chemismus. (Taste and chemism.) AAPM, pp. 367–71.

———. 1899 Geschmack und Chemismus. (Taste and chemism.) ZPSI, 20: 385–407.

*———. 1899 Geschmack und Chemismus. (Taste and chemism.) ZVDZ, 49: 376–88.

———. 1901 Geschmacksempfindung eines Anencephalus. (Taste sensation of an Anencephalus.) ZPSI, 27: 77–79.

———. 1903 Beiträge zur Physiologie de süssen Geschmackes. (Contribution to the physiology of the sweet taste.) AAPM, pp. 538–43.

———. 1903 Ueber das süssende Princip. (The sweet principle.) AAPM, pp. 113–19.

———. 1903 Ueber das wirksame Princip in den süsschmeckenden Verbindungen, das dem süssen Geschmack zu Grunde liegt, das sogenannte dulcigene Princip. (On the effective principle of the sweet taste complex, the basis of the sweet taste in the so-called dulcin principle.) AAPM, pp. 196–99.

———. 1904 Der salzige Geschmack und der Geschmack der Salze. (The salty taste and the taste of salts.) AAPM, pp. 483–558.

———. 1904 Le principe du goût doux dans le second groupe des corps sucrés. (The principle of sweet taste in the second group of sugar compounds.) AIPT, 13: 1–24.

———. 1904 Zur Physiologie des süssen Geschmacks. (The physiology of the sweet taste.) ZPSI, 35: 81–131.

———. 1905 Der Geschmackssinn in der Pharmacie und Pharmakologie. (The sense of taste in pharmacy and pharmacology.) DPGB, 15: 36–45.

———. 1905 Die stickstoffhaltigen Süssstoffe. (Sweet substances containing nitrogen.) AAPM, pp. 201–86.

———. 1905 Eine neue Methode zur klinischen Prüfung des Geschmackssinnes mittels eines Gustometers. (A new method for the clinical examination of the sense of taste by a gustometer.) DMWO, 31: 911–12.

———. 1905 Irrtümliches und Tatsächliches aus der Physiologie des süssen Geschmacks. (Errors and facts on the physiology of the sweet taste.) ZPSI, 38: 259–304.

———. 1905 Zur Untersuchung des Geschmackssinnes für klinische Zwecke. (Investigation of the sense of taste for clinical purposes.) DMWO, 31: 2057–58.

———. 1906 Der erste quantitative Gustometer zu klinischen Zwecken. (The first quantitative gustometer for clinical tests.) MEKL, 2: 1073.

———. 1906 Geschmack und Geruch. Physiologische Untersuchungen über den Geschmackssinn. (Taste and smell. Physiological studies on the sense of taste.) J. Springer, Berlin, 149 pp.

———. 1906 Subjektive Geschmacksempfindungen (Glycogeusia subjectiva, Kakogeusia subjectiva). (Subjective taste perception [Subjective glycogeusia, subjective cacogeusia].) ZKME, 59: 491–509.

———. 1907 Geschmack und Appetit. (Taste and appetite.) AMCZ, 76: 221–23.

———. 1907 Kompendiöser quantitativer Gustometer zu klinischen zwecken. (A compendious quantitative gustometer for clinical uses.) BKWO, 44: 396–98.

———. 1908 Die Schmackhaftigkeit und der Appetit. (Taste and appetite.) ZPSI, 1, 43: 224–36.

———. 1908 Die Zahl der Geschmacksqualitaten. (The number of taste qualities.) PAGP, 125: 522–26.

———. 1908 Geschmack und Appetit. (Taste and Appetite.) ZPDT, 11: 389–98.

———. 1909 Geschmack und Appetit. (Taste and appetite.) ZPSI, 2, 43: 315–44.

———. 1910 Unterscheidungsfähigkeit im Gebiete des Geschmacks und Geruchs. (Discriminatory power in the spheres of taste and smell.) PAGP, 131: 425–46.

———. 1914 Der Geschmack. (Taste.) ZIME, 35: 825–30.

———. 1914 Die Physiologie des Geschmacks. (The physiology of taste.) C. Kabitzsch, Würzburg, 63 pp.

———. 1916 Die Geschmacks-Lehre (Aesthetik) und der Genuss. Der ästhetische Genuss. Aesthetischer Geschmack. Gesicht, und Genuss. Appetitlichkeit. (The taste theory [esthetic] and pleasure. Esthetic pleasure. Esthetic taste. Appearance and pleasure. Appetite.) ZPMP, 6: 342–69.

———. 1925 Einfache quantitative Geschmacksprüfung. (Quantitative testing of taste.) BKWO, 4: 1143.

STERZ, H. 1876 Ein Fall von Irresein vortäuschender Geschmacksneurose. (A case of insanity with aberrant taste neurosis.) IRRE, 18: 137–41.

STEVENS, S. S. 1960 The psychophysics of sensory function. AMSC, 48: 226–53.

STICH, A. 1857 Beiträge zur Kenntniss der Chorda tympani. (Contribution to the knowledge of the chorda tympani.) ANCK, 8: 59–73.

———. 1857 Ueber die Schmeckbarkeit der Gase. (On the taste of gas.) ANCK, 8: 105–15.

STIER, E. 1941 Über Störungen des Geschmacks nach Kopfprellungen und ihre Lokalisation. (On taste disturbances after head contusions and their localization.) APNV, 113: 619–54.

STIRNIMAN, F. 1935 Versuche über Geschmack und Geruch am ersten Lebenstag. (Study of taste and smell in the first day of life.) JAKI, 146: 211–27.

———. 1936 Le goût et l'odorat du nouveau-né. Une contribution à la connaissance des réactions du nouveau-né. (Taste and smell in the newborn. A contribution to knowledge of the reactions of the newborn.) REFP, **12**: 453–85.

STIVERS, C. G. 1900 Testing the taste sense. SCPA, **15**: 373.

STOCQUART, 1889 Cas de perversion du goût. (Case of taste perversion.) AMCQ, **7**: 105. (Abstract.)

STOLLER, L. 1964. It's all in the taste. GIFL, **2**: 1–2.

STONE, H. 1965 The acidulant properties of L-aspartic acid. JFDS, **30**: 1068–69.

STONE, H. and OLIVER, S. 1966 Beidler's theory and human taste stimulation. PEPS, **1**: 358–60.

STONE, H., and OLIVER, S. 1966 Effect of viscosity on the detection of relative sweetness intensity of sucrose solutions. JFDS, **31**: 129–34.

STONE, L. S. 1933 Independence of taste organs with respect to their nerve fibers demonstrated in living salamanders. PSEB, **30**: 1256–2157.

———. 1940 The origin and development of taste organs in salamanders observed in the living condition. JEZO, **83**: 481–506.

STOUT, P. S. 1935 Dry mouth, vile taste, calculus in submaxillary gland. LARY, **45**: 962.

STRAIN, J. 1952 The influence of complete dentures upon taste perception. JPDE, **2**: 60–67.

STRANDSKOV, H. H. 1941 The distribution of human genes. SCMO, **52**: 203–15.

STRAUSS, H. 1925 Über Sensibilitätsstörungen an Hand und Gesicht, Geschmacksstörungen und ihre lokalisatorische Bedeutung. (Sensitivity disturbances on the hand and face, taste disturbances and their localized significance.) MPNE, **58**: 265–76.

STREBEL, O. 1928 Biologische Studien an einheimischen Collembolen. II: Ernährung und Geschmackssinn bei *Hypogastrura purpurascens* (Lubbock). (Biological studies on domestic collembola. II: Nutrition and taste sense in *Hypogastrura purpurascens* [Lubbock].) ZINS, **23**: 135–43.

STRIEK, F. 1924 Untersuchungen über den Geruchs und Geschmackssinn der Ellritze (*Phoxinus lavisa*). (Studies on the sense of smell and the sense of taste in the minnow.) ZVPH, **2**: 122–54.

STROTZKA, H. 1943 Ein Fall von Hyperpathie des Geruchs und Geschmacks. (A case of odor and taste hyperpathy.) WMWO, **93**: 143.

STSCHERBAK, A. E. 1893 Bemerkung über die Localisation des Geschmackcentrums beim Kaninchen. (Comment on the localisation of the taste center in the rabbit.) NEUZ, **12**: 261–62.

STÜRCKOW, B. 1959 Über den Geschmackssinn und den Tastsinn von *Leptinotarsa decemlineata* say Chrysomelidae. (On the taste and touch senses of *Leptinotarsa decemlineata* say Chrysomelidae.) ZVPH, **42**: 255–302.

———. 1960 Elektrophysiologische Untersuchungen am Chemorezeptor von *Calliphora erythrocephala* Meigen. (Electrophysiological studies on chemoreceptor of *Calliphora erythrocephala* Meigen.) ZVPH, **43**: 141–48.

———. 1962 Ein Beitrag zur Morphologie der labellaren Marginalborste der Fliegen *Calliphora* und *Phormia*. (A study of the morphology of the labellar marginal hairs of the flies *Calliphora* and *Phormia*.) ZZAC, **57**: 627–47.

———. 1963 Electrophysiological studies of a single taste hair of the fly during stimulation by a flowing system. PCZO, **3**: 102–4.

STUTZER, A. 1886 Ueber Saccharin. (On saccharin.) BIZT, **15**: 64–65.

SUGITA, H. 1962 (Measurement of taste.) EYGZ, **20**: 84–88. (In Japanese.)

SUÑÉ Y MOLIST, L. 1905 Disquisiciones sobre higiene olfactoria y gustativa. (Disquisition on olfactory and gustatory hygiene.) ARLO, **19**: 184–200.

SUPRAN, M. K., POWERS, J. J., RAO, P. V., DORNSEIFER, T. P., and KING, P. H. 1966 Comparison of different organic acids for the acidification of canned pimientos. FOTE, **20**: 215–20.

SUVOROVA, N. M. 1950 Sostoianie vkusovoi chuvstvitel'nosti pri normal'noi i patologicheskoi beremennosti. (The state of the gustatory sensitivity in normal and pathological pregnancy.) AKGI, **6**: 33–40. (English summary.)

SUZUKI, K. 1949 Taste blindness of Japanese. NATU, **163**: 177.

SZENDE, B. 1935 Izérzés vizsgálatok fülmütétek után. (Taste perception after ear operations.) ORHE, **79**: 876–77.

———. 1935 Untersuchungen über die Geschmacksempfindung nach Ohrenoperationen. (Taste perception after ear operations.) MOLA, **69**: 737–39.

SZTUCKI, B. 1934 Ueber die Schwellenkonzentrationen saurer Geschmacksreize. (Threshold concentrations of acid taste stimuli.) Inaugural Dissertation, Hoffmann, Berlin, 20 pp.

TACCARDI, B., and RAPUZZI, G. 1960 Risposta al $CaCl_2$ dei ricettori linguali della rana come test per l'attivitá di anestetici locali. (Response of the lingual receptors of the frog to $CaCl_2$ as a test for the activity of local anesthetics.) BSIB, **36**: 1761–63.

TAKEDA, K. 1961 The nature of impulses of single tarsal chemoreceptors in the butterfly, *Vanessa indica*. JCCP, **58**: 233–45.

TALLMAN, R. W. 1910 Taste and smell in articles in diet, in *Psychological Studies*. H. Gale, Minneapolis, Minn. 175 pp. (see pp. 118–39.)

TAMAR, H. 1956 Taste responses of opossum and bat. AJPH, **187**: 636. (Abstract.)

TANGL, H. 1939 Report of address by Harald Tangl, Sense of taste, of the University of Budapest. JAMA, **112**: 1616.

TANIKAWA, K. 1963 (Clinical and experimental studies on radiation-injury to taste.) NHGZ, **23**: 704–12. (In Japanese; English summary.)

TANKEL, H. I. 1951 A case of gustatory sweating. JNNP, 14: 129–33.

TANTURRI, V., and FUSER, L. 1941 I disturbi della olfatto e del gusto nei traumi cranici antichi e recenti. (Disturbances of olfaction and gustation in previous and recent cranial trauma.) RIOL, 15: 65–79.

TARAB, S. 1955 Troubles de la gustation après tonsillectomie. (Disorders of taste sensation after tonsillectomy.) PORL, 17: 260–62.

TARVER, M., HALL, B. A., and McDONALD, J. G. 1959 A statistical quality control approach to the selection of flavor panel members. ASQC, 13: 1–19.

TATEDA, H. 1961 Response of catfish barbels to taste stimuli. NATU, 192: 343–44.

———. 1964 The taste response of the isolated barbel of the catfish. CBCP, 11: 367–78.

TATEDA, H., and BEIDLER, L. M. 1964 The receptor potential of the taste cell of the rat. JGPS, 47: 479–86.

TATEDA, H., and MORITA, H. 1959 Initiation of spike potentials in contact chemosensory hairs of insect. I: The generation site of the recorded spike potentials. JCCP, 54: 171–76.

TÄUFEL, K. 1925 Studien über die Beziehungen zwischen dem chemischen Aufbau und dem Geschmack süss schmeckender Stoffe (Zuckerarten, Alkohole). (The relation between the chemical structure and taste of sweet-tasting substances [sugars and alcohols].) BIZE, 165: 96–101.

TÄUFEL, K., and KLEMM, B. 1925 Untersuchungen über natürliche und künstliche Süssstoffe. I: Studien über den Süssungsgrad von Saccharin und Dulcin. (Studies of natural and synthetic sweeteners. I: Studies on the degree of sweetness of saccharin and dulcin.) ZULE, 50: 264–73.

TÄUFEL, K., and WAGNER, C. 1951 Die Konstitution wässriger Lösungen von O-Bensoe-säure-sulfinid (Saccharin) and p-phenetylcarbamid (Dulcin.) (The constitution of aqueous solutions of O-benzoacid sulfamid [saccharin] and p-phenetylcarbamid [dulcin].) BDCG, 58(B): 909–12.

TAYLOR, C. W. 1961 A note on differential taste responses to P.T.C. (Phenyl-thio-carbamide.) HUBI, 33: 220–21.

TAYLOR, N. W. 1928 Acid penetration into living tissues. JGPS, 11: 207–19.

———. 1928 Physico-chemical theory of sweet and bitter taste excitation based on the properties of plasma membrane. PROT, 4: 1–17.

———. 1930 The nature of the nerve receptor for the acid taste as indicated by the absorption of organic acids by fats and proteins. PROT, 10: 98–105.

TAYLOR, N. W., FARTHING, F. R., and BERMAN, R. 1930 Quantitative measurements on the acid taste and their bearing on the nature of the nerve receptor. PROT, 10: 84–97.

*TAYLOR, R. G. 1963 Taste perception in older persons. IADR, 41: 78. (Abstract.)

TECKLENBURG, J. 1937 Ueber die Beeinflussung des Geschmacksfeldes auf der Zunge durch Anaesthetica. III. (The effect of anaesthetics on the taste area of the tongue. III.) Inaugural Dissertation, B. Sporn, Zeulenroda, Jena, 48 pp.

TEICHMANN, H. 1962 Die Chemorezeption der Fische. (Chemoreception in fish.) ERBI, 25: 177–205.

TEITELBAUM, P. 1955 Sensory control of hypothalamic hyperphagia. JCPP, 48: 156–63.

TEITELBAUM, P., and EPSTEIN, A. N. 1963 The role of taste and smell in the regulation of food and water intake, in Olfaction and Taste, Y. Zotterman (ed.). Macmillan, New York, 396 pp. (see pp. 347–60).

TENEN, S. S., and MILLER, N. E. 1964 Strength of electrical stimulation of lateral hypothalamus, food deprivation, and tolerance for quinine in food. JCPP, 58: 55–62.

TERRY, M. C. 1948 Diabetes mellitus in identical Negro twins and association of taste blindness and diabetes. JOHE, 39: 279–80.

———. 1950 Taste-blindness and diabetes in the colored population of Jamaica. JOHE, 41: 306–7.

TERRY, M. C., and SEGALL, G. 1947 The association of diabetes and taste-blindness. JOHE. 38: 135–37.

TÉTREAULT, L., GOUGER, P., and PANISSET, A. 1964 Étude du sodium en regard de la tension artérielle et de la réactivité vasculaire chez le normotendu. (Study on sodium in relation to arterial pressure and vascular reactivity in the normotensive subject.) UMCA, 93: 422–25. (English summary.)

TÉTREAULT, L., SASSEVILLE, H., and PESANT, P. 1963 Anomalie gustative chez les diabétiques. (Gustatory abnormalities in diabetics.) UMCA, 92: 1317–19. (English summary.)

THAMBIPILLAI, V. 1955–56 Taste threshold for phenyl-thio-urea in Malay school children. ANHG, 20: 232–38.

THATE, H. 1929 The relationship between constitution and taste among some derivatives of urea. RTCP, 48: 116–20.

THIBAULT, R. 1964 Propos sur la gustation. (Discourse on taste.) ACOD, 18: 89–100. (English, German, Italian, Spanish, Portuguese, and Russian summaries.)

THIEME, F. P. 1952 The geographical and racial distribution of ABO and pH blood types and tasters of PTC in Puerto Rico. AJHG, 4: 94–112.

THIERY, F. 1885 Untersuchungen über die Geschmacksempfindungen, die Kau- und Schlingbewegungen eines Zungenlosen (nach totaler Exstirpation des organs). (Investigations on taste perception, chewing and deglutition movements of a man without a tongue [after total extirpation of the organ].) Inaugural Dissertation, L. Schumacher, Berlin, 29 pp.

THOMAS, C. B., and COHEN, B. H. 1960 Comparison of smokers and nonsmokers. I. A preliminary report on the ability to taste phenylthiourea (P.T.C.). JHHB, **106**: 205–14.

THOMPSON, H. B. 1903 Taste and smell, in *Psychological Norms in Men and Women*. University of Chicago Press, Chicago, 188 pp. (see pp. 50–57).

THOMS, H., and NETTESHEIM, K. 1920 Untersuchungen über Geschmacksveränderungen des Süsstoffes Dulcin (p-Phenetholcarbamid) infolge chemischer Eingriffe. (Investigations on taste alterations of the sweet substance dulcin [p-phenethol carbamid] as a result of chemical change.) DPGB, **30**: 227–50.

THOMSSEN, E. G. 1928 Reflections on the chemical senses. APEO, **23**: 71–73, 161–62.

THORBJÖRNSON, B. 1936 Smak och lukt: Några synpunkter. (Taste and smell: Some observations.) TTDC, **66**: 9–13.

THORKILDSEN, V. 1935 Ageusi ved totalóreopmeisling. (Ageusia following total mastoidectomy.) NOMT, **9**: 570–71.

THORPE, W. H., CROMBIE, A. C., HILL, R., and DARRAH, J. H. 1946 The behavior of wireworms in response to chemical stimulation. JEBI, **23**: 234–66.

THOULD, A. K., and SCOWEN, E. F. 1964 Genetic studies of the syndrome of congenital deafness and simple goitre. ANHG, **27**: 283–93.

TIŁGNER, D. J., and BARYŁKO-PIKIELNA, N. 1959 Poziom progu i minimum wrazliwości zmyslu smaku. (Threshold and minimum sensitivity of the taste sense.) APYP, **10**: 741–54. (English summary.)

——. 1959 Wplyw metody ustalania progu wrazliwości smakowej na wynik. (Taste acuity and method of threshold assessment). APYP, **10**: 733–40. (English summary.)

TIMM, C. 1950 Theorie des Geschmackssinnes. (Theory of taste sensation.) ZLRO, **29**: 49–55.

TIMOFEEV, N. V. 1934 Izmeneniia ostroty vkusa pod vliianiem nekotorykh fiziologicheskikh sostoianii. (Modification of gustatory acuity under the influence of several physiological states. FZLZ, **17**: 1053–58. (German summary.)

TIMOFEEV, N. V., and KROLL-LIVSHITS, D. E. 1933 Izmenenie ostroty vkusa i rabochikh pod vliianiem uslovniakh raboty v nekotorykh proizvodstvakh i pri zabolevaniiakh s narusheniiami sekretsii zheludochnogo soka. (Changes of sharpness of taste in workers under conditions of work in several industries and under diseases with loss of secretion of gastric juices.) ASBU, **33**: 481–92. (German summary.)

——. 1934 Vliianie nekotorikh izmenenii v mineral'nom obmene na vysotu porogov razdrazheniia vkusa u sobak. (The effect of some changes in the mineral balance on the taste

threshold in dogs.) TVEM, **1**: 39–45. (German summary.)

TINBERGEN, L. 1939 Über den Bau der Geschmacksorgane auf den Proboscislippen und den Beinen von *Calliphora erythrocephala* Meigen. (On the structure of taste organs on the proboscis and on the legs of *Calliphora erythrocephala* Meigen.) ANZO, **4**: 81–92.

TITCHENER, E. B. 1893 Taste dreams. AJPC, **6**: 505–9.

——. 1901 Gustatory sensation, in *Experimental Psychology. A Manual of Laboratory Practice*. Macmillan, New York, 456 pp. (see 99–111).

——. 1915 The gustatory qualities, in *A Textbook of Psychology*. Macmillan, New York, 565 pp. (see pp. 129–42).

——. 1927 Gustatory sensation, in *Experimental Psychology, I*. Macmillan, New York, 214 pp. (see pp. 63–69).

TITLEBAUM, L. F., FALK, J. L., and MAYER, J. 1960 Altered acceptance and rejection of NaCl in rats with diabetes insipidus. AJPH, **199**: 22–24.

TITLEBAUM, L. F., and MAYER, J. 1963 Alteration of relative preference for sugar and saccharine caused by ventromedial hypothalamic lesions. EXPE, **19**: 539–40.

TODARO, F. 1872 Die Geschmacksorgane der Rochen. (The taste organ of roaches.) ZMWI, **10**: 227–29.

——. 1873 Gli organi del gusto e la mucosa bocco-branchiale dei Selaci. (The organ of taste and the bucco-bronchial mucosa of selachian.) RULN, **1**: 1–57.

——. 1873 Les organes du goût et la muqueuse bucco-branchiale des Séláciens. (The organs of taste and the bucco-bronchial mucosa of selachian.) AZEG, **2**: 534–58.

TOMASINI, S. 1896 Le allucinazioni del gusto ed il loro trattamento con l'acido gimnemico. (Hallucinations of taste and its treatment with gymnemic acid.) AFTE, **4**: 517–28.

TOMITA, H., and PASCHER, W. 1964 Über die Geschmacksfunktion nach Ausfall der sensorischen Zungennerven. (On functioning of taste after the loss of the sensory lingual nerves.) HNAO, **12**: 163–69.

TOMITA, T. 1958 Incentive motivation in rats as a function of palatability. APSK, **8**: 11–15.

TOMMASI, J. V. 1778 De gustu. (Taste.) Inaugural Dissertation, I. T. Trattnern, Vienna, 25 pp.

TORIGOE, H. 1958 (Influence of copper ion on the taste receptors of toad.) YOIZ, **9**: 495–98. (In Japanese.)

——. 1958 (Influence of the copper ion on the taste receptors of the human tongue.) YOIZ, **9**: 499–501. (In Japanese.)

——. 1958 (Relation between the thresholds of sweet taste and quantity of copper in human blood.) YOIZ, **9**: 489–94. (In Japanese.)

TORREY, T. W. 1931 The relation of taste-buds to their nerve-fibers. PNAS, **17**: 591–94.

———. 1934 The relation of taste buds to their nerve fibers. JCNE, **59**: 203–20.

———. 1936 The relation of nerves to degenerating taste buds. JCNE, **64**: 325–36.

———. 1940 The influence of nerve fibers upon taste buds during embryonic development. PNAS, **26**: 627–34.

TORRINI, G. 1935 La sensibilità gustativa negli operati di radiacale. (The taste sense after a radical operation.) ASIO, pp. 84–85.

———. 1940 La sensibilità gustativa nei due terzi anteriori della lingua o negli operati di radicale mastoidea. (Taste in anterior two-thirds of the tongue after radical mastoidectomy.) AIOR, **52**: 516–24.

TOSTESON, D. C., DEFRIEZ, A. I. C., ABRAMS, M., GOTTSCHALK, C. W., and LANDIS, E. M. 1951 Effects of adrenalectomy, desoxycorticosterone acetate and increased fluid intake on intake of sodium chloride and bicarbonate by hypertensive and normal rats. AJPH, **164**: 369–79.

TOULOUSE, E., and VASCHIDE, N. 1900 Méthode pour l'examen et la mesure du goût. (Method for examination and measurement of taste.) CORE, **130**: 803–5.

———. 1900 Topographie de la sensibilité gustative de la bouche. (Topography of the gustatory sensitivity of the mouth.) CORE, **130**: 1216–18.

TOURTUAL, E. T. 1827 Parallele des Geschmacks und Tastsinnes (Parallel of the senses of taste and touch), in *Die Sinne des Menschen*. F. Regensberg, Münster, 323 pp. (see pp. 101–11).

TRAVINA, A. A. 1952 Uslovnye refleksy no pochve razdrazheniia pishchevymi veshchestvamy vyvedennykh naruzhu uchastkov iazyka. (Conditioned reflexes in response to stimulation of surgically exposed portions of the tongue with alimentary substances.) ZVND, **2**: 126–32.

TRIPI, E. 1963 Un caso di diplegia facciale traumatica. (A case of traumatic facial diplegia.) RANE, **17**: 326–32.

TROLAND, L. T. 1929 Systems of gustatory and tactile qualities: Gustatory perception, in *The Principles of Psychophysiology*, I. Van Nostrand, New York, 429 pp. (see pp. 291–96).

———. 1930 Gustatory sensation, in *The Principles of Psychophysiology*, II. Van Nostrand, New York, 397 pp. (see pp. 280–95).

———. 1932 Gustatory projections, in *The Principles of Psychophysiology*, III. Van Nostrand, New York, 446 pp. (see pp. 38–39).

*TRONOVA, A. I. 1940 (On the influence of accesory stimulation on modification of gustatory sensitivity.) TIBI, **13**: 175–82.

TRUDEL, P. J. 1929 Untersuchungen über Geschmacksreaktionen der Fische auf "süsse" Stoffe. (Investigations on the gustatory reaction of fishes to sweet substances.) ZVPH, **10**: 367–409.

TRUJILLO-CENÓZ, O. 1957 Electron microscope study of the rabbit gustatory bud. ZZAC, **46**: 272–80.

———. 1961 Electron microscope observations on chemo- and mechano-receptor cells of fishes. ZZAC, **54**: 654–76.

TRUNZER, H. 1935 Kettengleichungen im Gebiete des Geschmackssinnes. Gleich süss schmeckende Lösungen. (Serial dilutions in the area of the sense of taste. Equal sweet tasting substances.) Inaugural Dissertation, Zeulenroda, Jena, 28 pp.

TSCHERMAK, A. VON. 1908 Über Simultankontrast auf verschiedenen Sinnesgebieten (Auge, Bewegungssinn, Geschmackssinn, Tastsinn und Temperatursinn). (On simultaneous contrast on different areas of the senses [visual, movement, taste, touch and temperature sense].) PAGP, **122**: 98–118.

TSENG, C. L., and CHU, E. J. 1931 Tastes of some derivatives of d-glutamic acid. ASMN, **5**: 1–18.

———. 1933 Tastes of glutamic acid and related compounds. II: Tastes of some derivatives of dl-glutamic acid. JCCO, 1: 188–98.

TSETSARKY, B. M. 1961 Ismenenie urovnia mobil'nosti vkusovikh sosochokov iazika pri razlichnykh zobolevaniiakh ukha. (Changes in the mobility level of gustatory papillae in different diseases of the ear.) VORL, **23**: 25–29. (English summary.)

TSUJI, T. 1957 Individual differences and inheritance of taste-ability for phenyl-thio-carbamide and related compounds. JJHG, **2**: 96–117.

*TSUZUKI, Y. 1947 Sweetness and configuration of sugars. KAGT, **17**: 342–46.

TSUZUKI, Y., and KAGAMI, K. 1954 (The sweetness of sugars.) TKSH, **49**: 453–62. (English summary.)

TSUZUKI, Y., KATO, S., and OKAZAKI, H. 1954 (Sweet flavor and resonance.) KAGT, **24**: 523–24. (In Japanese.)

TSUZUKI, Y., and MORI, N. 1954 Sweetness and configuration in rhamnose. NATU, **174**: 458–59.

TSUZUKI, Y., and YAMAZAKI, J. 1951 Sweetness of fructose and some other sugars, especially its variation with temperature. ICPA, **13**: 158–59.

———. 1953 On the sweetness of fructose and some other sugars, especially its variation with temperature. BIZE, **323**: 525–31.

———. 1953 (Sweetness of fructose and some other sugars.) JCSJ, **74**: 596–601. (In Japanese.)

TUCKER, B. R. 1911 Report of a case of tumor of the ponto-cerebella angle on the left side of the brain; with bilateral loss of smell and disturbance of taste. ODMS, **13**: 327–34.

TUCKERMAN, F. 1887–88 The anatomy of the papilla foliata of the human infant. JAPH, **22**: 499–501.

————. 1888 Note on the papilla foliata and other taste areas of the pig. ANAN, **3**: 69–73.

————. 1888 Observations on the structure of the gustatory organs of the bat. (*Vespertilio subulatus.*) JOMO, **2**: 1–6.

————. 1888 On the gustatory organs of *putorius vison.* ANAN, **3**: 941–42.

————. 1888 The tongue and gustatory organs of *Fiber zibethicus.* JAPH, **22**: 135–41.

————. 1889 An undescribed taste area in *perameles nasuta.* ANAN, **4**: 411–12.

————. 1889 On the development of the taste-organs of man. JAPH, **23**: 559–82.

————. 1889 On the gustatory organs of *Actomys monax.* ANAN, **4**: 334–35.

————. 1889 On the gustatory organs of *Erethizon dorsatus.* AMMH, **10**: 181.

————. 1889 On the gustatory organs of the American hare, *Lepus americanus.* AJSC, **38**: 277–80.

————. 1889 The gustatory organs of *Vulpes vulgaris,* JAPH, **23**: 201–5.

————. 1890 Further observations on the development of the taste-organs of man. JAPH, **24**: 130–31.

————. 1890 On the gustatory organs of some *Edentata.* IMAP, **7**: 335–39.

————. 1890 On the gustatory organs of some of the mammalia. JOMO, **4**: 151–93.

————. 1890 On the gustatory organs of the mammalia. PBSN, **24**: 470–82.

————. 1890 The gustatory organs of *Belideus ariel.* JAPH, **24**: 85–88.

————. 1890 The gustatory organs of *Procyon lotor.* JAPH, **24**: 156–59.

————. 1891 Observations on some mammalian taste-organs. JAPH, **25**: 505–8.

————. 1891 On the gustatory organs of *Sciurus hudsonius.* IMAP, **8**: 137–39.

————. 1892 Further observations on the gustatory organs of the mammalia. JOMO, **7**: 69–94.

————. 1892 On the terminations of the nerves in the lingual papillae of the Chelonia. IMAP, **9**: 1–5. (Abstract in ZEPH, **6**: 527, 1892.)

————. 1892 The gustatory organs of *Ateles ater.* JAPH, **26**: 391–93.

————. 1892–93 Note on the structure of the mammalian taste-bulb. ANAN, **8**: 366–67.

TURNER, W. A. 1896 On facial paralysis and the sense of taste. EDHR, **4**: 326–42.

————. 1897 Note on the course of the fibres of taste. EMJO, **2**: 261–62.

UCHIDA, T. 1957 An experiment on the gustatory sense of a newt, *Triturus pyrrogaster.* ZVPH, **39**: 357–60.

UCHIDA, Y. 1933 (Studies on taste in fish). KAGT, **3**: 196–200. (In Japanese.)

UFLAND, J. M. 1928 Izmeneniia ostroty vkusa u svintsovykh rabochykh. (Changes in sense of taste in lead workers.) PRPG, **1**: 31–38.

————. 1928 Veränderungen der Geschmacks-schärfe bei Bleiarbeitern. (Changes in acuity of taste in lead workers.) ZPSI, **59**: 128–35.

UMANSKII, K. G., SIDORCHUK, T. V., and SHUSTER, M. A. 1961 Vkusovaia chuvstvitel'nost' pri periphericheskom porazhenii litsevogo nerva. (Gustatory sensitivity in peripheral lesions of the facial nerve.) KLMI, **39**: 70–74.

URBANTSCHITSCH, V. 1876 *Beobachtungen ueber Anomalien des Geschmacks, der Tastempfindunges und der Speichelsecretion in Folge von Erkrankungen der Paukenhöle.* (Observation on abnormalities of taste, touch sensations and of saliva secretion as a result of illness in the tympanic cavity.) Enke, Stuttgart, 876 pp.

————. 1882 Beobachtung eines Falles von Anästhesie der peripheren Chorda tympani-Fasern bei Auslösbarkeit von Geschmacks- und Gefühlsempfindungen durch Reizung des Chorda tympani-Stammes. (Observation of a case of anaesthesia of the peripheral chorda tympani fibers by taste and touch sensations emitted through stimulation of the chorda tympani branch.) AONK, **19**: 135–47.

UTERHART, F. 1847 De functionibus nervi hypoglossi, Rami lingualis, nervi trigemini, Nervi glossopharyngei. (The function of the hypoglossal nerve, lingual branch, trigeminal nerve, glossopharyngeal nerve.) Inaugural Dissertation, Adlerianis, Rostock, 19 pp.

VALENTIN, G. 1839 De functionibus nervorum cerebralium et nervi sympathici. (The function of the cranial and sympathetic nerves.) Huber and Socii, Berne, 161 pp. (see pp. 39–45).

*————, 1848 in *Lehrbuch der Physiologie des Menschen.* Braunschweig, 713 pp. (see pp. 293–306).

————. 1853 Taste, in *A Textbook of Physiology.* Translated from German by W. Brinton. H. Renshaw, London, 684 pp. (see pp. 488–92).

————. 1864 Geschmack (Taste), in *Versuch einer Physiologischen Pathologie der Nerven, I.* C. F. Winter, Leipzig, 320 pp. (see pp. 252–55).

VALETTE, M. H. 1931 Les dispositifs vaso-sensoriels spécialises chez quelques mammifères. Étude analytique des organes de l'olfaction, du tact, de la gustation, de la vision et quelques organes annexes. (Specialized association of vessels and sensory zones in some mammals. Analytic study of the organs of olfaction, touch, taste, vision and some accessory organs.) AAHE, **13**: 281–360.

————. 1932 Dispositifs vaso-sensoriels spécialisés au niveau des organes du tact, de la gustation et de l'olfaction. Leur rôle de thermostabilisation. (Specialized vaso-sensory arrangements at the level of the organs of touch, taste and olfaction. Their role in thermostabilization.) RLOR, **53**: 553–94.

*VALLS MEDINA, A. 1958 *Estudio antropogenético de la capacidad gustativa para la feniltiocarbamida.* (Anthropogenetic study of the gustatory capacity for phenylthiocarbamide.) Proefschrift, Madrid.

VAN BENEDEN, 1835 Remarques sur le siège du goût dans la carpe. (Remarks on the origin of taste in the carp.) BARM, **2**: 103–7.

VAN BUSKIRK, C. 1945 The seventh nerve complex. JCNE, **82**: 303–30.

VASCHIDE, N. 1903 Contribution à la psycho-physiologie de la cavité buccale. (Contribution to the psycho-physiology of the buccal cavity.) BLOR, **6**: 15–18.

———. 1903 La gustatometrie. (Taste measurement.) BLOR, **6**: 93–103.

———. 1903 Un cas d'ageusie. (A case of ageusia.) BLOR, **6**: 19–24.

———. 1904 Mesure de la sensibilité gustative chez l'homme et chez la femme. (Measurement of taste sensitivity in males and females.) CORE, **139**: 898–900.

———. 1906 De l'analyse des perceptions gustatives. (Analyses of taste perception.) AIRB, **22**: 134–41.

———. 1907 Goût. (Taste.) RIDP, **7**: 570–709.

VASCHIDE, N., and MARCHAND, L. 1901 Anesthésie gustative et hypoesthésie tactile par lesion de la corde du tympan. (Gustatory anesthesia and tactile hyposthesia with lesion of the chorda tympani.) CRSS, **53**: 705–7.

VASCHIDE, N., and VARPAS, C. 1901 Contribution à l'étude de la psycho-physiologie de la corde du tympan à propos d'un cas de paralysie faciale. (Contribution to the psycho-physiological study of the chorda tympani in connection with facial paralysis.) BLOR, **5**: 169–74.

———. 1901 Contribution à l'étude psycho-physiologique des actes vitaux en l'absence totale du cerveau chez un enfant. (Contribution to the psycho-physiological study of vital actions in the total absence of a brain in an infant.) CORE, **132**: 641–43.

VASIL'EV, A. I. 1957 Kompleksnaia metodika izucheniia funktsii vkusovogo analizatora cheloveka. (Complex method of investigation of function of the taste analyzer in man.) TIFP, **6**: 172–82.

———. 1960 Nekotorye dannye o parnosti funktsii vkusovogo analizatora cheloveka, poluchennye pri strogo lokalizovannom khimicheskom razdrashenii iazyka. (Some data on the paired function of the gustatory analyzer investigated in strictly localized chemical stimulation of the tongue.) TIFP, **9**: 295–301.

VASTARINI-CRESI, G. 1915 Chiasma gustativo nella lingua dell'uomo e di alcuni mammiferi. (Gustatory chiasma of the tongue of man and some mammals.) IMAP, **31**: 380–410.

VATSURO, E. G. 1959 Characteristics of the taste analyser in the dog. ZVND, **9**: 68–75.

VELEY, V. H., and SYMES, W. L. 1910 Certain physical and physiological properties of Stovain and its homologues. PRLB, **83**: 413–20.

VENABLES, F. P. 1887 Sensitiveness of taste. CHNW, **56**: 221.

VENCLÍK, H., and HODÁCOVÁ, O. 1962 Poruchy chuti u stredousních operací. (Disorders of taste in middle ear surgery.) CEOT, **11**: 153–58. (Russian and English summaries.)

VERJAAL, A. 1954 De nervus facialis als traanen als smaakzenuw; localisatie van de periphere facialisparalyse. (Lacrimal and gustatory functions of facial nerve; localization of peripheral facial paralysis.) NTGE, **98**: 671–76.

VERKADE, P. E. 1946 A new sweetening material. FOMA, **21**: 483–85.

VERKADE, P. E., VAN DIJK, C. P., and MEERBURG, W. 1942 Ueber neue Süsstoffe und neue Lokalanästhetika. (New sweet compounds and new local anesthetics.) VVWN, **45**: 630–35.

———. 1946 Researches on the alkoxy-amino-nitrobenzenes. I: Partial reduction of 1-alkoxy-2, 4-dinitrobenzenes with sodium disulphide. The taste of the alkoxy-amino-nitrobenzenes thus obtained. RTCP, **65**: 346–60.

VERKADE, P. E., WEPSTER, B. M., and STEGERHOEK, L. J. 1959 Investigations on taste blindness with thiocarbamides. II (1): Intra-pair discrepancy of taste in pairs of identical twins. AGMG, **8**: 361–68.

VERKADE, P. E., and WITJENS, P. H. 1946 Researches on the alkoxy-amino-nitrobenzenes. II: Synthesis and taste of the ten possible ethoxy and n-propoxy compounds. Some remarks concerning the problem of the relation between taste and constitution. RTCP, **65**: 361–79.

VERLAINE, L. 1927 Le determinisme de deroulement de la trompe et la physiologie du goût chez les lépidoptères. (The determination of the development of the mouth and the physiology of taste of the lepidoptera.) ABSE, **67**: 147–82.

VERNIÈRE, A. 1827 Sur le sens du goût. (The sense of taste.) JSIE, **3**: 208–13.

———. 1828 Physiologische Untersuchungen über den Sinn des Geschmacks. (Physiological investigations on the sense of taste.) NGNH, **20**: 65–72, 81–89.

VERSON, E. 1868 Beiträge zur Kenntnis des Kehlkopfes und der Trachea. (Contribution to the knowledge of the larynx and the trachea.) SAMN **57**: 1093–1102.

VINCENT, H. C., LYNCH, M. J., POHLEY, F. M., HELGREN, F. J., and KIRCHMEYER, F. J. 1955 A taste panel study of cyclamate-saccharin mixture and its components. APHJ, **44**: 442–46.

VINCENT, S. B. 1916 The cutaneous sensitivity of the tongue as affected by the loss of the chorda tympani. PSBU, **13**: 69–70. (Abstract.)

VINTSCHGAU, M. VON. 1879 Beiträge zur Physiologie des Geschmackssinnes. I: Ueber die Geschmacksfähigkeit der Zungenspitze. (Contribution to the physiology of the sense of taste. I: On the ability of taste on the tip of the tongue.) PAGP, **19**: 236–53.

———. 1879 Beiträge zur Physiologie des Geschmackssinnes. II: Elektrische Reizung der Zunge. (Contribution to the physiology of the sense of taste. II: Electrical stimulation of the tongue.) PAGP, **20**: 81–114.

———. 1879 Beiträge zur Physiologie des Geschmackssinnes. III: Die Geschmacksarten. (Contribution to the physiology of the sense of taste. III: The basic tastes.) PAGP, **20**: 225–55.

———. 1880 Beobachtungen über die Veränderungen der Schmeckbecher nach Durchschneidung des n. Glossopharyngeus. (Observations on the changes of the taste buds after cutting the glossopharyngeal nerve.) PAGP, **23**: 1–13.

———. 1880 Physiologie des Geschmackssinnes (Physiology of taste), in *Handbuch der Physiologie der Sinnesorgane*, L. Hermann (ed.). Vogel, Leipzig, 461 pp. (see pp. 145–224).

VINTSCHGAU, M. VON, and HÖNIGSCHMIED, J. 1875 Versuche über die Reaktionzeit einer Geschmacksempfindung. I. (Studies on reaction time of taste sensation. I.) PAGP, **10**: 1–48.

———. 1876 Versuche über die Reaktionzeit einer Geschmacksempfindung. II. (Studies on reaction time of taste sensation. II.) PAGP, **12**: 87–132.

———. 1877 Nervus Glossopharyngeus und Schmeckbecher. (The glossopharyngeal nerve and taste goblets.) PAGP, **14**: 443–48.

———. 1877 Versuche über die Reaktionzeit einer Geschmacksempfindung. III: Reaktionszeit einer Geschmacksempfindung an den um wallten Papillen. (Study on reaction time of taste sensation. III: Reaction time of taste sensation on the circumvallate papillae.) PAGP, **14**: 529–92.

VITOLS, T. 1933 Über die Morphologie der Zunge der Letten. (On the morphology of the tongue in Latvians.) LBBR, **3**: 191–97.

VLEUTEN, M. VAN. 1938 Geruchs- und Geschmacksstörungen bei Schädelgrundbrüchen. (Disturbances of olfaction and taste in fractures of the base of the skull.) Inaugural Dissertation, K. and R. Hoffman, Charlottenburg, 30 pp.

VOGEL, B. 1931 Ueber die Beziehungen zwischen Süssgeschmack und Nährwert von Zuckern und Zuckeralcoholen bei der Honigbiene. (On the relationship between the sweet taste and the food value of sugars and alcohol sugars in the bee.) ZVPH, **14**: 273–347.

VOLTA, A. 1816 Estratto di un manoscritto sull' insussistenza della genesi del clorino, e dell' acali nell' acqua sottoposta all' azione degli elettro-motori (Summary of a manuscript on the absence of the generation of chlorine and alkali in water under the action of a Voltaic cell), in *Collezione dell' Opere*. G. Piatti, Firenze, 305 pp., Vol. 2, Part 2 (see pp. 289–302).

———. 1816 Sull-elettricità animale (Animal electricity), in *Collezione dell'Opere*. G. Piatti, Firenze, 268 pp. Vol. 2, Part 1 (see pp. 55–118).

VOLTZ, S. 1956 Über den chemischen Sinn der *Schaben Phyllodromia germania* und *Periplaneta americana* (On the chemical sense of the cockroaches *Phyllodromia germania* and *Periplaneta americana*.) ZOAN, **157**: 11–14.

VONDRÁCEK, V., and MARTONOVÁ, F. 1956 Chutové vnímání thiourey. (Taste perception of thiourea.) CLCE, **95**: 1136–38. (English, Russian, and French summaries.)

VOURI, E. E. 1927 Vallinystyjen suhteesta kielen poikkijuovaiseen lihastoon. (The relation of the vallate papillae to the transversely striated musculature of the tongue.) DUOD, **43**: 592–99.

VULPIAN, A. 1869 Remarques sur la distribution anatomique de la corde du tympan. (Remarks on the anatomical distribution of the chorda tympani.) APHP, **2**: 209–10.

———. 1873 Nouvelles recherches physiologiques sur la corde du tympan. (New physiological research on the chorda tympani.) CORE, **76**: 146–50.

———. 1878 Expériences ayant pour but de déterminer la véritable origine de la corde du tympan. (Experiences relating to the determination of the true origin of the chorda tympani.) CORE, **86**: 1053–57.

———. 1878 Expériences ayant pour but de déterminer la véritable origine de la corde du tympan. (Experiences relating to the determination of the true origin of the chorda tympani.) GAMP, **7**: 231–32.

———. 1885 Recherches sur les fonctions du nerf de Wrisberg. (Research on the function of the nerve of Wrisberg.) CORE, **101**: 1037–42, 1447–48.

WAGMAN, W. 1963 Sodium chloride deprivation: Development of sodium chloride as a reinforcement. SCIE, **140**: 1403–4.

WAGNER, E. C. 1953 Differentiation of taste bud cells following transection of their nerve supply. ANRE, **115**: 442. (Abstract.)

WAGNER, G. 1888 Ueber die Oxydation der Kohlenwasserstoffe, C_nH_{2n-2}. (On the oxidation of hydrocarbon.) BDCG, **21**: 3343–46.

WAGNER, H. W., GREEN, K. F., and MANLEY, M. B. 1965 Paired comparison method for measurement of sugar preference in squirrel monkeys. SCIE, **148**: 1473–74.

*WAGNER, K. G. 1949 Über einige wesentliche Voraussetzungen bei der geschmacklichen Prüfung süssschmeckender Substanzen. (On some essential assumptions from taste tests of sweet tasting substances.) ZUSU, 2: 7–9.

———. 1949 Über Geruchswahrnehmungen an Süsswaren. (On odor perception of sweet substances.) ZUSU, 2: 7–10.

———. 1950 Zur Chemie geruchlich und geschmacklich neutraler Substanzen. (The chemistry of odor and taste of neutral substances.) ZUSU, 3: 7.

WAGNER, M. W. 1965 Effects of two stressors on speed of preference shift for sugar solutions in the albino rat. JCPP, 59: 442–46.

———. 1965 Satiation effects on rate of intake and preference of glucose solutions. JCPP, 59: 115–17.

———. 1965 The effects of age, weight and experience on relative sugar preference in the albino rat. PSCI, 2: 243–44.

WAGNER, R. 1843 Function des Fünften Nervenpaars (Function of the fifth nerve pair), in Lehrbuch der Speziellen Physiologie. L. Voss, Leipzig, 511 pp. (see pp. 318–20).

———. 1846 Schmecken (Taste), in Lehrbuch der Speziellen Physiologie, 872 pp. (see pp. 1–12).

WAHL, O. 1936 Untersuchungen über ein geeignetes Vergällungsmittel für Bienenzucker. (Investigation of a suitable embittering agent for bee-sugar.) ZVPH, 24: 116–42.

WALLER, A. 1849 Minute examination of the organ of taste in man. PRLB, 5: 803–4.

———. 1849 Minute structure of the organ of taste in vertebrate animals. PRLB, 5: 751–53.

———. 1849 Minute structure of the papillae and nerves of the tongue of the frog and toad. PTRS, pp. 139–50.

WALLIS, D. I. 1961 Response of the labellar hairs of the blowfly, Phormia regina Meigen, to protein. NATU, 191: 917–18.

WALTHERUS, C. F. 1743 De gustatione et saporibus. (Taste and Flavor.) Inaugural Dissertation, Halae Magdeburgicae, 45 pp.

WANI, K. 1961 (Measurement of the point of subjective equality among citric acid, fumaric acid, and monosodium fumaric acid.) HIKA, 12: 878–81. (In Japanese.)

WARD, J. C., MUNCH, J. C., SPENCER, H. J., and GARLOUGH, F. E. 1934 Studies on strychnine. III: The effectiveness of sucrose, saccharin and dulcin in masking the bitterness of strychnine. JAPM, 23: 984–88.

WARFIELD, R. B. 1954 Taste and molecular structure. ACAF, p. 15A. (Abstract.)

WARREN, H. C. 1919 Taste sensations from uterine stimuli. PSBU, 16: 242–43.

WARREN, R. M. 1953 Taste perception. A literature survey. Project Report No. SD-6222, General Foods Corporation, Research and Development Department, Central Laboratories, Hoboken, N.J., 318 pp.

WARREN, R. M., and PFAFFMANN, C. 1959 Suppression of sweet sensitivity by potassium gymnemate. JAPY, 14: 40–42.

WARREN, R. P. 1963 Preference aversion in mice to bitter substance. SCIE, 140: 808–9.

WARREN, R. P., and PFAFFMANN, C. 1958 Early experience and taste aversion. JCPP, 52: 263–66.

WARREN, R. P., and VINCE, M. A. 1963 Taste discrimination in the great tit (Parus major). JCPP, 56: 910–13.

WASHBURN, M. F. 1917 Sensory discriminations: the chemical sense, in Animal Mind. 2nd ed. Macmillan, New York, 386 pp. (see pp. 62–116).

WASICKY, R., BARBIERE, E., and WEBER, H. 1942–43 Contribuição para o método de dosagem de princípios ativos em drogas e preparaçoes pello amargor. (Method of determining the active principle in drugs and preparations by their bitterness.) AFFS, 3: 113–19. (English summary.)

WEBER, E. H. 1847 Ueber den Einfluss der Erwärmung und Erkältung der Nerven auf ihr Leitungsvermögen. (On the effect of warm and cold on the nerves and their performance.) AAPA, pp. 342–56.

WEBER, W. 1942 Beitrag zur Methode, Statistik und Erblichkeit der Geschmacksempfindung für Phenylthiocarbamid. (Contribution to the method, statistical and hereditary, of taste perception for phenylthiocarbamide.) ERBA, 10: 154–67.

WEDDELL, G. 1955 Somesthesis and the chemical senses. ARPS, 6: 119–36.

WEDELL, C. H. 1935 Taste sensitivity in the white rat. PSBU, 32: 551. (Abstract.)

———. 1936 The taste sensitivity of the white rat. I: Sensitivity to quinine sulphate. JCPO, 21: 233–44.

WEETH, H. J., and HAVERLAND, L. H. 1961 Tolerance of growing cattle for drinking water containing sodium chloride. JANS, 203, 518–21.

WEINER, I. H., and STELLAR, E. 1951 Salt preference of the rat determined by a single-stimulus method. JCPP, 44: 394–401.

WEINGARTEN, K., and GLONING, L. 1953 Über zentrale Geschmacksstörungen. (Central gustatory disorders.) WZND, 8: 62–83.

WEINSTEIN, S. 1907 Untersuchungen über den salzigen Geschmack der Salze. (Studies on the salty taste of salts.) Inaugural Dissertation, J. J. Meier, Zürich, 24 pp.

WEIS, I. 1930 Versuche über die Geschmacksrezeption durch die Tarsen des Admirals, Pyrameis atalanta L. (Studies of taste sensitivity in the tarsi of the admiral butterfly, Pyrameis atalanta L.) ZVPH, 12: 206–48.

WEISKRANTZ, L. 1960 Effects of medial temporal

lesions on taste preference in the monkey. NATU, **187**: 879–80.

WEISS VALBRANCA, G., and PASCUCCI, F. 1946 Le variazioni della sensibilità gustativa in particolari situazioni fisiologiche ed in alcuni stati morbosi. I, II, III. (Variation in gustatory sensitivity in certain physiological situations and in some disease states. I, II, III.) RCCM, **46** (5): 46–69, 70–75, 76–88.

——. 1947 Le variazioni della sensibilità gustativa in particolari situazioni fisiologiche ed in alcuni stati morbosi. V: Il comportamento della soglia gustativa per le stimolazioni salate in rapporto alle modificazioni clorure-miche. (Variation in gustatory sensitivity in certain physiological situations and in some disease states. V: The behavior of gustatory thresholds for salty stimulation in relation to chloruremic modification.) RCCM, **47**(3): 540–50.

WELLS, M. J. 1963 Taste by touch: some experiments with octopus. JEBI, **40**: 187–93.

WENDEL, H. 1936 Untersuchungen über die Möglichkeit der Beeinträchtigung der Geschmacksempfindung durch Zahnersatz, insbesondere durch Gaumenplatten. (Investigation on the possibility of impairment of taste sensation through tooth replacement, especially through dental plates.) Inaugural Dissertation, Trapp, Bonn, 26 pp.

WENDT, G. R. 1952 Somesthesis and the chemical senses. ARPS, **3**: 105–30.

WENGER, M. A., JONES, F. N., and JONES, M. H. 1956 The chemical senses, in *Physiological Psychology*. Henry Holt & Co., New York, 472 pp. (see pp. 131–50).

WENZEL, B. M. 1954 The chemical senses. ARPS, **5**: 111–26.

WERKMEISTER-FREUND, R. 1933 Über Strahlenwirkung, insbesondere Geschmacksstörungen, in der Mundhöhle. (On radiation, especially taste disturbances, in the oral cavity.) ZSTO, **31**: 1171–85.

WERNER, K. 1933 Über das Verhalten der Geschmacksgleichungen bei Verdünnung der Ausgangslösung. (The behavior of taste equations with dilution of the original solution.) ZESI, **64**: 126–47.

WERNICH, A. 1870 Beiträge zu den Parästhesien des Geschmacks. (Contribution to the paraesthesia of taste.) APNV, **2**: 174–76.

WETZEL, R. J. 1959 The effect of experience with a taste reward. JCPP, **52**: 267–71.

*WHITACRE, J. 1946 Influence of salt on the judging of cooked vegetables. TAEP, **5**: 4 pp.

WHITESIDE, B. 1926 The regeneration of the gustatory apparatus in the rat. JCNE, **40**: 33–45.

——. 1927 Nerve overlap in the gustatory apparatus of the rat. JCNE, **44**: 363–77.

——. 1927 The innervation of the taste buds on the vallatae and foliatae papillae of the rat. ANRE, **35**: 28. (Abstract.)

WHITESIDE, B., and BLANCHARD, O. R. 1927 The effect of injury to the facial nerve upon taste perception. ANRE, **35**: 51.

WHYMPER, R. 1955 The relative sweetness of some sugar solutions—a new angle. MACO, **35**: 15–16, 19–20, 22.

WIDSTRÖM, G., and HENSCHEN, A. 1963 The relation between P.T.C. taste response and protein bound iodine in serum. SCLS, **15**(69): 257–61.

WIEDERSHEIM, R. 1884 Sinnesorgane (Sense organs), in *Grundriss der Vergleichenden Anatomie*. G. Fischer, Jena, 272 pp. (see pp. 132–38).

WIELEN, P. VAN DER. 1927 De codificatie van kleur, smaak en reuk in de pharmacopee. (Codification of color, taste and odor in pharmacopeia.) PHWE, **64**: 550–60, 594–99, 636–42.

WIGGERS, C. J. 1949 Taste, in *Physiology in Health and Disease*. 5th ed. Lea and Febiger, Philadelphia, 1242 pp. (see pp. 264–67).

WIGGERS, K. 1941 Onderzoekingen over den smaak van het drinkwater bij verandering van het keukenzoutgehalte. (The taste of drinking water after changing its sodium chloride content.) NTGE, **85**: 249–56. (French, German, and English summaries.)

WIGGLESWORTH, V. B. 1934 Chemical senses, in *Insect Physiology*. Methuen, London, 134 pp. (see pp. 108–9).

WILCZYNSKI, K. 1875 Jakiemi czesciami geby w ogole, a jezyka w szczegolnosci potrafimy rozpoznac smak niektorych istot. (With which part of the oral mucosa and especially the tongue can we recognize the taste of some substances? PRLK, **14**: 60–62, 72–73.

WILDNER, F. S. 1924 Notes on parageusia. AJCM, **31**: 466–67.

WILKES, S. R. 1941 Studies in taste: The qualitative stimulus threshold for sucrose, dextrose, and caffeine citrate in diabetes mellitus. Unpublished Master's thesis, Ohio State University, 112 pp.

WILKINS, L., and RICHTER, C. P. 1940 A great craving for salt by a child with corticoadrenal insufficiency. JAMA, **114**: 866–68.

WILL, F. 1885 Das Geschmacksorgan der Insekten. (Taste organs of insects.) ZWZO, **42**: 674–707.

WILLAMAN, J. J. 1918 Sweetness of invert sugar. AFOJ, **13**: 636.

——. 1928 The race for sweetness. SCMO, **26**: 76–86.

WILLAMAN, J. J., WAHLIN, C. S., and BIESTER, A. 1925 Carbohydrate studies. II: The relative sweetness of invert sugar. AJPH, **73**: 397–400.

WILLARD, J. T. 1885–86 On the sweetness of invert sugar, with some notes on its preparation. TSAS, **10**: 24–25.

WILLIAMS, R. J. 1931 "Taste deficiency" for creatine. SCIE, **74**: 597–98.

———. 1951 I. Introduction, general discussion and tentative conclusions, in *Individual Metabolic Patterns and Human Disease.* The University of Texas Publication No. 5109, 205 pp. (see pp. 7–21).

WILLIAMS, R. J., and LASSELLE, P. A. 1926 The identification of creatine. JACS, **48**: 536–37.

WILSON, J. G. 1905 The structure and function of the taste-buds of the larynx. BRAI, **28**: 339–51.

WINER, R. A., BARBER, T. X., and CHAUNCEY, H. H. 1965 Further studies on the influence of verbal suggestion on parotid gland response to gustatory stimuli. PSEB, **119**: 1–4.

WINER, R. A., CHAUNCEY, H. H., and BARBER, T. X. 1965 The influence of verbal or symbolic stimuli on salivary gland secretion. ANYA, **131**: 874–83.

WING, B. F. 1836 Fonctions de la membrane pituitaire. (Function of the pituitary membrane.) AGME, **12**: 92–94.

WINSOR, A. L., and KORCHIN, B. 1938 The effect of different types of stimulation upon the pH of human parotid secretion. JEPS, **23**: 62–79.

WINTHER, G. 1874 Udvendige smagspapiller hos Gobius niger Schonev. (Outer taste papillae of Gobius niger, Schonev.) NATI, **9**: 181–90.

WINTON, F. R., and BAYLISS, L. E. 1962 Taste and smell, in *Human Physiology.* 5th ed. Little, Brown & Co., Boston, 649 pp. (see pp. 517–19).

WIRTANEN, R. E., and OLMSTED, J. M. D. 1934 Taste fibers and the fifth nerve. JCNE, **60**: 1–3.

WISWESSER, W. J. 1955 Physiological aspects of testing contact chemoreception. VJSC, **6**: 16–21.

WITKOP, C. J., JR. 1964 Dental caries and phenylthiocarbamide taste ability, in Genes, chromosomes and dentistry. JADS, **68**: 845–58.

WITTICH, V. 1868 Ueber die Fortleitungsgeschwindigkeit in menschlichen Nerven. (The speed of transmission in human nerves.) ZRME, **31**: 87–125.

WOGER, K. 1952 Geschmacksphysiologische Betrachtungen unter besonderer Berücksichtigung der Kostprobe von Bieren. (Physiological taste observations with special consideration to taste tests on beer.) BRUW, **6**: 118–19.

WOHLFEIL, M. 1936 Ueber Geschmacksstörungen nach Mittelohrerkrankungen und Radikaloperationen. (Taste disturbances after middle-ear diseases and radical operations.) Inaugural Dissertation, Königsberg, 21 pp.

WOLBARSHT, M. L. 1957 Water taste in phormia. SCIE, **125**: 1248.

———. 1958 Electrical activity in the chemoreceptors of the blowfly. II: Responses to electrical stimulation. JGPL, **42**: 413–28.

———. 1963 Electrical signs of chemoreception. PCZO, **3**: 107–10.

WOLBARSHT, M. L., and DETHIER, V. G. 1958 Electrical activity in the chemoreceptors of the blowfly. I: Responses to chemical and mechanical stimulation. JGPL, **42**: 393–412.

WOLBARSHT, M. L., and HANSON, F. E. 1965 Electrical activity in the chemoreceptors of the blowfly. III: Dendritic action potentials. JGPL, **48**: 673–84.

WOLF, A. V. 1958 *Thirst. Physiology of the Urge to Drink and Problems of Water Lack.* Charles C Thomas, Springfield, Ill., 536 pp.

WOLF, G. 1964 Effect of dorsolateral hypothalamic lesions on sodium appetite elicited by desoxycorticosterone and by acute hyponatremia. JCPP, **58**: 396–402.

WOLF, G., and LAWRENCE, G. H. 1963 Saline preference curve for mice: Lack of relationship to pigmentation. NATU, **200**: 1025–26.

WOLF, G., and STEINBAUM, E. A. 1965 Sodium appetite elicited by sub-cutaneous formalin. JCPP, **59**: 335–39.

WOLF, O. 1880 Zur Function der Chorda tympani. (The function of the chorda tympani.) ZHNO, **9**: 152–58.

WOLFF, O. I. B. 1875 Das Riechorgan der Biene, nebst einer Beschreibung des Respirationswerkes der Hymenopteren, des Saugrüssels und Geschmacksorganes der Blumenwespen, einer vergleichenden Betrachtung der Riechhaut sämmtlicher Aderflügler-familien und Erläuterungen zur Geruchs und Geschmacksphysiologie. (The olfactory organ of bees, with a description of the respiratory apparatus of Hymenoptera, the antennae and smelling organ of wasps, a comparative consideration of the scent scales of flying families in general and in exposition of smell and taste physiology.) NOAL, **38**(2): 1–251.

WOODWORTH, R. S., and SCHLOSBERG, H. 1954 The chemical senses, in *Experimental Psychology.* Henry Holt & Co., New York, 948 pp. (see pp. 297–322).

WOTMAN, S., MANDEL, I. D., KHOTIM, S., THOMPSON, R. H., JR., KUTSCHER, A. H., ZEGARELLI, E. V., and DENNING, C. R. 1964 Salt taste thresholds and cystic fibrosis. AJDC, **108**: 372–74.

WRIGHT, M. R. 1951 Maintenance of denervated taste organs in adult *Triturus V. viridescens.* PSEB, **76**: 462–63.

———. 1955 Persistence of taste organs in tongue transplants of *Triturus V. viridescens.* JEZO, **129**: 357–68.

———. 1958 Persistence of taste organs in tongue grafted to liver. PSEB, **97**: 367–68.

———. 1964 Taste organs in tongue-to-liver grafts in the newt, *Triturus V. viridescens.* JEZO, **156**: 377–89.

WYKES, G. R. 1952 The preferences of honeybees for solutions of various sugars which occur in nectar. JEBI, 29: 511–19.

WYSS, H. VON. 1869 Über ein neues Geschmacksorgan auf der Zunge des Kaninchens. (A new taste organ on the tongue of the rabbit.) ZMWI, 7: 548–40.

———. 1870 Die becherförmigen Organe der Zunge. (The goblet shaped organs of the tongue.) AMAE, 6: 237–60.

YAKOVLEVA, I. Y. 1958 K voprosu o vkusovoi chuvstvitelnosti pri bolezni Ménière i kokhleovestibulyarnykh narusheniyakh pri sosudistykh zabolevaniyakh i travme cherepa. (Taste sensitivity in Ménière's disease and cochleo-vestibular disturbances in cases of vascular diseases and cranial trauma.) VORL, 3: 51–53. (English summary.)

———. 1958 K voprosu o vkusovoi chuvstvitelnosti pri opukholyakh oshnogo nerva. (Gustatory sensitivity in relation to tumors of the eighth nerve.) VORL, 2: 95–97. (English summary.)

———. 1959 Morfologiia perifericheskogo kontsa vkusovogo analizatora pri opukholiakh VIII nerva. (Morphology of the peripheral termination of the gustatory analyzer in tumors of the eighth nerve.) VORL, 3: 57–61. (English summary.)

YAMASHITA, S. 1961 Stimulating effectiveness of cations and anions on frog's tongue. KUMJ, 14: 170.

———. 1963 Stimulating effectiveness of cations and anions on chemoreceptors in the frog tongue. JJPH, 13: 54–63.

———. 1964 Chemoreceptor response in frog, as modified by temperature change. JJPH, 14: 488–504.

YAMASHITA, S., AKAIKE, N., and SATO, M. 1963 Stimulation of taste receptors of rat by certain salts. KUMJ, 16: 184–93.

YAMASHITA, S., and SATO, M. 1965 The effects of temperature on gustatory response of rats. JCCP, 66: 1–17.

YAMASHITA, S., YAMADA, K., and SATO, M. 1964 The effect of temperature on neural taste response of cats. JJPH, 14: 505–14.

*YAMAZAKI, J., TSUZUKI, Y., and KAGAMI, K. 1947 Sweetness of fructose. KAGT, pp. 175–76.

YANAGAWA, T., and NISHIDA, H. 1936 Studies on proteins. IV: On the taste-producing amino acids. OKGH, 16(10): 1–36.

YENSEN, R. 1958 Influence of salt deficiency on taste sensitivity in human subjects. NATU, 181: 1472–74.

———. 1958 Influence of water deprivation on taste sensitivity in man. NATU, 182: 677–79.

———. 1959 Some factors affecting taste sensitivity in man. I: Food intake and time of day. QJXP, 11: 221–29.

———. 1959 Some factors affecting taste sensitivity in man. II: Depletion of body salt. QJXP, 11: 230–38.

———. 1959 Some factors affecting taste sensitivity in man. III: Water deprivation. QJXP, 11: 239–48.

———. 1964 Taste sensitivity and food deprivation, blood sugar level and composition of meal. NATU, 203: 327–28.

YOSHIDA, M. 1962 Aji (Taste), in Kanno-kensa. (Handbook for Sensory Tests in Industry.) S. Miura and G. Masuyama (eds.). JUSE, Tokyo, 601 pp. (see pp. 104–20).

———. 1963 (Similarity among different kinds of taste near the threshold concentration.) JJPS, 34: 25–35. (In Japanese, English abstract.)

YOSHIKAWA, S. 1965 Mikakuto agi (Sense of taste), in Shokuhin no kanno-kensa-ho. (Sensory testing methods of foods.) Korinshoin, Tokyo, 199 pp. (see pp. 6–41).

YOUNG, P. T. 1940 Reversal of food preferences of the white rat through controlled pre-feeding. JGPS, 22: 33–66.

———. 1946 Palatability, bodily need, and habit as factors regulating the selection of food. AMPS, 1: 462. (Abstract.)

———. 1949 Studies of food preference, appetite, and dietary habit. IX. Palatability versus appetite as determinants of the critical concentrations of sucrose and sodium chloride. CPSM, 19: 1–44.

———. 1960 Isohedonic contour maps. PYRI, 7: 478.

———. 1966 Hedonic organization and regulation of behavior. PSRV, 73: 59–86.

YOUNG, P. T., and ASDOURIAN, D. 1957 Relative acceptability of sodium chloride and sucrose solutions. JCPP, 50: 499–503.

YOUNG, P. T., BURRIGHT, R. G., and TROMATER, L. J. 1963 Preference of the white rat for solutions of sucrose and quinine hydrochloride. AJPC, 76: 205–17.

YOUNG, P. T., and CHAPLIN, J. P. 1949 Studies of food preference, appetite, and dietary habit. X: Preferences of adrenalectomized rats for salt solutions of different concentrations. CPSM, 19: 45–74.

YOUNG, P. T., and CHRISTENSEN, K. R. 1962 Algebraic summation of hedonic processes. JCPP, 55: 332–36.

YOUNG, P. T., and FALK, J. L. 1956 The acceptability of tap water and distilled water to nonthirsty rats. JCPP, 49: 336–38.

———. 1956 The relative acceptability of sodium chloride solutions as a function of concentration and water need. JCPP, 49: 569–75.

YOUNG, P. T., FALK, J. L., and KAPPAUF, W. E. 1958 Running activity and preference as related to concentration of sodium-chloride solutions. AJPC, 71: 255–62.

YOUNG, P. T., and GREENE, J. T. 1953 Relative acceptability of saccharine solutions as revealed by different methods. JCPP, 46: 295–98.

YOUNG, P. T., and KAPPAUF, W. E. 1962 Apparatus and procedures for studying taste-preferences in the white rat. AJPC, 75: 482–84.

YOUNG, P. T., and MADSEN, C. H., JR. 1963 Individual isohedons in sucrose-sodium chloride and sucrose-saccharin gustatory areas. JCPP, 56: 903–9.

YOUNG, P. T., and RICHEY, H. W. 1952 Diurnal drinking patterns in the rat. JCPP, 45: 80–89.

YOUNG, P. T., and SCHULTE, R. H. 1963 Isohedonic contours and tongue activity in three gustatory areas of the rat. JCPP, 56: 465–75.

YOUNG, P. T., and SHUFORD, E. H., JR. 1955 Quantitative control of motivation through sucrose solutions of different concentrations. JCPP, 48: 114–18.

YOUNG, P. T., and TRAFTON, C. L. 1964 Activity contour maps as related to preference in four gustatory stimulus areas of the rat. JCPP, 58: 68–75.

———. 1964 Psychophysical studies of taste preference and fluid intake, in *Thirst*, M. J. Wayner (ed.). Macmillan, New York, 570 pp. (see pp. 271–85).

YUR'EVA, G. Y. 1958 The role of reactive groups in protein complexes in taste receptor stimulation. BIOP, 2: 653–56.

———. 1961 (New data on the role of protein sulfhydryl groups in taste sensitivity.) BIOF, 6: 189–93. (English summary.)

ZAIKO, N. S. 1956 Zakonomernosti iavleniia funktsional'noi mobil'nosti vkusovogo retseptornogo pribora cheloveka. (Mechanism of the functional mobility of the gustatory receptor in man.) BEBM, 41: 19–22.

———. 1961 K voprosu o fiziologicheskom deistvii pishchi raznogo kachestva i kolichestva na vkusovuiu chuvstvitel'nost'. (On the physiological effect produced by food of different quality and quantity on the sense of taste.) VPIT, 20: 9–14. (English summary.)

ZAIKO, N. S., KUZNETSOV, M. I., and CHELNOKOVA, N. A. 1963 Investigation of taste sensation in human subjects during prolonged inhalation of oxygen. BEBM, 56: 835–37.

ZAIKO, N. S., and LOKSHINA, É. S. 1963 Reflex reaction of the taste receptors of the tongue to direct stimulation of the gastric receptors. BEBM, 53: 9–11.

ZAMPARO, A. 1926 Sulla relazione tra costituzione chimica e sapore delle sostanze. (Relation between chemical constitution and taste of the substance.) BCFA, 65: 193–202.

ZANDER, R. 1897 Die Verbreitungsweise der Gefühls- und Geschmacks-nerven der Zungenschleimhaut. (The distribution of touch and taste nerves in the mucous membrane of the tongue.) SPOG, 38: 50.

———. 1897 Ueber das Verbreitungsgebiet der Gefühls- und Geschmacksnerven in der Zungenschleimhaut. (On the distribution of touch and taste nerves in the mucous membrane of the tongue.) ANAN, 14: 131–45.

ZANZUCCHI, G. 1936 Sulla cosidetta componente olfattiva del sapore metallico in rapporto a talune affezioni nasali. (So-called olfactory component of metallic taste in relation to nasal disturbances.) AIOR, 48: 654–61.

ZARNIKO, C. 1903 Über intraepitheliale Drüsen der Nasenschleimhaut. (On intraepithelial glands of the mucous membrane of the nose.) ZHNO, 45: 211–19.

ZELENÁ, J. 1964 Development, degeneration and regeneration of receptor organs, in *Progress in Brain Research. XIII: Mechanisms of Neural Regeneration*. M. Singer and J. P. Schade (eds.). Elsvier, Amsterdam, 241 pp. (see pp. 175–213).

ZENNECK, 1839 Die Geschmackserscheinungen. (Taste hallucinations.) REPP, 65: 224–40.

ZENNER, P. 1888 Ein klinischer Beitrag über den Verlauf des Geschmacksnerven. (A clinical contribution on the course of taste nerves.) NEUZ, 7: 457–60.

ZEROSI, C. 1940 Su un caso di anestesia ed ageusia linguale parzíale consecutiva ad anestesia tronculare del nervo dentario inferiore. (On a case of partial anesthesia and ageusia of the tongue following truncular anesthesia of the inferior dental nerve.) STIT, 2: 432–36.

ZEYNEK, R. VON. 1898 Ueber den elektrischen Geschmack. (On the electric taste.) ZEPH, 12: 617–21.

ZHUKOVICH, A. V. 1962 Ob otonevrologicheskikh simptomakh pri gipertonicheskoi bolezni. (Otoneurological symptoms in hypertensive vascular disease.) KLMI, 40: 94–99. (English summary.)

ZIEGLER, H. 1919 Über Störungen der Geruchs- und Geschmacksempfindung. (Disturbances of smell and taste.) MUVE, 26: 213–18.

ZIEHL, F. 1889 Ein Fall von isolierter Lähmung des ganzen Trigeminus Astes nebst einigen Beobachtungen über den Verlauf der Geschmacksfasern der Chorda tympani und die Innervation des Geschmacks überhaupt. (A case of isolated paralysis of the whole trigeminus branch besides some observations on the course of taste fibers of the chorda tympani and on the general innervation of taste.) VAPA, 117: 52–82.

———. 1890 Einige Bemerkungen zu der Erwiderung des Herrn Dr. L. Bruns in Hanover, meinen Aufsatz über die Innervation des Geschmacks betreffend. (Some comments on the answer of Dr. L. Bruns in Hanover, on the author's paper on innervation of taste.) VAPA, **120**: 193–94.

ZIELER, K. 1901 Zur Anatomie der umwallten Zungenpapillen des Menschen. (The anatomy of the circumvallate papillae in man.) ANHE, **16**: 761–80.

ZIEM, C. 1904 Zur Lehre von der Anosmie, Parosmie, und Parageusie. (Anosmia, parosmia and parageusia.) MOLA, **38**: 400–6.

ZILSTORFF-PEDERSEN, K. 1955 Anosmia and ageusia, presumably resulting from anoxia. AOLA, **45**: 370–72.

ZIMMERMAN, O. C. 1947 Heilung einer postkommationellen Ageusie nach Vierzigjähriger Dauer. (Recovery from a post-concussional ageusia of 40-years' duration.) SMWO, **77**: 1034–35.

ZITKA, W. 1952 Über die Ursachen der Geschmacksstörungen, die durch Gaumenplatten verursacht werden. (The reasons for taste disturbances caused by palatal plates.) ZAWE, **7**: 478–79.

ZLATOVEROFF, A. I., and ILLYINSKAYA, V. A. 1928 Klinicheskie nabliundeniia po voprosu o korkovoi lokalizatsii vkusa. (Clinical observations on localization of taste in cortex of brain.) MOMZ, **9**: 51–56.

ZOTTERMAN, Y. 1935 Action potentials in the glossopharyngeal nerve and in the chorda tympani. SAPH, **72**: 73–77.

———. 1936 Specific action potentials in the lingual nerve of cat. SAPH, **75**: 105–9.

———. 1949 The response of the frog's taste fibres to the application of pure water. APSC, **18**: 181–89.

———. 1950 The water taste of the frog. EXPE, **6**: 57–58.

———. 1956 Elektrophysiologie der Geschmacksreceptoren. (Electrophysiology of taste receptors.) BEME, 7: 205–8.

———. 1956 Species differences in the water taste. APSC, **37**: 60–70.

———. 1957 Electrophysiological investigations of the functions of gustatory nerve fibres. ADSC, **13**: 292–95.

———. 1958 Studies in the nervous mechanism of taste. ECRS, **5**: 520–26.

———. 1959 Studies on the nervous mechanism

of taste. JMKY, **15**(5): 1039–44.

———. 1959 The nervous mechanism of taste. ANYA, **81**: 358–66.

———. 1961 Studies in the neural mechanism of taste, in *Sensory Communication*, W. A. Rosenblith (ed.). John Wiley & Sons, New York, 844 pp. (see pp. 205–16).

ZOTTERMAN, Y., and DIAMANT, H. 1959 Has water a specific taste? NATU, **183**: 191–92.

ZUBEK, J. P. 1959 Intellectual and sensory processes in the aged. MDSJ, **15**: 731–33.

ZUCKERMANN, N. VON. 1913 Beobachtungen über den Ventriculus laryngis und die Zungenpapillen einiger "Melanesier." (Observations on the ventriculus larynx and the tongue papillae of some Melanesians.) ZEMA, **15**: 207–12.

ZUNTZ, N. 1892 Beitrag zur Physiologie des Geschmacks. (Contribution to the physiology of taste.) AAPA, p. 556.

ZWAARDEMAKER, H. 1899 Tast- en smaakgewaarwordingen bij het ruiken. (Touch and taste perception by smelling.) NTGE, **1**: 113–25.

———. 1899 Tast- en Smaakgewaarwordingen bij het Ruiken. (Touch and taste perception by smelling.) ZEPS, **21**: 143–47.

———. 1902 Mechanismus des Riechens: Geschmacks- und Tast- komponente. (Mechanism of smell: Taste and touch components.) ERPH, **1**: 898–900.

———. 1903 Geschmack. (Taste.) ERPH, **2**: 699–725.

———. 1903 Riechend Schmecken. (Tasting by smelling.) ARPI, pp. 120–28.

———. 1903 Riechend Schmecken. (Tasting by smelling.) OZPL, **4**: 408–20.

———. 1905 Al ruikende proevend. (Tasting by smelling.) OZPL, **6**: 15–20.

———. 1905 Riechend Schmecken. (Tasting by smelling.) ZPSI, **38**: 189–95.

———. 1914 Geruch und Geschmack (Smell and taste), in *Handbuck der physiologischen Methodik*, R. Tigerstedt (ed.). 3 vols. Leipzig, I, 46–108.

———. 1921 Methoden der Untersuchung des Geschmackes und der Geschmackstoffe. (Methods of investigation of taste and taste substances.) HBAM, **5**(7;3): 437–54.

APPENDIX

CODEN Abbreviations

A

AABI	Annals of Applied Biology
AACD	Amino Acid (Japan)
AACL	Archivio di Antropologia Criminale, Psichiatria e Medicina Legale
AAGE	Arkhiv Anatomii, Gistologii i Embriologii
AAHE	Archives d'Anatomie, d'Histologie et d'Embryologie (Strasbourg)
AALB	Atti della Accademia Nazionale dei Lincei. Memoire. Classe di Scienze Fisiche. Matematiche e Naturali. Sezione III. Botanica, Zoologia, Fisiologia, Patologia
AAMT	Accademia di Medicina (Torino)
AANL	Atti della Accademia Nazionali dei Lincei. Rendiconti, Classe di Scienze Fisiche, Matematiche e Naturali.
AAOH	Archiv für Augen und Ohrenheilkunde
AAPA	Archiv für Anatomie und Physiologie. Anatomische Abteilung
AAPM	Archiv für Anatomie, Physiologie und wissenschaftliche Medizin
ABAB	Annales de Biologie Animale, Biochimie, Biophysique
ABIL	Archives de Biologie (Liege)
ABME	Arquivos Brasileiros de Medicina (Rio de Janeiro)
ABNA	Amtliche Berichte über die Versammlung deutscher Naturforscher und Aerzte
ABSE	Annales et Bulletin Societe Entomologie (Belgium)
ACAF	American Chemical Society, Division of Agricultural and Food Chemistry
ACAP	Annali di Chimica Applicata
ACAT	Acta Anatomica
ACJL	Annalen der Chemie, Justus Liebigs
ACJO	American Chemical Journal
ACNC	Atti del Congresso Nazionale di Chimica Pura ed Applicata
ACNE	Acta Neurovegetativa (Vienna)
ACOD	Actualites Odonto-Stomatologiques
ACOR	Atti della Clinica Oto-Rino-Laringoiatrica dell Università di Palermo
ACPH	Annales de Chimie et de Physique
ACSA	Acta Chemica Scandinavica
ADSC	Advancement of Science
AEMP	Archives d'Electricité Medicale et de Physiotherapie du Cancer
AEMR	Annual Report, East Malling Research Station (Kent)
AEPP	Archiv für experimentelle Pathologie und Pharmakologie, Naunyn-Schmiedeberg's
AESA	Annals of the Entomological Society of America
AFSC	Aesculape (Paris)
AFAS	Association Francaise pour l'Avancement des Sciences, Bulletin (Paris)
AFFS	Anais da Faculdade de Farmacia e Odontologia da São Paulo
AFMC	Annali della Facolta di Medicina e Chirurgia di Perugia che Pubblicano gli Atti della Academia Anatomica-Chirurgia
AFOJ	American Food Journal

AFRE	Advances in Food Research
AFTE	Archivio di Farmacologia e Terapeutica
AGME	Archives Generales de Médecine
AGMG	Acta Geneticae Medicae et Gemellologiae (Rome)
AGSM	Acta Geneticae et Statistica Medica (Basel)
AGSW	Agricultural Science Review
AHBA	Archiv für Hygiene und Bakteriologie
AIAE	Archivio Italiano di Anatomia e di Embriologia
AIBL	Archives Italiennes de Biologie
AIFC	Association Internationale des Fabricants de Confiserie. Assemble Generale (Munich)
AIIZ	Aichi Igakkai Zasshi
AIMS	Archivio Italiano di Medicina Sperimentale
AIOR	Archivio Italiano di Otologia, Rinologia e Laringologia
AIPH	Archives Iternationales de Physiologie
AIPT	Archives Internationales de Pharmacodynamie et de Therapie
AIPZ	Acta Instituti Psychologici Universitet Zagreb
AIRB	Archives Internationales de Laryngologie, d'Otologie de Rhinologie et de Broncho-oesophagascopic
AJAE	Australian Journal of Agricultural Research
AJAN	American Journal of Anatomy
AJCM	American Journal of Clinical Medicine
AJCN	American Journal of Clinical Nutrition
AJDC	American Journal of Diseases of Children
AJEV	American Journal of Enology and Viticulture
AJHG	American Journal of Human Genetics
AJKS	Archiv der Julius Klaus—Stiftung für Vererbungsforschung Sozialanthropologie und Rassenhygiene
AJMD	American Journal of Mental Deficiency
AJMS	American Journal of the Medical Sciences
AJOG	American Journal of Obstetrics and Gynecology
AJPC	The American Journal of Psychology
AJPH	American Journal of Physiology
AJPN	American Journal of Physical Anthropology
AJSC	American Journal of Science
AJSU	American Journal of Surgery
AKGI	Akusherstvo i Ginekologiya
ALOR	Atti del 20th Congresso della Società Italiana di Laringologia, Otologia e Rhinologia
ALRO	Archivos Latinos de Rinologia, Laringologia, y Otologia (Barcelona)
AMAE	Archiv für Mikroskopische Anatomie und Entwicklungsmechanik
AMCQ	Archives de Medicine et de Chirurgie Pratique
AMCZ	Allgemeine Medicinische Central-Zeitung
AMDN	Annali di Medicina Navale
AMJA	American Journal of Anthropology
AMMH	American Monthly Microscopical Journal
AMNA	American Midland Naturalist
AMNL	Arquivos du Museu Nacional (Lisbon)
AMPS	The American Psychologist
AMPY	Annales Medico-Psychologiques
AMRY	American Mercury
AMSA	Abhandlungen der Mathematisch-Physischen Klasse der Saechsischen Akademie der Wissenschaften (Leipzig)
AMSC	American Scientist
AMUK	Acta Medica Universitatis Kagoshimaensis
AMZO	American Zoologist
ANAI	Annales de la Nutrition et de l'Alimentation
ANAN	Anatomischer Anzeiger

ANBE	Animal Behaviour
ANBR	Anales de Bromatologia (Madrid)
ANCK	Annales des Charitekrankenhaus (Berlin)
ANEF	Archives de Neurologie (France)
ANEN	Annales d'Endocrinologie
ANEU	Annals of Eugenics (Cambridge)
ANHE	Anatomische Hefte
ANHG	Annals of Human Genetics
ANMV	Annales des Maladies Venneriennes (Paris)
ANOL	Annales d'Oto-Laryngologie
ANPA	Archives Neerlandaises de Physiologie
ANPQ	Année Psychologique (Paris)
ANPS	Archives of Neurology and Psychiatry
ANRE	Anatomical Record
ANTH	The Anthropologist (Delhi)
ANVO	Anthropologische Vorträge
ANYA	Annals of the New York Academy of Sciences
ANZO	Archives Neerlandaises de Zoologie
AOGI	Annali di Ostetricia e Ginecologia (Milan)
AOIP	Archivio Italiano di Psicologia
AOLA	Acta Oto-Laryngologica (Stockholm)
AONK	Archiv für Ohren-, Nasen- und Kehlkopfheilkunde vereinigt mit Zeitschrift für Hals-, Nasen- und Ohrenheilkunde
AORH	The Annals of Otology, Rhinology, and Laryngology
AOSC	Acta Odontologica Scandinavica
APBU	American Pharmaceutical Association Bulletin
APEO	American Perfumer and Essential Oil Review
APHJ	American Pharmaceutical Association Journal, Scientific Edition
APHP	Archives de Physiologie Normale et Pathologique (Paris)
APKM	Archiv für pathologische Anatomie und Physiologie und klinische Medizin
APKY	Acta Phytotaxonomica et Geobotannica (Kyoto)
APNE	Acta Psychiatrica et Neurologica
APNP	Archivio di Psicologia, Neurologia e Psichiatria
APNV	Archiv für Psychiatrie und Nervenkrankheiten
APPN	Acta Physiologica et Pharmacologica Neerlandica
APSC	Acta Physiologica Scandivanica
APSE	Arkhiv Psikhiatrii Nevrologii i Sudenbnoi Psikhopatologie (St. Petersburg)
APSI	Archivio di Psichiatria
APSK	Annual of Animal Psychology (Tokyo)
APSS	Acta Physiologica Scandinavica, Supplement
APSY	Archives de Psychologie
APVZ	Apotekarski Vjesnik (Zagreb)
APYP	Acta Physiologica Polonica
ARBI	Archives of Biochemistry
ARBN	Arkhiv Biologicheskikh Nauk
ARCP	Anomalo Rivista di Antropologia Criminale e Psichiatria (Naples)
ARCS	Annals of the Royal College of Surgeons
ARDE	Archives of Dermatology
AREN	Annual Review of Entomology
AREO	Archiv für Entwicklungsmechanik der Organismen
ARFI	Archivio di Fisiologia
ARGP	Archives of General Psychiatry
ARKI	Archiv für Kinderheilkunde
ARLO	Archivos de Rinologia, Laringologia, y Otologia
ARNE	Archives of Neurology
AROP	Archives of Ophthalmology (Chicago)
AROT	Archives of Otolaryngology

ARPA	Archives of Pathology
ARPH	Annual Review of Physiology
ARPI	Archiv für Physiologie
ARPS	Annual Review of Psychology
ARSU	Archives of Surgery
ARZN	Arzneimittel-Forschung
ASAP	Archives Suisses d'Anthropologie Generale
ASBI	Archivio di Scienze Biologiche (Bologna)
ASBU	Arkiv Biologicheskikh Nauk (Archives des Sciences Biologiques U.S.S.R.)
ASGI	Associazione Genetica Italiana. Atti (Pavia)
ASIO	Atti della Società Italiana Laringologica, Otologica e Rinologica Congresso
ASJP	Australian Journal of Psychology
ASME	Archivio per le Science Mediche
ASMN	Academia Sinica, Memoir of the National Research Institute of Chemsitry (China)
ASPN	Archives des Sciences Physiques et Naturelles
ASQC	American Society for Quality Control, Transactions Annual Conventions
ASUP	Acta Societatis Medicorum Upsaliensis
ATNV	Atti della Società Toscana di Scienze Naturali Residente in Pisa, Processi Verbali
ATPA	Ateneo Parmense
AUMM	Annali Universali di Medicina (Milan)
AUSK	Akademija Umiejetnosci, Sprawozdia z Czynnosci i Posiedzen (Krakow)
AVBI	Archiv für Biontologie (Berlin)
AVMD	Journal of Aviation Medicine
AZEG	Archives de Zoologie Experimentale et Generale

B

BAAS	British Association for the Advancement of Science, Report of the Annual Meeting
BABS	Bulletin de l'Academie Royale de Belgique Classe de Sciences
BAME	Bulletin de l'Academie de Medecine (Paris)
BARM	Bulletin de l'Academie Royale de Medicine Belgique
BAZE	Breslauer Aerztliche Zeitschrift
BCFA	Bollettino Chimico Farmaceutico
BCHL	Boletim Clinico dos Hospitais Civis de Lisboa
BDCG	Berichte der Deutschen Chemischen Gesellschaft
BEBM	Byulleten Eksperimental noi Biologii i Meditsiny. English title: Bulletin of Experimental Biology and Medicine
BEHA	Behaviour
BEMB	Bulletin de Biologie et de Médecine Experimentale de l'U.R.S.S.
BEME	Berliner Medizin
BERP	Berichte der Deutschen Pharmazeutischen Gesellschaft
BERT	Behaviour Research and Therapy
BIAN	Bibliotheca Anatomica
BIBM	Biological Bulletin of the Marine Biological Laboratory
BIBU	Biological Bulletin
BIJO	Biochemical Journal
BILM	Biologica Latina
BIOF	Biofizika
BIOM	Biometrics
BIOP	Biophysics (U.S.S.R.)
BIOU	Biologische Untersuchungen (Stockholm)
BIUN	Bibliotheque Universelle
BIZE	Biochemische Zeitschrift
BIZN	Biologisches Zentralblatt
BIZO	Bibliotheca Zoologica
BIZT	Biedermanns Zentralblatt für Agriculturchemie und rationeller Landwirtschaftsbetrieb
BJAB	British Journal of Animal Behaviour

BJEP	The British Journal of Experimental Pathology
BJNU	British Journal of Nutrition
BJSG	British Journal of Psychology, General Section (London)
BJSP	British Journal of Statistical Psychology
BKWO	Berliner klinische Wochenschrift
BLOR	Bulletin de Laryngologie, Otologie, et Rhinologie
BLPY	Bulletin of the Laboratory of Psychology (Moscow)
BMJO	British Medical Journal
BMMH	Bulletins et Memoires de la Société de Médecine et des Hopitaux de Paris
BMOG	Bolletino delle Malattie dell' Orecchio, della Gola, del Naso
BMSJ	Boston Medical and Surgical Journal
BNEM	Bulletin of the New England Medical Center
BNIN	Bulletin of the Neurological Institute of New York
BNMV	Berichte des Naturwissenschaftlich-medizinischen Vereines in Innsbruck
BOBC	Boletín de la Sociedad de Biologia de Concepción (Chile)
BOSM	Bolletino delle Scienze Mediche
BPSS	Biological Prototypes and Synthetic Systems
BRAI	Brain
BRGI	Brewer's Guild Journal
BRUW	Brauwelt, Ausgabe B
BRWS	Brauwissenschaft
BRYG	Brygmesteren, Medlemsblad for Dansk Brygmester-Forening
BSCT	Bulletin de la Société Centrale de Médecine du Department du Nord (Lille)
BSIB	Bollettino della Società Italiana di Biologia Sperimentale
BSMP	Bollettino della Società Medico-Chirurgica (Pavia)
BSMU	Bulletin of the School of Medicine, University of Maryland
BSSH	Bulletin de la Société Scientifique d'Hygiene Alimentaire et d'Alimentation Ration-nelle de l'Homme
BSZF	Bulletin de la Société Zoologie de France (Paris)
BTMD	Bulletin of Tokyo Medical and Dental University
BUAB	Bulletin of Animal Behaviour (London)
BUBF	Bulletin Biologique de la France et de la Belgique
BUCT	Bulletin of the Central Food Technological Research Institute, Mysore (India)
BUDI	Bulletin Department of Anthropology, India (Calcutta, Delhi)
BUME	Bulletin Medical (Paris)
BUSG	Bulletin der Schweizerischen Gesellschaft für Anthropologie und Ethnologie
BUUV	Bulletin Universel des Sciences et de l'Industrie. Section 3; Bulletin des Sciences Medicale
BUVM	Bulletin Vancouver Medical Association

C

CAJM	Central African Journal of Medicine
CBCP	Comparative Biochemistry and Physiology
CCPI	Canadian Chemistry and Process Industries
CEAP	Contribuicoes parao Estudo de Antropologia Portuguesa
CELL	La Cellule Recueil de Cytologie et d'Histologie (Lorraine)
CEMW	Centralblatt für die Medizinischen Wissenschaften
CENE	Chemical and Engineering News
CEOT	Ceskoslovenska Otolaryngologie (Prague)
CEPE	Ceskoslovenska Pediatrie
CHBE	Chemische Berichte
CHCA	Chemistry in Canada
CHDR	The Chemist and Druggist
CHIN	Chemistry and Industry (London)
CHIZ	Chiba-Igakkai-Zasshi (Journal of the Chiba Medical Society)
CHMI	Die Chemie
CHNW	The Chemical News and Journal of Industrial Science

CINM   La Chimica et L'Industria (Milan)
CJPS   Canadian Journal of Psychology
CLCE   Casopis Lékaru Ceskych
CLJL   Clinical Journal (London)
CLOD   Clinica Odontoiatrica
CLOP   Clinica Odonto-Protesica
CLTE   Clinica Terapeutica
CMIA   Clinica Medica Italiana (Archivio Clinico)
CMKZ   Chemiker-Zeitung
CNEW   Chemical News (London)
CNFP   Confectionery Production
CNRB   Canadian Journal of Research. Section B: Chemical Sciences
CNRM   Canadian Journal of Research. Section E: Medical Sciences
COLS   Collier's
COME   Concours Medical
COPA   Copeia
CORE   Comptes Rendus Hebdomadaires des Seances de l'Academie des Sciences
CORL   Clinica Oto-Rino-Laringologica de la Università di Napoli
CORV   Contemporary Review (London)
COUR   La Clinica Otorinolaringoiatrica
CPBT   Chemical and Pharmaceutical Bulletin (Tokyo)
CPCM   Contribution. W. Pepper Laboratory of Clinical Medicine (University of Pennsyl-
        vania)
CPCN   Chemical Products and Chemical News
CPSM   Comparative Psychology Monographs
CRME   Crónica Médica (Lima)
CRSS   Comptes Rendus des Sceances de la Société de Biologie
CUCE   Columbia University Teacher's College, Contribution to Education
CUSC   Current Science (India)

                                        D

DAJK   Dainihon Jibiinkokakai-Kaiho
DAKM   Deutches Archiv für Klinische Medizin
DANB   Doklady Akademiia na Naukite (Sofia)
DANK   Doklady Akademii Nauk S.S.S.R.
DCIN   Drug and Cosmetic Industry
DCNN   Decheniana
DDZE   Deutsche Destillateur Zeitung
DEBI   Developmental Biology
DECB   Dermatologisches Centralblatt
DECO   Dental Cosmos
DEKL   Deutsche Klinik (Berlin)
DESS   Deutsche Essigindustrie
DESU   Dental Survey
DEVO   Deutsche Vogelwelt
DIAS   Dissertation Abstracts
DIIN   Dental Items of Interest
DIME   Dia Médico (Buenos Aires)
DJMC   Dublin Journal of Medical and Chemical Science
DLRU   Deutsche Lebensmittel—Rundschau
DMCN   Developmental Medicine and Child Neurology
DMWO   Deutsche Medizinische Wochenschrift
DMZK   Deutsche Monatsschrift für Zahnheilkunde
DPGB   Deutsche Pharmazeutische Gesellschaft. Berichte
DRRE   Dragoco Report
DSME   Dictionnaire Encyclopedique des Sciences Medicales
DTZU   Deutsche Zuckerindustrie

DUOD   Duodecim, Laaketieteellinen Aikakauskirja
DZGG   Deutsche Zeitschrift für die gesamte Gerichtliche Medizin
DZNE   Deutsche Zeitschrift für Nervenheilkunde
DZTP   Deutsche Zeitschrift für Tiermedizin und vergleichende Pathologie

E

EAAN   Eastern Anthropologist
ECRS   Experimental Cell Research, Supplement
EDHR   Edinburgh Hospital Reports
EENT   Eye, Ear, Nose and Throat Monthly
EMCP   Encyclopedic Medico-Chirurgicale Psychiatrie
EMJO   Edinburgh Medical Journal
ENCE   Encephale (Paris)
ENDO   Endocrinology

ERBA   Erbarzt
ERBI   Ergebnisse der Biologie
ERNF   Ernaehrungsforschung
ERPH   Ergebnisse der Physiology
EUNE   Eugenical News
EXPE   Experientia
EYGZ   Eiyogaku Zasshi (Japanese Journal of Nutrition)

F

FARR   Farm Research
FEPR   Federation Proceedings
FIME   Fisiologia e Medicina (Rome)
FKFS   Fukuoka, Japan. Kyushu University Faculty of Science Memoirs
FLAV   Flavours
FMTE   Food Materials and Equipment
FNBI   Folia Neuro-Biologica
FOCN   Food in Canada
FOEG   Food Engineering
FOFO   Forschungen und Fortschritte
FOIN   Food Industries
FOMA   Food Manufacture
FOPA   Food Packer
FOPP   Food Processing and Packaging
FOPR   Food Processing
FORE   Food Research
FOTE   Food Technology
FOZA   Fortschritte der Zahnheilkunde
FOZO   Fortschritte der Zoologie
FPJV   The Fruit Products Journal and American Vinegar Industry
FPNJ   Folia Psychiatrica et Neurologica Japonica
FRDE   Fruits et Leurs Dérivés
FRFF   Frosted Food Field
FRPD   Friskies Pet Digest
FSHS   Florida State Horticultural Society
FUIZ   Fukuoka Ikwadaigaku-Zasshi
FZLZ   Fiziologicheskii Zhurnal S.S.S.R. Imeni I. M. Sechenova

G

GAMP   Gazette Medicale de Paris
GAMV   Gazzetta Medico-Veterinaria
GAST   Gastroenterology
GBKL   Geneeskundige Bladen uit Kliniek en Laboratorium (Haarlem)

GCIT   Gazzetta Chimica Italiana
GEMJ   Gegenbaurs Morphologisches Jahrbuch
GERI   Geriatrics
GIFL   Givaudan Flavorist
GIGE   Giornale di Gerontologia
GISM   Giornale Internazionale delle Scienze Mediche
GMCB   Gross Medical College Bulletin (Denver)
GMDT   Giornale della Accademia di Medicina di Torino
GMES   Gaceta Médica Española (Madrid)
GMIT   Gazzetta Medica Italiana (Milan)
GMPV   Gazzetta Medica Italiana, Provincie Venete
GOCL   Gazzetta degli Ospedali e della Cliniche
GPMO   Genetic Psychology Monographs
GRME   Grenzgebiete der Medizin
GYHE   Gyogyszereszi Hetilap

H

HALE   The Harvey Lectures
HAZA   Hanzaigaku Zasshi
HBAM   Handbuch der Biologischen Arbeitsmethoden
HBNE   Handbuch der Neurologie (Berlin)
HDTY   Heredity
HERE   Hereditas
HHLR   Heymann's Handbuch der Laryngologie und Rhinologie
HIHJ   Hillside Hospital Journal
HIKA   Hinshitsu-Kanri (Statistical Quality Control)
HLGT   Stricker's Handbuch der Lehre von Geweben des Menschen und der Tiere
HMAM   Handbuch der mikroskopischen Anatomie des Menschen
HNAO   Hals, Nasen und Ohrenarzt
HNOK   Hals, Nasen und Ohrenheilkunde
HNPP   Handbuch der Normalen und Pathologischen Physiologie
HPME   Handbuch der Physiologie des Menschen
HPPA   Helvetica Physiologica et Pharmacologica Acta
HTKR   Handbuch der Therapie innerer Krankheiten
HUBI   Human Biology
HYGI   Hygeia

I

IADR   International Association for Dental Research
IAME   Iatrikos Menytor Athenai
ICAC   International Congress of Applied Chemistry
ICPA   International Congress of Pure and Applied Chemistry
ICPH   Industrie Chemique, Le Phosphate
ICPS   International Congress of Physiological Sciences
ICPY   International Congress of Psychology
IJMR   Indian Journal of Medical Research
IJMS   The Dublin Journal of Medical Science
IKAD   Izvestiya Akademii Nauk Kazakhskoi S.S.R., Seriya Meditsiny i Fiziologii
IMAP   Internationale Monatsschrift für Anatomie und Physiologie
IMPZ   Imparziale. Giornale degli Interessi Scientifici Pratici Morali e Professionali della
        Classe Medica
INDE   L'Information Dentaire
INEW   Industrial and Engineering News
INPS   Industrielle Psychotechnik
IRCY   International Review of Cytology
IRRE   Der Irrenfreund, Psychiatrische Monatsschrift für praktische Aerzte
ISCJ   Iowa State College Journal of Science

| ISUJ | The International Sugar Journal |
| IUST | Iowa University. Studies in Psychology |

J

JACP	Journal of the Academy of Natural Science (Philadelphia)
JACS	Journal of the American Chemical Society
JADA	Journal of the American Dietetic Association
JADS	Journal of the American Dental Association
JAFC	Journal of Agricultural and Food Chemistry
JAHD	Journal of Oral Surgery, Anesthesia and Hospital Dental Service
JAIH	Journal of the American Institute of Homeopathy
JAKI	Jahrbuch für Kinderheilkunde
JAMA	Journal of the American Medical Association
JANS	Journal of Animal Science
JAPH	Journal of Anatomy and Physiology
JAPM	Journal of the American Pharmaceutical Association, Scientific Edition
JAPS	Journal of Applied Psychology, Scientific Edition
JAPY	Journal of Applied Physiology
JASI	Journal of Agricultural Science
JASP	Journal of Abnormal and Social Psychology
JBBC	Journal of Biophysical and Biochemical Cytology
JBEN	Journal Belge de Neurologie et de Psychiatrie
JBLS	Johns Hopkins University Biological Laboratory Studies
JCCO	Journal of the Chinese Chemical Society
JCCP	Journal of Cellular and Comparative Physiology
JCED	Journal of Chemical Education
JCEM	Journal of Clinical Endocrinology and Metabolism
JCEN	The Journal of Clinical Endocrinology
JCHM	Journal de Chimie Medicale, de Pharmacie, de Toxicologie
JCIN	Journal of Clinical Investigation
JCLB	Journal of Cell Biology
JCNE	Journal of Comparative Neurology
JCNP	Journal of Comparative Neurology and Psychology
JCOQ	Journal of the Colorado-Wyoming Academy of Science
JCPH	Journal of Consulting Psychology
JCPO	The Journal of Comparative Psychology
JCPP	Journal of Comparative and Physiological Psychology
JCSJ	Journal of the Chemical Society of Japan. Pure Chemistry Section
JDRE	The Journal of Dental Research
JEAB	Journal of the Experimental Analysis of Behavior
JEBI	The Journal of Experimental Biology
JEEN	Journal of Economic Entomology
JENZ	Journal of Entomology and Zoology
JEPS	Journal of Experimental Psychology
JEZN	Jenaische Zeitschrift für Naturwissenschaft
JEZO	The Journal of Experimental Zoology
JFDS	Journal of Food Science
JFPN	Jahresbericht über die Fortschritte der Physiologie
JGPL	Journal of General Physiology
JGPS	Journal of General Psychology
JGPY	Journal of Genetic Psychology
JHCY	Journal of Histochemistry and Cytochemistry
JHHB	The Johns Hopkins Hospital Bulletin
JHOE	Journal of Home Economics
JIAS	Journal of the Iowa Academy of Science
JIEC	The Journal of Industrial and Engineering Chemistry
JIPH	Journal of Insect Physiology

JJHG	Japanese Journal of Human Genetics
JJPA	The Japanese Journal of Pharmacology
JJPH	The Japanese Journal of Physiology
JJPS	Japanese Journal of Psychology
JJSS	Journal of the Japanese Stomatological Society
JLEP	Journal of Educational Psychology
JLOT	Journal of Laryngology and Otology
JMCP	Journal de Médecine, de Chirurgie et de Pharmacologie (Brussels)
JMKY	Japan Medical Congress (Nippon Igakkai Dai)
JNEU	Journal of Neuropsychiatry
JNMD	The Journal of Nervous and Mental Disease
JNNP	Journal of Neurology, Neurosurgery and Psychiatry
JOAN	Journal of Anatomy
JOCE	Journal of Organic Chemistry
JOEN	The Journal of Endocrinology
JOGE	Journal of Gerontology
JOGN	Journal of Genetics
JOHE	The Journal of Heredity
JOHY	Journal of Hygiene
JOMO	Journal of Morphology
JONE	Journal of Neurophysiology
JONP	Journal de Neurologie et de Psychiatrie
JONU	Journal of Nutrition
JOOM	Journal of Oriental Medicine
JOPD	The Journal of Pediatrics
JOPH	Journal de Physiologie (Paris)
JOPK	Journal der Physik (Halle)
JOPS	Journal of Psychology
JORN	Journal für Ornithologie
JPCH	Journal of Physical Chemistry
JPDE	The Journal of Prosthetic Dentistry
JPEP	Journal de Physiologie Experimental et Pathologie, Magendie
JPET	The Journal of Pharmacology and Experimental Therapeutics
JPGA	Japanese Journal of Gastroenterology
JPHY	Journal of Physiology (London)
JPMA	Japanese Journal of Medical Sciences. I: Anatomy
JPMN	Journal of Psychological Medicine (New York)
JPMP	Japanese Journal of Medical Sciences: III: Biophysics
JPMS	Journal of Pharmaceutical Sciences
JPNE	Jahrbücher für Psychiatrie und Neurologie
JPNP	Journal de Psychologie Normale et Pathologique
JPPG	Journal de Physiologie et de Pathologie General
JPSJ	Journal of the Physiological Society of Japan
JPSY	Journal de Psychologie
JRIB	Journal of the Royal Institute of Great Britain
JSBJ	Journal of the Society of Brewing (Japan)
JSFA	Journal of the Science of Food and Agriculture
JSHU	Journal of Science of the Hiroshima University
JSIE	Journal des Progres des Sciences et Institutions Medicales en Europe, en Amerique
JSML	Journal des Sciences Medicales de Lille
JSOJ	Journal of the Agricultural Chemical Society (Japan)
JTBI	Journal of Theoretical Biologie
JTKC	Journal of the Tokyo Chemical Society
JULR	Journal of Ultrastructure Research

K

| KAGT | Kagaku (Science) (Tokyo) |
| KAUQ | Kansas University Quarterly |

KLMI	Klinicheskaya Meditsina
KLWO	Klinische Wochenschrift
KMJB	Königsberger Medizinische Jahrbücher
KMMS	Kyushu Memoirs of Medical Sciences
KOZE	Kolloid-Zeitschrift
KSGZ	Kyushii Shika Gakkai Zasshi Kyushu (Dental Society Journal)
KUMJ	Kumamoto Medical Journal
KWPS	Kwartalnik Psychologiczyy

L

LANC	Lancet
LARY	Laryngoscope
LBBR	Latvijas Biologijas Biedribas Raksti
LEFO	Die Lehrerfortbildung
LIFS	Life Sciences
LIME	Lille Medical Journal
LIVJ	Lijecnicki Vjesnik
LMMS	Liverpool and Manchester Medical and Surgical Reports
LYME	Lyon Medical

M

MACO	Manufacturing Confectioner
MANA	Man: A Monthly Record of Anthropological Science
MBAR	Magyar Belorvosi Archivum (Budapest)
MCGU	Medicina y Cirugia de Guerra (Madrid)
MCTR	Medico-Chirurgical Transactions (London)
MDSJ	Medical Services Journal (Canada)
MEAL	Medizinische Annalen (Heidelberg)
MEDS	Medicinskt Archiv (Stockholm)
MEIS	Minzoku Eisei (Race Hygiene)
MEKL	Medizinische Klinik (Munich)
MENE	Medical News (New York)
MENM	Mensch en Maatschappij
MENP	Medical News (Philadelphia)
MERA	Meditsinskaya Radiologiya
MERC	Medical Record
MEVI	Medicinsky Viestnik
MEWE	Die Medizinische Welt
MEXP	Medicina Experimentalis
MEZE	Medicinal Zeitung (Dayton, Ohio)
MGLH	Mitteilungen aus dem Gebiete der Lebensmitteluntersuchung und Hygiene (Same as TCAH)
MGMC	Mitteilungen aus den Grenzgebieten der Medizin und Chirurgie
MIAN	Minerva Anestesiologica
MIME	Minerva Medica
MIOT	Minerva Otorinolaringologica
MJAU	Medical Journal of Australia
MJRE	Medical Journal and Record
MKAR	Mitteilungen Serie A: Rebe und Wein (Klosterneuburg)
MLPS	Manchester Literary and Philosophical Society Memoirs
MMAA	Minerva Medicolegale; Archivio di Antropologia Criminale
MMWO	Münchener Medizinische Wochenschrift
MNVS	Mitteilungen des Naturwissenschaftlichen Vereins für Steiermark
MOKI	Monatsschrift für Kinderkeilkunde
MOLA	Monatsschrift für Ohrenheilkunde und Laryngo-Rhinologie
MOMJ	Monthly Microscopical Journal
MOMZ	Moskovskii Meditsinsky Zhurnal

MOOD   Mondo Odontostomatologico
MORG   Morgagni (Milan)
MOUI   Monatsschrift für Unfallheilkunde und Invalidenwesen
MPNE   Monatsschrift für Psychiatrie und Neurologie
MPTI   Monatshefte für Praktische Tierheilkunde
MRAR   Morphologische Arbeiten
MSAI   Medicina Sperimentale—Archivio Italiano
MSTA   Memoires de L'Academie Stanislas
MUVE   Monatsschrift für Unfallheilkunde und Versicherungsmedizin
MVMJ   Mississippi Valley Medical Journal
MZOI   Monitore Zoologico Italiano
MZSN   Mittheilungen aus der Zoologischen Station zu Neapel

N

NAGN   Nederlandsch Archief voor Genees- en Naturkunde
NAGZ   Nagasaki Igakkawai Zassi
NAKG   Nachrichten von der Königlichen Gesellschaft der Wissenschaften zu Göttingen
NAOF   Natur und Offenbarung
NAOZ   Nauchnoe Obozrienie
NARS   Naturwissenschaftliche Rundschau
NATI   Naturhistorisk Tidsskrift (Copenhagen)
NATU   Nature
NATW   Naturwissenschaften
NAUC   Naturwissenschaftliche Umschau der Chemiker-Zeitung
NEPS   Nevropatologya i Psikhiatrya
NERV   Nervenzarzt
NEUM   Neue Medizinische Welt
NEUR   Neurology
NEUS   Neuropsichiatria (Genoa)
NEUZ   Neurologisches Zentralblatt
NGNH   Notizen aus dem Gebiete der Natur- und Heilkunde
NHGZ   Nippon Igaku Hoshasen Gakkai Zasshi (Nippon Acta Radiol.)
NIKW   Nippon Kwagaku Kwaishi
NNPP   Neurologia, Neurochirurgia i Psychiatria Polska
NOAL   Nova Acta Leopoldina (*also* Verhandlungen der Kaiserlichen Leopoldinisch-
        Carolinischen Akademie der Naturforscher)
NOMT   Nordisk Medicinisk Tidskrift (Stockholm)
NRME   Nuovo Raccoglitore Medico
NSLF   Nervnaya Sistema, Leningradskii Gesudarst-vennyi Universitet IM. A. A. Zhdanova,
        Fiziologicheskii Institut
NTGE   Nederlandsch Tijdschrift voor Geneeskunde
NTMA   Naucni Trudove Meditsinska Akademiia
NTUR   Natur (Leipzig)
NTVM   Nauchni Trudove Visshiya Meditsinski Institut Sofiya
NURE   Nutrition Reviews
NVKU   Nevrologicheskii Viestnik, Kazan Universitet
NWSC   New Scientist
NYMJ   New York Medical Journal
NYSC   New York Agricultural Experimental Station Bulletin (Cornell University)
NYSJ   New York State Journal of Medicine
NZMJ   New Zealand Medical Journal

O

ODMS   Old Dominion Journal of Medicine and Surgery
OFAJ   Okajimas Folia Anatomica Japonica
OFRR   Research Reviews, Office of Naval Research, Department of the Navy, Washington,
        D.C.

OIZA   Okayama Igakkai Zasshi
OJSC   Ohio Journal of Science
OKGH   Osaka Kogyo Gijutsu Shikenjo Hohoku
OPEP   Obozrienie Psikhiatrii Nevrologii e Eskperimental noi Psikhologii (Petrograd)
ORBE   Ornithologischer Beobachter
ORHE   Orvosi Hetilap (Budapest)
ORLI   Otorinolaringologia Italiana
OVWV   Oesterreichische Vierteljahreschrift für Wissenschaften. Veterinar Kunde (Vienna)
OZPL   Onderzoekingen Physiologisch Laboratorium (Utrecht)

P

PAAS   Publication of the American Association for the Advancement of Science
PAEN   Problemes Actuels d'Endocrinologie et de Nutrition
PAGP   Pflügers Archiv für die Gesamte Physiologie des Menschen und der Tiere
PAHE   Pharmaceutica Acta Helvetiae
PAKO   Parfumer und Kosmetik
PAPO   Pharmaceutische Post
PARE   Pharmacological Reviews
PBME   Perspectives in Biology and Medicine
PBSN   Proceedings of the Boston Society of Natural History
PCZO   Proceedings of the International Congress of Zoology
PEDI   Pediatrics
PEDR   Pediatrie
PEES   Pediatria Española (Madrid)
PEHE   Pediatric Herald
PEOR   Perfumery and Essential Oil Record
PEPS   Perception and Psychophysics
PFIO   Problemy Fiziologicheskoi Optiki
PFMB   Permanente Foundation Medical Bulletin (Oakland, Calif.)
PFSH   Proceedings of the Florida State Horticultural Society
PHAR   Die Pharmazie
PHJO   The Pharmaceutical Journal and Pharmacist
PHRE   Physiological Reviews
PHST   Philosophische Studien (Leipzig)
PHWE   Pharmaceutische Weekblad
PHZI   Pharmazeutische Zeitung
PHZO   Physiological Zoology
PISN   Pisani (Palermo)
PMCB   Pester medicinisch-chirurgische Presse (Budapest)
PMOS   Perceptual and Motor Skills
PNAS   Proceedings of the National Academy of Sciences. U.S.
PNMP   Psychiatrie, Neurologie und Medizinische Psychologie
POAS   Proceedings of the Oklahoma Academy of Science
POBB   Press Otolaryngologique Belge (Brussels)
POLE   Polski Tygodnik Lekarski
PORL   Practica Oto-Rhino-Laryngologica
POSC   Poultry Science
PPEZ   Pishchevaya Promyshlennost S.S.S.R. Sbornik Statei i Materialov
PPRS   Philosophical Proceedings of the Royal Society (London)
PREB   Proceedings of the Royal Society of Edinburgh. Section B: Biology
PRIB   Proceedings of the Royal Irish Academy. Section B. Biological, Geological and
        Chemical Science
PRIR   Priroda
PRJA   Proceedings of the Japanese Academy
PRLB   Proceedings of the Royal Society. Series B. Biological Sciences (London)
PRLK   Przeglad Lekarski
PRMC   Proceedings of the Mayo Clinic (Rochester, Minn.)

PRMD   La Prática del Médico
PRME   La Presse Medicale
PROT   Protoplasma
PRPG   Professional 'naia Patologiia i Gigiena (Moscow)
PRSM   Proceedings of the Royal Society of Medicine
PSBU   Psychological Bulletin
PSCI   Psychonomic Science
PSEB   Proceedings of the Society for Experimental Biology and Medicine
PSHE   Psyche (A Journal of Entomology)
PSIC   Psychonomic Science
PSMD   Il Policlinico, Periodico di Medicina, Chirurgia ed Igiene (Rome)
PSME   Psychosomatic Medicine
PSNE   Psychiatria et Neurologia
PSPR   Il Policlinico, Sezione Practica (Rome)
PSRV   Psychological Review
PTRB   Philosophical Transactions of the Royal Society. Series B: Biological Sciences (London)
PTRS   Philosophical Transactions of the Royal Society (London)
PUPC   Proceedings of the International Union of Physiological Sciences, International Congress
PWCP   Proceedings, The World Congress of Psychiatry
PYMO   Psychological Monographs
PYRC   Psychological Record
PYRI   Psychological Reports
PYSO   The Physiologist
PZSL   Proceedings of the Zoological Society of London

Q

QBNU   Quarterly Bulletin of Northwestern University Medical School
QJEH   Quarterly Journal of Experimental Physiology
QJMS   Quarterly Journal of Microscopical Science
QJSA   Quarterly Journal of Studies on Alcohol
QJXP   Quarterly Journal of Experimental Psychology
QRBI   Quarterly Review of Biology

R

RABL   Revista de la Sociedad Argentina de Biología y su Filial la Sociedad de Biología del Litoral
RACL   Radiologia Clinica
RADL   Radiology
RANE   Rassegna di Neuropsichiatria e Scienze Affini
RAOG   Rassegna d'Ostetricia e Ginecologia (Naples)
RARE   Radiation Research
RBBI   Revista Brasileira de Biologia
RBCM   Revista Balear de Ciencias Médicas
RBIL   Rivista di Biologia (Perugia)
RBME   Revista Brasileira de Medicina (Rio de Janeiro)
RBOR   Revista Brasileira de Oto-Rino-Laringologia
RBSD   Revue Belge de Science Dentaire
RBTU   Revista Brasileira de Tuberculose e Doencas Toracicas
RCCM   Rivista Critica di Clinica Medica
RCIR   Revista Científica (Rio de Janeiro)
RCMB   Revista de Ciencias Médicas de Barcelona
RCPI   Rivista di Clinica Pediatrica
REEA   Revista Española de las Enfermedades del Aparato Digestivo y de la Nutrición
REFP   Revue Francaise Pediatrie
RENE   Revue Neurologique

REOG   Revista Española de Obstétricia y Ginecología
REPP   Repertorium für die Pharmacie
RESC   Le Revue Scientifique
RFEC   Revue Francaise de'Etudes Cliniques et Biologiques
RFFM   Report, Faculty of Fisheries, Prefectural University of Mie
RIDP   Richet's Dictionnaire de Physiologie
RIEI   Riechstoff Industrie
RIGI   Rivista Italiana di Ginecologia
RILR   Reale Istituto Lombardo di Scienze e Lettere. Rendiconti (Milan)
RIME   La Riforma Medica
RINE   Rivista di Neurologia
RIOL   Rassegna Italiana di Oto-Rino-Laringologia
RIPS   Rivista di Psicologia (Italy)
RLOR   Revue de Laryngologie, Otologie, Rhinologie
RMGI   Revista Médica Germano-Iberio-Americana
RMLI   Revue Medicale de Liege
RMSR   Revue Medicale de la Suisse Romande
RNPS   Review of Neurology and Psychiatry
RNSA   Rivista di Neuropsichiatria e Scienze Affini (Parma)
RNVE   Rassegna di Neurologia Vegetativa
RONO   Revue d'Oto-Neuro-Ophtalmologie
RPGA   Revista de Psicología General y Aplicada (Madrid)
RPLS   Reports, Psychological Laboratory, University of Stockholm
RPNM   Rivista di Patologia Nervosa e Mentale
RPOG   Revue Pratique d'Obstetrique et de Gynecologie
RPPA   Revue de Psychothérapie et de Psychologie Appliquée
RPPE   Revue de Psychiatrie et de Psychologie Experimentale
RQPP   Rivista Quindicinale di Psicologia, Psichiatria, Neuropatologia ad uso dei Medici e dei Giruesti
RSEC   Report of the Sense Inspection Conference
RSPS   Rassegna di Studi Psichiatrici
RTCP   Recueil des Travaux Chimiques de Pays-Bas
RULN   Ricerche Universita Laboratorio di Anatomia Normale (Rome)
RUMR   Russische Medizinische Rundschau
RUVR   Russkii Vrach
RVOO   Rivista Oto-Neuro-Oftalmologica
RVSM   Revista Veneta di Scienze Mediche
RWLP   Rozprawy Wydzialu Lekarskiego Polska Akademia Umiejetnosci (Krakow)

S

SAMN   Sitzungsberichte der Akademie der Wissenschaften in Wien, Mathematisch-Naturwissenschaftliche Klasse
SANP   Schweizer Archiv für Neurologie und Psychiatrie
SANT   Journal de la Santé (Paris)
SAPH   Skandinavisches Archiv für Physiologie
SBLE   Sbornik Lekarsky
SBNP   Sperimentale: Archivivio di Biologia Normale e Patalogia
SCAM   Scientific American
SCCT   Sammlung Chemischer und Chemisch-Technischer Vorträge
SCIE   Science
SCLS   Scandinavian Journal of Clinical and Laboratory Investigation, Supplement
SCMO   The Scientific Monthly
SCPA   Southern California Practitioner
SCPR   Science Progress
SCTN   Scottish Naturalist
SEMD   Semaine Medicale (Paris)
SEME   Le Semana Médica (Buenos Aires)

SHGO   Shika Geppo (Dental Science Monthly Report)
SILO   Società Italiana di Laringologia, Otologia e Rinologia, AHi di Congresso (Catania)
SJPS   Scandinavian Journal of Psychology
SMDJ   Scottish Medical Journal
SMEJ   Sei-Kwai Medical Journal
SMPB   Sitzungsberichte der Mathematisch–Psysikalischen Klasse der Bayerischen Akademie der Wissenschaften zu München
SMWO   Schweizerische Medizinische Wochenschrift
SNLE   Science News Letter
SOME   Sovetskaya Meditsina
SOPE   Sovetskaya Psikhonevrologiia
SPAW   Sitzungsberichte der Koeniglichen Preussischen Akademie der Wissenschaften
SPER   Sperimentale
SPML   Spice Mill
SPOG   Schriften der physikalischoekonomischen Gesellschaft zu Königsburg
STIT   Stomatologia Italiana
STMM   Stomatologiia Instituta Myasnoi i Molochnoi Promyshlennosti (Moscow)
STON   Stomatologia (Milan)
STOC   Statistical Quality Control
STRK   Die Stärke
SVLA   Svenska Lakartidningen
SWWA   Sitzungsberichte der Akademie der Wissenschaffen in Wien. Mathematik-Naturwissenschaftliche Klasse. Abteilung III: Anatomie und Physiologie des Menschen und der Tiere sowie theoretische Medizin.
SXQU   The Sigma Xi Quarterly
SZFA   Semons Zoologische Forschungsreisen in Australien

T

TAAC   Transactions of the American Association of Cereal Chemists
TAAO   Transactions of the American Academy of Ophthalmology and Otolaryngology
TAEP   Texas Agricultural Experiment Station, Progress Note
TALA   Transactions of the American Laryngological Association
TALR   Transactions of the American Laryngological, Rhinological and Otological Society
TAMS   Transactions of the American Microscopical Society
TANA   Transactions of the American Neurological Association
TAND   Tandleagebladet
TBMI   Transactions of the Boston Society for Medical Improvements. Extracts
TCAH   Travaux de Chimie Alimentaire et d'Hygiene (Same as MGLH)
TCOE   Tennessee, Contribution to Education
TEFO   Technische Fortschrittsberichte
TFBF   Trudy 1-Sessii. Fiziologov, Biokhimikov i Farmakologov (Moscow)
THEP   Therapeutikon
THGE   Therapie der Gegenwart
THMO   Therapeutische Monatshefte
TIAE   Trabajos del Instituto de Antropología y Ethnología (Bernardino de Sohagun) (Barcelona)
TIBI   Trudy Instituta Imeni V. M. Bekhterova po Izucheniyu (Moscow)
TIFP   Trudy Instituta Fiziologii Imeni I. P. Pavlova
TIPF   Trudy Institut Normal noi i Patologicheskoi Fiziologhii (Moscow)
TISA   Transactions of the Illinois State Academy of Science
TJEM   Tohoku Journal of Experimental Medicine
TKKO   Tanpakushitsu, Kakusan, Koso (Protein, Nucleic Acid, Enzymes)
TKSH   Tokyo Kogyo Shikensho Hokoku (Reports of the Government Chemical Industrial Research Institute, Tokyo)
TNLA   Tidsskrift for den Norske Laegeförening (Oslo)
TOCJ   Taste and Odor Control Journal
TPSF   Tohoku Psychologica Folia

TRCB   Transactions of the Royal Society of Canada. V: Biological Sciences
TRCM   Transactions of the Royal Society of Canada. III: Chemical, Mathematical and Physical Sciences
TRES   Transactions of the Royal Entomological Society of London
TRME   La Tribune Medicale
TSAS   Transactions of the Kansas Academy of Science
TSPP   Transactions of the First Session, Moscow Society of Physiologists, Biochemists and Pharmacologists
TTDC   Teknisk Tidskrift. Upplaga C Kemi och Bergsvetenskap
TUNE   Turtox News
TVEM   Trudy Vsesoyuznogo Instituta Eskperimental noi Meditsiny
TWIZ   Taiwan Igakkai Zasshi (Journal of the Medical Association, Formosa)

U

UCPS   University of California (Berkeley) Publications in Psychology
UCRE   The Urologic and Cutaneous Review
UGLA   Ugeskrift for Laeger
UMCA   Union Medicale du Canada
UMSC   Die Umschau
UMSP   L'Union Medicale: Journal des Interêts Scientifiques et Pratiques
UNMT   Untersuchungen zur Naturlehre des Menschen und der Tiere
UNPH   Union Pharmaceutique, Repertoire de Pharmacie, Archives de Pharmacie et Journal de Chime Medicale
UPIY   Ushinskii Pedagogic Institute, Yaroslavl, U.S.S.R., Scientific Report
UPSF   Upsalaluakareforenings Forhandlingar
USFB   United States Bureau of Fishery Bulletin
USFC   United States Fish Commission Bulletin
UWIB   University of Wisconsin Bulletin, Science Series

V

VALS   Valsalva
VAPA   Virchow's Archiv für Pathologische Anatomie und Physiologie und für Klinische Medizin
VEOF   Vestnik Oftalmologii
VETR   Veterinary Record
VGMS   Vierteljahresschrift für gerichtliche Medizin und öffentliches Sanitätswesen
VGNA   Verhandlungen der Gesellschaft deutscher Naturforscher und Aerzte
VJSC   Virginia Journal of Science
VMGW   Verhandlungen der physikalisch Medizinischen Gesellschaft zu Würzburg
VMSJ   Virginia Medical and Surgical Journal (Richmond)
VNGB   Verhandlungen der Naturforschenden Gesellschaft in Basel
VOED   Voeding
VONE   Voprosy Neirokhirurgii
VORL   Vestnik Oto-Rino-Laringologii
VORT   Vortrag in Mainz
VPIT   Voprosy Pitaniya
VRRA   Vestnik Rentgenologii i Radiologii
VSNG   Verhandlungen der Schweizerischen Naturforschenden Gesellschaft
VVWN   Verslag van de gewone vergadering der wis- en naturkundige afdeeling (Proceedings for de Akademie van wettenschappen, Amsterdam. Afdeeling naturkunde)

W

WAME   War Medicine
WHNE   What's New (Abbott Laboratories)
WICZ   Wiener Chemiker-Zeitung
WIKR   Wiener klinische Rundschau
WIMB   Wiener Medizinische Blätter

WIVI   Wines and Vines
WKWO   Wiener Klinische Wochenschrift
WLCO   Wallerstein Laboratories Communications
WMEP   Wiener Medizinische Presse
WMWO   Wiener Medizinische Wochenschrift
WSBR   Wochenschrift für Brauerei
WZND   Wiener Zeitschrift für Nervenheilkunde und deren Grenzgebiete

X

XAAI   U.S.D.A. Agriculture Information Bulletin

Y

YJBM   Yale Journal of Biology and Medicine
YOIZ   Yonago Igaku Zasshi

Z

ZACH   Zeitschrift für Angewandte Chemie
ZAEN   Zeitschrift für Anatomie und Entwicklungsgeschichte
ZAPB   Zeitschrift für Angewandte Psychologie. Beihefte
ZAPP   Zentralblatt für allgemeine Pathologie und Pathologische Anatomie
ZAWE   Zahnärztliche Welt
ZEBL   Zeitschrift für Biologie
ZEEL   Zeitschrift für Elektrochemie
ZEKI   Zeitschrift für Kinderheilkunde
ZEMA   Zeitschrift für Morphologie und Anthropologie
ZENF   Aus der Natur; Zeitschrift für alle Naturfreunde
ZEPH   Zentralblatt für Physiologie
ZEPS   Zeitschrift für Psychologie mit Zeitschrift für Angewandte Psychologie und
        Charakterkunde
ZERA   Zeitschrift für Rassenphysiologie
ZESI   Zeitschrift für Sinnesphysiologie
ZEWA   Zentralblatt für die ganze wissenschaftliche Anatomie. Suppl. Anat. Anz.
ZGEM   Zeitschrift für die gesamte experimentelle Medizin
ZGIM   Zeitschrift für die gesamte innere Medizin und ihre Grenzgebiete
ZGNP   Zeitschrift für die gesamte Neurologie und Psychiatrie
ZHGE   Zeitschrift für Hals-, Nasen- und Ohren-Heilkunde
ZHNG   Zentralblatt für Hals, Nasen und Ohrenheilkunde sowie deren Grenzgebiete
ZHNO   Zeitschrift für Hals, Nasen und Ohrenheilkunde
ZHPT   Ziemssens Handbuch der spezialen Pathologie und Therapie
ZIME   Zentralblatt für innere Medizin
ZINS   Zeitschrift für Insektenbiologie
ZJZP   Zoologische Jahrbücher. Abteilung für allgemeine Zoologie und Physiologie der
        Tiere
ZKME   Zeitschrift für Klinische Medizin
ZLRO   Zeitschrift für Laryngologie, Rhinologie, Otologie und ihre Grenzgebiete
ZLRT   Zeitschrift für Laryngologie, Rhinologie, Otologie (Stuttgart)
ZMAF   Zeitschrift für Mikroskopisch-Anatomische Forschung
ZMEE   Zeitschrift für Medizinische Elektrologie
ZMVK   Zeitschrift für Menschliche Vererbungs-und Konstitutionslehre
ZMWI   Zentralblatt für die Medizinischen Wissenschaften
ZNGE   Zeitschrift für Untersuchung der Nahrungs-und Genussmittel sowie der
        Gebrauchsgegenstaende
ZNPP   Zhurnal Nevropatologii i Psikhiatrii
ZOAN   Zoologischer Anzeiger
ZOKH   Zhurnal Obshchei khimii
ZOOL   Zoologica
ZPCH   Zeitschrift für Physiologische Chemie, Hoppe-Seylers

ZPCL	Zeitschrift für Physikalische Chemie (Leipzig)
ZPDT	Zeitschrift für Physikalische und Diätetische Therapie
ZPMP	Zeitschrift für Psychotherapie und Medizinische Psychologie
ZPSI	Zeitschrift für Psychologie und Physiologie der Sinnesorgane
ZRDV	Zhurnal po Rannemu Detskomu Vozrastu
ZRKO	Zhurnal Russkogo Fiziko-Khimichesko Obshchestva
ZRME	Zeitschrift für rationelle Medizin
ZSTO	Zeitschrift für Stomatologie
ZTPS	Zeitschrift für Tierpsychologie
ZUIN	Zuckerindustrie
ZULE	Zeitschrift für Untersuchung der Lebensmittel
ZUSU	Zucker- und Süsswarenwirtschaft
ZVDZ	Zeitschrift der Vereine der Deutschen Zucker-Industrie
ZVND	Zhurnal Vysshei Nervnoi Deyatel 'Nosti Imeni I. P. Pavlova (Same as Pavlov Journal of Higher Nervous Activity U.S.S.R.)
ZVPH	Zeitschrift für Vergleichende Physiologie
ZWBC	Zeitschrift für Wissenschaftliche Biologie, Abteilung C. Zeitschrift für Vergleichende Physiologie
ZWZA	Zeitschrift für wissenschaftliche Zoologie, Abteilung A
ZWZO	Zeitschrift für wissenschaftliche Zoologie
ZZAC	Zeitschrift für Zellforschung und mikroskopische Anatomie

INDEX

Freeman, 1936
Hahn, 1934, 1943, 1951
Hennies, 1933
Kiesow, 1903b
Kuraoka, 1928, 1929
McBurney, 1963

AFFECT
Beebe-Center, 1946
Carlsmith, 1963
Christensen, 1960, 1961, 1962
Engel, 1928
Herring, 1930
Pfaffmann, 1960, 1961, 1962, 1964, 1966
Regnault, 1921
Roby, 1950
Shuford, 1955, 1959

AGE
Allara, 1939, 1940, 1941
Becker, 1909
Byrd, 1959
Cicala, 1964
Cohen, 1959
Cooper, 1959
Glanville, 1964
Goldschmidt, 1927
Heiderich, 1906
Kalmus, 1962
Kaplan, 1965
Khairushev, 1961
Laird, 1939
Lumia, 1959b, 1960, 1961
Mattei, 1901
Nachman, 1959
Parisella, 1964
Scott, 1948
Shafar, 1965
Taylor, 1963
Zubek, 1959

ALCOHOL
Anderson, 1963
Arrola, 1963
Beerstecher, 1950
Berg, 1955
Carr, 1936
Dicker, 1958
Fava, 1956
Gregson, 1966
Hallenberg, 1914
Hellekant, 1965
Hinreiner, 1955
Kato, 1956
Le Magnen, 1961
Lester, 1952
Margulies, 1950
Mello, 1964
Müssle, 1891
Myers, 1961
Parisella, 1964
Richter, 1940
Rodgers, 1964
Slosson, 1890

AMPHIBIA
Abbott, 1948
Anderson, 1950

Andrew, 1949
Arnold, 1900
Beale, 1865, 1869
Billroth, 1858
Bruni, 1933
Casella, 1955, 1957, 1963
Chernetski, 1964
Cole, 1910
Cole, 1930
Engelmann, 1868
Hartmann, 1863
Hoyer, 1859
Kallius, 1901
Key, 1861
Kimura, 1961b, 1962
Koketsu, 1951, 1953
Kusano, 1957, 1960
Lazzaroni, 1962
Maddox, 1869
Pumphrey, 1935
Rapuzzi, 1960, 1961, 1962, 1963, 1965
Retzius, 1892, 1905
Schulze, 1870
Seo, 1932
Taccardi, 1960
Torigoe, 1958
Waller, 1849
Yamashita, 1961, 1963, 1964
Zotterman, 1949, 1950

APPETITE, HUNGER, SATIETY
Ahokas, 1950
Behrman, 1965
Bellomo, 1941
Furchtgott, 1960
Gastaut, 1955
Goetzl, 1949, 1950, 1951
Grace, 1964
Gussev, 1940, 1941
Hammer, 1951
Harris, 1933
Janowitz, 1949
Kato, 1960
Margulies, 1950
McCleary, 1953
McGinty, 1965
Meyer, 1952
Moore, 1965
Pangborn, 1959
Richter, 1936–47
Schur, 1937
Scott, 1946–50
Shuford, 1959
Smith, 1956, 1957, 1958
Soulairac, 1943–1958
Sternberg, 1907, 1908, 1909
Teitelbaum, 1955
Tenen, 1964
Young, 1946–56

ASTRINGENCY
Bate-Smith, 1954
Bissar, 1939
Christian, 1950
Gronberg, 1919
Herlitzka, 1908

Shiga, 1956
Sollmann, 1921
AUDITION AND TASTE
Allen, 1940
Ash, 1951
Barnes, 1933
F., 1910
Fisher, 1965
Kottmeyer, 1961
Pierce, 1907
Schneider, 1947, 1952, 1953
Srinivasan, 1955
BIRDS
Bath, 1905, 1906
Baume-Halensee, 1908
Botezat, 1904, 1906, 1910
Brindley, 1965
Duncan, 1960, 1962, 1963
Engelmann, 1934–43
Fuerst, 1962
Gillespie, 1922
Greschik, 1917
Halpern, 1962
Harriman, 1966
Hermann, 1899
Kallius, 1905
Kare, 1957, 1959, 1960, 1961, 1963, 1964, 1965
Kitchell, 1959
Lindenmaier, 1959
Liszt, 1917
Moore, 1944, 1946
Pick, 1959, 1962
Rensch, 1925
Salverda-TerLaag, 1936
Soedarmo, 1961
Warren, 1963
BITTER
Bailey, 1885–86
Bourliere, 1959
Charonnat, 1939
Diemair, 1950
Green, 1942
Kaplan, 1964
Kuckulies, 1936
Langton, 1938
Lumia, 1961
Maestrini, 1912
Mata, 1963
Moncrieff, 1951
Nündel, 1936
Nyquist, 1949
Quevenne, 1847–48
Rapaport, 1954, 1956
Ratcliff, 1954
Reid, 1956
Sakai, 1964
Sato, 1956
Scholl, 1937
Shimizu, 1957, 1958
Sonohara, 1934
Taylor, 1928
Ward, 1934
Warren, 1963
Wasicky, 1942–43

BLOOD FACTORS
Bartalena, 1962
Bednar, 1929
Bruni, 1933
Canniggia, 1947
Chlenov, 1957
Cruz-Coke, 1964
McCreesh, 1958
Reid, 1943
Schwartz, 1938
Scow, 1954
Torigoe, 1958
CARBONATED WATER
Adachi, 1964
Anonymous, 1940
Kawamura, 1964
CAT
Appelberg, 1958, 1959
Bartoshuk, 1965
Bonvallet, 1952
Bremer, 1923
Cohen, 1955, 1957
Elliott, 1937
Emmers, 1964
Frings, 1951
Guth, 1958
Hayes, 1942
Hellekant, 1965
Ishiko, 1964
Kerr, 1962
Kimeldorf, 1960
Landgren, 1959
Macht, 1951
Nagaki, 1964
Patton, 1952
Pfaffmann, 1935, 1936, 1955
Schofield, 1876
Zotterman, 1936
CHILDREN, INFANTS
Beidler, 1966
Canciullo, 1958
Cardullo, 1951
Dix, 1912
Eckstein, 1927, 1928
Flasarova, 1959
Gallucci, 1932
Gauger, 1929
Genzmer, 1892
Goldschmidt, 1927
Gustafson, 1953
Horowitz, 1958
Jensen, 1932
Jonas, 1964
Jong, 1964
Kellog, 1945
Kiesow, 1904
Koeppe, 1939
Kroner, 1882
Kulakovskaja, 1929
Kussmaul, 1896
Lalonde, 1961
Lichtenstein, 1893–94
Mahner, 1909
Marchand, 1902

Martin du Pan, 1955
Mattei, 1901
Merton, 1958
Morse, 1954
Motta, 1961
Nelson, 1928
Nemanova, 1941
Neumann, 1896
Osepian, 1958
Ponzo, 1905, 1907
Rakhawy, 1964
Sanctis, 1898
Schmidt, 1910
Sonohara, 1934
Stahr, 1901
Stirniman, 1935, 1936
Thambipillai, 1955–56
Tuckerman, 1887–88
CRUSTACEA
Barber, 1951, 1953, 1956
Hopkins, 1932
Laverack, 1963
Levandowsky, 1965
DENTURES, DENTAL CONDITIONS
Ackermann, 1885
Chung, 1964
Coy, 1956
Filderman, 1962
Giddon, 1954
Harrison, 1965
Jaffe, 1955
Laird, 1939
Landa, 1945
Manly, 1952
Matot, 1961
Mones, 1950
Nucci, 1951
Pickerill, 1914
Singer, 1963
Strain, 1952
Wendel, 1936
Witkop, 1964
Zitka, 1952
DISEASE
Abasov, 1961
Ables, 1960
Aitken, 1933
Alajouanine, 1939
Anonymous, 1964
Aronov, 1962
Artom, 1923
Becker, 1964
Beiguelman, 1964
Bekény, 1951
Bellows, 1939
Brand, 1964
Büssem, 1894
Clementi, 1935
Da Costa, 1889
David, 1965
Davids, 1822
Delhougne, 1930
Demshanko, 1961
Derouet-Boissiere, 1839

Digiesi, 1961, 1962
D'Onofrio, 1923
Edinger, 1903
Elek, 1944
Erb, 1870, 1875
Faber, 1947
Fabbi, 1954
Falck, 1853
Féré, 1892
Feron, 1822
Fischer, 1962, 1963
Fraser, 1961
Furstner, 1952
Gastaut, 1955
Gereb, 1948
Gluschkoff, 1958
Gowers, 1880
Grain, 1943
Harris, 1949
Henkin, 1962, 1963, 1964
Hollingsworth, 1963
Iakovlera, 1957
Jullian, 1900
Kalmus, 1960, 1962
Kaplan, 1965
Kato, 1960
Kitchin, 1959
Klippel, 1897
Krarup, 1958, 1959
Laterza, 1953
Lorian, 1960
Lumia, 1959
Lunedei, 1946
Lussana, 1869
Maier, 1904
Manlapas, 1965
Marcus, 1934
Martin, 1946
Mashanskii, 1956
Mayer, 1935
Mayer-Gross, 1928, 1946
Mayr, 1904
Motta, 1961
Müller, 1911
Neumann, 1864
Nevraeva, 1959
Paleani, 1910
Pascucci, 1947
Pfeifer, 1907
Potts, 1903
Pruett, 1939
Pulec, 1964
Schelling, 1965
Schwanke, 1936
Segall, 1948
Smith, A., 1964, 1965
Sobel, 1929
Sottner, 1964
Stamm, 1839
Stanojević, 1924
Terry, 1947, 1948, 1950
Tétreault, 1963
Timofeer, 1933
Titlebaum, 1960

Tsetsarky, 1961
Weiss Valbranca, 1946, 1947
Wilkes, 1941
Wotman, 1964
Yakovlera, 1958, 1959
Zhukovich, 1962
Dog
Andersson, 1950
Clementi, 1935, 1958
Hellekant, 1965
Holliday, 1940
Iriuchijima, 1961
Koizumi, 1953
Krol'lifshits, 1933, 1934, 1935
Lapina, 1960
Malloizel, 1903
Murskii, 1959
Olmsted, 1921
Osepian, 1959
Schofield, 1876
Timofeev, 1934
Vatsuro, 1959
Drug Effects
Ahokas, 1950
Aleksandrova, 1955
Anrep, 1879
Biriukov, 1938
Boltz, 1939
Dicker, 1958
Ehrenberg, 1949
Ferrari, 1904, 1905
Fischer, 1938
Fischer, 1963, 1964, 1965
Fontan, 1964
Fontana, 1902
Forchheimer, 1916
Gavaudan, 1947
Grossman, 1953
Guyot, 1856
Hallman, 1953
Kiesow, 1894
Knapp, 1884
Knüchel, 1905
Kraupa-Runk, 1916
Kusano, 1959
Le Magnen, 1953
Lewin, 1894
Luciani, 1952
Mata, 1963
Müller, 1964
Ponzo, 1909
Schneeberg, 1952
Simons, 1927
Skouby, 1955
Skramlik, 1956, 1957
Tecklenburg, 1937
Ward, 1934
Wasicky, 1942–43
Electric Taste
Békésy, 1964, 1965
Bordier, 1899
Brühl, 1903
Bujas, 1935–49
Dzendolet, 1957, 1962

Galioto, 1961
Gertz, 1919
Harper, 1961
Hermann, 1891
Heüman, 1911, 1941
Hofmann, 1897
Ichioka, 1963
Kamei, 1936
Laserstein, 1891
Loubimow, 1896
Neumann, 1864
Palmberg, 1860
Penfield, 1937
Pfaff, 1794
Pierrel, 1955
Rosenthal, 1860
Vintschgau, 1879
Volta, 1816
Zeynek, 1898
Electron Microscopy
Baradi, 1962, 1963
DeLorenzo, 1958–63
Farbman, 1965
Iriki, 1960
Trujillo-Cenóz, 1957, 1961
Enzymes
Arvy, 1961
Baradi, 1951, 1959, 1963
Bourne, 1948
Ellis, 1959
Koshtoiants, 1958
Newbrun, 1962
Nonnis-Marzano, 1961
Rakhawy, 1960, 1962, 1963
Sakai, 1964
Shimizu, 1958
Fish
Allison, 1931–32, 1934
Aronov, 1962
Bardach, 1962, 1965
Cole, 1931
Dykgraaf, 1933
Edwards, 1930
Hasler, 1957
Herrick, 1902, 1905, 1906, 1907
Hoagland, 1933
Jourdan, 1881
Kamrin, 1953
Klenk, 1930
Konishi, 1958, 1961, 1963, 1964
Krinner, 1934
Kuroda, 1932
Lenhossék, 1894, 1895
Parker, 1908, 1912, 1917, 1922
Scharrer, 1947
Schulze, 1863
Sheldon, 1909
Tateda, 1961, 1964
Teichmann, 1962
Todaro, 1872, 1873
Trudel, 1929
Trujillo-Cenóz, 1961
Uchida, 1933
Van Beneden, 1835

Wells, 1963
FLAVOR
Aman, 1955
Anonymous, 1942, 1943
Brillat-Savarin, 1926
Chappell, 1953
Childs, 1944
Clendenning, 1940
Crocker, 1945, 1948
Fincks, 1886
Jacobs, H. L., 1964
Kawamura, 1964, 1965
Le Magnen, 1945
Lockhart, 1955
Maybee, 1939
Mills, 1960
Rapaport, 1952
Scott, 1946
Showalter, 1945
Sivetz, 1949
GYMNEMIC ACID
Belletrud, 1907
Berthold, 1887, 1888
Dyer, 1887
Hooper, 1887
Kiesow, 1894
Lovell, 1961
Mhaskar, 1930
Oefele, 1894
Podiapolsky, 1896
Power, 1904
Quirini, 1891
Tomasini, 1896
Warren, 1959
HORMONES
Allara, 1950, 1952
Aria Vallejo, 1950
Bare, 1949
Rice, 1943
Soulairac, 1943–58
INSECTS
Abraham, 1944
Anderson, 1932
Baton-Browe, 1962
Bauer, 1938–39
Bonnet, 1924
Browne, 1960, 1962, 1963
Butler, 1940
Chadwick, 1946, 1949
Copeland, 1924
Crow, 1932
Deonier, 1935, 1938, 1939
Dethier, 1937–65
Eger, 1937
Eltringham, 1933
Engelmann, 1872
Evans, 1957–63
Forel, 1910, 1921
Frings, 1945, 1946, 1948, 1954
Frisch, 1927–39
Gazagnaire, 1886
Haslinger, 1935
Hassett, 1950
Hodgson, 1953–65

Holbrook, 1950
Hudson, 1958
Ishikawa, 1963
Künckel, 1878, 1881
Kunze, 1915, 1927, 1933
Larsen, 1962, 1963
Löhner, 1916
Marlowe, 1942
McIndoo, 1928, 1934
Mellon, 1961
Millot, 1936
Minnich, 1921–32
Morita, 1957, 1959, 1963
Peters, 1963
Ritter, 1936
Roys, 1958
Ruiter, 1963
Schmidt, 1938
Slifer, 1959
Steinhardt, 1963, 1966
Stürckow, 1959, 1960, 1962, 1963
Takeda, 1961
Tateda, 1959
Tinbergen, 1939
Vogel, 1931
Voltz, 1956
Wallis, 1961
Weis, 1930
Will, 1885
Wolbarsht, 1957, 1958, 1965
Wolff, 1875
Wykes, 1952
INTERACTION OF TASTE MODALITIES
Anderson, 1955
Anonymous, 1943
Dallenbach, 1943
Fabian, 1943
Feller, 1965
Funakoshi, 1963
Gregson, 1963, 1965, 1966
Hara, 1955
Kamen, 1959, 1961
Kamenetzky, 1958
Lockhart, 1952
Pangborn, 1960, 1961, 1962, 1964
Pilgrim, 1961
MENSTRUATION
Beiguelman, 1964
Fornasari, 1951
Glanville, 1965
METHODS
Bayton, 1954
Beebe-Center, 1948, 1949
Camerer, 1885
Dawson, 1963
Dove, 1953
Dussik, 1933
Ekman, 1961
Filipello, 1956
Galioto, 1961
Grandjean, 1943
Gregson, 1962, 1964, 1965
Gridgeman, 1958
Gustafson, 1953

Jones, 1956, 1961
Krarup, 1958
Lewis, 1948
MacKenzie, 1955
MacLeod, 1950, 1952
Marlowe, 1942
Pfaffmann, 1934, 1935, 1948
Pulec, 1964
Purdum, 1942
Quix, 1903
Roasenda, 1925, 1932
Russell, 1966
Skramlik, 1937
Sternberg, 1905, 1906, 1907
Tarver, 1959
Tilgner, 1959
Toulouse, 1900
Vasil'ev, 1957
Wagner, 1965

NUTRITION
Beythien, 1949
Borisov, 1903
Cosmelli, 1954
Hartridge, 1945
Hillix, 1959
Horowitz, 1953
Le Magnen, 1956, 1959, 1963
Pfaffmann, 1951
Popelski, 1903
Pyke, 1944
Richter, 1936–45
Striek, 1924

OBESITY
Digiesi, 1964
Fuller, 1955
Maller, 1964
Pangborn, 1958

OLFACTION AND TASTE
Allen, 1940
Amici, 1958
Bähr, 1919
Benjamin, 1960
Beyer, 1904
Crosland, 1926, 1928
Felderman, 1935
Gilliland, 1921
Goetzl, 1949, 1951
Kneeland, 1853
Lavin, 1959
MacDonald, 1888
Mainland, 1945
Nagel, 1904, 1905
Naïdus, 1940
Parker, 1912, 1913
Patrick, 1899
Picht, 1829
Rocén, 1920
Schutz, 1952
Wagner, 1949
Zanzucchi, 1936
Zwaardemaker, 1899, 1902, 1903, 1905

PHENYLTHIOCARBAMIDE (P.T.C.) AND
RELATED COMPOUNDS
Akesson, 1959

Allison, 1951, 1952–53, 1959
Anonymous, 1964
Azevêdo, 1965
Barnicot, 1949–50, 1951
Bat-Miriam, 1962
Beach, 1953
Becker, 1964
Beiguelman, 1962, 1964
Bhattacharya, 1964
Blakeslee, 1932, 1933, 1935
Botsztejn, 1942
Boyd, 1936–62
Brand, 1963
Brandtzaeg, 1958
Brdicka, 1964
Büchi, 1955–61
Cardullo, 1951
Chiarelli, 1959
Chikauki, 1952
Chung, 1964
Cohen, 1949, 1951
Cook, 1933
Cunha, 1956
Das, 1955–63
Dencker, 1959
Ehrhardt, 1952
Evans, 1962–63
Evans, 1958
Falconer, 1947
Fernandes, 1957
Fernberger, 1932
Fischer, 1959–63
Fox, 1931, 1932
Fraser, 1961
Freire-Maia, 1960
Fukuoka, 1936
Gamna, 1958
Gottschick, 1937
Grande, 1952
Griffin, 1960
Grünwald, 1962, 1963
Guinsburg, 1953
Hall, 1945
Haro, 1951, 1963
Harris, 1949
Hartmann, 1939
Hogben, 1935
Hollingsworth, 1963
Hoover, 1956
Hopkins, 1942
Hoyme, 1955
Huard, 1953
Hutt, 1947
Jacobs, B. B., 1962
Jong, 1964
Julien, 1938
Junqueira, 1957
Kalmus, 1957, 1962, 1964
Kaplan, 1963
Kitchin, 1959
Klein, 1952
Kumar, 1955
Lattes, 1952
Lee, 1934

Leguebe, 1960, 1963
Lessa, 1953
Levine, 1932
Lugg, 1955–62
MacRoberts, 1964
Manlapas, 1965
Matson, 1938, 1940
Mauro, 1963
Merton, 1958
Miki, 1960
Modrzewska, 1953
Mohr, 1951
Montenegro, 1964
Morton, 1954
Nakajima, 1959
Omm, 1958
Parr, 1934
Partridge, 1962
Pons, 1955, 1960, 1961
Pullin, 1963
Richter, 1941, 1942
Riddell, 1944
Rife, 1944, 1953, 1954
Rikimaru, 1934, 1936, 1937
Roger, 1931
Saldanha, 1954–63
Salmon, 1935
Schinz, 1942
Schrijver, 1933
Segall, 1948
Serra, 1950
Setterfield, 1936
Sewall, 1939
Sheba, 1962
Shepard, 1960, 1961, 1963
Simmons, 1951, 1953
Skramlik, 1943
Skude, 1959–63
Snyder, 1931, 1932, 1937, 1941
Soltan, 1958
Sottner, 1964
Srivastava, 1959, 1961
Steggerda, 1937
Strandskov, 1941
Suzuki, 1949
Taylor, 1961
Terry, 1947, 1948, 1950
Thambipillai, 1955–56
Thieme, 1952
Thomas, 1960
Tsuji, 1947
Valls Medina, 1948
Verkade, 1949
Vondráček, 1956
Weber, 1942
Widström, 1963
Williams, 1926, 1931
Witkop, 1964
PREGNANCY
Baravelli, 1961
Barvelare, 1938
Bidone, 1901
Guidizi, 1946
Hansen, 1935

Langer, 1936
Noferi, 1946
Nonnis-Marzano, 1961
Panebianco, 1950
Richter, 1938
Schettino, 1925, 1926
Schmidt, 1925
Scott, 1948
Suvorova, 1950
PRIMATES, SUB-HUMAN
Anderson, 1963
Bagshaw, 1953
Benjamin, 1960
Blomquist, 1962
Blum, 1943
Bornstein, 1940
Brown, 1889
Ferrier, 1875
Fishman, 1959
Gordon, 1959
Murray, 1960
Oppenheimer, 1932
Patton, 1944, 1946
Schäfer, 1888
Schrier, 1965
Schwartzbaum, 1961
Wagner, 1965
Weiskrantz, 1960
PROTEINS, AMINO ACIDS
Barnes, 1959, 1960
Berg, 1942, 1953
Case, 1961, 1963
Crocker, 1948
Halpern, 1962
Heiduschka, 1925
Iur'eva, 1958, 1960, 1961
Krauss, 1964
Levandowsky, 1965
Ninomiya, 1965
Piutti, 1886
Rapuzzi, 1963
Richter, 1938, 1939, 1941
Scott, 1946
Sollmann, 1921
Solms, 1965
Wallis, 1961
Widström, 1963
Yanagawa, 1936
Yur'eva, 1958, 1961
RADIATION
Botsztejn, 1942
Freund, 1933
Garcia, 1957, 1958
Hunt, 1965
Kalmus, 1959
Kimeldorf, 1960
MacCarthy-Leventhal, 1959
Morris, 1964
Smith, J. C., 1963, 1964
Tanikawa, 1963
Werkmeister-Freund, 1933
REGENERATION
Arey, 1942
May, 1925

Olmsted, 1936
Whiteside, 1926
REPTILES
Bath, 1905, 1906
Baume-Halensee, 1908
Giersberg, 1920
Herrick, 1893
Kallius, 1901
Leydig, 1872
Nonoyama, 1936
Rensch, 1927
RIBONUCLEOTIDES
Kawamura, 1964
Kuninaka, 1960, 1961
Sato, 1965
RODENTS
Abbott, 1953
Ables, 1960
Allara, 1950, 1952
Allen, 1922–23
Andrew, 1951
Arvola, 1963
Arvy, 1961
Bare, 1949
Barnett, 1953
Barvelare, 1938
Beebe-Center, 1948
Behrman, 1965
Beidler, 1954, 1960
Benjamin, 1952–65
Boyd, 1941
Bremer, 1923
Brucke, 1948
Burright, 1963
Campbell, 1958
Carr, 1952
Chaplin, 1947
Chiang, 1963
Cicala, 1964
Clark, 1943
Covian, 1963
Deutsch, 1960
Dicker, 1958
Drasch, 1887
Ectors, 1936
Edmonds, 1960
Emmers, 1960, 1962, 1963
Epstein, 1955, 1962
Erbengi, 1964
Erickson, 1958, 1959, 1963
Fish, 1944, 1946
Fisher, 1964, 1965
Fishman, 1955, 1957
Fleisher, 1956
Fregly, 1955–59
Frommer, 1961
Gad, 1891
Grace, 1964
Griffini, 1884
Guth, 1957
Hagstrom, 1957, 1958, 1959
Halpern, 1959, 1962, 1965
Harriman, 1953, 1955, 1964
Hausmann, 1933

Heidenhain, 1914
Hermann, 1884, 1885
Herxheimer, 1959, 1960
Hoshishima, 1962
Huber, 1917
Iriki, 1960
Jacobs, B. B., 1962
Jacobs, 1955, 1964
Kaplick, 1953
Kappauf, 1963
Katsumi, 1961
Kimeldorf, 1960
Kimmel, 1941
Kimura, 1956, 1961
Kissileff, 1962
Kitamura, 1936
Koh, 1958, 1961
Le Magnen, 1953–61
Lenhossék, 1893
Lester, 1952
Lewis, 1960
Lindsley, 1950
Maller, 1964, 1965
Mark, 1943
McCreesh, 1958
McLaurin, 1964
Mello, 1964
Mook, 1963
Morgane, 1961
Morrison, 1959, 1966
Murray, 1953, 1961
Nachman, 1957–63
Nejad, 1962
Nelson, 1947
Oakley, 1960, 1962
Okada, 1931, 1932
O'Kelly, 1958
Parisella, 1964
Pfaffmann, 1950, 1955, 1961
Rapaport, 1954, 1956
Retzius, 1913
Rice, 1943
Richter, 1936–54
Rodgers, 1964
Roeske, 1897
Rowinski, 1953
Sato, 1965
Schaffer, 1914
Scott, 1946
Shuford, 1955, 1959
Simonetta, 1928
Soulairac, 1943–58
Stahr, 1902, 1903
Stscherbak, 1893
Tateda, 1964
Titlebaum, 1960, 1963
Tomita, 1958
Tosteson, 1951
Trujillo-Cenóz, 1957
Wagner, 1965
Wedell, 1935, 1936
Weiner, 1951
Whiteside, 1927
Wolf. 1963, 1964, 1965

Wyss, 1869
Young, 1940–66

SALIVA

Anonymous, 1950
Arias Vallejo, 1950
Barber, 1964
Biriukov, 1938
Brunacci, 1910–17
Camerer, 1869
Chauncey, 1958–64
Cragg, 1937
DeLaurenzi, 1925
DeWardener, 1957
Diamant, 1959
Digiesi, 1963
DiStefano, 1940
Feller, 1965
Griffin, 1960
Grisogani, 1925
Kawamura, 1964
Köster, 1900, 1902
Kuraoka, 1928
McBurney, 1963
Newbrun, 1962
Oster, 1953
Shepard, 1963
Shinjo, 1950
Skude, 1961
Winer, 1965
Winson, 1938

SALTS

Adachi, 1962
Adamtzik, 1936
Andersen, 1963
Anderson, 1955
Balavoine, 1945, 1948
Barvelare, 1938
Beebe-Center, 1955, 1959
Beilharz, 1961, 1963
Bell, 1960, 1963
Böhme, 1936
Brown, 1914
Carr, 1952
Chaplin, 1947
Chiang, 1963
Christensen, 1960, 1962
Cole, 1910
Covian, 1953
Cox, 1953
Crocker, 1932
Dahl, 1962
Denton, 1958, 1961, 1963
Deutsch, 1960
DeWardener, 1957
Digiesi, 1961, 1962, 1963
Edmonds, 1960
Epstein, 1955
Falk, 1961, 1963
Fisher, 1964, 1965
Fregly, 1955–59
Galvin, 1948
Gayda, 1912
Grace, 1964
Gronberg, 1919

Harriman, 1953, 1955, 1964, 1966
Heinemann, 1937
Henken, 1962
Herlitzka, 1908, 1909
Hertel, 1933
Herxheimer, 1959, 1960
Höber, 1898
Holway, 1937
Irvin, 1952
Kionka, 1922
Kissileff, 1962
Koketsu, 1953
Laverack, 1960
Le Magnen, 1953, 1955
Lewis, 1960
Lockhart, 1950, 1952
Loewenstein, 1962
Lumia, 1960
Mark, 1943
McBurney, 1963
McCutcheon, 1963
McFadden, 1937
Moncrieff, 1950
Nachman, 1962, 1963
Nagel, 1896
Nikitina, 1960
O'Kelly, 1958
Pangborn, 1962, 1964
Parker, 1906
Pearson, 1958
Peirce, 1957, 1959, 1960
Pfaffmann, 1948, 1949, 1950, 1962
Plate, 1929
Renshaw, 1934
Rice, 1943
Richter, 1936, 1937, 1938, 1939, 1941, 1956
Schulz, 1937
Schulze, 1937
Scofield, 1934
Scott, 1950
Skramlik, 1957
Sternberg, 1904
Titlebaum, 1960
Tosteson, 1951
Wagman, 1963
Weeth, 1961
Weiner, 1951
Weinstein, 1907
Whitacre, 1946
Wiggers, 1941
Wilkins, 1940
Wolf, 1963, 1964, 1965
Wotman, 1964
Yamashita, 1963
Yensen, 1958, 1959
Young, 1949, 1956, 1957, 1958, 1963

SEX DIFFERENCES

Bailey, 1888
Bernstorff, 1932
Boyd, 1937–38
Dehn, 1894
Glanville, 1964
Kaplan, 1965
Laird, 1939

Hausmann, 1933
Herxheimer, 1959, 1960
Herzfeld, 1887
Hurwitz, 1965
Ison, 1964
Jacobs, H. L., 1955, 1958, 1962
Jacobs, M. B., 1951
Jones, 1951
Jordon, 1940
Kamen, 1959
Kamenetzky, 1958
Laverack, 1960
Lester, 1952
Lichtenstein, 1948
Lippmann, 1895
Lockhart, 1950, 1952
Loginov, 1941, 1943
Margulies, 1950
McCleary, 1951
Miller, 1946
Mills, 1960
Moncrieff, 1948
Müssle, 1891
Murray, 1953
Neuman, 1943
Nieman, 1958, 1960
Ogilvie, 1922
Pangborn, 1958–64
Paul, 1921, 1922
Renner, 1939
Richter, 1940, 1941, 1942, 1947
Rodgers, 1964
Roederer, 1952
Sale, 1922
Schrier, 1965
Schutz, 1957
Shallenberger, 1963, 1965
Shuford, 1955, 1959
Snow, 1909
Soedarmo, 1961
Spengler, 1927, 1928
Sternberg, 1903, 1904, 1905
Stone, 1966
Titlebaum, 1963
Trunzer, 1935
Tsuzuki, 1947–54
Wagner, 1965
Wagner, 1949, 1965
Whymper, 1955
Wilkes, 1941
Willaman, 1918, 1925, 1928
Willard, 1885–86
Yamazaki, 1947
Young, 1949, 1955, 1957, 1963
SYNTHETIC SWEETNERS
Alberti, 1935, 1939
Anonymous, 1960
Bergmann, 1922
Boedecker, 1920
Bottle, 1964
Capretta, 1964
Collier, 1962
Cordell, 1964
Dyson, 1938, 1939

Fink, 1949
Fisher, 1965
Frisch, 1952
Garcia, 1957
Grinstead, 1960
Hager, 1893
Hagstrom, 1954
Hamor, 1961
Hausmann, 1933
Helgren, 1955
Holleman, 1923
Hughes, 1957
Jacobs, H. L., 1964
Jacobs, M. B., 1957, 1955
Klemm, 1924
Kroll, 1942
Lapicque, 1941
Le Magnen, 1954
Lemberger, 1908
Lester, 1952
Magidson, 1923
Mannessier-Mameli, 1935, 1941
McCance, 1933
McLaurin, 1964
Moncrieff, 1949
Morris, 1964
Neuman, 1943
Noyce, 1951
Oddo, 1937, 1940
Paul, 1921a, 1922
Pauli, 1920, 1921
Richards, 1951
Schwartz, 1962
Siedler, 1916
Smith, L. C., 1963, 1964
Smith, M. P., 1956, 1957, 1960
Speckan, 1922
Staub, 1942
Sternberg, 1903
Stutzer, 1886
Täufel, 1925
Thomas, 1920
Titlebaum, 1963
Veley, 1910–11
Verkade, 1942, 1946
Vincent, 1955
Young, 1953, 1963
TACTILE, TOUCH, TEXTURE
Dubois, 1890
Dubriel, 1931
Kiesow, 1901, 1903
Künckel, 1878
Landgren, 1957
Laverack, 1960, 1961
Moos, 1869
Pariser, 1961
Roederer, 1952
Tourtual, 1827
Wells, 1963
Zwaardemaker, 1899
TEMPERATURE
Békésy, 1964, 1965
Chinaglia, 1915
Dobriakova, 1941, 1944

Goudriaan, 1925, 1930
Hoffmann, 1961
Jensen, 1932
Karashima, 1934
Kiesow, 1901
Komuro, 1921
Krol'lifshits, 1933, 1935
Landgren, 1957
Lasareff, 1922
Maurizi, 1961
McFadden, 1937
Michael, 1933
Nagaki, 1964
Nelson, 1928
Renshaw, 1933, 1934
Sato, 1960, 1963, 1965
Schreiber, 1887
Scofield, 1934, 1939
Snow, 1909
Weber, 1847
Yamashita, 1964, 1965

THEORIES
Baradi, 1951b
Beidler, 1954, 1961
Békésy, 1966
Frentzel, 1896
Hahn, 1936
Haycraft, 1885
Koshtoiants, 1958
Lasareff, 1922
Lehmann, 1884
Nickles, 1861
Nicol, 1960
Schneider, 1952
Timm, 1950

THRESHOLDS
Barysheva, 1936
Berg, 1955
Berlatzky, 1927, 1928
Brown, 1914
Camerer, 1869
Cicala, 1964
Cox, 1953
DeWardener, 1957
Digiesi, 1961
Fodor, 1922
Frings, 1945, 1946
Galioto, 1961
Gayda, 1912
Gertz, 1923
Gregson, 1962
Habs, 1938
Hahn, 1938, 1940, 1948
Hallenberg, 1914
Harriman, 1953
Harris, 1960
Henkin, 1962, 1963, 1964
Hinreiner, 1955
Janowitz, 1949
Kloehn, 1948
Koh, 1958, 1961
Liljestrand, 1922
Linker, 1964
Lumia, 1959–61

McCutcheon, 1963
Miyaji, 1956
Pangborn, 1959
Renqvist, 1920
Renshaw, 1933
Rubin, 1962
Sakaguchi, 1956
Sanders, 1948
Sato, 1956
Shiga, 1956
Sinnot, 1937
Skramlik, 1948
Sztucki, 1934
Tilgner, 1959

TRIGEMINAL
Bernhardt, 1876
Carmichael, 1933
Cushing, 1903
D'Ajutolo, 1940
Dana, 1886
Economo, 1911
Garcin, 1935
Gowers, 1880, 1897, 1902
Harris, 1952
Krause, 1895, 1896
Scheier, 1893, 1894
Schiff, 1886
Schmidt, 1895
Senator, 1882
Sigerson, 1880
Uterhart, 1847
Wagner, 1843
Wirtanen, 1934
Ziehl, 1889

TWINS
Ardashnikov, 1936
Bell, 1959
Dencker, 1959
Ford, 1941
Habs, 1938
Ogawa, 1940
Rümler, 1943
Segall, 1948
Verkade, 1959

UNGULATES
Andersson, 1957
Andreev, 1954
Baldwin, 1959
Beilharz, 1961, 1963
Bell, 1959, 1960, 1963
Bernard, 1962, 1964
Brücher, 1884
Denton, 1958, 1961, 1963
Kaljevitch, 1921
Peirce, 1957, 1959, 1960
Pick, 1959
Weeth, 1961

VISION AND TASTE
Allen, 1940
Ash, 1951
Dejerine, 1891
Dobriakova, 1938–44
Downey, 1911
Eberson, 1897

Féré, 1891
Gregson, 1966
Kekcheev, 1936
Lassche, 1962
Margolin, 1941
Nakhminovich, 1952
Pangborn, 1960, 1963
Sanctis, 1898
Sollier, 1891
VITAMINS
Barbera, 1950
Behrman, 1965
Bernard, 1961, 1962

Harris, 1933
Remaggi, 1959
Richter, 1937, 1938, 1939, 1941
Scott, 1946–50
Seifter, 1960
"WATER" TASTE
Bartoshuk, 1964, 1965
Casella, 1955
Diamant, 1960
Liljestrand, 1955
Mellon, 1961
Zotterman, 1949, 1950, 1956, 1959

Index

THE CHEMICAL SENSES AND NUTRITION
Edited by Morley R. Kare and Owen Maller

designer: Gerard Valerio
typesetter: Monotype Composition Company, Inc.
typeface: Baskerville
printer: Universal Lithographers, Inc.
paper: Glatco Offset C–60
binder: Moore & Co., Inc.
cover material: Columbia Riverside Chambray RVC–3771